THE ESTATE OF JACQUELINE KENNEDY ONASSIS

APRIL 23–26, 1996

The Mark Shaw Collection / Photo Researchers

Georgetown, 1960

THE ESTATE OF JACQUELINE KENNEDY ONASSIS

Sale 6834

Auction:

Tuesday, April 23, 1996 at 7:30 pm
Wednesday, April 24, 1996 at 10 am, 2 pm and 6 pm
Thursday, April 25, 1996 at 10 am, 2 pm and 6 pm
Friday, April 26, 1996 at 10 am and 2 pm

Absentee Bids

This catalogue may be referred to as 6834 "JKO"
Fax for bids only: (212) 606-7016

Admission

Admission to the exhibition and auction will be limited to ticket holders. For further information, please call (212) 606-7000.

Catalogue

$90 (hardcover)
$45 (softcover)

William F. Ruprecht, Principal Auctioneer, License No. 0794917

See special Copyright notice on page 7.

SOTHEBY'S

1334 York Avenue (at 72nd Street) New York, NY 10021
Telephone: (212) 606-7000

1/96

Contents

Specialists in Charge

General Information

Phone (212) 606 7136
Fax (212) 606 7599

American Decorative Arts and Furniture

William W. Stahl, Jr. (212) 606 7110
Leslie B. Keno (212) 606 7130
Nancy C. Druckman (212) 606 7225

American Paintings

Peter Rathbone (212) 606 7280
Dara Mitchell

Antiquities

Richard M. Keresey (212) 606 7328
R. Seth Bright

Books and Manuscripts

Selby Kiffer (212) 606 7385
Elizabeth Muller

Contemporary Art

Robert Monk (212) 606 7254
Leslie Prouty

European Furniture

Phillips Hathaway (212) 606 7213
Gillian M. Arthur
Thierry Millerand

General Fine Arts

Jennifer Roth (212) 606 7516

Impressionist Paintings

Alexander Apsis (212) 606 7360
John Tancock
(Scholarship and Research)
David Norman
Laurel Beckett
Mollie Brocklehurst

Indian & Southeast Asian Art

Carlton C. Rochell, Jr. (212) 606 7304

Jewelry

John Block (212) 606 7392
Paul Russo

Fashion Jewelry

Valerie Vlasaty (212) 606 7392
Mish Tworkowski

Nineteenth Century European Paintings

Nancy Harrison (212) 606 7140
Benjamin Doller
Evelyn Tompkins Mandy

Old Master Paintings

George Wachter (212) 606 7230
Scott Schaefer

Porcelain

Letitia Roberts (212) 606 7180

Prints

Mary Bartow (212) 606 7117

Rugs and Carpets

Mary Jo Otsea (212) 606 7996

Russian Art, Icons, Objects of Vertu

Gerard Hill (212) 606 7150

Silver

Kevin Tierney
John Culme (212) 606 7160

Sale Inquiries

Client Advisory Services

For assistance in buying at this auction
Roberta Louckx (212) 606 7415
Mallory Hathaway (212) 606 7447
Raul Suarez (212) 606 7274
Lisa Heller (212) 606 7468
Geraldine Nager (212) 606 7568
Mish Tworkowski (212) 606 7419
Brooke Douglass (212) 606 7521
Tiffany Dubin (212) 606 7263
Fax (212) 606 7269

Absentee Bids

Frederica Lauder (212) 606 7414
Fax (212) 606 7016

Client Services Desk

(212) 606 7116

24 Hour Recorded Information

Sales Results
(212) 606 7901

Current Auctions and exhibitions
(212) 606 7245

Payment and Shipping

Buying
Joy Serette (212) 606 7498
Fax (212) 606 7488

Shipping
Mary Klindt
(212) 606 7511

Subscriptions

(800) 444 3709 From within the U.S.
(212) 606 7044 From outside the U.S.

Sotheby's World Wide Web Site:

http://www.sothebys.com

Special Notice

Conditions of Sale

The following Conditions of Sale and Terms of Guarantee are Sotheby's, Inc. and the Consignor's entire agreement with the purchaser relative to the property listed in this catalogue. The Conditions of Sale, Terms of Guarantee, the glossary, if any, and all other contents of this catalogue are subject to amendment by us by the posting of notices or by oral announcements made during the sale. The property will be offered by us as agent for the Consignor, unless the catalogue indicates otherwise. By participating in any sale, you acknowledge that you are bound by these terms and conditions.

Please refer to the Glossaries at the back of this catalogue.

1 Goods auctioned are often of some age. The authenticity of the Authorship of property listed in the catalogue is guaranteed as stated in the Terms of Guarantee and except for the Limited Warranty contained therein, all property is sold "AS IS" without any representations or warranties by us or the Consignor as to merchantability, fitness for a particular purpose, the correctness of the catalogue or other description of the physical condition, size, quality, rarity, importance, medium, provenance, exhibitions, literature or historical relevance of any property and no statement anywhere, whether oral or written, whether made in the catalogue, an advertisement, a bill of sale, a salesroom posting or announcement, or elsewhere, shall be deemed such a warranty, representation or assumption of liability. We and the Consignor make no representations and warranties, express or implied, as to whether the purchaser acquires any copyrights, including but not limited to, any reproduction rights in any property. We and the Consignor are not responsible for errors and omissions in the catalogue, glossary, or any supplemental material.

2 Prospective bidders should inspect the property before bidding to determine its condition, size, and whether or not it has been repaired or restored.

3 A buyer's premium will be added to the successful bid price and is payable by the purchaser as part of the total purchase price. The buyer's premium is 15% of the successful bid price up to and including $50,000, and 10% on any amount in excess of $50,000.

4 We reserve the right to withdraw any property before the sale and shall have no liability whatsoever for such withdrawal.

5 Unless otherwise announced by the auctioneer, all bids are per lot as numbered in the catalogue.

6 We reserve the right to reject any bid. The highest bidder acknowledged by the auctioneer will be the purchaser. In the event of any dispute between bidders, or in the event of doubt on our part as to the validity of any bid, the auctioneer will have the final discretion to determine the successful bidder, cancel the sale, or to reoffer and resell the article in dispute. If any dispute arises after the sale, our sale record is conclusive. Although in our discretion we will execute order or absentee bids or accept telephone bids as a convenience to clients who are not present at auctions, we are not responsible for any errors or omissions in connection therewith.

7 If the auctioneer decides that any opening bid is below the reserve of the article offered, he may reject the same and withdraw the article from sale, and if, having acknowledged an opening bid, he decides that any advance thereafter is insufficient, he may reject the advance.

8 Subject to fulfillment of all of the conditions set forth herein, on the fall of the auctioneer's hammer, title to the offered lot will pass to the highest bidder acknowledged by the auctioneer, and such bidder thereupon (a) assumes full risk and responsibility therefor (including, without limitation, liability for or damage to frames or glass covering prints, paintings or other works), and (b) will immediately pay the full purchase price or such part as we may require. In addition to other remedies available to us by law, we reserve the right to impose from the date of sale a late charge of 1½% per month of the total purchase price if payment is not made in accordance with the conditions set forth herein. All property must be removed from our premises by the purchaser at his expense not later than 10 business days following its sale and, if it is not so removed, (i) a handling charge of 1% of the total purchase price per month from the tenth day after the sale until its removal will be payable to us by the purchaser, with a minimum of 5% of the total purchase price for any property not so removed within 60 days after the sale, and (ii) we may send the purchased property to a public warehouse for the account, risk and expense of the purchaser.

If any applicable conditions herein are not complied with by the purchaser, the purchaser will be in default and in addition to any and all other remedies available to us and the Consignor by law, including, without limitation, the right to hold the purchaser liable for the total purchase price, including all fees, charges and expenses more fully set forth herein, we, at our option, may (x) cancel the sale of that, or any other lot or lots sold to the defaulting purchaser at the same or any other auction, retaining as liquidated damages all payments made by the purchaser, or (y) resell the purchased property, whether at public auction or by private sale, or (z) effect any combination thereof. In any case, the purchaser will be liable for any deficiency, any and all costs, handling charges, late charges, expenses of both sales, our commissions on both sales at our regular rates, legal fees and expenses, collection fees and incidental damages. We may, in our sole discretion, apply any proceeds of sale then due or thereafter becoming due to the purchaser from us or any affiliated company, or any payment made by the purchaser to us or any affiliated company, whether or not intended to reduce the purchaser's obligations with respect to the unpaid lot or lots, to the deficiency and any other amounts due to us or any affiliated companies. In addition, a defaulting purchaser will be deemed to have granted and assigned to us and our affiliated companies, a continuing security interest of first priority in any property or money of or owing to such purchaser in our possession or in the possession of any of our affiliated companies, and we may retain and apply such property or money as collateral security for the obligations due to us or to any affiliated company of ours. We shall have all of the rights accorded a secured party under the New York Uniform Commercial Code. Payment will not be deemed to have been made in full until we have collected good funds. In the event the purchaser fails to pay any or all of the total purchase price for any lot and Sotheby's nonetheless elects to pay the Consignor any portion of the sale proceeds, the purchaser acknowledges that Sotheby's shall have all of the rights of the Consignor to pursue the purchaser for any amounts paid to the Consignor, whether at law, in equity, or under these Conditions of Sale.

9 **All lots in this catalogue are offered subject to a reserve, which is the confidential minimum price acceptable to the Consignor.** No reserve will exceed the low presale estimate stated in the catalogue, or as amended by oral or posted notices. We may implement such reserve by opening the bidding on behalf of the Consignor and may bid up to the amount of the reserve, by placing successive or consecutive bids for a lot, or bids in response to other bidders. In instances where we have an interest in the lot other than our commission, we may bid up to the reserve to protect such interest. In certain instances, the Consignor may pay us less than the standard commission rate where a lot is "bought-in" to protect its reserve.

10 Unless exempted by law, the purchaser will be required to pay the combined New York State and local sales tax, any applicable compensating use tax of another state, and if applicable, any federal luxury or other tax, on the total purchase price. The rate of such combined tax is 8¼% in New York City and ranges from 4% to 8½% elsewhere in New York.

11 These Conditions of Sale and Terms of Guarantee, as well as the purchaser's and our respective rights and obligations hereunder, shall be governed by and construed and enforced in accordance with the laws of the State of New York. By bidding at an auction, whether present in person or by agent, order bid, telephone or other means, the purchaser shall be deemed to have consented to the exclusive jurisdiction of the state courts of, and the federal courts sitting in, the State of New York.

12 We are not responsible for the acts or omissions in our packing or shipping of purchased lots or of other carriers or packers of purchased lots, whether or not recommended by us. Packing and handling of purchased lots is at the entire risk of the purchaser. If we obtain on behalf of the purchaser an export license for an item containing an endangered species, there will be a charge of $150 for each license obtained.

13 In no event will our liability to a purchaser exceed the purchase price actually paid.

Terms of Guarantee

Sotheby's warrants the authenticity of Authorship of each lot contained in this catalogue on the terms and conditions set forth below.

The foregoing Terms of Guarantee do not apply to Books, Manuscripts and Memorabilia. Please see the following page for those Terms of Guarantee.

NOTICE FOR JEWELRY

No reference to imperfections is made in individual catalogue descriptions of property offered for sale. All lots are sold "AS IS" in accordance with Paragraph 1 of the Conditions of Sale, and we make no representation or warranty as to the condition of any lot sold. We disclaim responsibility for, and prospective bidders should not rely on, any description in the catalogue or any other source, including without limitation any gemological report, of the condition, size or quality of any lot.

Anyone wishing further information on any of the property included in this catalogue may write or call the Jewelry Department (212) 606-7392.

During the auction, a color slide of each lot will be shown as it is sold. This is only to assist the audience and the slide is not meant to represent the actual size, color or quality of the item offered.

1 *Definition of Authorship.* "Authorship" is defined as the creator, period, culture, source of origin, as the case may be, as set forth in the BOLD TYPE HEADING of a lot in this catalogue, as amended by any oral or written salesroom notices or announcements. **If there is a "Glossary" of terms in this catalogue, please note that any such heading represents a qualified statement or opinion and is not subject to these Terms of Guarantee.** Sotheby's makes no warranties whatsoever, whether express or implied, with respect to any material in the catalogue, other than that appearing in BOLD TYPE HEADING and subject to the exclusions in 5 and 6 below.

2 *Guarantee Coverage.* Subject to the exclusions in 5 and 6 below, Sotheby's warrants the Authorship (as defined above) of a lot for a period of five years from the date of sale of such lot and only to the original purchaser of record at the auction. If it is determined to Sotheby's satisfaction that the BOLD TYPE HEADING is incorrect, the sale will be rescinded as set forth in 3 and 4 below, provided the lot is returned to Sotheby's at the original selling location in the same condition in which it was at the time of sale. It is Sotheby's general policy, and Sotheby's shall have the right to have the purchaser obtain, at the purchaser's expense, the opinion of two recognized experts in the field, mutually acceptable to Sotheby's and the purchaser, before Sotheby's determines whether to rescind a sale under the above warranty. If the purchaser requests, Sotheby's will provide the purchaser with the names of experts acceptable to it.

3 *Non-Assignability.* The benefits of this warranty are not assignable and shall be applicable only to the original purchaser of record and not to any subsequent owners (including, without limitation, heirs, successors, beneficiaries or assigns) who have, or may acquire, an interest in any purchased property.

4 *Sole Remedy.* It is specifically understood and agreed that the rescission of a sale and the refund of the original purchase price paid (the successful bid price, plus the buyer's premium) is exclusive and in lieu of any other remedy which might otherwise be available as a matter of law, or in equity. Sotheby's and the Consignor shall not be liable for any incidental or consequential damages incurred or claimed.

5 *Exclusions.* This warranty does not apply to: (i) Authorship of any paintings, drawings or sculpture created prior to 1870, unless the lot is determined to be a counterfeit (a modern forgery intended to deceive) which has a value at the date of the claim for rescission which is materially less than the purchase price paid for the lot; or (ii) any catalogue description where it was specifically mentioned that there is a conflict of specialist opinion on the Authorship of a lot; or (iii) Authorship which on the date of sale was in accordance with the then generally accepted opinion of scholars and specialists; or (iv) the identification of periods or dates of execution which may be proven inaccurate by means of scientific processes not generally accepted for use until after publication of the catalogue, or which were unreasonably expensive or impractical to use.

6 *Limited Warranty.* As stated in paragraph 1 of the Conditions of Sale, neither Sotheby's nor the Consignor makes any express or implied representations or warranties whatsoever concerning any property in the catalogue, including without limitation, any warranty of merchantability or fitness for a particular purpose, except as specifically provided herein.

Terms of Guarantee for Books, Manuscripts and Memorabilia

We guarantee the authenticity and condition of each book and manuscript and memorabilia of historical interest catalogued herein on the terms and conditions set forth below.

1 *Physical Condition.* Except for books in original parts, serial publications and any lot containing more than one item, or unless otherwise indicated in the respective catalogue description, we guarantee that each book and manuscript is complete in both text and illustrations and generally is in such physical condition as may reasonably be expected considering the age and provenance. If within two weeks from the date we deliver a purchased book or manuscript, the original purchaser of record tenders to us such purchased book or manuscript in the same condition as when sold and it is established that the catalogue description of the physical condition of such lot (as amended by any posted notices or oral announcements during the sale) is not substantially correct based upon a fair reading of the catalogue as a whole including the terms of any Glossary contained herein, the sale of such lot shall be rescinded and the original purchase price refunded.

2 *Authenticity.* Unless otherwise indicated in the respective catalogue description or unless physical inspection would reveal self-evident lack of authenticity, we guarantee the authenticity of the signature of autographed material, the accuracy of the edition number designation of books and the provenance of memorabilia of historical interest, the value of which derives solely from its historical significance. If within five years from the date of sale of a purchased lot, the original purchaser of record tenders to us a purchased lot in the same condition as when sold and it is established that the catalogue description of the lot as it relates to its authenticity (as defined above and as amended by any posted notices or oral announcements during the sale) is not substantially correct based upon a fair reading of the catalogue as a whole, including the terms of any Glossary contained herein, the sale of such lot will be rescinded and the original purchase price refunded.

3 *Non-Assignability.* It is specifically understood that the benefits of this Guarantee are not assignable and shall be applicable only to the original purchaser of the lot from us and not to the subsequent owners or others who have or may acquire an interest therein.

4 *Sole Remedy.* It is further specifically understood that the remedy set forth herein, namely the rescission of the sale and refund of the original purchase price paid for the lot, is exclusive and in lieu of any other remedy which might otherwise be available as a matter of law.

5 *Exclusions.* The guarantee covers only the catalogue description of the physical condition and/or authenticity of property as explicitly set forth in 1 and 2 above, and does not extend to (i) any such catalogue description which may be proven inaccurate by means of scientific processes not generally accepted for use until after publication of the catalogue or (ii) the secondary and supplemental descriptive material which appears in each entry in the catalogue and which is not material to the description of physical condition or authenticity (as defined in 2 above) of the lot. Although due care is taken to insure the correctness of said supplemental material, the guarantee does not extend to any possible errors or omissions therein.

The Mark Shaw Collection / Photo Researchers

The Estate of Jacqueline Kennedy Onassis

In deciding what to do with our mother's possessions, we were guided first and foremost by her deep knowledge and love of history. She was proud to have played a part in the history of our country, and in accordance with her wishes, we have given objects and documents which help chronicle the Kennedy Administration and her role as First Lady to the John F. Kennedy Library Foundation which will make them available to the public.

Beyond that, our mother believed in individuals more than in institutions. She was able to evoke the lives and people of other times and places, describing to us the ancient pharaohs, court society at Versailles, or life on a Nantucket whaling ship so vividly that we felt we had visited these wondrous places. For our mother, history came alive through objects and paintings, as well as books. Because the things she collected link her with history, and because she cared about them, they represent more than just a record of her life and travels. As they go out into the world, we hope that they bring with them not only their own beauty and spirit, but some of hers as well.

Caroline Kennedy John Kennedy

The Mark Shaw Collection / Photo Researchers

A Personal Reminiscence

My reminiscences of Jackie are as vivid today as ever. She was unique, unlike any other person I've known. There was this charismatic presence about her, made up in part by her intelligence, wit, and sense of the ridiculous. You never could be bored when you were with Jackie, because you never knew quite what to expect from her. She had this love of intrigue that often led to some sort of conspiritorial act. For instance, in 1964 when she decided to move from Washington to New York and we went apartment hunting, to avoid publicity she came up with the idea that I would play the part of the prospective buyer while she'd come along disguised as the children's nanny! She looked upon it as a game and she loved every moment of it. Jackie was a wonderful listener. When you told her a story that sparked her imagination, particularly if it included a dash of intrigue, she was not satisfied until you'd told her every last detail — and even then she'd ply you with all sorts of questions that were running through her mind.

I have countless memories of happy and fun times spent with Jackie; I only wish I could tell all of them. But, what I say here is written in the hope that for you who never knew her well - or not at all - it will give an indication of her captivating personality, her attributes and her accomplishments.

In School

Mr and Mrs. John V. Bouvier and their daughter Jacqueline, at a Southampton, New York, horse show in 1934.

UPI / Bettmann

I first met Jacqueline Bouvier in the 5th grade at the Chapin School in New York City. Jackie, with her distinctive looks and magnificent thick braids, was one of the most popular girls in the class. She was liked because she was a loyal and attentive friend and because she was very funny. Furthermore, she was unusually intelligent and quick witted, with a vivid imagination.

While she could be strong willed and stubborn, at the same time she was always fair and willing to compromise. Beyond this, Jackie held the distinction of being the naughtiest girl in the class, and this was in the days when good manners and proper behavior were key factors in our education. We were in awe of her escapades - escapades that invariably ended with Jackie being sent to Miss Stringfellow, the headmistress, for a stern warning to "behave or else." Actually, Jackie's antics showed considerable creative thought, like when she got hold of the braids of the girl sitting at the desk in front of her and dipped them into her inkwell or when she climbed on top of the coat lockers and dropped water bombs on students as they passed below. At some point, Miss Stringfellow, thoroughly tired of Jackie's pranks and knowing of her love of horses, tried a more unusual approach to her behavior, this time coaxing Jackie to model herself after a horse! "Why not think of yourself as a horse?" she asked. "And if you were a horse, of course you'd want to be a thoroughbred and behave like one." Predictably, it didn't have much effect, but the thing about Jackie was that whatever she did - however naughty she was - she was never mean. Just full of spirit, boundless energy and humor.

Cecil Beaton

Jacqueline Lee Bouvier and her sister Caroline Lee Bouvier.

Teachers loved Jackie for her intelligence and her inquisitive mind. Because of her eagerness to learn and her retentive memory, and to keep her mind occupied, they often gave her double homework assignments. Once when our homework included memorizing a number of Longfellow verses, Jackie came to class having memorized the entire poem. But, she never drew attention to or flaunted her intelligence. She did not want to be known as a brain.

Jackie and I left Chapin when our familes moved away from the city, but our paths crossed again when we attended Miss Porter's School, a boarding school in Farmington, Connecticut. It was there that we established a

UPI // Bettmann

Jacqueline Kennedy at the Jeu de Paume in Paris, June 2, 1961

bond of friendship that lasted over the years and which in later life, particularly in times of tragedy, took on special meaning. At Miss Porter's, Jackie was an avid reader, her favorite courses being English Literature and History of Art. She was greatly influenced by the teachers who taught her these subjects, both of whom commented that she was one of the brightest and most challenging students they had encountered. While Jackie was popular among her classmates, by nature she was a loner. After evening study hall, for instance, when friends would get together to socialize, Jackie seldom joined in, happily staying in her room, reading, writing poetry or drawing. She could draw just about anything - people, animals, objects of any sort, all in perfect scale. And she wrote poetry and made up whimsical children's stories, which she would also illustrate. At school, Jackie was in the dramatic club as well as the riding club. She was an accomplished rider and spent a great deal of her free time in the barn tending to her horse, Danseuse, known as Donny. At one point, she decided that my education would not be complete without my learning to ride Donny. To get over my fear of horses, she had me walk under Donny's belly 20 times a day! I did this for what seemed like forever, until one day Jackie took me up to a playing field and put me bareback on Donny. In those days, a student could be expelled for riding a horse without family permission, but it was not something we gave much thought to. Everything went well, until a gong sounded in the stable which signalled the horses' midday meal. Donny, ears perked, took off heading for the stable at lightning speed. I frantically clung to her mane but eventually was thrown, injuring my arm. I was terrified at the thought of confessing what had happened to the infirmary nurse. But not Jackie. She always had a way out of any tight situation. "Tell the infirmary you fell out of a tree." And, of course, that's what I did, and, of course, it worked.

In The White House

West Sitting Room, The White House, 1961.

The John F. Kennedy Library

In June 1963, Jackie and I again were reunited when I went to work at the White House as Social Secretary. When I told Jackie I had no training for a job of this sort, she couldn't see why that made any difference. "It's a very simple job," she said. "It's mostly fun!" While I never thought the job simple, Jackie did more than her share to make it fun. And fun was when she'd put on a disguise and we'd venture outside the White House gates unescorted. Or, when the Goodyear blimp came to Washington and we took Caroline and John on a spur-of-the-moment jaunt over the Virginia countryside, while the Secret Service agents, with no advance notice, were forced to follow the blimp's course by car, weaving through the roads at breathtaking speed. I'd been on the job only a few weeks when I was faced with my first State Dinner. It was to be in honor of the King of Afghanistan. Jackie, knowing that the Washington press would be watching my every move that evening, was determined that the entertainment be so unusual, so spectacular, that they would write about me the next day in the most glowing terms. And so, she came up with the idea of fireworks on the South Lawn; a first for the White House. And thus began the saga of Jackie's brilliant idea! The evening of the dinner, President Kennedy told me he thought eight minutes of fireworks was too long; they should be cut to four minutes. So, I went to Mr. Zambelli, the fireworks guru of the day and the person who'd supplied the fireworks, and gave him the President's message. Without saying anything to me, Mr. Zambelli decided that since the White House had already paid for eight minutes of fireworks, he should give us our money's worth by putting eight minutes of explosives into four! Once the President and the King were seated on the White House balcony, the fireworks began. 'Began' is hardly the word to describe what followed as Mr. Zambelli's explosives ignited. There was one thunderous blast after another. The original outburst was so monumental that the President's Secret Service agent and the King's bodyguard leapt forward to protect them - from what they had no idea! What followed

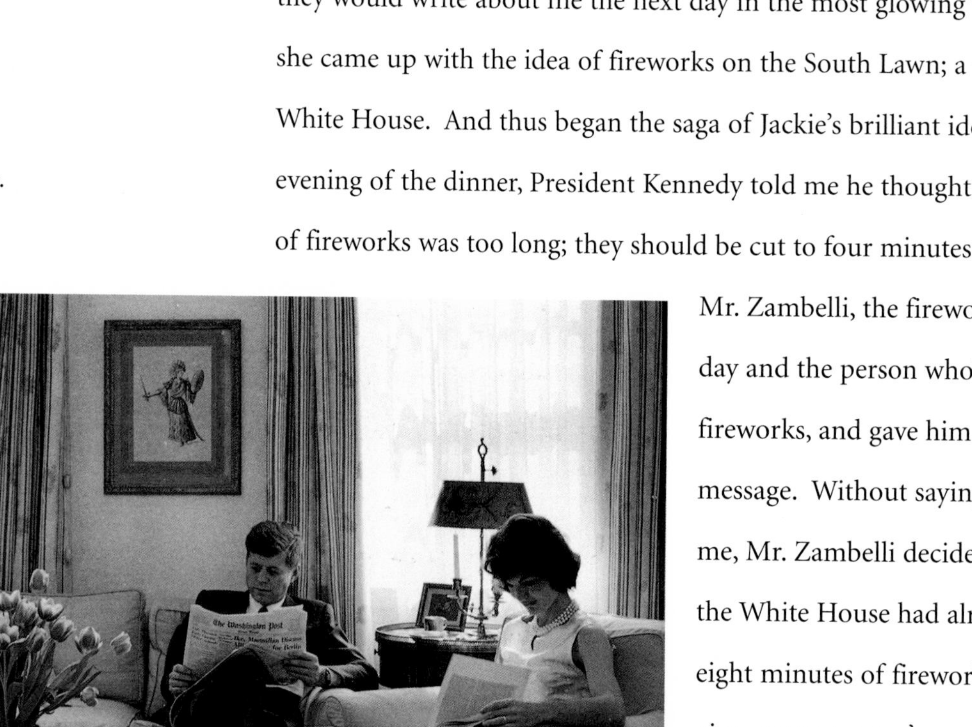

Senator and Mrs. Kennedy in their Georgetown residence.

Ed Clark / Life Magazine / Time Inc.

Jacqueline Kennedy working on the redecoration of The White House, 1961.

was the most spectacular display of fireworks ever seen; so spectacular, that the White House switchboard was inundated with telephone calls from Washington residents wondering if a bomb had been dropped in the middle of the city or a plane had crashed. Luckily, President Kennedy was enchanted by the event and the next day the press wrote rave reviews about the fireworks and myself, barely mentioning the King. "See Nancy," Jackie said, "you upstaged the King of Afghanistan," thereby giving me the credit that was due her. This was a typical gesture of friendship on her part.

To the extent it was possible, Jackie's life in the White House centered around her children. More than anything, she wanted Caroline and John to lead normal lives, and in this respect she was ever conscious of shielding them from the press. There were certain hours of the day that she spent with her children and during those hours she was not to be disturbed; there was never an exception to this rule. It was a welcome distraction to sense the presence of small children in the White House. Caroline's school was there and every day at recess, when the children were playing on the South Lawn, President Kennedy would step outside the Oval Office, clap his hands, and the children would come running to greet him, ready for the handout of candies which he kept in his pocket. It was not unusual, either, to see a dog wandering out of the Cabinet room or jumping into the swimming pool. And sometimes you would see Caroline riding her pony, Macaroni, on the South Lawn or skipping rope with two of her Secret Service agents! Jackie's greatest accomplishment as the wife of the President (she disliked the term First Lady; she thought it sounded like a race horse),

The John F. Kennedy Library

Jacqueline Kennedy in Hyannisport, Massachusetts in the Summer of 1959.

was the restoration of the White House, a monumental undertaking which, when completed, reflected her sense of history, style and taste.

The White House Guidebook was her idea. Prior to its publication, visitors to the White House had nothing to take away with them to interpret and remember their visit. Jackie had a flair for entertaining and came up with the idea of seating guests at State Dinners at round tables rather than the usual rectangular one. It was less formal and gave people the opportunity to talk in groups of three or four, not just to those on either side. In addition, she brought to the White House the finest performers, among them Pablo Casals, Isaac Stern, and the American Ballet Theatre. She also initiated a series of Shakespeare performances; the first ones to be held at the White House since President Taft's administration.

The staff at the White House was particularly fond of Jackie. She was considerate of them and they were amused by her. After one of the State Dinners, she wrote a handwritten memo to the housekeeper saying, "Anne - Please thank all the help at the White House who stay up 'till dawn at these parties & never complain and tell them how much we appreciate it — and give them an extra day off or a distinguished service cross or something - Put up a thank you message from JFK and me." And for Christmas she once gave Mr. West, the chief usher (majordomo) of the White House an embroidered pillow that said, "You don't have to be crazy to live here but it helps!"

The White House days were cut short when tragedy struck in late 1963. As the country grieved over President Kennedy's death, Jackie was a symbol of selflessness, courage and dignity. She behaved like no one else could have. She behaved like the thoroughbred in Miss Stringfellow's reprimand. President Charles de Gaulle of France said, "She gave an example to the whole world of how to behave."

In New York City

Jackie moved from Washington to New York in the fall of 1964 to start a new life for her and her children. I think she saw her return to the city as coming home. And more than anything, she hoped - perhaps even expected - that in a city of such size and diversity, she'd be able to find the anonymity she longed for. But, this was unrealistic, and intellectually she probably knew it. Jackie, by this time, was more than a household name. She was a public figure, and the press and the rest of the world were not about to let her forget it. The thing about Jackie is that she never thought of herself as famous. She thought to be famous a person had to accomplish something in her own right - that fame had nothing to do with being the wife of a president. She continually sought to affirm her role as a private citizen, even relinquishing her lifetime franking privilege. But there was nothing she or anyone could do to discourage the curiosity of the press or the amount of mail she received each day, both constant reminders of her public image. People continually wrote asking for her autograph and she never could understand why; in fact, she couldn't understand why anyone would want to collect autographs. There was nothing the least pretentious about Jackie; I don't

Two Hellenistic Terracotta Horses, 3rd Century, B.C. Lot 35.

Brooks Kraft / Sygma

Above: Jacqueline Kennedy Onassis, Caroline Kennedy and John F. Kennedy, Jr. at the rededication ceremony at the Kennedy Presidential Library in Boston on October 29, 1993. Right: The Living Room in Jacqueline Kennedy Onassis' New York City apartment, showing lots 6, 46, 627, 629, 1007 and 1012.

think she knew the meaning of the word. And, she made a point in seeing that Caroline and John would never appear pretentious or consider themselves special in any way. She succeeded in spite of press and public interest. It was not easy, either. Once on an airplane with Caroline and John, the stewardess told me that she'd serve them their meal before the other passengers. Preferential treatment like that upset Jackie and she did her best to counteract it.

The apartment Jackie moved into was one we had seen when we went apartment hunting when she wore her nanny disguise. She furnished it with works of art and other possessions that she brought with her from the White House. While Jackie had the practiced eye of a collector, she did not consider herself one and she acquired art that pleased her, rather than as an investment. Essentially, there was nothing grand or ostentatious about her apartment. It was inviting and comfortable, with a pleasing, lived-in feeling to it. She was not in the habit of changing or rearranging furniture. Once everything was in place, she kept it that way, replacing worn upholstery or slipcovers with identical materials. The day Jackie moved into the apartment, we spent the day unpacking, emptying cartons, putting books in bookcases. Around 8:00 in the evening, the doorbell rang and Jackie, in her bluejeans and looking quite disheveled, opened the door. There stood two distinguished-looking couples in full evening attire. When they recognized Jackie they were taken aback. They said they were expected for dinner at Mrs. Whitehouse's. It turned out that the elevator man, unnerved by the mere thought of Jackie's presence in the building, was unable to associate the name Whitehouse with anyone or anything but her.

In New York, Jackie devoted her time and energy to projects having

to do with the arts. She joined a number of boards, but restricted the use of her name to organizations in which she was an active participant. She did not lend her name for the sake of its usefulness. As a board member of the Municipal Art Society, her greatest achievement was the role she played in saving Grand Central Terminal from architectural mutilation; at one point leading a whistle-stop train expedition to Washington to lobby on behalf of the terminal's preservation.

John Wootton, Lord Bateman's Arabian, *signed, dated* Fecit 1733-34 *and inscribed with the title, oil on canvas, 40 by 50 in. (101.6 by 127 cm.), Lot 266.*

Jackie was a health and exercise enthusiast. Every day, she'd walk to work, always bringing celery and carrot sticks neatly wrapped in tinfoil to eat at her desk. To stay fit, she'd jog around the reservoir. Whenever she'd set out for the park at dusk on a winter's evening, I'd warn her of all the horrible things that could happen to her, and true to form, she never paid any attention. By nature she was fearless and I think experience had taught her to trust her fate.

In the late '70's, Jackie turned to publishing as a career. She was ideally suited for this type work, having just the right credentials for the making of a good editor - a love of books, an inquisitive and creative mind, and a discerning taste for literature. It was strictly all business when she went to Doubleday as an Associate Editor. There were no frills, no preferential treatment. She worked out of a small, inside office and was committed to editing about 12 books a year.

It did not take long for her to prove to be an enthusiastic and accomplished editor. She had a talent for acquiring manuscripts and was

UPI / Bettmann

Jacqueline Kennedy in Hyannis, Massachusetts, 1964.

adept at creating ideas for books on all sorts of subjects, like architecture, dance, photography, Russian history- even butterflies! And, she was the person who thought of publishing Naguib Mahfouz, the Egyptian Nobel Prize winning novelist, in this country.

Jackie loved being with her grandchildren, eagerly awaiting their weekly visits. With her flagrant imagination, she was able to hold their attention for hours on end. There was this enormous red wooden chest in which she kept all sorts of hidden treasures for them: pirate loot, Gypsy trinkets, beaded necklaces, rings with colored stones. As soon as they arrived, everything from the chest was dumped out on the bedroom floor and the children would dig in. They'd deck themselves out with jewelry, and put on costumes they'd made from old scarves and odd bits of material. Jackie then would take them on a so-called "fantasy adventure." She'd weave a spellbinding tale while leading them through the darkened apartment, opening closet doors in search of ghosts and mysterious creatures. Once they were finished playing, they'd have their traditional afternoon tea party sitting on the living room floor. The children loved these visits, but no more so than Jackie.

Jackie made life fun. She was irrepressible, witty and wise. To all those who knew her personally and those who did not, she will always be remembered as utterly unique. She is greatly missed.

Nancy Tuckerman

THE ESTATE OF JACQUELINE KENNEDY ONASSIS

SESSION ONE

TUESDAY, APRIL 23,

7:30 P.M.

The Living Room and Dining Room of Jacqueline Kennedy Onassis' New York City apartment, showing lots 3, 15, 72, 82, 94, 234, 239, 240, 246, 250, 263, 273, 309, 323, 341, 352 and 1003.

1

1

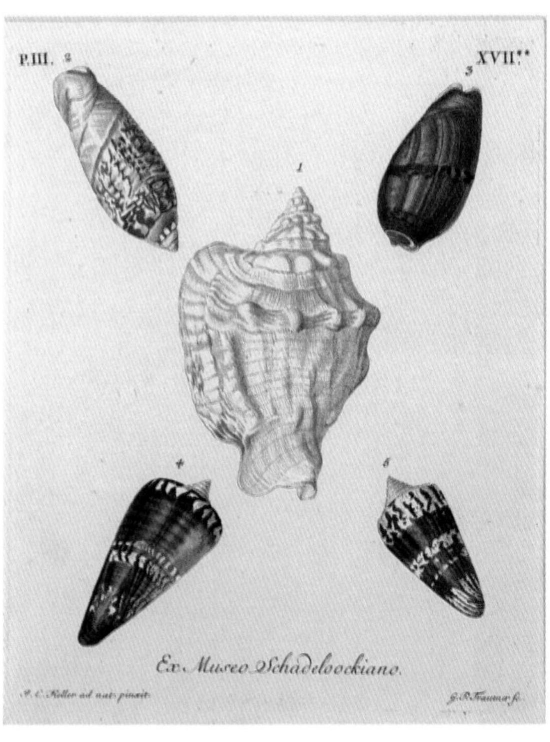

2

2

1 **G. P. Trautner (and others) (Engravers)**

SEASHELLS

Two hand-colored engravings, with margins and in apparently good condition, framed* (not examined out of the frames) (2)
First plate 7 ½ by 6 ⅜ in. (19 by 16.2 cm.);
second plate 7 ⅞ by 6 in. (20 by 15.2 cm.)

$700–800

2 **G. P. Trautner (and others) (Engravers)**

SEASHELLS

Two hand-colored engravings, with margins and in apparently good condition, framed* (not examined out of the frames) (2)
First plate 7 ⅞ by 6 ½ in. (20 by 16.5 cm.);
second plate 8 by 6 ⅛ in. (20.3 by 15.6 cm.)

$700–800

3

3 **A Louis XV/XVI Ormolu and Patinated Bronze Mantel Clock, third quarter 18th Century, the ormolu base signed Vion**

The drum-shaped case with a later white enamel dial and now fitted with a modern small movement, raised on an ebonized horse (traces of gilding beneath) above a rectangular base cast with guilloche, rockwork, laurel swags and a rosette.
Height 12 ¾ in. (32.4 cm.)

François Vion, *maître fondeur,* 1764.

A drawing of this clock case (reproduced below), attributed to François Vion, is conserved in the Bibliothèque Doucet, Paris and is reproduced by Ottomeyer and Proschel, *Vergoldete Bronzen*, 1986, Vol. I, p. 180, fig. 3.7.8.

This mantel clock was among the furnishings in the Second Floor Oval Room of the White House during President and Mrs. Kennedy's residence.

$5,000–7,000

4

4 **A French Painted Paper Four-Panel Screen, early 19th Century**

Decorated on one side with stylized figures and pavilions, and ribbon-tied baskets of flowers with marbleized panels below, the reverse with sprays of flowers and leaves.
Height 6 ft. 2 in. (1.88 m.), width of each panel 19 in. (48.3 cm.)

This screen was among the furnishings in Mrs. Kennedy's dressing room at the White House.

$3,000–5,000

5 **A Set of Six Louis XVI Style Painted Chaises en Cabriolet**

Each with an oval caned backrest, the oval caned seat raised on circular tapered fluted legs.

These chairs were among the furnishings in the West Sitting Room of the White House during President and Mrs. Kennedy's residence, and, earlier, in the dining room of their house in Georgetown.

$2,500–3,500

5

6

6 **Peter Paillon, English (circa 1720-1785/90)**

STUDY OF A SNOW OWL

gouache and watercolor, signed and dated lower right *P. Paillon, 1755*
19½ by 14¾ in. (49.5 by 37.5 cm.)

This painting was among the furnishings in Mrs. Kennedy's bedroom at the White House.

$2,000–3,000

Below: *Jacqueline Kennedy's bedroom in the White House, showing lots 6, 10, 13, 26, 238, 251, 301, 351, 905 and 1016.*

The John F. Kennedy Library

The John F. Kennedy Library

Left: *A small hall off the main cross hallway, upstairs in the Kennedy White House, showing lot 7.*

7 **A Classical Parcel-Gilded Brass-Mounted and Ebonized Mahogany Swivel-Top Card Table, School of Charles Honore Lannuier, New York, circa 1815**

The shaped baize-lined top with ebonized edge above a plain apron with brass skirt, above a single winged gilded caryatid support, two leaf-carved and fluted columns behind, the mahogany plinth supported on four carved and gilded paw feet, (restored). *Length 36 in. (91.4 cm.)*

$35,000–45,000

This card table relates to a group of New York card tables with soaring winged terms supporting the frieze.

The first is part of a suite made for Stephen Van Rensselaer IV who built a home in Albany in 1817 for his bride Harriet Elizabeth Bayard and consists of a pair of card tables, two corner tables, a pier table and a bed. The suite is now in the Collection of the Albany Institute of History and Art.

The second pair of card tables was made for Baltimore merchant James Bosley and is *en suite* with two armchairs, five side chairs and two upholstered window benches.

The third pair was made for Philip Hone, who was a prominent businessman, diarist, and the Mayor of New York during the year 1826. The pair of tables was probably purchased for the house Mr. Hone completed in 1813 at 44 Courtland Street which was, in his own words, "one of the most genteel residences in the city." One of the pair is in the collection of The Metropolitan Museum of Art. The other was sold in these rooms on October 24, 1993, sale 6483, lot 358, and is now in a private collection and on loan to The Metropolitan Museum of Art (see Marshall B. Davidson and Elizabeth Stillinger, *The American Wing at The Metropolitan Museum of Art*, New York, 1985, p. 73, fig. 90).

The design source for the winged term figures and hooked animal leg is most likely Pierre de la Mesangere's *Collection des meubles et objects de Gout*, Paris, 1802, where these appear on a center table and bed respectively.

The present offered table shares approximately the same top profile as the other known tables but the edges of the leaf and the stationary top are both convex, instead of being flat and cove-molded respectively, as seen on the other known examples. Additionally, while the other tables employ ormolu mounts on the frieze, this table was made with a plain frieze. The edge of the plinth base on the lower section is flat with an absence of a blocked upper and lower outside edge. While the feet relate to those on other known New York City pieces, their distinctive design with flat uncarved sides and leaf-carved top does not appear on other documented pieces made by Lannuier. The fluted baluster and leaf-carved colonnettes on the presently offered table, however, are nearly identical to those on numerous card tables documented to Lannuier.

This card table was among the furnishings in the White House during President and Mrs. Kennedy's residence.

7

8

8 **An Empire Style Ormolu-Mounted Slant-Front Desk, late 19th/early 20th Century**

With an architectural pediment above a rectangular top, the slant front opening to reveal a fitted interior and mounted with empire style ormolu leafage and cornucopia, the case with an overhanging frieze drawer above three long drawers, flanked by free-standing columns, the whole raised on bun feet.
Height 46 in. (116.8 cm.), length 33 in. (83.8 cm.), depth 18 in. (45.7 cm.)

This desk belonged to John B. Bouvier and was subsequently given to his daughter, Jacqueline. It was among the furnishings in the West Sitting Room of the White House during President and Mrs. Kennedy's residence.

$1,500–2,000

9 **A Very Fine and Rare Classical Ormolu-Mounted and Carved Mahogany Marble-Top Pier Table, New York, circa 1815**

The grey-veined King of Prussia marble top above a frieze with a central plaque, with ormolu mount in the form of a winged chariot, the dies with leaf-carved rectangular plaques, the brass-inlaid apron continuing to ormolu-mounted columnar uprights and a mirror, ending in brass paw feet.
Height 41 ½ in. (105.4 cm.), length 50 ½ in. (128.3 cm.)

Cast-brass frontal paw feet are characteristic of high-style New York classical seating and case furniture. However, the presently offered pier table is rare due to the presence of four cast feet which are each fully carved.

The leaf-carved panels on the frieze, carving above the feet, and rare free-standing columns flanking the mirror plate, combined with a well-balanced overall design, make this pier table particularly exceptional. For nearly identical brass paw feet on a sideboard, see Nancy McClelland, *Duncan Phyfe and the English Regency*, New York, 1939, p. 172.

This pier table was among the furnishings of the White House during President and Mrs. Kennedy's residence.

$8,000–12,000

9

10 **An Empire Style Mahogany Stool, American, 19th Century**

With florally woven silk drop-in seat.
Length 12 ½ in. (31.7 cm.)

This stool bearing label, "Footstool JBK bedroom in White House for Caroline to climb onto window seat."

$100–150

10

11

11 **A. Berghaus**

MISS LANE'S RECEPTION AT THE WHITE HOUSE

signed *Berghaus*, l.l.; inscribed *Miss Lane's Reception*, l.c.; also inscribed *All the ladies have on bonnets, cloaks, shawls / Gentlemen divested of over-coats-hats in their hands. The room is oval and everything is blue and gold: The White House*, on the reverse
pencil on paper
6 7/8 by 10 1/8 in. (17.5 by 25.7 cm.)

According to a letter from Victor Spark which is affixed to the reverse, this work was executed circa 1855-1860.

Provenance:
Victor D. Spark, New York
Acquired from the above, January, 1962

This drawing was among the furnishings in the Second Floor Oval Room of the White House during President and Mrs. Kennedy's residence.

$1,000–1,500

12

13

12 **Continental School, 18th Century**

STUDY OF AN OSTRICH

watercolor
15 by 10½ in. (38.1 by 26.7 cm.)

Provenance:
Herbert N. Bier, London, February 18, 1963

$3,000–5,000

13 **French School, 19th Century**

A PARK VIEW

oil on board
8 by 6¼ in. (20.3 by 15.9 cm.)

Provenance:
The Veerhoff Galleries, Inc., Washington, D.C.

This painting was among the furnishings in the West Sitting Room and Mrs. Kennedy's bedroom at the White House.

$800–1,200

The John F. Kennedy Library

Above: *The West Sitting Room, The White House, 1961, showing lots 5, 8, 13, 14, 38, 82, 1021 and 1022.*

14

14 **A Louis XV Style Gilded and Silver-Plated Three-Light Bouillotte Lamp**

With an adjustable chinoiserie decorated *tôle peinte* shade, three voluted candle branches above a scalloped circular base. *Fitted for electricity. Finish distressed.*
Height 26 in. (66 cm.)

This lamp was among the furnishings in the West Sitting Room of the White House during President and Mrs. Kennedy's residence, and previously they were in their house in Georgetown.

$700–900

15 **A Pair of Paris Porcelain Gold-Ground Vases Mounted as Lamps, 1815-20**

Each shield-shaped body with a gold ground (some touch-ups) tooled with various neoclassical devices and reserved on the front with a panel painted with two classically-dressed children seated or walking in a landscape, and on the reverse with a chocolate-brown-ground roundel finely painted in cameo technique with the head of a classical maiden or warrior, the sides with stylized bird's-head handles (both repaired on one vase) terminating in masks above scrolls and pendent grape clusters, the circular foot on a black integral square base, (lower body of each and one ankle and foot repaired); *now drilled and fitted for electricity.*
Height of vases 14½ in. (36.8 cm.)

These lamps were among the furnishings in the Second Floor Oval Room of the White House during President and Mrs. Kennedy's residence.

$1,500–2,000

15

16

16 **Jacqueline Duhéme**

JACKIE AND LEE ON A CAMEL

signed *J. Duhéme*, l.r.
watercolor on paper
Sight: 6 ¼ by 7 in. (15.9 by 17.8 cm.)

The French naive artist Jacqueline Duhéme, friend of Matisse, Picasso and Eluard, first became intrigued by President Kennedy and his family as likely subjects for her paintings during their visit to Paris in June 1961. "I was not the only Parisian to be surprised!" she wrote, "I think everyone was absolutely overwhelmed by the radiant charm and the simplicity of Jack and Jackie Kennedy. To us, in France, the image of world politics is something usually a bit more austere."

The John F. Kennedy Library

She went on to explain that, having been so captivated by the President and First Lady, her pleasure was expressed in a few "little doodles" which were subsequently accepted for publication by the French women's magazine, *Elle*. Soon afterwards, Mlle. Duhéme received word from Pierre Salinger, President Kennedy's press secretary, that her drawings had been admired and that she was invited to the White House. She confessed to have been taken completely by surprise. Notwithstanding, she packed her best clothes and her painting kit and headed for Washington.

Jackie and Lee on a Camel would appear to have been inspired by an incident which took place during a visit to Karachi, when "Mrs. Kennedy met Bashir Ahmed, the Pakistani camel driver who had come to the United States [in 1960] as the guest of Vice-President Johnson. The First Lady presented Bashir with a letter from the Vice-President and gave presents to his family; then she and her sister Princess Radziwill ventured a ride on Bashir's camel" (Mary Van Rensselaer Thayer, *Jacqueline Bouvier Kennedy*, Garden City, New York, 1961, p. 266).

$500–700

Above: *Jaqueline Kennedy and Lee Radziwill in India, 1962.*

17 **A Coalport Porcelain 'Peacock' Pattern Part Dinner Service, 1815-20**

Each piece printed in black and enamelled in a *famille-rose* palette of iron-red, yellow, blue, black and shades of rose and green, and heightened in gilding with a pair of peafowl perched on rocks amidst peonies and other flowering plants within or above a gilt spearhead border, the gilt-edged rim with a gilt chain border interrupted with blue foliate panels above on most pieces four trailing floral vines; comprising:
Oval soup tureen with scroll handles and cover (restored chips and a hair crack), *length 14¾ in. (37.5 cm.)*
Pair of oval sauce tureens, covers and stands, *lengths 7½ and 8½ in. (19 and 21.6 cm.)*
Pair of square vegetable dishes and covers (one repaired), *widths 9⁹⁄₁₆ and 9¾ in. (24.3 and 24.8 cm.)*
Sixteen soup plates (four with a hair or star crack, and three with a chip), *diameters 9⅝ to 9¾ in. (24.4 to 24.8 cm.)*
Twelve dinner plates (some wear), *diameters 9⅜ to 9½ in. (23.8 to 24.1 cm.)*
Fifteen dessert plates (most with crackled glaze, three with a star crack on the base, and one of those and another with a chip), *impressed numeral 2 marks, diameters 8½ to 8¹¹⁄₁₆ in. (21.6 to 22.1 cm.)*
(50)

The 'Peacock' pattern originated in Chinese Export porcelain around 1760, and services of this design are known to have been shipped to Portugal, Brazil and England, where by 1815 the Spode factory had begun to reproduce the pattern in 'New Stone' (an ironstone pottery), the greyish color of which nicely resembled the Chinese Export porcelain glaze. While the first Spode pieces in this pattern may well have been made as replacements for depleted Chinese Export services, the design met with instant success, and remained in production continuously at Spode for 150 years. Presumably, Coalport's version of the pattern was put into production hastily to meet the initial demand, but it never rivaled Spode's success, and surviving examples of Coalport's 'Peacock' pattern are uncommon.

This part dinner service belonged to Jacqueline Kennedy Onassis' mother, Janet Lee Auchincloss.

$4,000–6,000

18 **A Coalport Porcelain 'Peacock' Pattern Square Salad Bowl, 1815-20**

En suite with the preceding lot, each side of the exterior and the center of the interior decorated with the peafowl perched on rocks amidst flowers above or within a roundel of gilt spearheads, the sides of the interior with trailing floral vines beneath the gilt chain border and gilt-edged rim (forking crack).
Width 9¹⁵⁄₁₆ in. (25.2 cm.)

See note to lot 17.

$300–500

19 **A Pair of Coalport Porcelain 'Peacock' Pattern Oval Sauce Tureens, Covers and Stands, 1815-20**

En suite with the two preceding lots, the tureens (one hair cracked) decorated on either side, and the covers (both hair cracked and one chipped) and stands decorated across the top or center with the peafowl design beneath or within the gilt chain border around the rim, the tureens with the gilt spearhead border around the footrim. (4)
Lengths 7½ and 8½ in. (19 and 21.6 cm.)

See note to lot 17.

$600–800

20 **A Set of Twelve Coalport Porcelain 'Peacock' Pattern Plates, 1815-20**

En suite with the three preceding lots, (four with a small rim chip).
Diameters 9⅜ to 9½ in. (23.8 to 24.1 cm.)

See note to lot 17.

$900–1,200

21 **A Set of Eleven Coalport Porcelain 'Peacock' Pattern Plates, 1815-20**

En suite with the four preceding lots, (some imperfections, and one repaired).
Diameters 9⅜ to 9½ in. (23.8 to 24.1 cm.)

See note to lot 17.

$500–700

22 **A Pair of Coalport Porcelain 'Peacock' Pattern Dessert Plates, 1815-20**

En suite with the five preceding lots, (one with a star crack in the glaze on the base), *impressed numeral 2 marks.*
Diameters 8⁹⁄₁₆ and 8¹¹⁄₁₆ in. (21.7 and 22.1 cm.)

See note to lot 17.

$200–300

23 **A Pair of Coalport Porcelain 'Peacock' Pattern Plates, circa 1830**

Similarly decorated to the six preceding lots, but the porcelain of a whiter body, *impressed potter's marks and painter's letter P in blue enamel.*
Diameters 9⅝ and 9¾ in. (24.4 and 24.8 cm.)

See note to lot 17.

$200–300

17 - 23

24

24 **A Regency Rosewood Reading and Games Table, early 19th Century**

Inset with a panel of gilt-tooled green leather, rising on an adjustable ratchet and sliding to reveal a backgammon well, the demilune ends hinged and opening for writing implements and game pieces, the apron with pull-out chessboard slide at one side and work basket support at the other, and the whole on trestle supports and inlaid with brass stringing.
Height 28½ in. (72.4 cm.), length 29 in. (73.7 cm.), depth 16 in. (40.6 cm.)

This table was among the furnishings in the West Sitting Room of the White House during President and Mrs. Kennedy's residence.

$3,500–4,500

25

25 **A Chinese Export Porcelain Oval Dish for the American Market, circa 1876**

Painted in black, yellow, blue, turquoise, iron-red and brown in the center with seven figures before an encampment beneath a spread-winged eagle bearing in his beak a banderole inscribed THE SURRENDER OF BURGOYNE, the rim with floral sprigs beneath a flowering vine border around the edge, (extensively restored).
Length 11¼ in. (28.6 cm.)

An oval platter decorated with this scene of the surrender of General John Burgoyne at Saratoga on October 17, 1777, was sold in these rooms on May 20, 1972, lot 366; and is illustrated by David Sanctuary Howard, *New York and the China Trade*, p. 120, no. C91, who indicates that it "is sketchily copied from John Trumbull's painting, which is now at Yale University, but the Chinese artist has omitted Burgoyne's sword and shown him shaking hands with [the American General Horatio] Gates." A similarly decorated bowl is illustrated by Geoffrey A. Godden, *Oriental Export Market Porcelain*, p. 295; and a shaped square dish was in the collection of John Alex McCone, sold also in these rooms on January 22, 1992, lot 202.

$200–300

26

26 **A Pair of Italian Neoclassical Style Blue and White Painted Armchairs**

Each with a horseshoe-shaped back-rest, out-curved wooden armrests raised on curved supports, the bow-fronted seat raised on square tapered legs.

These armchairs were among the furnishings in Mrs. Kennedy's bedroom at the White House, and previously, they were in their house in Georgetown.

$1,500–2,000

27 **An Early Victorian Mother-of-Pearl-Inset Papier-Mâché Dressing Table, circa 1845**

The shaped rectangular top painted and mother-of-pearl inlaid with pagodas and figures in a landscape, the interior with a well, conforming frieze and raised on four scrolled legs, joined by a serpentine-sided platform stretcher, distressed.
Height 29½ in. (74.9 cm.), length 20½ in. (52.1 cm.), width 14 in. (35.6 cm.)

Provenance:
Parke-Bernet, New York, December 15-16, 1961, Sale 2074, lot 140

This table was among the furnishings in Mrs. Kennedy's dressing room at the White House.

$1,500–2,000

27

Pairs, left to right: 30, 28, 29

28 **A Pair of English Enamel Table Candlesticks, South Staffordshire, late 18th Century**

Painted with puce figural vignettes on a white ground, (some chips and repairs).
Height 9½ in. (24.1 cm.)

These candlesticks were among the furnishings of the White House during President and Mrs. Kennedy's residence.

$900–1,200

29 **A Pair of English Enamel Table Candlesticks, South Staffordshire, circa 1800**

Painted with sprays of flowers on a white ground, (extensively chipped and repaired).
Height 10¼ in. (26 cm.)

These candlesticks were among the furnishings of the White House during President and Mrs. Kennedy's residence.

$600–800

The John F. Kennedy Library

Above: *President Kennedy's bedroom, The White House, 1962, showing lot 31.*

30 **A Pair of English Enamel Candlesticks, South Staffordshire, late 18th Century**

Painted with flowers on a white ground, (extensively chipped and repaired).
Height 9½ in. (24.1 cm.)

These candlesticks were among the furnishings of the White House during President and Mrs. Kennedy's residence.

$600–800

31 **Circle of John Nost Sartorius**

'SMOLENSKO' AHEAD and A CHESTNUT COLT WITH JOCKEY UP: A PAIR OF PAINTINGS

the first titled
oil on canvas
11½ by 14 in. (29.2 by 35.6 cm.)

'Smolensko', by 'Sorcerer', was owned by Sir Charles Bunbury (1740-1821), 6th Bart. The Bunbury family owned large estates in Suffolk. Sir Charles Bunbury was a member of the House of Commons for over forty years. He was a prominent member of the racing community and was a co-founder of the Derby at Epsom and the 2,000 Guineas in 1813. In the present work his jockey is probably Tom Goodison, who rode him to victory at Epsom. The jockey is wearing the pink and white striped silks of Sir Charles Bunbury. 'Smolensko' was the third horse belonging to Sir Charles Bunbury to win the Derby at Epsom.

The second horse in this pair is ridden by a jockey wearing the green and white striped silks of Thomas, 3rd Baron Foley (1780-1863). It is probable that this chestnut colt is 'Soothsayer', the winner of the St. Leger in 1811. Lord Foley bought 'Soothsayer' after the St. Leger victory. 'Soothsayer's' last win was in 1813 at an important match race at Newmarket against the 1811 Derby winner 'Phantom.' Although 'Soothsayer' and 'Smolensko' never raced against each other, they were both by 'Sorcerer' and owned by friends and fellow members of the Jockey Club which could explain their pairing for these works.

These paintings were among the furnishings in President Kennedy's bedroom at the White House.

$2,000–3,000

31

31

32 **An American Hide-Covered Child's Rocking Horse, early 20th Century**

In the form of a roan with leather saddle and bridle, and on a brass-mounted maple platform.
Length 4 ft. 2 in. (127 cm.)

This rocking horse was among the furnishings in Caroline Kennedy's nursery at the White House.

$2,000–3,000

32

The John F. Kennedy Library

Above: *Caroline Kennedy's Nursery, The White House, showing lot 32.*

33

33 **A Victorian Mahogany Youth Chair, probably French, second half 19th Century**

The tub-shaped backrest with red velvet upholstery, and with straight arms, basket footrest, sliding tray and molded cabriole legs.
Height 38 in. (96.5 cm.)

This high chair was used by John F. Kennedy, Jr. while in residence at the White House.

$1,500–2,000

34 **An American Silver-Cased 25 ft. 9 in. Tape Measure, Tiffany & Co., New York, circa 1965**

With flexible steel graduated rule, the otherwise plain circular case engraved with the initials JBK (Jacqueline Bouvier Kennedy), chrome plated winder.
Diameter 3 in. (7.6 cm.)

$500–700

34

35

35 **Two Hellenistic Terracotta Horses, Canosa, 3rd Century B.C.**

Each vigorously modeled steed rearing with the head slightly turned, one to the right, the other to the left, and wearing a bridle with applied disk ornament, the reins molded in relief on the neck, and with short wavy mane and top-knot, the details painted in traces of red, yellow, and black over a white gesso ground.
Length 12 ⅛ in. (30.8 cm.)

Compare Louvre Museum, *Encyclopédie Photographique de l'Art*, vol. II, Paris, 1936, p. 256, and Sotheby's, New York, December 14th, 1993, no. 62.

$12,000–18,000

36 **A Black-glazed Trefoil Oinochoe, Magna Graecia, Apulia, circa mid-4th Century B.C.**

With torus foot, ribbed ovoid body, flange at the base of the neck, and high faceted handle, the vessel ornamented with a band of ovolo kymation carved on the overhanging rim, an applied gilt terracotta wreath encircling the shoulder, a collar of ivy leaves and berries encircling the neck, and a beaded band around the base of the handle.
Height 13 ¼ in. (33.7 cm.)

$20,000–30,000

36

37

37 **A Silver-Plated Beaker, Christofle, mid 20th Century**

Engraved *JK*
Height 3 in. (7.6 cm.)

$100–150

38

38 **A German Earthenware Large Tub, Franz Anton Mehlem, Bonn, circa 1910**

Of tapering cylindrical shape, lightly molded with gilt floral garlands, 'French' ribbons and grapevines interspersed with colorful floral bouquets, wreaths and sprigs between gilt-edged green borders around the rim and footrim, (the glaze crackled), *BONN FRANZ ANT. MEHLEM castle mark printed in green, and various pattern and model numbers painted in puce and impressed.*
Height 12⅜ in. (31.4 cm.)

This tub was among the furnishings in the West Sitting Room of the White House during President and Mrs. Kennedy's residence.

$800–1,200

39

39 **A Hellenistic Marble Torso of Aphrodite, 2nd/1st Century B.C.**

Of slender graceful form, her body turned to the left and bending forward to untie her sandal, her cloak formerly falling from the left shoulder.
Height 6 ¼ in. (15.9 cm.)

Provenance:
J. J. Klejman, New York

Compare Comstock and Vermeule, *Sculpture in Stone, The Greek, Roman and Etruscan Collections of the Museum of Fine Arts Boston*, 1976, p. 114, no. 175; also compare Margarete Bieber, *The Sculpture of the Hellenistic Age*, New York, 1961, fig. 394, now in The Metropolitan Museum of Art, and *Antiquities from the Collection of Christos G. Bastis*, New York, 1987, no. 132.

$6,000–9,000

40 **A Pair of Louis XVI Painted Fauteuils en Cabriolet, last quarter 18th Century**

Each tapered upholstered rectangular backrest with *chapeau de gendarme* top rail carved with leaf tips and beading; the out-curved armrests raised on fluted baluster-shaped supports, the bow-fronted seat raised on circular, tapered fluted legs; painted off-white.

These chairs were among the furnishings in the West Sitting Room of the White House during President and Mrs. Kennedy's residence.

$10,000–15,000

"Behold me at length on the vaunted scene of Europe," Thomas Jefferson wrote home from Paris in 1784, where he had gone to assist John Adams and Benjamin Franklin in trade negotiations. For this lover of fine arts, Europe was a glittering paradise. "Were I to proceed to tell you how much I enjoy their architecture, sculpture, painting, music," he observed, "I should want words." The following year Jefferson replaced Franklin as American minister in Paris. He remained there, living in the Hôtel de Langeac on the borders of the Champs Elyssée, until October 1789, just two months after the destruction of the Bastille and the start of the French Revolution. Having been granted a leave of absence to settle his private affairs and to take his two daughters home, he returned to the United States, fully expecting to resume his duties in Paris after a six-month leave. But when he disembarked at Norfolk in late November, the newspapers at once informed him of his nomination by President Washington to the post of Secretary of State in the new government. Never again did Jefferson leave his native country. When his household effects in Paris were eventually packed for shipment to America in the early 1790s they filled eighty-six crates described in a sixteen-page inventory.

Susan R. Stein, curator at Monticello, Thomas Jefferson's former home near Charlottesville, Virginia, has recently published her findings based on documentary evidence relating to his acquisition of furniture in France (*The Worlds of Thomas Jefferson at Monticello,* 1983). Judging from the inventory or shipping list, the Hôtel de Langeac at the time of Jefferson's incumbency contained abundant seating furniture: in all there were forty-eight chairs of one sort or another, as well as sofas, tables, beds, commodes, and other items. Using the list as her source, Mrs. Stein has divided the seating furniture according to form. "These," she writes, "included twenty-two armchairs, twenty-two side chairs, and four *bergères* (easy chairs)." It is believed that much of the furniture sent from France to Monticello remained there until Jefferson's death. An inventory of his household goods taken in 1815 mentions "6 sophas with gold leaf" and "44 chairs with gold leaf" which were undoubtedly among his acquisitions from Paris. In order to pay off his debts, his daughter, Martha Jefferson Randolph, held a sale in January 1827 shortly after his death at which his effects were dispersed, chiefly among buyers from his own family and neighbors from Albemarle and nearby counties.

The armchairs in the present lot may have been purchased by Captain John M. Perry at or soon after the 1827 sale; certainly they were found eighty years later in a stable loft at Montebello, the mansion he built in the vicinity of Charlottesville between 1818 and 1820. Sometime after the Montebello estate changed hands in 1907 the chairs were sold and found their way into the Fisher family of Baltimore. In 1962 they were sold by Mrs. Janon Fisher to Jacqueline Kennedy. No doubt the chairs were close at hand when later that same year, at a dinner honoring twenty-nine Nobel Prize winners, President John F. Kennedy in a famous toast referred to his celebrated predecessor's erudition and accomplishments; his guests embodied, he said, "the most extraordinary collection of talent, of human knowledge, that has ever been gathered together at the White House, with the possible exception of when Thomas Jefferson dined alone."

A clearly erroneous theory concerning the origin of the armchairs is predicated by the existence of a photograph taken in the 1870s or '80s which shows the corner of Dr. John McCalla's parlor in his house in Washington, D.C. The room contains an armchair, now in the Baltimore Museum of Art, which, with the exception of the upholstery, appears to be identical to the present examples. A contemporary handwritten caption on the reverse of the photograph reads, "...7 - A chair owned and used by Marie Antoinette at the Trianon; was bought by Thomas Jefferson at the time of the Revolution with the others of the set and brought to this country and used at Monticello."

40

41 **Ebonized Baby Grand Piano, Henry F. Miller, Boston**

Together with a Piano Bench.

$3,000–5,000

41

42

42 **A Bessarabian Style Machine-Made Carpet, after a design by Stéphane Boudin, 20th Century**

The overall pattern of brown and white ovals containing coral or blue flowers separated by chartreuse strapwork, within a small geometric border. *Approximately 18 ft. by 7 ft. 11 in. (5.49 by 2.41 m.)*

This rug, after a design by Stéphane Boudin (1888-1967), is of the same pattern as those supplied under his supervision to Lady Olive Baillie for her dining room at Leeds Castle, Kent, England, and President and Mrs. Kennedy for the White House State Dining Room. W.A.A. Wells, the present Agent and Curator of Leeds Castle, writes that the version under his care is described as "a loop pile tufted carpet, the ivory field with a repeating walnut floral medallion design in shades of green, saffron and rose."

Jacqueline Kennedy and Boudin were introduced to each other about 1956 by a mutual friend. Mrs. Kennedy shared the view of many who thought him one of the most celebrated interior designers of his generation. "When you saw him work," she told *The New York Times Magazine*, "you saw what no American decorator could do. In France, you are trained as an interior architect…[he gave the rooms] a sense of state, ceremony, arrival and grandeur."

Stéphane Boudin's career began under his father, Alexandre Boudin, a maker of trimmings, tassels and other passementeries. At the age of thirty-five in 1923 he joined the well-known Parisian decorating firm of Maison de Jansen, which had been founded in 1880. By 1936 he had become the firm's president and under his guidance it began a program of purchasing eighteenth and nineteenth century interiors for installation in houses on both sides of the Atlantic. Indeed, Boudin was fascinated by period detail and for his schemes was able to draw inspiration from his own considerable knowledge as well as Jansen's library of prints, drawings and photographs. It was this aspect of his accomplishments which particularly impressed Mrs. Kennedy.

Something of the grandeur of Boudin's White House interiors, which he created under the watchful eye of Jacqueline Kennedy, was conveyed in the 1995 exhibition at Boscobel. An illustrated catalogue, *A Frenchman in Camelot / The Decoration of the Kennedy White House by Stephane Boudin*, with essays by James A. Abbott and Elaine M. Rice, was published in conjunction with this event.

$2,000–3,000

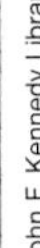
The John F. Kennedy Library

Leeds Castle Enterprises Ltd.

Above: *State Dining Room, The White House, 1963.*

Left: *The Dining Room, Leeds Castle, Maidstone, Kent, England*

43 **A Study of a Spotted-Billed or Gray Pelican (*Pelecanus philippensis*), a Natural History Illustration Painted by the Artist Zayn al-Din for Lady Impey, Calcutta, Company School, dated 1780**

Watercolor on European (Whatman) paper, inscribed in English and Persian "In the Collection of Lady Impey at Calcutta. Painted by Zayn al-Din. Native of Patna, 1778"
29 ¾ by 21 ¼ in. (75.6 by 54 cm.)

$20,000–30,000

The great series of natural history illustrations made in Calcutta for Lady Impey between 1777 and 1783 is the earliest and undoubtedly the finest of such series commissioned by the British in India. Sir Elijah Impey (1732-1809) was appointed first Chief Justice in Bengal in 1774. His appointment, accompanied by his knighthood, was a direct result of the regulating Act of 1774, which necessitated the establishment of law courts in Calcutta for the administration of English law in Bengal. When Sir Elijah left for India with his wife Mary aboard the *Anson*, they took their household servants with them in addition to a moonshee from whom Sir Elijah could learn the Persian necessary for his new legal posting. On landing, he set about collecting manuscripts and miniatures almost immediately, having his personal collector's seal cut within the year. Though now obscured by the mounting, impressions of this seal are to be found on the reverse of most of the natural history drawings.

But it was Lady Impey, bound to the house by family duties and her many children, who collected exotic creatures in the garden of their Calcutta house. From 1777, she employed Shaykh Zayn al-Din to record the animals and birds on a true-to-life scale satisfactory to the eighteenth-century passion for recording new species. Zayn al-Din came from Patna where, it can be assumed, he had been trained in the Mughal techniques of miniature painting. After three years he was joined by two Hindu painters, Bhawani Das and Ram Das, both also from Patna. The project continued until Impey was recalled to London in 1783, by which time over 300 illustrations had been completed. The Impeys brought the collection with them to London, where the drawings were of interest to contemporary ornithologists.

After Sir Elijah's death, the collection was sold with many of his other possessions on May 21, 1810, by Phillips of New Bond Street. At the time of the sale there were 197 drawings of birds, 76 fishes, 8 flowers, 28 reptiles and 17 beasts. The largest group was purchased by Archibald Elijah Impey (1766-1831), a natural son of Sir Elijah Impey. His widow, Mrs. Sarah Impey, bequeathed their collection of sixty-four illustrations to the Linnaean Society, London, in 1855.

Examples from the Impey series of natural history drawings are in the collections of the Victoria and Albert Museum, London, the Wellcome Institute, London, the Radcliffe Science Library, Oxford, the Binney Collection, San Diego, and in private collections in Europe and America. Other leaves have been sold at auction. See Sotheby's, London, April 29, 1992, lot 1 and October 22, 1993, lot 229; Christie's, London, June 13, 1983, lots 19-27, and Christie's, New York, October 3, 1990, lot 66.

Exhibited:
Toby Falk and Gael Hayter, *Birds in an Indian Garden*, exhibition catalogue, Michael Goedhuis, Ltd., (Colnaghi Oriental) and Mallet & Son (Antiques) Ltd., London, June 12 to July 14, 1984, color illus. The authors comment that "this cumbersome-looking bird is a deceptively intelligent hunter and is therefore to be found in a wide variety of water areas. Hunting in flocks, pelicans drive shoals of fish into the shallows where they are scooped into the capacious pouched bills."

References:
Archer, M. & W. G., *Indian Painting for the British. 1770-1880*, Oxford, 1955, figs. 44-77; Welch, S. C., *Room for Wonder. Indian Painting during the British Period*, New York, 1978, nos. 6-9; E. A. Impey, *About the Impeys*, Worcester 1963; Toby Falk and Gael Hayter, *Birds in an Indian Garden*, exhibition catalogue, London, Michael Goedhuis, Ltd., (Colnaghi Oriental) and Mallet & Son (Antiques) Ltd., 1984; Welch, S. C., *India. Art and Culture 1300-1900*, Metropolitan Museum of Art, New York, 1985, no. 28

گکن بهہ
In the Collection of Lady Impey at Calcutta
Painted by زین الدین a Native of Patna 1780

43

44 **A Study of a Milky Stork (*Mycteria cinerea*) Eating a Snail, a Natural History Illustration Painted by the Artist Zayn al-Din for Lady Impey, Calcutta, Company School, dated 1781**

Watercolor on European (Whatman) paper, inscribed in English and Persian with measurements of the bird and "In the Collection of Lady Impey at Calcutta. Painted by Zayn al-Din. Native of Patna, 1781"
21 ¼ by 29 ¾ in. (54 by 75.6 cm.)

$20,000–30,000

The Milky or Southern Painted Stork is found in Cambodia, Malaya, Java and Sumatra.

Exhibited:
Toby Falk and Gael Hayter, *Birds in an Indian Garden*, exhibition catalogue, Michael Goedhuis, Ltd., (Colnaghi Oriental) and Mallet & Son (Antiques) Ltd., London, June 12 to July 14, 1984, color illus.

Please refer to note corresponding to previous lot.

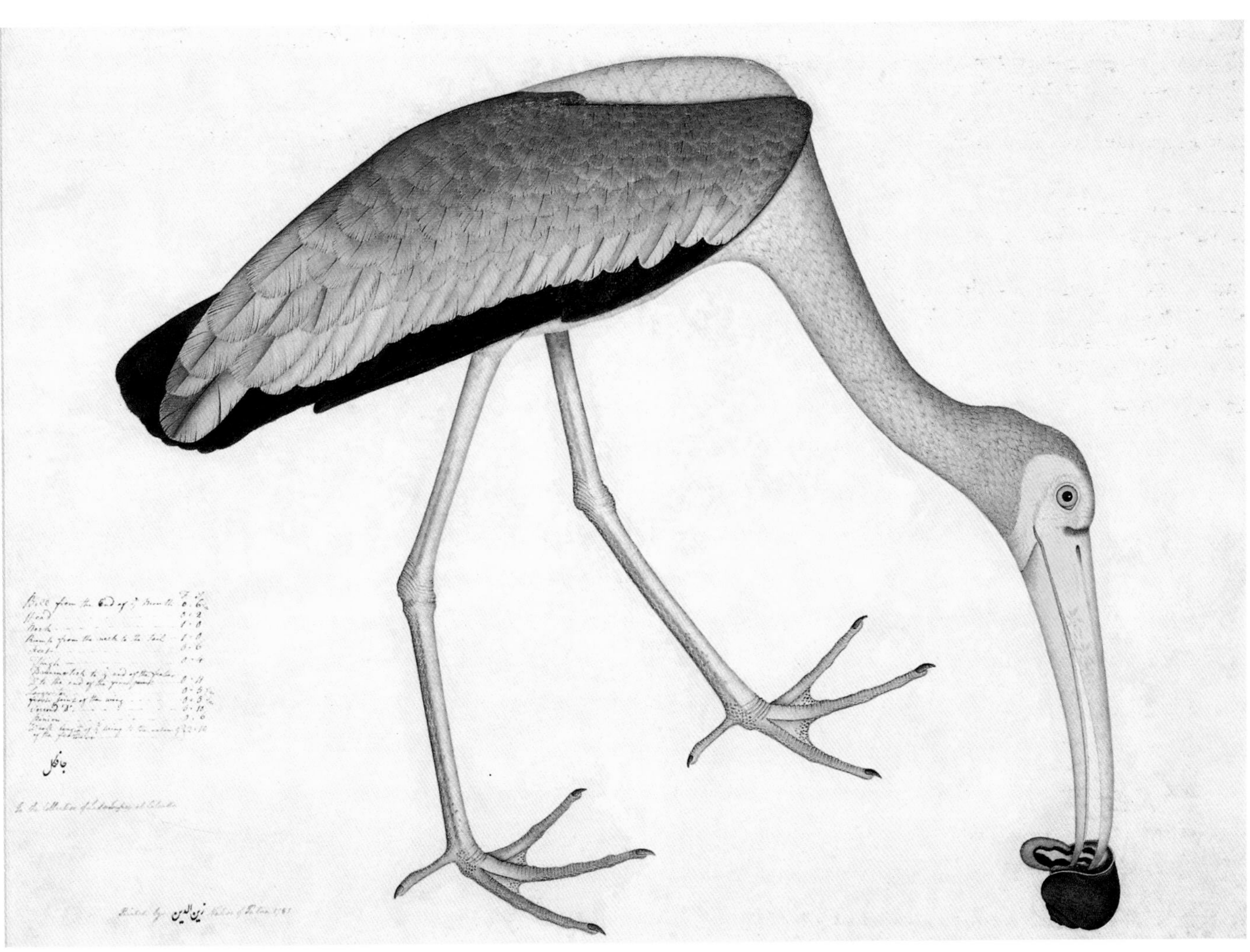

44

45 **John Singer Sargent (1856-1925)**

HEAD OF AN ARAB

signed *John S. Sargent* and dedicated *To George Aitken*, l.r.
watercolor and body color on paper
12 ½ by 10 ¼ in. (31.7 by 26 cm.)

$100,000–125,000

By the early 1900s, watercolor had become John Singer Sargent's favored medium. He preferred its immediacy and portability, which he considered crucial for his extended travels. In the winter of 1905, Sargent made a second trip to the Middle East in an attempt to gather fresh material for the completion of the Boston Public Library mural, *The History of Religion* (six lunettes connecting the Pagan and Christian ends of the library hall, which were installed in 1916). Annette Blaugrund notes in her essay, "Sargent's Watercolors", that "Sargent clearly demonstrates a change in his watercolor style" during his second trip to the Middle East (*John Singer Sargent*, New York, Whitney Museum of American Art, October 1986-April 1987, p. 225). *Head of an Arab*, executed circa 1905-1906, was one of many figural studies completed on this particular excursion through Syria and Palestine. Using the white unpainted surface of the paper for highlights, Sargent applied ultramarine blue and sienna brown in varying intensity to capture his subject adding gouache for accents evident in the rendering of the face. Eleven of the Bedouin subjects which were executed during this trip are in the permanent collection at the Brooklyn Museum and all bear strong similarities to *Head of an Arab.*

This painting will be included in the forthcoming J. S. Sargent *catalogue raisonné* by Richard Ormond and Elaine Kilmurray, in collaboration with Warren Adelson and Elizabeth Oustinoff.

Provenance:
George Aitken (acquired directly from the artist)
Mrs. Maime Woolf (his niece)
Miss S. O. Welch
Spink and Sons, 1968
Leroy Davis, New York, 1969
Acquired by the present owner from the above

Exhibited:
New York, Andrew Crispo Gallery, *Ten American Masters of Watercolor*, May-June, 1974, illustrated in color no. 132
New York, Davis & Langdale Co., *British Drawings, 1760-1925: A Loan Exhibition*, May 1985, no. 58, illustrated

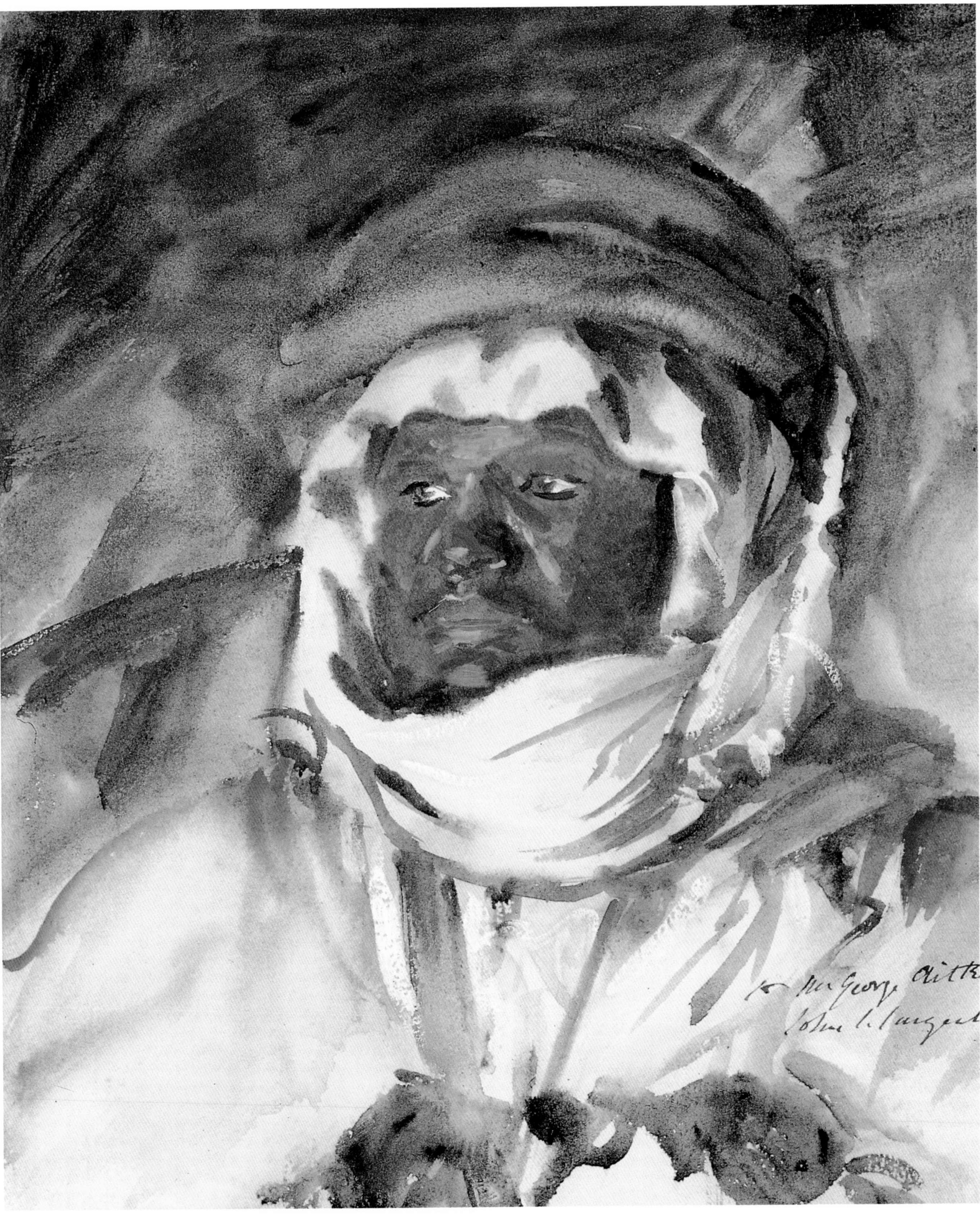

45

46 **John Singer Sargent** (1856-1925)

VENETIAN GIRL

watercolor on paper
20 by 13¾ in. (50.8 by 34.9 cm.)

$80,000–120,000

Beginning in 1880 and continuing over the course of three decades, John Singer Sargent made regular visits to Venice. During his sojourns, he documented the city and its inhabitants in both watercolor and oil, but watercolor freed him to explore diverse subjects and to work in a spontaneous and personal manner. Throughout his career, Sargent used watercolor as a sketching medium, but it was not until the years following the turn of the century that he concentrated on mastering varying watercolor techniques. Donelson Hoopes observed: "Very quickly, Sargent was applying a vigorous brush to paper with a *brio* that is unmatched. Watercolor seemed to release him from constraints about pictorial 'manners'" (Donelson F. Hoopes, *Sargent Watercolors*, New York, 1976, p. 19).

Venetian Girl shares qualities frequently found in many of Sargent's portrayals of Venetian women in interiors. Both the watercolors and the oil paintings incorporate brilliant blacks and chromatically rich whites set against a spare background of warm ochres and cool greys. The present watercolor depicts a young woman with her face in half-shadow as she engages the viewer with her warm smile and extended arm which holds an open fan. *Venetian Girl* relates to *Italian Girl with Fan* (1882, 92¾ by 52½ inches, Cincinnati Art Museum; The Edwin and Virginia Irwin Memorial) which depicts a single standing female figure wearing a cream dress and burgundy shawl holding a large blue fan. Both works have a mysterious and exotic tone which is characteristic of Sargent's paintings executed in Venice.

This painting will be included in the forthcoming J. S. Sargent *catalogue raisonné* by Richard Ormond and Elaine Kilmurray, in collaboration with Warren Adelson and Elizabeth Oustinoff.

Provenance:
Emily Sargent (the artist's sister)
Acquired by the present owner, circa 1969

Exhibited:
London, England, The Royal Academy, 1926, no. 101 (as *A Venetian Girl*)
London, England, Tate Gallery, *Opening Exhibition of the Sargent Gallery*, June-October 1926 (as *A Venetian Girl*)
New York, Andrew Crispo Gallery, *Ten Americans: Masters of Watercolor*, May-June 1974, illustrated no. 128 (as *Venetian Lady*)

47 **Babb, James T.**

The White House Library: A Short-Title List. *Washington: The White House Historical Association, 1967*

(9 x 5¾ in.). Photographic frontispiece of the White House library. Half red pebble-grain cloth over taupe buckram, spine gilt-lettered, gray endpapers. Gray board slipcase printed with the federal eagle and letterpress spine label.

LIMITED EDITION, number 84 of 300 numbered copies of the first edition, signed on the limitation page by Lady Bird Johnson and with an unaccomplished White House Library gift bookplate tipped in. This copy is also SIGNED on the front free endpaper by Jacqueline Kennedy. The renewal of the White House library—"intended to contain books which best represent the history and culture of the United States, works most essential for an understanding of our national experience"—was begun by Mrs. John F. Kennedy in 1962 and seen to completion by Mrs. Johnson.

$1,500–2,500

THE FIRST EDITION OF THE SHORT-TITLE LIST OF THE WHITE HOUSE LIBRARY HAS BEEN LIMITED TO THREE HUNDRED NUMBERED COPIES, EACH HERE SIGNED BY MRS. LYNDON B. JOHNSON

Lady Bird Johnson

THIS COPY IS NUMBER 84

47

48 **Kennedy, John F.**

Profiles in Courage. *New York: Harper & Row, (1964)*

(9 x 5¾ in.). Photographic frontispiece portrait of President Kennedy, photographic plates. Blue morocco, covers gilt-panelled, spine gilt in six compartments with red morocco lettering-pieces, red morocco doublures, red moiré silk linings, gilt edges. Blue cloth slipcase.

PUBLISHER'S PRESENTATION COPY, with a calligraphic inscription written below the half-title: "This volume, the first of two specially bound copies of The Memorial Edition of 'Profiles in Courage', is presented by the publisher to Mrs. John F. Kennedy." The second copy of this edition of *Profiles in Courage* specially bound by the publisher was presented to Robert F. Kennedy.

$3,000–5,000

PROFILES IN COURAGE

This volume, the first of
two specially bound copies of
the Memorial Edition of
"Profiles in Courage",
is presented by
the publisher to
Mrs. John F. Kennedy

48

48

49 **Kennedy, John F.**

Why England Slept. *New York: Wilfred Funk, 1940*

(8 x 5½ in.). Blue sheep gilt, front cover gilt with the supralibros of ROSE F. KENNEDY, gilt edges; extremities worn, endpapers foxed.

THE DEDICATION COPY OF JOHN F. KENNEDY'S FIRST BOOK; the printed dedication reads "To My Mother and Father." *Why England Slept* was a revised and expanded version of JFK's Harvard senior thesis, the publication of which was suggested and advanced by Joseph P. Kennedy. The volume also contains the presidential bookplate of John F. Kennedy.

$3,000–5,000

49

Photograph of the family visiting Runnymede is included in Lot 50.

50 **Kennedy, John F.**

Inauguration of the British Memorial to John F. Kennedy by Her Majesty Queen Elizabeth II at Runnymede on the 14th May 1965. *[London, 1965]*

(10¼ x 8⅝ in.). Extra-illustrated with 8 tipped-in silverprint photographs (each 9½ x 7¼ in. or the reverse). Blue morocco by Tollit & Harvey, covers with gilt-fillet border, front cover gilt with title and the SUPRALIBROS OF JACQUELINE BOUVIER KENNEDY ("J. B. K."), marbled endleaves; binding slightly rubbed and buckled.

The official printing of the order of service and speeches for the dedication of the Runnymede Memorial. The photographs bound at the end of Mrs. Kennedy's copy depict the carved memorial stone, the arrival of the Kennedy family, the royal dais, and other views of the ceremony.

$1,500–2,500

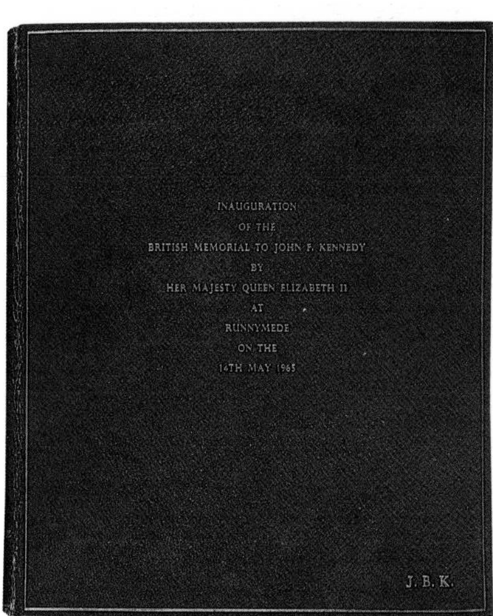

50

87TH CONGRESS, 1ST SESSION

HOUSE DOCUMENT NO. 218

Inaugural Addresses

OF THE

PRESIDENTS OF THE UNITED STATES

FROM

GEORGE WASHINGTON 1789

TO

JOHN F. KENNEDY 1961

UNITED STATES GOVERNMENT PRINTING OFFICE
WASHINGTON, D.C.
1961

John F. Kennedy

INAUGURAL ADDRESS

JANUARY 20, 1961

Mr. Chief Justice, President Eisenhower, Vice President Nixon, President Truman, reverend clergy, fellow citizens, we observe today not a victory of party, but a celebration of freedom—symbolizing an end, as well as a beginning—signifying renewal, as well as change. For I have sworn before you and Almighty God the same solemn oath our forebears prescribed nearly a century and three quarters ago.

The world is very different now. For man holds in his mortal hands the power to abolish all forms of human poverty and all forms of human life. And yet the same revolutionary beliefs for which our forebears fought are still at issue around the globe—the belief that the rights of man come not from the generosity of the state, but from the hand of God.

We dare not forget today that we are the heirs of that first revolution. Let the word go forth from this time and place, to friend and foe alike, that the torch has been passed to a new generation of Americans—born in this century, tempered by war, disciplined by a hard and bitter peace, proud of our ancient heritage—and unwilling to witness or permit the slow undoing of those human rights to which this Nation has always been committed, and to which we are committed today at home and around the world.

74578 O—61——18

267

51

yet both racing to alter that uncertain balance of terror that stays the hand of mankind's final war.

So let us begin anew—remembering on both sides that civility is not a sign of weakness, and sincerity is always subject to proof. *Let us never negotiate out of fear. But let us never fear to negotiate.*

Let both sides explore what problems unite us instead of laboring those problems which divide us.

Let both sides, for the first time, formulate serious and precise proposals for the inspection and control of arms—and bring the absolute power to destroy other nations under the absolute control of all nations.

Let both sides seek to invoke the wonders of science instead of its terrors. Together let us explore the stars, conquer the deserts, eradicate disease, tap the ocean depths, and encourage the arts and commerce.

Let both sides unite to heed in all corners of the earth the command of Isaiah—to "undo the heavy burdens and to let the oppressed go free."

And if a beachhead of cooperation may push back the jungle of suspicion, let both sides join in creating a new endeavor, not a new balance of power, but a new world of law, where the strong are just and the weak secure and the peace preserved.

All this will not be finished in the first 100 days. Nor will it be finished in the first 1,000 days, nor in the life of this administration, nor even perhaps in our lifetime on this planet. But let us begin.

In your hands, my fellow citizens, more than in mine, will rest the final success or failure of our course. Since this country was founded, each generation of Americans has been summoned to give testimony to its national loyalty. The graves of young Americans who answered the call to service ~~are found around~~ the globe.

Now the trumpet summons us again—not as a call to bear arms, though arms we need; not as a call to battle, though embattled we are; but a call to bear the burden of a long twilight struggle, year in, and year out, "rejoicing in hope, patient in tribulation"—a struggle against the common enemies of man: tyranny, poverty, disease, and war itself.

Can we forge against these enemies a grand and global alliance, North and South, East and West, that can assure a more fruitful life for all mankind? Will you join in that historic effort?

In the long history of the world, only a few generations have been granted the role of defending freedom in its hour of maximum danger. I do not shrink from this responsibility—I welcome it. I do not believe that any of us would exchange places with any other people or any other generation. The energy, the faith, the devotion which we bring to this endeavor will light our country and all who serve it—and the glow from that fire can truly light the world.

And so, my fellow Americans, ask not what your country can do for you: Ask what you can do for your country.

269

52

51 **Presidents of the United States**

Inaugural Addresses of the Presidents of the United States from George Washington 1789 to John F. Kennedy 1961. *Washington: GPO, 1961*

(9 x 5¾ in.). The address (or addresses for two-term presidents) of each chief executive is headed by an engraved vignette portrait (portraits of Tyler, Fillmore, Johnson, and Arthur, who did not make inaugural addresses, appear on a page facing the table of contents). Blue wrappers printed in red; spine and edges faded; adhesive residue from removed bookplate.

PRESIDENT KENNEDY'S COPY OF THE *INAUGURAL ADDRESSES OF THE PRESIDENTS OF THE UNITED STATES*, WITH HIS OWN ADDRESS MARKED AND CORRECTED IN HIS HAND.

On the title-page, Mrs. Kennedy has made the note "Hyannis July 1963, J. marked his passages in Inaug—& corrected it." President Kennedy's address, delivered on 20 January 1961, is printed on pages 267–270; he has marked the speech in blue ink with eleven marginal brackets indicating particularly important passages, including the stirring admonitions "And so, my fellow Americans, ask not what your country can do for you: Ask what you can do for your country. My fellow citizens of the world: Ask not what America will do for you, but what together we can do for the freedom of man."

On page 269, Kennedy has also made a substantive change to his text, scoring through the words "are found around" in the sentence "The graves of young Americans who answered the call to service are found around the globe," and writing in the margin the substitution "surround," which he has signed with the initials "JK."

$10,000–15,000

52 detail

52 **Stetson Brown Leather Hatbox**

Bearing a tag stating *The President. 15½ by 15 in. (39.4 by 38.1 cm.)*

$200–300

53 **Robert Rauschenberg**

DRAWING FOR PRESIDENT OF THE USA WITH DANTE

signed, titled, dated *1960* and inscribed *D-35* on the reverse
gouache, pencil and solvent transfer on artist's board
22 ¾ by 28 ¾ in. (58.4 by 73 cm.)

$80,000–100,000

From 1962 to 1964, Rauschenberg painted an important series of silkscreen paintings which combined an innovative use of materials with a rich iconographic vocabulary. The artist developed his technique of transferring media images onto paper and canvas in works of the late 1950s and early 1960s, such as the present drawing. Like the Cubists, Rauschenberg created "collaged" compositions by arranging images at varying angles and juxtapositions. At this time, a few of the most prevalent and evocative images were portraits of President John F. Kennedy and symbols of his office.

Three basic themes emerged in this series: Americana and patriotism, communications and mass media, and a populist Everyman. Within the American theme, images of President Kennedy were the most powerful and appeared in eight of the colored silkscreen paintings, including *Retroactive I* (collection of the Wadsworth Athenaeum, Hartford) and *Axle* (collection of the Museum Ludwig, Cologne). The artist felt that Kennedy "'re-established what a president is supposed to be—somebody special' … Rauschenberg saw Kennedy as a hero, as someone larger than life, and this view of the late president is clearly manifested in his art" (Roni Feinstein, *Robert Rauschenberg: the Silkscreen Painting, 1962-64*, New York, 1990, p. 82).

The present drawing, done in 1960, focuses on Kennedy's role as a campaigner. The office of President is symbolised by the images of the Oval Office, a bald eagle, George Washington, and a detail of a flag. The campaign theme is further suggested by the use of images that do not recur in the later paintings, including a map of the United States and a picture of Pat and Richard Nixon. The most significant addition to Rauschenberg's graphic vocabulary is the rare portrait of Mrs. Kennedy. Silkscreen images of Jacqueline Kennedy are most often associated with the work of Andy Warhol, but in this drawing, the image is a reference to the extreme popularity and effectiveness of the future First Lady on the campaign trail.

53

54 **Aaron Shikler (American, b. 1922)**

STUDY FOR THE WHITE HOUSE PORTRAIT OF JACQUELINE KENNEDY

signed with artist's initials *AAS* and dated *'68*, l.l.
oil on panel
13 ¾ by 5 ¾ in. (34.9 by 14.6 cm.)

$10,000–15,000

Aaron Shikler was born in Brooklyn, New York in March 1922. In the early 1940s, he studied painting at The Barnes Foundation in Marion, Pennsylvania, and the Tyler School of Art, Temple University, in Philadelphia. In 1949, Shikler returned to his hometown, working in Hans Hoffman's studio for several years. From 1953 to the present, Shikler has had approximately twenty-five one-person exhibitions, most of which were hosted by Davis & Langdale, New York. Shikler is considered by some critics as one of our great contemporary portrait painters.

In 1968, Jacqueline Kennedy's secretary contacted Aaron Shikler to commission a portrait of Caroline and John. Shikler believes that Mrs. Kennedy selected him because she had admired the portrait that he painted of her nieces and nephew, the Lawford children. When Shikler arrived at Mrs. Kennedy's New York apartment for a sketching session, Mrs. Kennedy remarked that "…they [Caroline and John] look just right to me now. I would like to remember them at this age. As they are, just now" (Aaron Shikler, "The Painting of a Legend," *McCall's*, March 1971, p. 79). Caroline was ten and John was seven. The final portrait of Caroline and John includes Mrs. Kennedy reading to them on a sofa in the apartment.

During one of the sketching sessions, Mrs. Kennedy asked Shikler if he would do her official White House portrait as well. Shikler recalls: "I wanted to create a painting that Mrs. Kennedy would feel was right and that would, at the same time, fall within the meaningful tradition of the White House, a tradition which she had done so much to preserve and enhance. I needed to paint a picture of the First Lady of the Land at the same time that I painted a picture of Jacqueline Bouvier Kennedy Onassis" (*ibid*, p. 118).

For the White House portrait, Mrs. Kennedy chose to have herself depicted in a long black skirt and a high-collared white blouse. Shikler executed numerous sketches of Mrs. Kennedy; some in casual poses and others more formal. Shikler recalls that "she was particularly pleased by a charcoal drawing of her reading a book" (*idem.*), but they both agreed that it was not formal enough for the official portrait. Eventually Mrs. Kennedy and Shikler chose a sketch that depicted Mrs. Kennedy standing before her fireplace, confronting the viewer with her direct gaze. Upon its completion, Shikler decided that he was not satisfied with the final version. He felt it was too girlish and coy and it failed to convey her reserve and her strength.

Shikler states: "The painting I finally did of her was the result of many studies I had done of her, a composite concept. She might have preferred another study for the White House. She might have wanted something a little more mysterious, a little less finished." However, he emphasized that "she left me completely alone" (Sally Quinn, "Aaron Shikler Talks About Kennedys," Washington *Post*, March 26, 1971). The official White House portrait depicts Mrs. Kennedy standing in a similar pose as the first portrait, wearing a full-length off-white dress with her head slightly turned to one side. Shikler explained that "he wanted a brighter, less troubled image, one that would immediately evoke how he—and the rest of the country—saw her: as an ethereal woman of almost mythological dimensions" (Byron Dobell, "The Forgotten Portrait," *Town & Country*, pp. 77-78).

54

55 **Elaine De Kooning**

PORTRAIT OF JOHN F. KENNEDY

signed with initials and dated *63*
charcoal on paper
35 by 26 in. (88.9 by 66 cm.)

$3,000–4,000

In the fall of 1962 Thomas Hart Benton and Robert Graham, director of the Graham Gallery, visited President Harry S. Truman. President Truman asked them about the possibility of a portrait of President Kennedy being done for his library in Independence, Missouri. As a result, Elaine de Kooning (1920-1989) traveled to Palm Beach and did many sketches of President Kennedy between Christmas, 1962, and New Year's Day, 1963. "In succeeding sessions of sketching, I was struck by the curious faceted structure of light over his face and hair—a quality of transparent ruddiness. This play of light contributed to the extraordinary variety of expressions. His smile and frown both seemed to be built-in to the bone. Everyone is familiar with the quick sense of humor revealed in the corners of his mouth and the laugh lines around the eyes, but what impressed me most was a sense of compassion" (Elaine de Kooning, *The Spirit of Abstract Expressionism*, New York, 1994, p. 202). Besides de Kooning, the President sat for only two other artists during his time in office. These were Pietro Annigoni, whose portrait of him was published as the cover of the "Man of the Year" issue of *Time* in 1962, and Wiliam Draper. Two other portraits, drawn at the same time, are offered as lots 759 and 760. A fourth portrait is in the Permanent Collection of the John F. Kennedy Library Foundation.

Provenance:
Graham Gallery, New York

Exhibited:
Washington Gallery of Modern Art, 1964
Pennsylvania Academy of Fine Arts, 1964
Graham Gallery, New York, 1965
Kansas City Art Institute, 1965 (catalogue no. 22)

Eddie Johnson

Elaine De Kooning drawing President Kennedy in Palm Beach

55

56 **Oak Rocking Chair**

With caned backrest and seat, loose cushions, padded arms and turned legs ending in rockers, stamped under left arm *Manufacturer of the original Carolina Rocker P & P Chair Company Asheboro, North Carolina*; upholstered by Larry Arata.
Height 43 ¼ in. (109.9 cm.), width 28 in. (71.1 cm.), depth 34 in. (86.4 cm.)

$3,000–5,000

"A rocker is a rocker and there isn't much you can do to make it look like anything else," Jacqueline Kennedy once said. Rocking chairs were recommended by Dr. Janet Travell to ease President Kennedy's severe back pain. In deference to the President's need for comfortable seating, the comment was one of surrender; Mrs. Kennedy was, after all, attempting to restore the White House state rooms, wherein, she explained, "everything...must have a reason for being there." But in a sense there was a very good historical reason why a rocking chair should have been included among the furnishings of the Oval Room: it is said that no less a personage than Dr. Benjamin Franklin devised the form by applying rockers to the lower extremities of a straight chair.

The pioneer minister Manasseh Cutler wrote after a visit to Franklin's home in July, 1787: "...the Doctor invited me into his library, which is likewise his study.... [He showed us] his great armed chair, with rockers." While Cutler's reference is the earliest dated citation for the usage in the *Oxford English Dictionary*, the antiquarian Dr. Irving I. Lyon found rocking chairs listed in inventories of estates of Hartford County, Connecticut, rather earlier: 1772 in Windsor and 1775 in Enfield. While in the eighteenth century straight slat-back chairs were converted into rockers, there are published advertisements as early as 1810 of fancy chair manufactories that produced rocking chairs, not as a new curiosity, but as an accepted and well-known type.

After 1840 the so-called Boston Rocker, a direct descendant of the Windsor rocker of the 1820s and 1830s, with flat rockers, turned and slightly raked legs, turned stretchers, a wood seat fashioned in a peculiar roll, arms curving over at the ends to fit the hands, and a high back of two stiles and seven slender spindles surmounted by a horizontal dressing with curved outline at the level of the sitter's head, were made in large quantities. About 1825, an Empire touch was added to the entire chair—rolling crest, seat and arms. The *Bridgeport Standard* of July 26, 1845, contains two advertisements in which the 'Boston rocker' is specifically mentioned. The rectangular headpiece was steamed and bent in a shallow curve, and the spindles were also steamed and bent to fit the back. As the Boston rocker began to become more a matter of quantity production in factories, material was conserved and work simplified. A plainer headpiece came into vogue, developing at length, about 1835, into the standard stenciled headpiece of the later Boston rocker, with the top rounded and the straight bottom edge cut with two semicircular notches. Boston rockers were made in great quantities in widely separated places, and become pretty generally standardized in form and construction after 1840. Most were made with pine or whitewood seats, while legs and spindles were made of oak, hickory, ash or maple. The price was low and they were widely distributed by peddlers.

Continued on next page.

The John F Kennedy Library

President Kennedy in the Second Floor Oval Room in The White House.

Rocking chairs abounded in Jacksonian America. The Englishwoman Anne Royall abhorred them. She stumbled over their bold crescent projections, departing the country in 1828 with "hardly a sound toe left." Nevertheless, the rocking chair became established in general use during this period. The critical English traveler and writer Harriet Martineau on a visit here in the mid 1830s was reflecting a fairly general attitude among foreigners when she wrote in her *Retrospect of Western Travel* of "The disagreeable practice of rocking in the chair... How this lazy and ungraceful indulgence ever became general, I cannot imagine, but the [American] nation seems so wedded to it, that I see but little chance of its being forsaken."

57

57 Walnut Humidor

With presentation plaque *To J.F.K. Good Health - Good Smoking, Milton Berle - 1/20/61.*
Height 12½ in. (31.7 cm.), length 12½ in. (31.7 cm.), width 13 in. (33 cm.)

$2,000–2,500

SOTHEBY'S

1334 York Avenue
New York, NY 10021
Tel: (212) 606-7000

THE ESTATE OF JACQUELINE KENNEDY ONASSIS

AUCTION RESULTS
(continued)

April 23–26, 1996

Sale Number 6834

LOT	U.S.$	LOT	U.S.$	LOT	U.S.$	LOT	U.S.$	LOT	U.S.$	LOT	U.S.$
745	11,500	**777**	7,475	**813**	5,175	**849**	5,750	**885**	9,775	**921**	2,875
746	18,400	**778**	14,950	**814**	8,050	**850**	4,600	**886**	9,775	**922**	2,875
747	7,475	**779**	6,900	**815**	3,450	**851**	3,450	**887**	2,875	**923**	3,450
748	12,650	**780**	25,300	**816**	6,900	**852**	5,750	**888**	5,750	**924**	3,450
749	20,700	**781**	25,300	**817**	9,200	**853**	3,450	**889**	2,875	**925**	9,775
750	16,100	**782**	5,175	**818**	123,500	**854**	4,025	**890**	12,650	**926**	5,750
751	13,800	**783**	40,250	**819**	4,600	**855**	5,750	**891**	34,500	**927**	4,600
752	7,475	**784**	6,325	**820**	9,775	**856**	5,175	**892**	4,600	**928**	16,100
753	5,750	**785**	8,050	**821**	9,775	**857**	4,600	**893**	31,050	**929**	37,375
754	387,500	**786**	7,475	**822**	18,400	**858**	12,650	**894**	9,775	**930**	6,325
755	772,500	**787**	6,900	**823**	6,900	**859**	12,650	**895**	40,250	**931**	5,750
756	65,750	**788**	12,650	**824**	5,750	**860**	4,600	**896**	13,800	**932**	31,050
757	63,000	**789**	6,900	**825**	4,887	**861**	4,025	**897**	4,600	**933**	6,325
758	28,750	**790**	7,475	**826**	6,900	**862**	4,025	**898**	4,025	**934**	8,625
758A	34,500	**791**	6,900	**827**	12,650	**863**	3,450	**899**	3,450	**935**	9,775
759	51,750	**792**	5,175	**828**	6,325	**864**	12,650	**900**	5,750	**936**	6,325
760	63,000	**793**	11,500	**829**	8,050	**865**	6,325	**901**	5,175	**937**	8,625
761	10,350	**794**	23,000	**830**	4,025	**866**	3,450	**902**	6,900	**938**	6,325
762	10,350	**795**	10,350	**831**	4,600	**867**	3,450	**903**	14,950	**939**	4,600
763	39,100	**796**	5,750	**832**	6,325	**868**	4,025	**904**	10,350	**940**	4,025
764	8,625	**797**	5,750	**833**	21,850	**869**	8,625	**905**	12,650	**941**	4,025
765	63,000	**798**	4,600	**834**	6,325	**870**	5,750	**906**	3,450	**942**	11,500
766	8,050	**799**	4,888	**835**	4,025	**871**	4,600	**907**	4,025	**943**	4,600
766A	11,500	**800**	4,888	**836**	2,300	**872**	5,175	**908**	4,600	**944**	6,900
766B	3,162	**801**	8,050	**837**	6,325	**873**	3,450	**909**	4,025	**945**	4,600
766C	11,500	**802**	12,650	**838**	5,750	**874**	3,450	**910**	4,600	**946**	21,850
767	12,650	**803**	13,800	**839**	6,900	**875**	3,450	**911**	7,475	**947**	63,000
768	13,800	**804**	7,475	**840**	12,650	**876**	2,300	**912**	5,750	**948**	27,600
769	5,750	**805**	24,150	**841**	17,250	**877**	4,600	**913**	14,950	**949**	16,100
770	8,050	**806**	11,500	**842**	7,475	**878**	4,600	**914**	6,900	**950**	4,025
771	74,000	**807**	5,175	**843**	13,800	**879**	10,925	**915**	8,050	**951**	9,200
772	6,900	**808**	21,850	**844**	6,325	**880**	4,025	**916**	9,200	**952**	5,750
773	5,175	**809**	17,250	**845**	9,775	**881**	4,025	**917**	6,900	**953**	14,950
774	5,750	**810**	5,175	**846**	3,162	**882**	3,450	**918**	3,450	**954**	11,500
775	6,900	**811**	13,800	**847**	37,950	**883**	2,875	**919**	3,450	**955**	9,200
776	5,750	**812**	12,650	**848**	4,600	**884**	6,900	**920**	3,450	**956**	28,750

FOR INFORMATION ABOUT SALE RESULTS OR CATALOGUE SUBSCRIPTIONS, PLEASE CALL 1-800-444-3709 (FROM THE U.S. ONLY) OR 203-847-4646 (FROM OUTSIDE THE U.S.)

SOTHEBY'S

1334 York Avenue
New York, NY 10021
Tel: (212) 606-7000

THE ESTATE OF JACQUELINE KENNEDY ONASSIS

AUCTION RESULTS
(continued)

April 23–26, 1996

Sale Number 6834

LOT	U.S.$	LOT	U.S.$	LOT	U.S.$	LOT	U.S.$	LOT	U.S.$	LOT	U.S.$
957	14,950	**993**	17,250	**1029**	10,350	**1066**	5,750	**1101A**	3,450	**1113**	3,737
958	8,625	**994**	10,350	**1030**	8,625	**1067**	6,900	**1101B**	5,462	**1114**	2,300
959	13,800	**995**	13,800	**1031**	2,530	**1068**	6,900	**1101C**	4,600	**1115**	4,025
960	10,350	**996**	36,800	**1032**	5,865	**1069**	5,750	**1101D**	4,887	**1116**	3,737
961	18,400	**997**	41,400	**1033**	4,600	**1070**	11,500	**1101E**	6,900	**1117**	3,450
962	8,050	**998**	32,200	**1034**	4,600	**1071**	5,175	**1101F**	4,312	**1118**	10,350
963	3,450	**999**	8,050	**1035**	5,175	**1072**	5,750	**1101G**	5,175	**1119**	8,625
964	2,875	**1000**	8,050	**1036**	5,175	**1073**	6,325	**1101H**	25,300	**1120**	9,775
965	6,325	**1001**	14,950	**1037**	5,750	**1074**	6,900	**1101 I**	10,925	**1121**	7,475
966	6,900	**1002**	17,250	**1038**	7,475	**1075**	8,625	**1101J**	13,800	**1122**	9,430
967	4,025	**1003**	28,750	**1039**	6,325	**1076**	9,775	**1101K**	6,325	**1123**	8,625
968	48,300	**1004**	29,900	**1040**	4,025	**1077**	6,900	**1101L**	5,750	**1124**	8,625
969	40,250	**1005**	12,650	**1041**	3,737	**1078**	4,600	**1101M**	40,250	**1125**	12,650
970	23,000	**1006**	26,450	**1042**	5,462	**1079**	8,050	**1101N**	10,925	**1126**	20,700
971	7,475	**1007**	19,550	**1043**	4,600	**1080**	4,025	**1101O**	3,162	**1127**	9,775
972	8,625	**1008**	12,650	**1044**	4,025	**1081**	8,050	**1101P**	6,900	**1128**	29,900
973	8,050	**1009**	29,900	**1045**	4,312	**1082**	7,475	**1101Q**	4,887	**1129**	4,600
974	20,700	**1010**	36,800	**1046**	4,312	**1083**	7,475	**1101S**	3,162	**1130**	10,350
975	10,350	**1011**	6,900	**1047**	3,737	**1084**	3,162	**1101T**	6,325	**1131**	5,750
976	11,500	**1012**	40,250	**1048**	4,600	**1085**	19,550	**1101U**	7,475	**1132**	6,900
977	6,900	**1013**	24,150	**1049**	5,175	**1086**	9,200	**1101V**	5,462	**1133**	12,650
978	4,600	**1014**	25,300	**1050**	4,600	**1087**	9,775	**1101W**	9,775	**1134**	4,312
979	6,900	**1015**	9,200	**1051**	6,325	**1088**	5,750	**1101X**	4,025	**1135**	5,750
980	9,200	**1016**	41,400	**1052**	14,950	**1089**	5,175	**1101Y**	18,400	**1136**	12,650
981	3,450	**1017**	18,400	**1053**	11,500	**1090**	3,162	**1101Z**	8,050	**1137**	11,500
982	4,025	**1018**	12,650	**1054**	4,887	**1091**	4,600	**1102**	189,500	**1138**	28,750
983	4,600	**1019**	19,550	**1055**	5,175	**1092**	7,475	**1103**	40,250	**1139**	43,700
984	8,625	**1020**	10,350	**1056**	10,925	**1093**	7,475	**1104**	37,375	**1140**	24,150
985	5,175	**1021**	112,500	**1057**	8,050	**1094**	10,925	**1105**	7,475	**1141**	4,600
986	4,600	**1022**	4,025	**1058**	6,900	**1095**	10,350	**1106**	5,750	**1142**	24,150
987	5,750	**1023**	6,325	**1059**	8,050	**1096**	6,900	**1107**	5,175	**1143**	6,325
988	4,600	**1024**	4,025	**1060**	7,475	**1097**	12,650	**1108**	6,900	**1144**	48,875
989	31,625	**1025**	1,955	**1061**	6,900	**1098**	6,900	**1109**	4,312	**1145**	12,650
990	4,600	**1026**	28,750	**1062**	5,175	**1099**	6,325	**1110**	6,325	**1146**	25,300
991	12,650	**1027**	4,600	**1063**	4,600	**1100**	4,025	**1111**	4,887	**1147**	23,000
992	11,500	**1028**	3,162	**1065**	3,737	**1101**	9,200	**1112**	3,450	**1148**	23,000

FOR INFORMATION ABOUT SALE RESULTS OR CATALOGUE SUBSCRIPTIONS, PLEASE CALL 1-800-444-3709 (FROM THE U.S. ONLY) OR 203-847-4646 (FROM OUTSIDE THE U.S.)

THE ESTATE OF JACQUELINE KENNEDY ONASSIS

SESSION TWO

WEDNESDAY, APRIL 24,

10:00 A.M.

The Living Room and Dining Room of Jacqueline Kennedy Onassis' New York City apartment, showing lots 12, 35, 40, 72, 120, 274, 308, 333, 341, 352 and 1002.

58

59

58 **A Derby Porcelain Part Breakfast and Coffee Service, circa 1820**

Each piece painted in underglaze-blue, iron-red, green, turquoise, salmon, purple and gilding with an oriental pattern of three ducks swimming amongst flowering plants, the interior rim with two or three flowering branches beneath the gilt edge, (some repairs and imperfections), *crowned crossed batons and D marks and numeral 9 in iron-red*; comprising:
Eight breakfast cups, *diameter 4 ¼ in. (10.8 cm.)*
Six breakfast saucers, *diameter 6 ⅜ in. (16.2 cm.)*
Eight coffee cans, *height 2 ½ in. (6.3 cm.)*
Seven saucers, *diameter 5 ¼ in. (13.3 cm.)*
Three small plates, *diameter 6 ⅞ in. (17.5 cm.)*
(32)

$600–900

59 **A French Porcelain Green-Ground Inkwell and Cover, Modern**

Of kidney shape and with a white- and gold-dotted dark green ground reserved on the front and reverse with a gilt-edged oval panel colorfully painted with two exotic birds in a landscape, the top pierced with three gilt-metal-edged apertures, the central aperture inset with a removable inkwell and fitted with a hinged cover, spurious interlaced L's and SEVRES mark in blue enamel. (2)
Length 4 ½ in. (11.4 cm.)

$150–250

60

60 **A Staffordshire Saltglaze Silver-Mounted Cast-House Teapot, 1745-55**

Molded as a rectangular three-story building with a large door on either side, one surmounted by a *fleur-de-lis* and a lion rampant, the other by the Royal Arms of Holland, and both beneath a winged cherub's head below the roof, the spout (reduced) molded on either side with a serpent above a human head, and the reverse with a plain S-scroll handle, (footrim chips, star cracks on the base, and a hair crack by the spout); the spout end and the rim mounted in late 19th-Century Dutch silver, and the cover replaced in silver, *maker's mark CEH, probably for C. E. Held, Jr., Amsterdam, 1895-1921, and Dutch control marks.*
Height 5 in. (12.7 cm.)

A block mold for this popular teapot form, and three variations of the model, are illustrated by Arnold R. Mountford, *The Illustrated Guide to Staffordshire Salt-Glazed Stoneware*, pls. 89-91.

$500–700

61 **A Lenox Porcelain Butter or 'Dessert' Plate from the State Dinner Service Made for President Franklin D. Roosevelt, dated 1934**

The cavetto encircled by a gilt line, and the top of the rim printed in brown, red, blue and green with the Great Seal of the United States, the shield-emblazoned eagle, beneath a border of gilt roses, foliage and feathers within a gilt-edged and -starred cobalt-blue band, *THE WHITE HOUSE 1934, letter L enclosed within boughs, LENOX MADE IN USA and WM. H. PLUMMER & CO. LTD. NEW YORK CITY mark printed in gold.*
Diameter 6¼ in. (15.9 cm.)

This small plate is from the service commissioned for use at the White House by President and Mrs. Franklin Delano Roosevelt, who, upon moving into the presidential mansion in 1933, discovered that the state china remaining from previous administrations was insufficient for formal entertaining. According to Margaret Brown Klathor, *Official White House China*, pp. 154 and 155, who provides a detailed history of this service, "the announcement that the White House was to get a new state service was made on November 20, 1934.... Criticism of the extravagance of ordering a new service for $9,000 while the country was in the midst of a depression obviously prompted Mrs. Roosevelt to quickly justify the order for new china at her press conference on December 4, [during which] she said that she felt that the order would give work to an American firm and that it would, on the whole, be more economical to order a full set," rather than to continue to replace individual pieces from earlier services.

"The new porcelain was ordered from the New York firm of William H. Plummer, and the purchase order [dated] October 13, 1934 [lists] 1,722 pieces...at a total cost of $9,301.20," including the ten dozen '6-inch dessert plates' in which the present plate was included, at $5.10 each. "The set arrived at the White House in January 1935 and was first used at the annual state dinner given for the heads of foreign missions on January 24, the largest affair of its kind in the history of the White House" at that time: a gathering of 99 ladies and gentlemen, seated "at the huge horseshoe-shaped table in the state dining room."

The design of the china, personally chosen by the President, included Mrs. Roosevelt's touch of the border of roses and feathers: elements of the Roosevelt coat of arms, which she felt made "the china more interesting historically,...[and while] the public had been critical" of both this personal reference and the final cost, the Roosevelts were redeemed by the "very complimentary" reception of the service by the press.

Other pieces from this service are in the collections of the White House and the Smithsonian Institution in Washington, D.C.; in the Franklin D. Roosevelt Library in Hyde Park, New York; and in the Lenox China Museum in Trenton, New Jersey.

$400–600

66

62 **A Chinese Export Porcelain Famille-Rose Fluted Hexagonal Spoon Tray, circa 1750**

Painted in the center in rose, yellow, blue and green with flowering peony and chrysanthemum sprigs, the rim with an iron-red-edged gilt trellis diaper border (worn) interrupted with three panels of rose foliate motifs.
Length 4 ⅞ in. (12.4 cm.)

$100–150

63 **A Chinese Export Porcelain Fluted Hexagonal Spoon Tray and a Scalloped Berry Dish, circa 1750 and 1770**

The spoon tray painted in worn *famille-rose* enamels and gilding with peonies and prunus in a fenced garden beneath an iron-red-edged gilt trellis diaper border around the rim (chipped) interrupted with six small floral panels; and the dish painted in rose and green with a floral spray in the center and within four rose- and gilt-edged cartouches around the *bianco-sopra-bianco* 'Dulong'-patterned rim (small chips, and a central star crack). Together with an English porcelain spirally writhen saucer, circa 1805, painted with rose and gold paterae interrupting a flowering vine border, (damaged). (3)
Length 5 ⅛ in. (13 cm.); diameters 6 ⅝ and 5 ¼ in. (16.8 and 13.3 cm.)

$100–150

64 **A Chinese Export Porcelain Fluted Hexagonal Teapot Stand, 1775-80**

Colorfully painted in the center with a Chinese lady standing at the window of a pavilion and observing another lady bringing tea to a gentleman standing by a table in a courtyard, the rim with a black cell diaper border beneath an iron-red and black cell diaper band at the gilt rim edge, (slight wear).
Width 4 ¾ in. (12.1 cm.)

$200–300

65 **A Chinese Export Porcelain Armorial Saucer, circa 1745**

The center painted in iron-red, black, blue, green, gold and white with an unidentifiable Continental coat of arms above a rose banderole inscribed with the motto *SINE LABORE NIHIL* and flanked by turquoise-green grasses beneath a helmet and elaborate iron-red and *grisaille* scrolls, the rim with a gilt cipher at the top interrupting a border of pink and gold rococo scrollwork issuing brown and green leafy boughs and surrounding at the sides two gold sun faces.
Diameter 4 ¾ in. (12.1 cm.)

$150–200

66 **A Set of Twelve Davenport Earthenware 'Canton' Pattern Soup Plates and Ten Dinner Plates, dated 1836-40**

Each transfer-printed in sepia with a chinoiserie scene of a couple conversing in a park near a flower-filled urn and before a gazebo and an exotic building on the banks of a river within a wide border of trellises, scrolls and floral sprays on the wavy-edged rim (one plate cracked; and several with slight discoloration), *impressed DAVENPORT and anchor marks and date numerals 6 and 36 for June 1836, or 2 and 40 (?) for February 1840, and CANTON within an oval above DAVENPORT marks and some with numeral 8 printed in sepia.* (22)
Diameters 10 ½ and 10 ⅜ in. (26.7 and 26.4 cm.)

$800–1,200

67 **A Set of Eleven Ashworth Ironstone Pudding Plates, 1865-75**

Each printed in maroon and painted in a *famille-rose* palette of iron-red, rose, yellow, shades of green, blue, salmon and gold with a Chinese pheasant perched on a rock amidst flowering peonies and prunus, the rim with four panels of a bird or a cricket amongst flowering branches alternating with four green-ground panels with bowls of fruit set on foliate scrolls and separated by gilt-edged salmon foliate scrolls, (one with a small chip), *Royal Arms and IRONSTONE CHINA marks printed in maroon, impressed ASHWORTH REAL IRONSTONE marks, and pattern number 4/255 and a painter's mark in gold or colored enamels.*
Diameter 8 9/16 in. (21.7 cm.)

Provenance:
The collection of Mrs. McFadden Staempfli, sold at Sotheby Parke Bernet, Inc. in New York City on October 15, 1980, lot 336;
Bardith, Ltd., New York City

$700–1,000

68 **A Staffordshire Earthenware Transfer-Printed Circular Dish and Cover, circa 1835**

Each piece printed in brown with a gentleman conversing with a mother and daughter near a house in a wooded landscape within a stippled border edged with floral sprigs and foliate scrolls below a band of circlets at the gadrooned edge (restored chips and discoloration on both), the knop on the ogee-domed cover (hair crack beneath) formed as a basket of flowers heightened in brown enamel.
Diameter 10 7/8 in. (27.6 cm.)

$125–175

67

68

69

70, 72, 71

69 **A Set of Seven Bing & Grondahl Porcelain Teacups and Nine Saucers, Modern**

Each piece printed in colors with a floral bouquet and two floral sprigs on and beneath a dentil-edged molded scalework border around the gilt-edged rim, the angular handles on the cups heightened in gilding, (four cups cracked, a fifth cup and two saucers chipped), *B&G COPENHAGEN PORCELAIN MADE IN DENMARK and 475 marks printed in green.* (16)
Height 2 7⁄16 in. (6.2 cm.); diameter 5 7⁄8 in. (14.9 cm.)

$75–100

70 **A Metal Cup**

Reproduction of a Minoan cup, inspired by the treasure found at Vapheio, depicting a bull being caught peacefully by the means of a decoy cow.
Height 3 3⁄8 in. (8.6 cm.)

$75–100

71 **A Group of Miscellaneous Decorations**

Comprising four brass bowls; six metal coasters; two basketweave cups; a pierced brass letter rack, a woven metal basket with handle and liner; three woven metal baskets, and a low metal container. (17)
Diameter of largest 10 in. (25.4 cm.)

$75–100

72 **A Regency Cream-Painted and Floral-Decorated Jardinière**

With tapered cylindrical sides and floral painted foot.
Height 5 in. (12.7 cm.)

This jardinière was among the furnishings in Mrs. Kennedy's dressing room at the White House.

$100–150

73, 74

73 **A Collection of Miscellaneous Woven Baskets**

(Approximately 14 pieces)

$150–200

74 **An American Pine and Turned Maple Long Table**

The rectangular multi-board top above a plain apron, a shallow shelf below fitted with two deep and long drawers, the whole supported on turned tapering legs ending in ball feet.
Height 29 in. (73.7 cm.), length 6 ft. 4½ in. (1.94 m.)

$1,500–2,500

75 **A Regency Chinoiserie-Decorated Cartouche-Shaped Dressing Mirror, early 19th Century**

(Distressed)
Height 24 in. (61 cm.), width 17½ in. (44.4 cm.)

$1,200–1,500

76 **A Button-Tufted Overstuffed Upholstered Settee**

Covered in floral brocade, cream damask slipcover. Together with two pillows.
Length 7 ft. (2.13 m.)

$1,000–1,500

77 **A Japanese Gilt-Decorated Black-Lacquered Cabinet**

In two parts, the upper with shelves painted olive-green and fitted with two drawers, the lower section with a pair of grille doors, on bracket feet; the sides painted with pavilions and a continuous landscape in gilt on a black ground.
Height 5 ft. 6 in. (1.68 m.), width 34 in. (86.4 cm.), depth 10¼ in. (26 cm.)

$1,500–2,500

78 **A Victorian Mother-of-Pearl-Inlaid Papier-Maché Caned Slipper Chair, mid-19th Century**

$700–900

75

76

77

78

79

79 **A Contemporary Four-Panel Wallpaper Screen**

Each arched wood-framed panel inset with contemporary Chinese wallpaper painted with flowering plants, birds and figures; the opposing side with striped wallpaper.
Height of each panel 8 ft. 6 in. (2.59 m.), width of each panel 28 in. (71.1 cm.)

$3,000–5,000

80 **A Gilt-Decorated Black Lacquer, Papier-Mâché and Wood Work Table, 19th Century**

The shaped oblong hinged top opening to a well, the lid inset with a mirror panel, above a shaped apron continuing to squared cabriole legs, distressed.
Height 28¾ in. (73 cm.), length 20½ in. (52.1 cm.), width 16½ in. (41.9 cm.)

$600–800

80

81

81 An Embossed and Watercolor Bird Picture, in the manner of Samuel Dixon

Depicting various birds and butterflies, one bird nesting, in a gilt-metal black-japanned frame.
10½ by 14 in. (26.7 by 35.6 cm.)

$1,200–1,800

82 After Edgar Degas

THREE STUDIES OF HORSES

reproduction of a drawing, framed*
(not examined out of the frame)
7⅜ by 4⅜ in. (18.7 by 11.1 cm.)

This reproduction was among the furnishings in the West Sitting Room of the White House during President and Mrs. Kennedy's residence.

$100–150

82

83 **Chinese School, 19th Century**

A pair of watercolors, each depicting figures on a junk, matted and framed.
7 by 12¾ in. (17.8 by 32.4 cm.)

$400–600

84 **Continental School, circa 1900**

YOUNG MAN IN A GALLERY

gouache on board
13½ by 9 in. (34.3 by 22.9 cm.)

This painting was among the furnishings of the White House during President and Mrs. Kennedy's residence, and, previously, of their house in Georgetown.

$500–700

83

84

85

86

85 Neapolitan School, 18th Century

WOMAN IN SEDAN CHAIR ATTENDED BY TWO MEN IN BLUE COATS

inscribed on medallion *40–Napoli*
pen and black ink with watercolor

Image 9 ⅝ by 13 in. (24.4 by 33 cm.)

$2,000–3,000

86 American School, 19th Century

RED AND WHITE FLOWERS

oil on milk glass
12 by 18 in. (30.5 by 45.7 cm.)

$300–500

87 **A Pair of Chinese Export Porcelain Blue and White Hexagonal Garden Seats, 20th Century**

Each decorated in underglaze-blue with a ground of scrolling foliate vines bearing large blossoms and surrounding precious objects between molded borders of bosses outlined with a band of 'cracked-ice and prunus', the sides pierced with interlocking cash medallions and the top pierced with a single cash medallion, all patterned with 'cracked-ice and prunus', (very minor chips).
Height 18 ¾ in. (47.6 cm.)

$1,500–2,500

88 **A Pair of Chinese Export Porcelain Blue and White Barrel-Form Garden Seats, 20th Century**

Each painted in bright underglaze-blue on the top and around the body with a ground of scrolling foliate vines bearing large blossoms interrupted by pierced cash medallions, the upper edge of the body encircled by a stylized *ruyi*-head border above a band of molded bosses repeated around the lower body above stands of bamboo, (some wear and chips), *one with characters inscribed beneath.*
Heights 18 and 18 ½ in. (45.7 and 47 cm.)

$1,200–1,800

89 **A Pair of Chinese Porcelain Blue and White Jardinières and a Pair of Stands, 20th Century**

Each U-shaped pot painted with peony and hibiscus blossoms and scrolling foliate vines surrounding a border of eight blossom roundels beneath the *ruyi*-head-bordered scalloped rim (one cracked, the other with a chip), the bottom pierced with drainage holes, and the stands painted with waves and clouds beneath a lappet-bordered scalloped rim, *spurious seal marks in underglaze-blue.*
Height overall 6 ⅝ in. (16.8 cm.)

$400–600

90 **Three Chinese Porcelain Blue and White Character-Decorated Vessels, late 19th Century**

Comprising an ovoid deep bowl and cover surmounted by a small cup, a baluster-form jar, and a footed circular stand; each decorated all over in underglaze-blue with long calligraphic inscriptions, the rim (minor chips) mounted in metal.
Height of largest 7 ½ in. (19 cm.)

$500–700

91 **A Chinese Porcelain Blue and White Cylindrical Stacking Container and Cover, 20th Century**

Formed as a deep dish surmounted by three shallow dishes and a low domed cover, each transfer-printed in underglaze-blue of medium tone with vertical foliate bands alternating with undulating stripes bisected by square medallions, (some rim chips).
Height 9 ⅜ in. (23.8 cm.)

$250–350

92 **A Chinese Porcelain Blue and White Reticulated Two-Tier Square Box and Cover, 19th Century**

Each side with a slightly recessed panel pierced with interlocking cash medallions within blue-ground borders patterned with blossoms and tassel devices, the slightly domed cover similarly decorated, (some shallow chips). (2)
Width 9 in. (22.9 cm.)

$500–700

93 **A Pair of Dutch Delft Blue and White Flower Bricks, Modern**

Reproductions made for Colonial Williamsburg from London delftware originals of circa 1760, each decorated on the front and reverse with two rows of flowering mimosa plants, and on the ends with a single flowering plant, the top pierced with six holes on either side of a central rectangular aperture, *Delft, the Colonial Williamsburg insignia and MADE IN HOLLAND marks printed in blue.*
Lengths 6 1/16 and 6 ⅛ in. (15.4 and 15.6 cm.)

The 'Mimosa' pattern flower brick, attributed to London, circa 1740, from which the present pair was reproduced, is illustrated by John C. Austin, *British Delft at Williamsburg*, p. 266, no. 635, who comments that "fragments [of delftware] with the mimosa pattern have been excavated on many sites in Williamsburg."

$50–75

94 **Two Chinese Porcelain Blue and White Rectangular Trays, 20th Century**

Each with canted corners and painted in underglaze-blue, one depicting an Immortal in a landscape, and the other depicting birds among flowers and rockwork.
Lengths 8 ¾ and 9 ¼ in. (22.2 and 23.5 cm.)

$250–350

87
88
88
89
89
91
90
976
94
90
92
94
93
90

95

96

95 **A Chinese Export Porcelain Small Bowl and a Pair of Small Jars and Covers for the Siamese Market, 19th Century**

The bowl with a blue-ground exterior reserved with colorful deities between iron-red, yellow, turquoise, rose and white patterned borders, the interior with a central blossom medallion beneath a turquoise ground and colorful floral border around the iron-red-edged rim; and the compressed spherical jars and domed covers with an iron-red ground decorated in rose, green and white with floral motifs, and reserved on the bodies with four black-ground medallions between grey borders. (3)
Diameter of bowl 4 15⁄16 in. (11 cm.), height of jars 1 15⁄16 in. (4.8 cm.)

$300–500

96 **A Chinese Export Porcelain 'Green Fitzhugh' Reticulated Oval Stand, late 19th Century**

Characteristically decorated in the center with a peony sprig within a beast and trellis diaper medallion edged in spearheads and dumbbells and surrounded by four clusters of flowers and precious objects, the rim with a turquoise, blue and yellow fret-pierced border within a green trellis diaper band at the gilt edge, (in half and reglued, and some wear to the central enamels).
Length 11 7⁄16 in. (29.1 cm.)

$100–150

97 **A Chinese Export Porcelain Bowl, 19th Century**

Painted around the exterior in a *famille-verte* palette heightened in gilding with a continuous scene of a Siamese dignitary and attendants in an island pavilion observing further figures in boats coursing over green waves in which large fish frolic between blue-dotted gilt lappet borders around the iron-red-edged rim (chip and hair crack) and above the green footrim.
Diameter 7 ⅞ in. (20 cm.)

$250–350

98 **A Chinese Porcelain Peach Bloom Amphora-Form Vase, late 19th Century**

With a tapered neck and high shouldered narrow ovoid body, the whole covered in a deep red glaze, *spurious four-character Xuande mark in underglaze-blue.*
Height 6 ⅜ in. (16.2 cm.)

$400–600

99 **A Japanese Lacquer Brush Box, 19th Century**

Painted with fans and leaves, chipped.
Length 9 ¼ in. (23.5 cm.)

$250–350

97

98

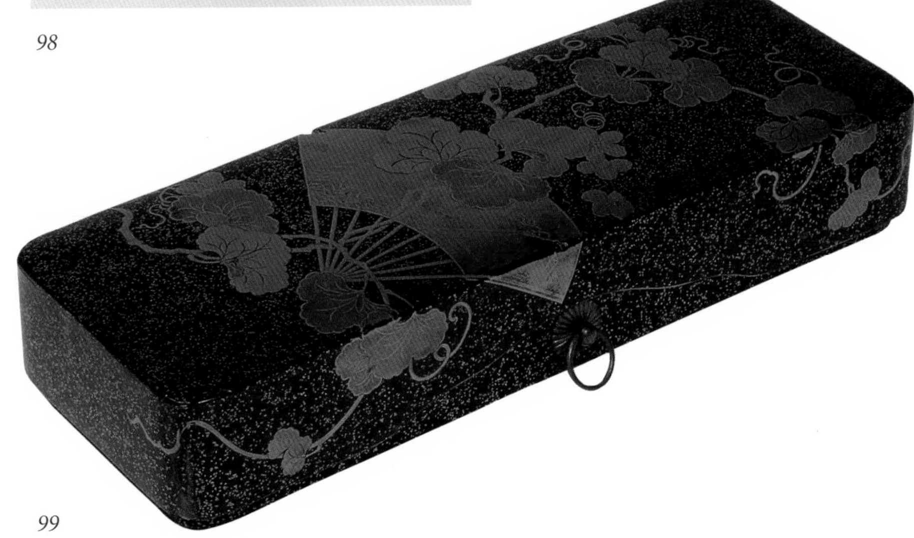

99

100 **A Chinese Ivory and Tortoiseshell Gourd Container and a Pair of Tusk-Section Bracelets**
Height of container: 6¾ in.

$150–200

101 **A Chinese Jadeite and Enamel-Mounted Silver Hand Mirror**

The reverse mounted with a green jadeite pierced disk surrounded by small stones, with a belt hook handle.
Length 9¼ in. (23.5 cm.)

$600–800

102 **A Chinese Cloisonné Enamel Bird-Form Box**

Height 3½ in. (8.9 cm.)

$125–175

103 **A Cambodian Silver Betel Box, 20th Century**

With two sections in the form of a recumbent feline, its ears separately cast, the body with finely incised fur interspersed by foliate medallions.
Length 4 in. (10.2 cm.)

$100–150

100

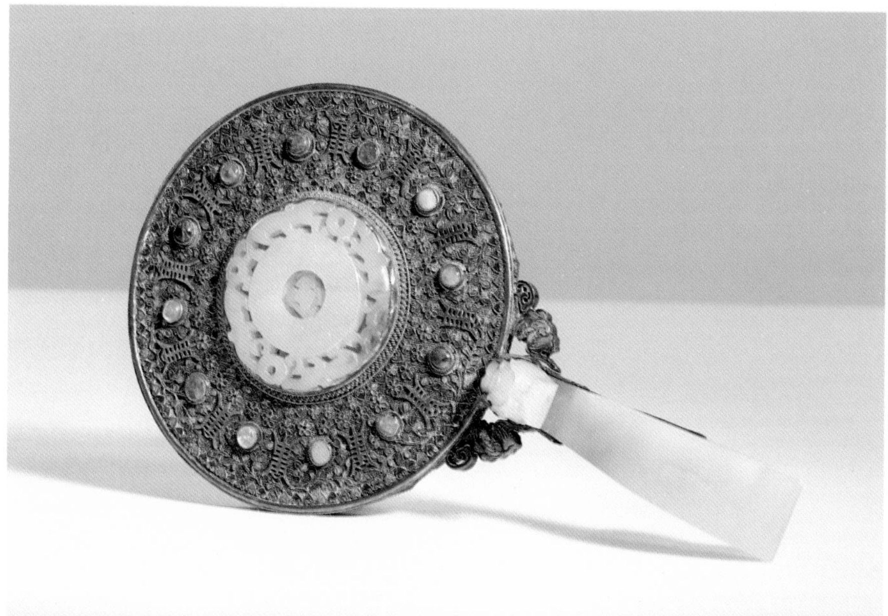

101

102, 103, 104

105

108, 106, 106, 106, 106, 106, 106, 107

104 **A Japanese Porcelain Group of a Mouse on a Corncob, late 19th Century**

Naturalistically modelled as a small white mouse with finely incised hair and other details, the tail curling and extending to the short stalk of the partially nibbled and chestnut-brown-glazed cob beneath, *the tip of the stalk with an incised character.*
Length 9 in. (22.9 cm.)

$700–1,000

105 **An Empire Style Gilt-Bronze Hand Mirror, 19th Century**

The baluster handle terminating in a ring and with eagle attachment to circular mirror frame.
Length 11 in. (27.9 cm.)

$500–700

106 **A Set of Three Silver Salts and Three Matching Peppers, American, circa 1915-20**

The slender vase-shaped bodies chased with leaves and engraved with the initial K in gothic script, stamped '9088'.
Height 6 in. (15.2 cm.)

$400–600

107 **A Silver Caster, American, circa 1920**

On spreading circular foot, the otherwise plain baluster body engraved with the initial K in gothic scrip, detachable cover, stamped '<M>1002'.
Height 6¼ in. (15.9 cm.)

$100–150

108 **An American Silver Sugar Caster, Ensko, New York, early 20th Century**

In George II style, of baluster form, vase-shaped finial.
Height 6⅜ in. (16.2 cm.)

$60–100

109 **A Set of Twelve White Metal Table Mats, mid 20th Century**

Of reeded circular form, the center of each engraved with the initials JJK in monogram, cork undersides.
Diameter 8 in. (20.3 cm.)

The initials are those of John and Jacqueline Kennedy.

$600–800

110 **An English Electroplate Salver, unmarked, probably Birmingham, early 20th Century**

In 1770s style, shaped circular, the border applied with cast gadroons and shells above three volute supports, later engraved 'J.L.B.K.' (Jacqueline Lee Bouvier Kennedy), the underside inscribed 'From the Charlotte Chamber of Commerce Jan. 15, 1959.'
Diameter 8 in. (20.3 cm.)

$50–100

109

110

groups, left to right: 111, 112, 114, 113

111 **Four Indian Electroplate Tumblers, 20th Century**

Of tapering cylindrical form, variously engraved or flat-chased.
Height 4 ¼ to 6 ¼ in. (10.8 to 15.9 cm.)

$100–150

112 **A Pair of Electroplate Wine Coasters, unmarked, probably English, mid 20th Century**

The sides pierced with pales, dots and paterae, turned wood bases.
Diameter 5 ¾ in. (14.6 cm.)

These wine coasters were among the furnishings in Senator and Mrs. Kennedy's Georgetown residence.

$200–400

113 **A Set of Five Cambodian Silver Finger Bowls and Five Underplates, respectively stamped Bouthan Cambodge and Bouthan Cambodia, 20th Century**

The bowls hemispherical, the plates shaped circular, each on three button supports, all repoussé and chased with bands of foliage.
Diameter of bowls 4 ⅛ in. (10.5 cm.), diameter of plates 6 in. (15.2 cm.)

$400–600

115

114 **A Pair of Electrogilt Wine Coasters, unmarked, probably English, circa 1960**

The straight sides pierced and die-stamped with interlaced reeded motifs, turned wood bases, the undersides covered in blue paper.
Diameter 4 ½ in. (11.4 cm.)

$50–100

115 **A Pair of French Silver Wine Coasters, Jean-Baptiste-Claude Odiot, Paris, 1809-19**

Circular, the cast and pierced sides decorated with formal fruiting vines below everted lips of stiff leaves, the otherwise plain base plates engraved with armorials including the motto *Labor amnio vincit.*
Diameter 5 ⅛ in. (13 cm.)

$1,000–1,500

116, 117, 118, 14

116 **An American Silver Three-Piece After-Dinner Coffee Service, Gorham Mfg. Co., Providence, Rhode Island, mid 20th Century**

The plain baluster bodies each on four hoof supports, comprising: coffee pot, cream pitcher and two-handled sugar bowl, stamped 609.
Height of coffee pot 7½ in. (19 cm.)

$450–650

117 **A Painted Papier-Mâché Tray, late 19th Century**

Decorated with green flowers on a black ground, (chipped).
Length 20 in. (50.8 cm.)

$80–120

118 **A Louis XV Provincial Fruitwood Bureau Plat, mid-18th Century**

The rectangular top inset with a leather writing surface, the frieze with two drawers, raised on cabriole legs fitted with ormolu *sabots.*
Height 28½ in. (72.4 cm.), width 4 ft. (121.9 cm.), depth 28¼ in. (71.8 cm.)

This bureau plat was among the furnishings in President and Mrs. Kennedy's Georgetown residence.

$7,000–9,000

119

119 **A Regency Style Gilt-Decorated Black-Japanned Kneehole Dressing Table, 19th Century**

The rectangular top above a frieze drawer and two drawers in each pedestal, the whole raised on bracket feet and decorated with Chinese-style animals, birds and vases of flowers in shades of gold on a black ground.
Height 30½ in. (77.5 cm.), length 38½ in. (97.8 cm.)

$1,800–2,200

120 **An Upholstered Settee**

With plain back, three-cushion seat and buttoned box-pleated apron, yellow upholstery faded.
Length 6 ft. 10 in. (2.08 m.)

$500–800

120

121 **An Upholstered Club Chair**

With floral chintz slipcover.

$200–250

122 **A Chinese Export Gilt-Decorated and Black-Lacquered Tilt-Top Table, second quarter 19th Century**

The oblong top with canted corners, on a baluster stem with shaped rectangular base on paw feet.
Height 26 ½ in. (67.3 cm.), length 20 in. (50.8 cm.), width 16 in. (40.6 cm.)

$2,000–2,500

121

122

123

124

123 **An American Victorian Maple Caned Rocking Chair, Late 19th/Early 20th Century**

With serpentine top rail, shaped cane backrest, scrolled arms, caned seat and sabre legs, on rockers, (restored).

$300–400

124 **A Louis XV Ebonized Table à Écrire, mid 18th Century**

The rectangular leather-inset top fitted with a three-quarter wooden gallery, the serpentine frieze containing one drawer, raised on cabriole legs. *Height 27¾ in. (70.5 cm.), width 29½ in. (74.9 cm.), depth 16½ in. (41.9 cm.)*

Provenance:
Richard V. Hare

$5,000–7,000

125 **A Set of Eight Burleigh Earthenware 'Nantucket' Dessert Plates, Burgess & Leigh Ltd., circa 1983**

Each transfer-printed in underglaze-blue in the center with Nantucket Island, and around the rim with four vignettes of local buildings: 'The Oldest House Built 1686', 'Stone Alley & Town Clock', 'Sankaty Lighthouse Mass.' and 'Old Windmill Built 1740', alternating with panels of roses within starred scroll borders, *'A Reproduction of a Nineteenth Century Staffordshire Design, Nantucket Historical Association, Mottahedeh By Burleigh STAFFORDSHIRE, ENGLAND marks encircling the Nantucket Historical Association insignia printed in underglaze-blue.*
Diameter 8 ¾ in. (22.2 cm.)

$200–300

126 **A Set of Twelve Grosvenor Bone China 'Merlin' Pattern Dinner Plates, 20th Century**

Each decorated in gold on the scalloped rim with a border of leaves, berries and buds within the gilt edge, *GROSVENOR BONE CHINA ENGLAND marks and one with the pattern name printed in gold, and TIFFANY & C.º NEW YORK marks printed in brown.*
Diameter 10 ¾ in. (27.3 cm.)

Provenance:
The collection of Mrs. Hugh D. Auchincloss, Hammersmith Farm, Newport, Rhode Island

$400–600

127 **Seven Nevers Faïence Polychrome Plates, 19th Century**

Each painted in shades of blue, green, yellow, ochre and manganese: two variously decorated with fruit within a scalloped band and foliate border, one with a basket of flowers within a wavy swag-and-dot border, one with a central cornflower sprig within smaller sprigs and foliate motifs around the rim (chips), one with a bird within a scalloped roundel and a scallop-and-circlet border around the rim (chips), one with two birds perched in two trees above a fence in a hilly landscape within a scallop-and-dot border, and one with a pair of billing doves within a roundel and a dotted swag border around the rim (chip); (usual minor abrasions on the edges).
Diameters 8 ⅞ to 9 ⅛ in. (22.5 to 23.2 cm.)

$500–800

125

126

127

128

128 A Set of Twelve Gold-Ground Pottery Octagonal Plates, Modern

Each with a lightly molded beadwork border, (some with slight wear from use).
Width 9⅜ in. (23.8 cm.)

$300–500

129

130, 131, 134, 132, 133

137, 135, 136 (part), 135, 137

129 **An American Electroplate Part Flatware Set, Gorham Mfg. Co., Providence, Rhode Island, circa 1950**

Each tapering handle with trifid end chased with leaves and engraved 'K', comprising: five Dinner Forks, five Dessert Forks, six Dinner Knives, seven Butter Knives, 1 Cheese Knife, six Teaspoons, six Soup Spoons, and one Sugar Shovel. Together with a wood case. (38)

$100–200

130 **A Silver-Plated Silent Butler, probably English, mid 20th Century**

Plain oblong, the domed hinged cover engraved with an elephant and castle crest above the initials 'JLB' (Janet Lee Bouvier), straight turned wood handle.
Width 7½ in. (19 cm.)

$200–400

131 **An English Silver Compote, maker's mark of Black, Starr & Frost of New York as retailers, London, 1925**

Circular, the domed foot and bowl applied with cast Regence pattern borders, the interior engraved with the initials 'JLB', stamped 'Made in England for Black, Starr & Frost'.
Diameter 10¼ in. (26 cm.)

$700–1,000

132 **An American Silver Platter, International Silver Co., Meriden, Connecticut, early 20th Century**

Of plain circular outline with die-stamped neoclassical molded border of urns and foliage, the center engraved with the initials 'JLB' (Janet Lee Bouvier), stamped 'H 458 Wedgwood Patented'.
Diameter 12 in. (30.5 cm.)

$250–350

133 **An Oak Piling Fragment, purportedly from the London Bridge**

Bearing a silver plaque with inscription: *To Janet Lee (Bouvier) on her Wedding Day from Tilden Smith. 7th July 1928. Portion of the pile of the First London Bridge Constructed by Alfred the Great.*
Length 5 in. (12.7 cm.)

$400–600

134 **An English Electroplate Salver, Barker Brothers Silversmiths Ltd. of Birmingham, early 20th Century**

Shaped circular, applied Chippendale border, the center engraved with the initials 'JLB' (Janet Lee Bouvier).
Diameter 10 in. (25.4 cm.)

$80–120

135 **A Pair of American Silver Three-Light Candelabra**

Gadroon bordered circular, each with two scroll branches and three bell-shaped sconces, monogrammed, loaded.
Height approximately 15 in. (38.1 cm.)

These candelabra were a wedding gift to Senator and Mrs. John F. Kennedy.

$1,000–1,500

136 **A Group of Silver and Silver-Plated Articles**

Comprising: a silver-plated ice bucket, a silver circular tray, an English small silver ashtray, a pair of ice tongs, an ice pick initialed 'JBK' (Jacqueline Bouvier Kennedy), a bottle opener, and ten silver-plated coasters. (16)

$200–300

137 **A Pair of American Silver Three-Light Candelabra, Tiffany & Co., New York, 1947-55**

The reeded circular bases each engraved with the initials 'JBK' (Jacqueline Bouvier Kennedy) below knopped stems, each with two reeded scroll branches, three plain bell-shaped sconces and detachable nozzles, stamped '222953 M'.

Height approximately 7 in. (17.8 cm.)

These candelabra were a wedding gift to Senator and Mrs. John F. Kennedy.

$500–700

138 **An American Silver Plate, Gorham Mfg. Co., Providence, Rhode Island, circa 1953**

Circular, molded border, inscribed, stamped '474'.
Diameter 8 ¼ in. (21 cm.)

The inscription reads 'To Jacqueline and John / September 12, 1953 From Dennis J. Roberts / Governor of Rhode Island'.

$200–300

139 **A Pair of Parcel-Gilt Silver Table Candlesticks, maker's mark 665M1, Italy, 1960s, retailed by Tiffany & Co. of New York**

Realistically modeled as palm trees rising from circular rocky bases, both fitted with detachable triple palm leaf sconces, stamped 'Tiffany & Co. Sterling Made in Italy.'
Height 14 in. (35.6 cm.)

$1,200–1,800

140 **A Silver Cigarette Box, unmarked, probably European, mid 20th Century**

Rectangular, the hinged lid set with rows of amethyst-colored pastes.
4 by 5 ½ in. (10.2 by 14 cm.)

$250–350

138

139

140

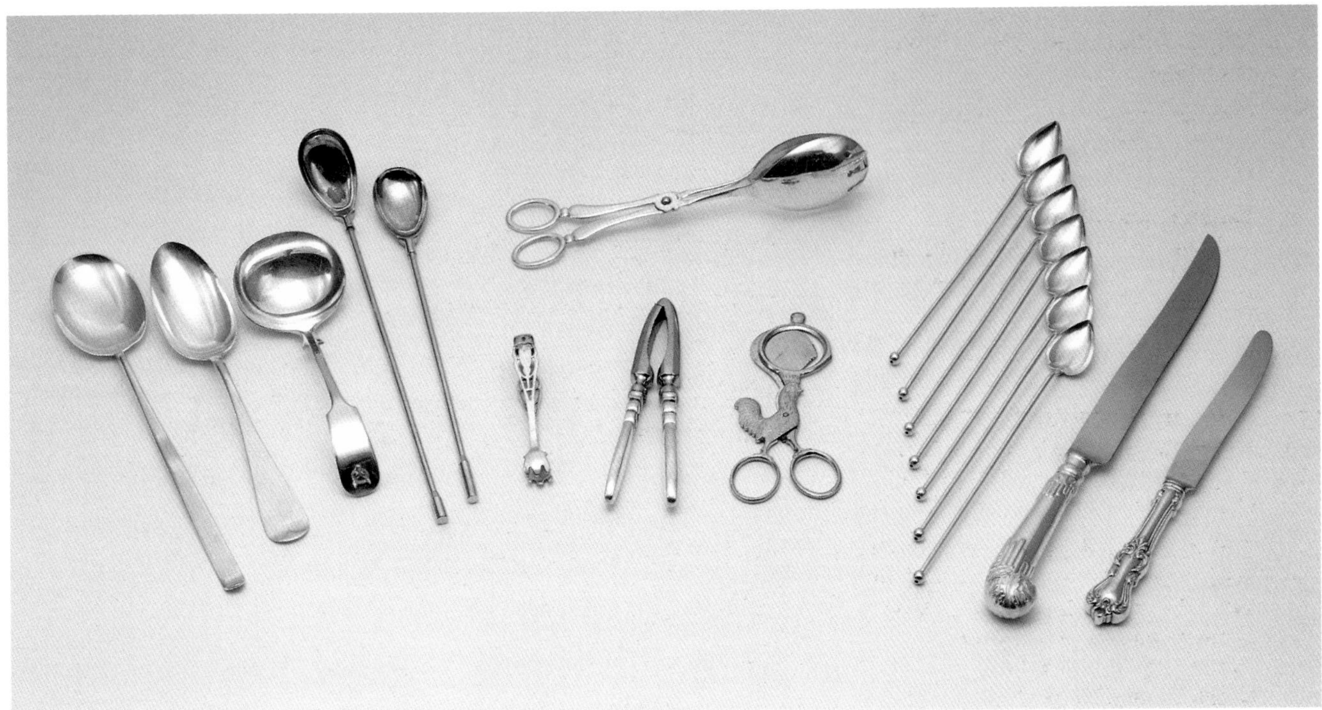

141, 142

141 **Various Items of Silver Flatware, circa 1860-20th Century**

Comprising: seven Iced Tea Spoons, heart-shaped bowls, *American, 20th Century;* a pair of Sugar Tongs (broken), *American, 20th Century;* an Old English pattern Tablespoon, *'Sterling. A.W. Turner', circa 1860;* and a pair of silver-mounted 'Cactus' pattern Nut Crackers, *Georg Jensen Silversmiths, Copenhagen, mid-20th Century.* (11)

$300–500

142 **Various Items of Electroplate Flatware, American, English, &c., 20th Century**

Comprising: a pair of Martini Stirrers, a Sauce Ladle with fox-mask-applied terminal, an Egg Slicer, a Carving Knife with foliate pistol handle, a long-handled Spoon, a scissor-form Salad Server, and a scroll pattern Dessert Knife. (7)

$100–150

143 **An English Electroplate Cake Stand, Mappin & Webb Ltd. of Sheffield, circa 1925**

The flattened wirework frame supporting three detachable beaded circular dishes.
Height 17¼ in. (43.8 cm.)

$80–120

144,143

144 **A Silver-Plated Cocktail Shaker, Reed & Barton**

Of plain tapered cylindrical form, monogrammed 'JBK' (Jacqueline Bouvier Kennedy).

$100–200

145 **Three Georgian Old English Pattern Teaspoons, Eley & Fearn, 1803, William Bateman, 1816, and Robert Peppin, 1823, all London**

Variously crested.

$150–200

146 **An English Silver-Gilt Bowl, maker's mark of Tiffany & Co. as retailer, London, 1968**

Of heavy gauge, lobed shaped circular with lightly hammered surface, stamped 'Tiffany & Co England Sterling'.
Diameter 10¼ in. (26 cm.)

$800–1,200

145

147 **A Set of Eight French Gold-Plated Beakers, Christofle, probably 1960s**

On ribbed domed circular bases below plain bell-shaped bowls, stamped 'Coll-Gallia'.
Height 3⅛ in. (7.9 cm.)

$400–600

147, 146, 147

148 **An Italian Silver Cigarette Box, maker's mark 309 F1, stamped 'A. Formari Roma'**

Rectangular with reeded surface, the interior with two inscriptions, one in facsimile, wood lined.
Length 6¼ in. (15.9 cm.)

The first inscription reads 'Voyage Aux Indes Et Au Pakistan (12.26 Mars 1962) Rome. New Delhi. Fatehpor. Sikri. Agra. Benares. Udaipur. Jaipur. New Delhi. Lahore. Rawalpindi. Peshawar. Karachi. Teheran. Londres'.

The second, in facsimile, reads 'Pour Jacqueline "La Maharanée d'Amérique"! Affectueusement Benno.'

$400–600

148

149

150

151

149 **A Set of Ten H. Bittner & Co. Porcelain 'Soldiers of the American Army' Plates, 20th Century**

Each printed in colors with a different pair of soldiers *from a design by F. Kredel* within a gilt line around the cavetto and rim edge, (four damaged), *the reverse entitled 'Soldiers of the American Army 1775-1941', each scene identified and described, LIMITED EDITION SET NO. 13, EXCLUSIVE WITH Abercrombie & Fitch Co., New York, and DESIGNS COPYRIGHTED BY H. BITTNER & CO. marks printed in sepia.*
Diameter 10⅝ in. (27 cm.)

The soldiers depicted are from: "Thompson's Pennsylvania Rifle Battalion 1778"; "Congress' Own and the Continental Artillery 1780"; "Regular Infantry 1814"; "U.S. Military Academy 1825"; "7th Regiment New York State Militia 1861"; "7th Cavalry 1876"; "Cuban Expedition 1898"; "Staff and Pioneer Infantry A.E.F. 1918"; "The Air Corps and Parachute Units 1940"; and "The Armored Force 1941."

$200–300

150 **A Partial Set of Six Copeland Spode Creamware 'Fox Hunting' Dinner Plates, dated 1952**

Each printed in sepia and enamelled in green, brown, iron-red, black and blue with a different scene of the hunt after identified drawings by John Frederick Herring, Senior, the scalloped rim (three cracked) with a crimson band border, *identifications, and COPELAND SPODE ENGLAND fret marks printed in sepia, impressed Copeland Spode England and date cipher Y 52, and 2/9344 and a painter's mark in colored enamels.*
Diameter 10⅝ in. (27 cm.)

The scenes depicted are identified as:
2 "THE FIND"
4 "OFF TO DRAW"
7 "THE MEET"
8 "THE DEATH"
9 "GOING TO HALLOA"
10 "DRAWING THE DINGLE"

$200–300

151 **A Set of Ten W. Adams & Co. Earthenware 'Fairy Villas' Pattern Small Dessert Plates, 20th Century**

Each transfer-printed in underglaze 'flow blue' with a chinoiserie scene of a figure near a rococo folly on the bank of a river plied by a sailboat within a trefoil-edged roundel and a border of floral clusters alternating with panels of flower-filled vases interrupting a dotted band around the wavy-edged rim (two cracked and those and six others with a chip), *ROYAL SEMI-PORCELAIN above a cartouche surrounding 'Fairy Villas', and W. Adams & C<u>o</u> TUNSTALL ENGLAND marks printed in underglaze-blue.*
Diameter 7¾ in. (19.7 cm.)

$150–250

152 **A Victorian Gilt-Decorated Black Papier-Mâché Tray, 19th Century**

Serpentine-sided with gilt banding. *Length 24 in. (61 cm.), width 19 in. (48.3 cm.)*

$100–150

153 **An Anglo-Indian Quillwork Desk Tray, late 19th Century**

With rectangular quill-basket sides, rim and base inlaid with bone, *losses. Height 3¾ in. (9.5 cm.), length 11½ in. (29.2 cm.), width 8¼ in. (21 cm.)*

$150–175

152

153

154, 155, 156, 157, 158

159, 160, 159

154 **Five Pairs of Turned Ivory Baluster Salt Shakers and Pepper Grinders**

(Some damaged).
Heights 4 and 3 in. (10.2 and 7.6 cm.)

$250–350

155 **Three Pairs of Turned Ivory Baluster Salt Shakers and Pepper Grinders**

(Some damaged).
Height 3 in. (7.6 cm.)

$150–200

156 **Four Pairs of Turned Ivory Baluster Salt Shakers and Pepper Grinders**

(Some damaged).
Heights 3 and 4 in. (7.6 and 10.2 cm.)

$200–300

157 **Four Pairs of Turned Ivory Baluster Salt Shakers and Pepper Grinders**

(Some damaged).
Heights 3 and 4 in. (7.6 and 10.2 cm.)

$200–300

158 **Two Pairs of Turned Ivory Baluster Salt Shakers and Pepper Grinders and Six Pepper Grinders**

(Some damaged).
Heights 3 and 4 in. (7.6 and 10.2 cm.)

$250–350

159 **A Pair of Blue Marbleized Wood Columnar Table Lamps**

On plinth base.
Height 21 ½ in. (54.6 cm.)

$300–500

160 **A Charles X Style Gilt and Patinated Bronze-Mounted Marble Candelabrum Mounted as a Lamp, 19th Century**

The green mottled marble columnar support surmounted by an oil lamp after the antique fitted with three candle arms, raised on a concave-sided triangular base. *Fitted for electricity.*
Height 24 in. (61 cm.)

$1,000–1,500

161, 162

163, 164

161 **A Victorian Polished Steel and Brass Trivet, 19th Century**

The wheel-pierced top on front cabriole legs.
Height 12½ in. (31.7 cm.), length 13 in. (33 cm.), depth 10¾ in. (27.3 cm.)

$400–600

162 **A George III Brass and Wrought-Iron Standing Trivet, 19th Century**

With pierced rectangular top, on frontal cabriole legs ending in shaped feet.
Height 9 in. (22.9 cm.), length 14 in. (35.6 cm.), width 9 in. (22.9 cm.)

$500–700

163 **A Federal Red-Painted Pine Two-Drawer Side Table, American, 19th Century**

The rectangular top above a plain apron enclosing two drawers with turned wood knobs, supported on square tapering legs.
Height 28½ in. (72.4 cm.), length 47 in. (119.4 cm.)

$2,000–3,000

164 **A Group of Galvanized Metal Flower Holders**

Together with a wooden tin cistern, *height 21½ in. (54.6 cm.)*, and a coopered wooden jardinière.

$150–250

lead & put on 3d page if convenient

Walt Whitman's Lecture at Association Hall on the
Death of President Lincoln comes off
to-night ~~at Asso~~ to-day being the fifteenth
anniversary of the sad event. ~~at Asso-
ation Hall~~

165

165 Whitman, Walt

Autograph note signed in text, 1 page (3 x 7½ in.) removed from a larger sheet, 6 lines with several autograph emendations and additions, being the draft for a press announcement of Whitman's 1880 address on the assassination of Abraham Lincoln. Matted, framed, and glazed with an 1887 photogravure portrait of Whitman by George C. Cox.

Headed by a direction to the printer to "lead & put on 3d page if convenient," the poet's announcement reads: "Walt Whitman's Lecture at Association Hall on the Death of President Lincoln comes off to-night — to-day being the fifteenth anniversary of the sad event." Whitman strongly identified with the martyred sixteenth president, and he wrote one of his most important poems ("When Lilacs Last in the Door-yard Bloom'd"), as well as one of his most popular ("O Captain! My Captain!") in eulogy of him.

$1,200–1,800

166

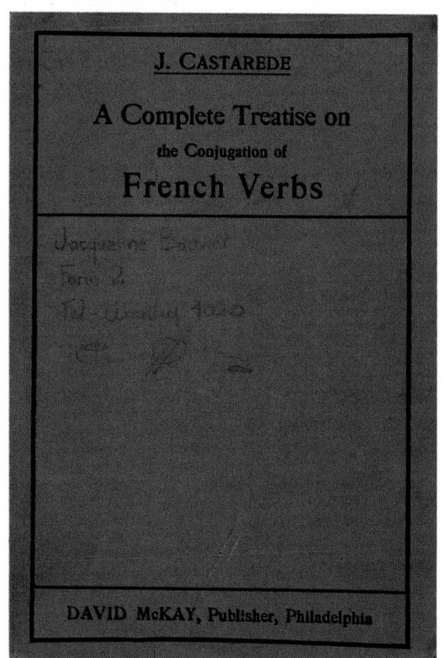

166

166 **Castarède, J.**

A Complete Treatise on the Conjugation of French Verbs. *Philadelphia: David McKay, [n.d.]*

(8¾ x 6 in.). Publisher's red cloth wrappers; frayed.

JACQUELINE BOUVIER'S SCHOOLGIRL FRENCH TEXTBOOK, SIGNED AND INSCRIBED BY HER ON THE FRONT COVER "Jacqueline Bouvier, Form 2, Tel–Woodley 4020 [small decorative design].

$500–800

167 **Bouvier, Jacqueline and Lee**

One Special Summer. *New York: Delacorte Press, 1974*

(13 x 10½ in.). Facsimile manuscript written and illustrated by the Bouvier sisters, pictorial color title-page, numerous black-and-white line drawings and color illustrations in text (some full-page), decorative initials. Textured and marbled blue paper over boards, blue foil panels with cartoon outlines of Jacqueline snapping a photo of Lee, spine lettered in blue foil, uniform slipcase with facsimile photograph of Lee and Jacqueline aboard the *SS Queen Elizabeth*; faint marginal discoloration on lower board.

Limited edition, one of 500 copies.

This copy is not signed, and is presumably an advance copy given to Mrs. Onassis. The book chronicles a European vacation taken by Jacqueline and Lee Bouvier by themselves in the summer of 1951. Intended as a gift for their mother, the original journal was composed "in a state of joy and laughter, which was our mood throughout the trip...Jackie did the drawings, the poetry, the parts on Rome and Spain. I described most of our adventures—on the *Queen Elizabeth*, in London, Paris, Venice, Rome and Florence." It was retrieved from the family attic some 23 years later as a potential source of materials for a book of remininiscences on which Lee Radziwill was then working. "As I reread and thought about it," she writes in the introduction, " it seemed too much—a kind of separate entity—to include as part of my book. And so here it is, just as we did it in 1951, with not a word or a pen stroke changed." A wonderfully fresh and candid view of the Bouvier sisters.

$100–150

168 **Sloane, Eric**

Remember America. *New York: Funk & Wagnalls, 1975*

(11 x 14 in.). Numerous reproductions of drawings and paintings by Sloane. Green cloth spine, gilt-lettered white cloth covers, dust-jacket; minor wear and soiling to covers.

PRESENTATION COPY OF THE "BICENTENNIAL EDITION," INSCRIBED AND SIGNED TO MRS. KENNEDY BY SLOANE AND WITH A LARGE DRAWING OF A COVERED BRIDGE on the front free endpaper. The inscription reads: "To the J. K. O. Library, with infinite admiration. Eric Sloane, 1984."

$300–500

169 **Decorative Arts**

Group of 6 volumes, various sizes. Illustrated. Publisher's cloth, some with dust-jackets. Various places, various dates.

Constantino Bulgari. *Argentieri gemmarie orafi d'Italia.* 2 vols., 1959. — Hubert Landais. *French Porcelain.* 1961. BOOKPLATE of Jacqueline Bouvier Kennedy. — Paul Jokelson. *Antique French Paperweights.* 1955. BOOKPLATE of Jacqueline Bouvier Kennedy; INSCRIBED by the author "en respectueux hommage," 4 April 1961. — Ernst Lehner. *Alphabets and Ornaments.* [1968]. With several sheets of ornament tracings on tracing paper, ANNOTATED by Mrs. Onassis. — and another.

$400–600

170 **Decorative Arts**

Group of 4 volumes, various sizes. All illustrated. Publisher's cloth, with dust-jackets. Various places, various dates.

Hugh Honour. *Chinoiserie: The Vision of Cathay.* 1961. BOOKPLATE of Jacqueline Bouvier Kennedy. — Albert Sack. *Fine Points of Furniture: Early American.* 1955. INSCRIBED by author "To Mrs. John F. Kennedy." — R. W. Symonds & B. B. Whineray. *Victorian Furniture.* 1962. BOOKPLATE of Jacqueline Bouvier Kennedy. — A. Kenneth Snowman. *Eighteenth Century Gold Boxes of Europe.* 1990. INSCRIBED by author "For Jacqueline, who knows all about these lovely objects ..."

$500–700

171 **Russia**

Pauline de Rothschild. *The Irrational Journey.* New York, (1967). — Phyllis Penn Kohler, ed. and trans. *Custine's Eternal Russia: A New Edition of Journey for Our Time.* (Coral Gables, Florida, 1976).

Together 2 volumes, various sizes. Publisher's boards and wrappers, respectively; rather worn.

These two volumes were evidently used by Mrs. Onassis during the research of her *In the Russian Style.* The rear endpapers of Rothschild's work are filled with brief autograph notes by Mrs. Onassis making reference to the text. Kohler's book is signed on the title-page "J.K.O." Both works have many page corners turned down and have been ruled in the margins for quick reference.

$700–1,000

172 **Winter Antiques Show**

East Side House Winter Antiques Show: The Eighth Annual Show and Sale by the Most Distinguished Dealers in America ... Seventh Regiment Armory ... January 19th through January 25th, 1962. *(New York, 1962)*

(10 ⅞ x 8½ in.). Numerous illustrations. Blue cloth gilt, front cover gilt with the supralibros of MRS. JOHN F. KENNEDY; extremities bumped.

MRS. KENNEDY'S COPY of the catalogue for the 1962 Winter Antiques show, with her name gilt-lettered on the front cover and bearing her Jacqueline Bouvier Kennedy bookplate.

$500–700

173 **Dedini, Eldon**

"I don't know, lately, everything looks like Jackie Kennedy to me." *N.p., [1962]*

(11½ x 17 in.), sight. Cartoon ink drawing of the Sphinx as a likeness of Jackie Kennedy, with text, signed by the artist. Framed, matted and glazed.

The cartoon was published in the 26 May 1962 issue of *The New Yorker.*

$300–500

174 **Ballet**

A group of 13 volumes, various sizes. Illustrated. Publisher's cloth, some with dust jackets. Various places, various dates.

Horizon. Volume III, number 3, January, 1961. Bookplate of Jacqueline Bouvier Kennedy, inscribed by George Balanchine "For dear Mrs. Kennedy with much appreciation from G. Balanchine" and with note from Lincoln Kirstein to Mrs. Kennedy stating "Balanchine wanted you to have this piece about him. He said if you felt up to it, the first two ballets at tomorrows matinee might interest you." — Alexander Bland. *The Nureyev Valentino.* 1977. With lengthy inscription from Lincoln Kirstein. — Yuri Slonimsky. *The Bolshoi Theatre Ballet.* 1956. Signed by all the dancers of the company, 13 November 1962. — Nathalia Makarova. *A Dance Autobiography.* 1979. Inscribed by the author "To dear Jackie." — Leroy Leatherman. *Portrait of the Lady as an Artist: Martha Graham.* 1966. Inscribed by Graham "For Mrs. John F. Kennedy" and signed by the author as well as the photographer Martha Swope. — and 8 other volumes inscribed to Mrs. Kennedy or with her bookplate.

$600–800

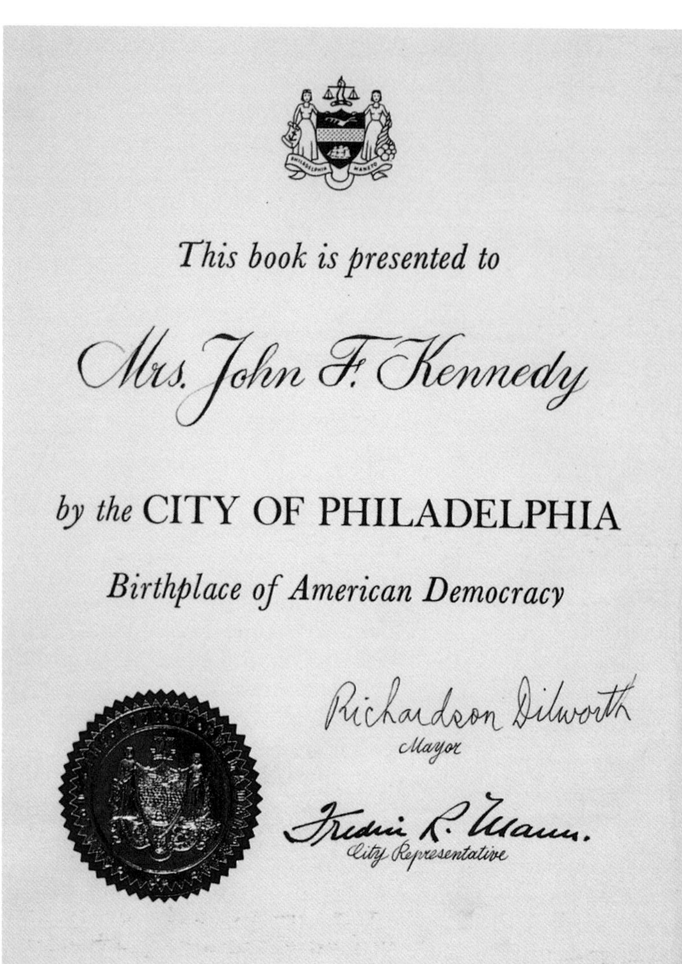

175

175 Tatum, George B.

Penn's Great Town: 250 Years of Philadelphia Architecture Illustrated in Prints and Drawings. *Philadelphia: University of Pennsylvania Press, (1961)*

(12¼ x 9⅜ in.). Numerous halftone reproductions of prints and drawings. Blue buckram, front cover gilt-stamped with seal of the City of Philadelphia and title, pictorial endleaves. Blue buckram folding-case with supralibros MRS. JOHN F. KENNEDY; a trifle worn.

LIMITED EDITION, COPY 2 OF 200 NUMBERED COPIES. PRESENTATION COPY, with printed and calligraphic inscription to Mrs. Kennedy, signed by Mayor Richardson Dilworth and City Representative F. R. Mann and with the embossed gilt seal of the city.

$400–600

176 Mailer, Norman

Harlot's Ghost. *New York: Random House, 1991*

(9⅛ x 6 in.). Publisher's half blue cloth, dust-jacket.

PRESENTATION COPY, INSCRIBED BY MAILER on the front free endpaper, "Jackie, I don't know if you will care to read this or not, but I want you to have it. With respect, Norman. Sept. '91."

$300–500

177 Liberman, Alexander

Greece: Gods and Art; introduction by Robert Graves, descriptions by Iris Love. New York, Viking Press, 1968

(12¾ x 9½ in.). Blue cloth, dust-jacket. Warmly INSCRIBED: "To Jacqueline Onassis, with profound admiration. Alexander Liberman."

$400–600

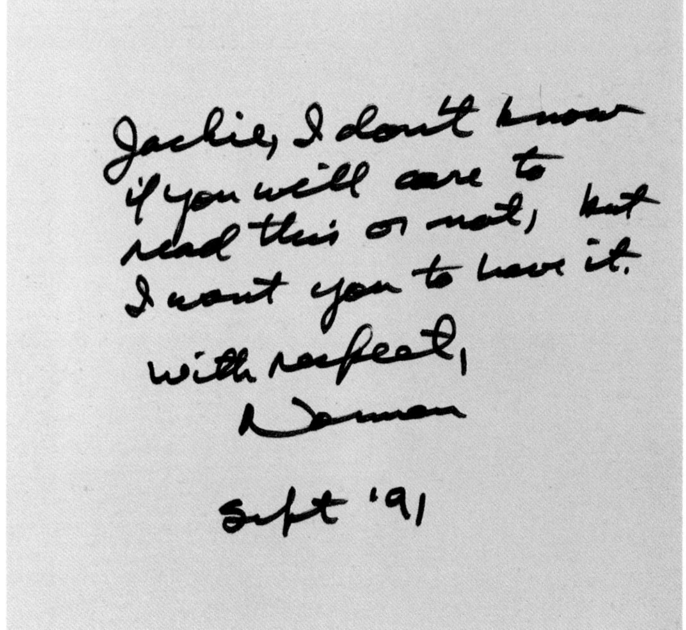

176

178 **Music**

A group of 14 volumes, various sizes. Mostly illustrated. Publisher's cloth or paper. Various places and dates. Including 3 INSCRIBED as below.

Barotmeu Ferra. *Chopin and George Sand.* 1935. With Jacqueline Bouvier Kennedy bookplate. — Charles O'Connell. *Victor Book of Symphonies.* 1948. A gift to "Jacqueline and Jack" from "Genevieve McDermott." — Nicolas Nabakov. *Old Friends and New Music.* 1951. Inscribed to "Mrs. J. Kennedy with affection (pour lire en route) ... a change from 'Lolita' Nicolas N.6-7." With bookplate of Jacqueline Bouvier Kennedy. — Selden Rodman and James Kearns. *The Heart of Beethoven.* 1962. Signed presentation to "President and Mrs. Kennedy. This hand-bound first copy ... high hope for the future of the Arts in America." — Ruth Berges. *Opera and Sidelights.* 1961. With Jacqueline Bouvier Kennedy bookplate. — *The Best of Rolling Stone.* 1993. Edited by Mrs. Onassis. — and others.

$400–600

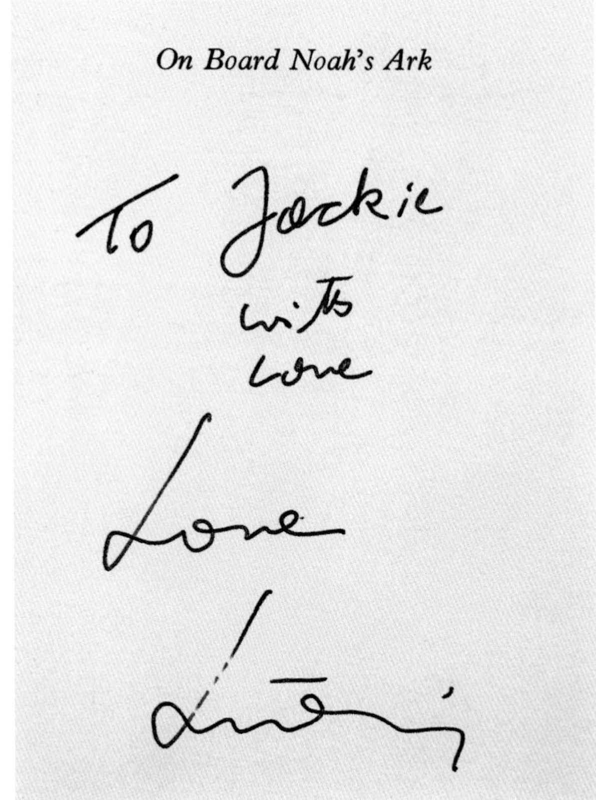

180

179 **Pope-Hennessy, Sir John**

Group of 4 volumes, various sizes. Most illustrated. Publisher's cloth, most with dust wrappers. Various places, various dates. All inscribed.

The Piero della Francesca Trail. 1991. INSCRIBED "To Jackie, a small tribute from John." — *Paradiso: The Illuminations to Dante's Divine Comedy by Giovanni di Paolo.* 1993. With typed presentation note signed, laid in. — *Donatello, Sculptor.* 1993. INSCRIBED "To Jackie from John P-Hennessy." — *On Artists and Art Historians.* 1994. INSCRIBED "To Jackie, with every Affectionate wish from John, 14.iv.1994"

$800–1,200

180 **Bemelmans, Ludwig**

On Board Noah's Ark. *New York: Viking, (1962)*

(8¼ x 5½ in.). Color frontispiece and text reproductions. Publisher's half red cloth, illustrated endpapers, dust-jacket.

PRESENTATION COPY, inscribed and signed by the author on the half-title: "To Jackie with love, Love Ludwig."

$400–600

181 **Moryson, Fynes**

An Itinerary ... containing his Ten Yeeres Travell through the Twelve Dominions of Germany, Bohmerland, Sweitzerland, Netherland, Denmarke, Poland, Italy, Turky, France, England, Scotland, and Ireland. *London: Printed by John Beale, 1617*

(12¾ x 8⅝ in.). Woodcut maps and plans, woodcut initials and tailpieces; occasional marginal repair and restoration. Brown morocco gilt, marbled endpapers, gilt edges; extremities scuffed.

First edition of Moryson's celebrated travel book, containing one of the earliest appearances of the phrase "merry Christmas." Inscribed by the famous antiquarian bookseller John Fleming: "To Jackie Kennedy Onassis in memory of an earlier Christmas ... Christmas in June 1984." With the bookplates of Boies Penrose.

$800–1,200

182 **Rowse, A. L.**

Homosexuals in History: A Study of Ambivalence in Society, Literature and the Arts. *New York: Macmillan, (1977)*

(9 x 6 in.). Photographic plates. Publisher's black cloth, dust-jacket.

The rear fly-leaves and free endpaper are filled with brief autograph notes by Mrs. Onassis about various authors and artists discussed in the text. Many page corners in the volume have been turned down for quick reference.

$600–800

183 **Modern History**

Group of 6 volumes, various sizes, all INSCRIBED to Mrs. Onassis. Publisher's cloth or wrappers, 3 with dust-jackets. Various places, various dates.

Cornelius Ryan. *The Last Battle.* 1966. "For Jackie – in memory of the man who wanted me to write this book." — Jean-Jacques Servan-Schreiber. *Le Défi américain.* 1967. "Pour Madame J. F. Kennedy, en hommage respectueux". — David Ormsby-Gore (Lord Harlech). *Must the West Decline?* 1966. "To Jackie – with love – and gratitude for having the fortitude to come and listen to one of the lectures." — and 3 others.

$500–800

Above: *Jacqueline Kennedy working on the redecoration of the White House.*

184 **United States Capitol Historical Society**

We, the People: The Story of the United States Capitol. *Washington, D.C.: Historical Society, 1963*

(10 x 7 in.). Color illustration in text throughout. Red morocco gilt with "Mrs. Kennedy" stamped in gilt on the upper cover, original wrappers bound in; light wear.

MRS. JACQUELINE KENNEDY'S COPY. Limited to 150 copies.

$300–400

185 **White House Guides**

A group of various editions, with successive revisions, of *The White House: An Historic Guide* (first published in the summer of 1962 at the request of the First Lady, Jacqueline Kennedy). Approximately 40 copies from the Kennedy years, 7 from Johnson's administration and 1 from Nixon's.

Together approximately 48 volumes, variously publisher's cloth and paper.

Jacqueline Kennedy as First Lady said that she planned to accomplish two things: "To make the White House the most beautiful 'house' and a point of pilgrimage to all Americans;" and to provide a guidebook as a souvenir of a White House visit. A nonprofit corporation called the White House Historical Association was chartered on November 3, 1961, and sale of *The White House: An Historic Guide* for one dollar a copy began in the foyer of the East Wing on the morning of July 4, 1962. The initial printing of 250,000 copies was exhausted in three months. The Association went to press again in the fall of 1962 and once again in the winter of 1962. Today, the *Guide* is in its 19th edition; the publication continues to be an all-time best-seller among guidebooks, with more than 4,400,000 copies sold to date.

When the cornerstone of the White House was laid on October 12, 1792, Pierre Charles L'Enfant discussed the site and design for what he called the "President's Palace," and described the President's House as a combination of the "sumptuousness of a palace" with the "convenience of a house and the agreeableness of a country seat." Built of light brown Aquia, Virginia, sandstone, the building was first whitewashed in 1797; generally referred to as the White House by Jefferson's day, it was not officially so designated until 1902. By 1800 the White House was occupied, but it was not completed until 1803. In 1807 Benjamin Henry Latrobe redesigned the north and south façades, adding monumental porticoes that were carried out in slightly altered form by James Hoban in 1824 (south) and 1829 (north). Latrobe also redecorated the interiors, landscaped the grounds in a picturesque manner with terraces, and added low, single-story wings to provide for storage and other household necessities on the east and west. Hoban was again in charge of construction after 1815, as at Monticello, for three years, rebuilding after the August 1814 burning by British troops. The interiors were gutted, but the earlier walls remained sound.

The White House is a unit of the National Park System; it represents "Reservation No. 1," established by the Congress of the United States as public land in 1791 and placed under the jurisdiction of the Park Service by President Franklin D. Roosevelt's Executive Order of June 10, 1935. In the summer of 1961, the National Park Service transferred Nash Castro from its Omaha regional office to Washington, D.C., as assistant superintendent of the National Capital Parks, which was then headed by T. Sutton Jett Castro . In addition for being mad responsible for certain administration functions of the National Capital Parks, Castro assumed liaison activities between the Park Service and the White House. He made his first visit to the White House in August 1961 at the invitation of J. B. West, its chief usher and chief administrative officer. Very shortly after this visit, Mr. West called Castro and described the new First Lady's proposed White House restoration program. Mrs. Kennedy wanted visitors to the "restored" White House to have an opportunity to take home with them a momento of some kind. John Walker, director of the National Gallery of Art and a member of the informal Fine Arts Committee was asked to assist with the project. The initial idea was to print postcards of the various state rooms and other Executive Mansion amenities and make them available to visitors for a small charge. Mrs. Kennedy planned for the proceeds to be used to enhance the ongoing restoration program through the acquisition of furniture, paintings, and objets d'art reflective of the history of the White House. Eventually it was her idea to have a White House guidebook published. Nash Castro proposed the establishment of a nonprofit corporation for the purpose of benefiting the interpretive program: he recommended the name, the White House Historical Association, a proposal approved in principle by Mrs. Kennedy. At her suggestion the plan was discussed with Clark M. Clifford, who advised President Kennedy on many legal matters. Since the White House had never been adequately identified in the law as a unit of the National Park System, Senator Clinton Anderson of New Mexico introduced a bill on August 5, 1961, proposing that the White House be established as a national monument, a unit of the National Park System. There was one serious obstacle: President Kennedy made it known that he did not wish to live in a national monument. A change had to be made.

In committee the bill was revised to provide merely that the White House would continue to be known as the White House and administered pursuant to the Act of August 25, 1916, the organic act creating the National Park Service. The legislation was enacted in record time and signed into law by President Kennedy and the way was cleared toward the establishment of the nonprofit corporation, called the White House Historical Association. The charter and proposed bylaws were filed in the District of Columbia, where the corporation was chartered on November 3, 1961. John Walker, J. B. West, and Nash Castro discussed the composition of the board of directors and agreed that the incorporators would be Mr. Walker, Mr. Clifford, and David E. Finley, chairman of the Commission of Fine Arts. It was also agreed that the board would be composed of certain *ex officio* members, officials of the government, such as the director of the National Park Service and the secretary of the Smithsonian Institution, as well as citizens at large—ideas presented to Mrs. Kennedy, who approved them.

The first organizational meeting was held in the early fall of 1961 in David Finley's office in the Interior Building. Underwriting the costs of publication of the Guidebook was a prime topic. Conrad L. Wirth, a trustee of the National Geographic Society and director of the National Park Service, suggested the idea of asking the Society if it might assist with the publication. Melville Bell Grosvenor, president of the National Geographic Society, made an initial contribution of $120,000 to underwrite, as a public service, to cover the initial costs of photography and editing. Robert L. Breeden, of the *National Geographic*, was assigned the task of developing the concept. Mr. Breeden worked closely with Franc Shor, his colleague at the magazine, and with Lorraine Waxman Pearce, a recent graduate of the Winterther Museum Program and curator of the White House, who wrote the text. With a "dummy" of the guidebook, a meeting was held in the Yellow Oval Room of the White House in early 1962 with Mrs. Kennedy; those present were Dr. Grosvernor, Mr. Shor, Mr. Breeden, Mr. West, Mrs. Pearce, Mr. Jett, and Mr. Castro. For more than two hours, Mrs. Kennedy studied every page of the dummy with great care and thoroughness, making a number of suggestions informed by her own professional background in journalism. The time that elapsed between the charter of the White House Historical Association and the sale of the first guidebook was a mere eight months.

The White House Historical Association, after moving several times in its thirty-four year history, is presently located at 740 Jackson Place. The President's House and with it the people of the United States are the beneficiaries of the Association's dedicated work. Our of the earnings from its publications—particularly *The White House: An Historic Guide*—has provided funds for important paintings and furnishings for the White House. This is an important part of the enduring legacy of Jacqueline Kennedy.

Bibliography:
Nash Castro, "The Association's Twentieth Year," *White House History*, Washington, D.C.: White House Historical Association, 1983, pp. 23-87.
Pamela Scott and Antoinette J. Lee, *Buildings of the District of Columbia*, New York: Oxford University Press, 1993, pp. 149-154.

$300–500

187

LORD DERBY

'KING OF LANCASHIRE'

188

186 Kennedy, John F.

The John F. Kennedy Memorial at Runnymede: Dedicatory Remarks May Fourteenth, Nineteen Hundred Sixty-Five. *(Privately printed and bound for Mrs. John F. Kennedy, December 1965)*

(10½ by 7¾ in.,*uncut*). Polished red calf, covers with double gilt-fillet border, front cover gilt with presidential seal, marbled endpapers; spine slightly faded.

LIMITED EDITION, ONE OF ONE HUNDRED COPIES PRINTED FOR MRS. KENNEDY.

In memory of John F. Kennedy, Great Britain gave to the United States an acre of English ground at Runnymede, where the Magna Carta had been signed in 1215. The present volume contains the addresses of the principal speakers at the dedication of the memorial: Queen Elizabeth II, Harold Macmillan, Harold Wilson, and Dean Rusk.

$400–600

187 McCarthy, Joe

The Remarkable Kennedys. *New York: Dial Press, 1960*

(8 x 5½ in.). Publisher's red cloth, blue cloth spine, dust-jacket; dust-jacket slightly worn, spine darkened.

PRESENTATION COPY OF A CAMPAIGN BIOGRAPHY, INSCRIBED AND SIGNED: "To Jack and Jackie Kennedy—with gratitude for the help and the tolerance they gave me while I was working on this book, which may not be the greatest book ever written about the Kennedys, but is probably one of the quickest ones to read. Joe McCarthy." Also with the presidential bookplate of John F. Kennedy.

$600–800

188 Churchill, Randolph S.

Lord Derby: "King of Lancashire." *London: Heinemann, 1959*

(8¼ x 5½ in.). Photographic plates, maps. Publisher's gray buckram gilt, top edges stained black, dust-jacket; front hinge cracked, jacket worn with loss at foot of spine.

PRESENTATION COPY, inscribed by Churchill on the half-title: "Jacqueline, with love from Randolph. Washington, June 1960." The volume also contains the presidential bookplate of John F. Kennedy.

$400–600

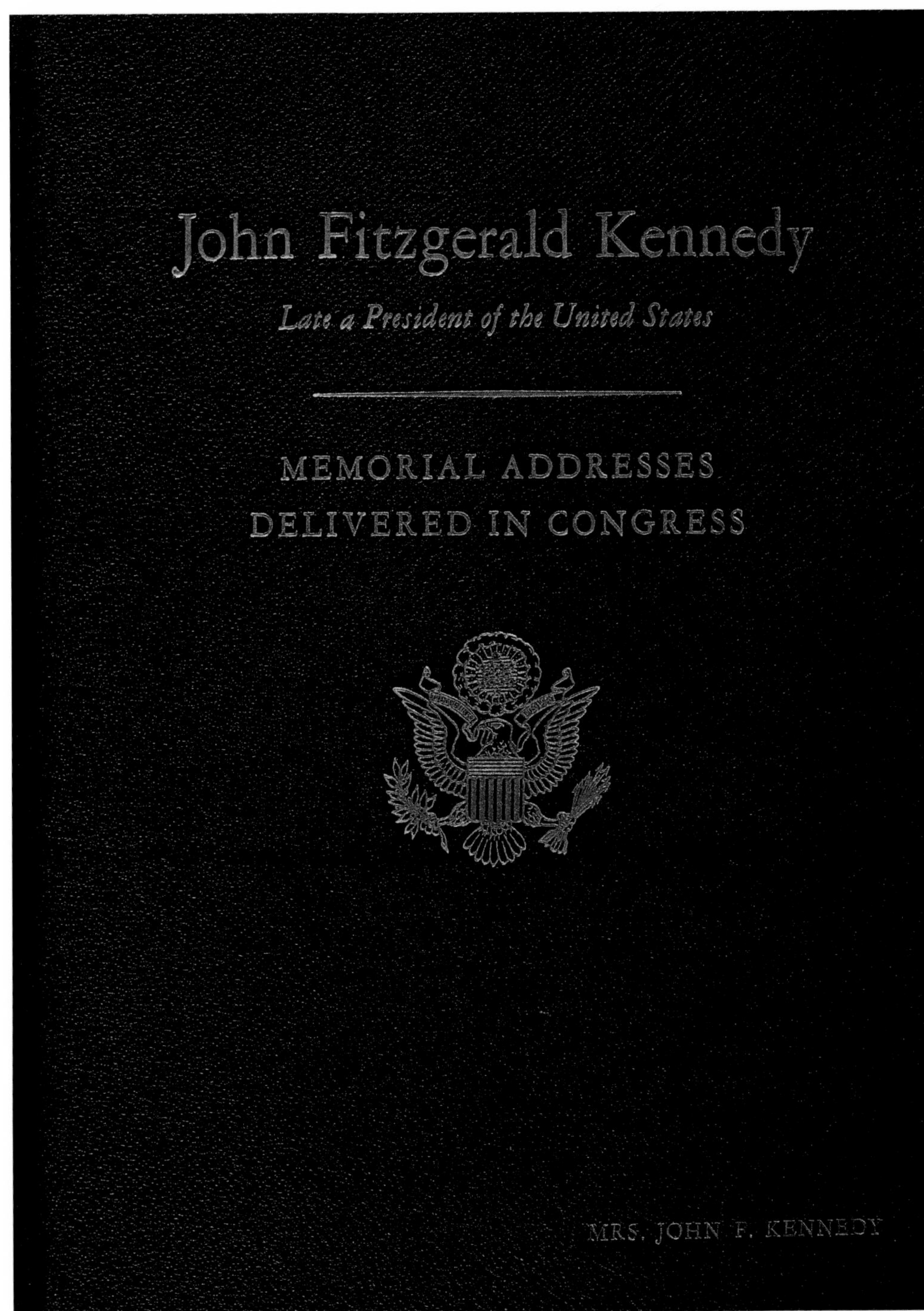

189

189 **Kennedy, John F.**

Memorial Addresses in the Congress of the United States and Tributes in Eulogy of John Fitzgerald Kennedy, Late a President of the United States. *Washington: Government Printing Office, 1964*

(10¼ x 7⅛ in.). Photographic frontispiece portrait of Kennedy. Blue morocco, front cover gilt with title, federal eagle, and the supralibros of Mrs. John F. Kennedy, spine vertically gilt with President Kennedy's name and dates, white moiré silk linings. Black cloth slipcase.

Mrs. Kennedy's copy of the compilation of addresses and tributes given in the Senate and House of Representatives on the life and service of President Kennedy. The volume was compiled under the direction of the Joint Committee on Printing and was published in an edition of 32,250. The present copy is one of 10,300 printed for the use of the Senate and designated Senate Document No. 59 of the second session of the eighty-eighth Congress.

$3,000–5,000

193

190 Holt, J. C.

Magna Carta. *Cambridge: University Press, 1965*

(8⅜ x 5⅝ in.). Photographic plates. Blue morocco gilt, marbled endpapers, gilt edges. Blue cloth slipcase.

ONE OF THREE COPIES SPECIALLY BOUND BY THE PUBLISHER FOR PRESENTATION. Holt's authoritative history of *Magna Carta* was published to commemorate the 750th anniversary of the sealing of the charter at Runnymede, the site of the British memorial to President Kennedy. Identically bound copies were also presented to Queen Elizabeth II and President Lyndon B. Johnson. A presentation slip from Cambridge University Press is laid in.

$1,000–1,500

191 National Cultural Center

Creative America. (Texts by John F. Kennedy, James Baldwin, Robert Frost, et al.). *New York, Ridge Press, 1962*

(11 x 8½ in.). Glazed pictorial boards.

INSCRIBED "To Jackie with the affectionate regards of her friend LeMoyne Billings" (editor of the volume); also signed "Jacqueline Kennedy, March 28, 1963" and with her bookplate. Unusual in containing all three evidences of ownership.

$400–600

192 Eban, Abba

Heritage: Civilization and the Jews. *New York: Summit, (1984)*

(10 x 7⅞ in.). Color illustrations. Publisher's half blue cloth, dust-jacket.

PRESENTATION COPY, inscribed and signed on the front fly-leaf: "To Jackie in friendship and respect, Abba Eban, New York, January 17, 1990."

$400–600

193 Ben-Gurion, David

Israel: Years of Challenge. *New York: Holt, Rinehart and Winston, (1963)*

(8¼ x 5½ in.). Photographic plates. Publisher's white cloth, pictorial dust-jacket.

PRESENTATION COPY, inscribed and signed on the title-page by the author: "To Mrs. Jacqueline B. Kennedy with deep admiration. D. Ben-Gurion, Sdeh-Boker, 18.12.63." Prime Minister Ben-Gurion, one of the founding fathers of Israel, was a close ally of President Kennedy, who strongly advanced the United States commitment to a free Israel. Sdeh-Boker was the kibbutz where Ben-Gurion lived in his retirement.

$1,500–2,500

Portrait of a
President

For Jacqueline Bouvier Kennedy
With admiration, and respect,
from the father of a
five-year-girl—
William Manchester
Wesleyan University
Middletown, Conn.
11 X 62

194

194 **Manchester, William**

Portrait of A President. *Boston: Little, Brown and Co., 1962*

(8 x 5½ in.). Frontispiece portrait of the President. Publisher's cloth with printed dust jacket. With the Jacqueline Bouvier Kennedy book-plate.

Inscribed by the author "For Jacqueline Bouvier Kennedy with admiration and respect…" This informal and candid biography contains much of interest on the President's wife and his family. An attractive association.

$400–600

195 **Oratio Dominica**

Oratio Dominica. *Parma: Bodoni, 1806* [Facsimile, *Parma: Franco Maria Ricci, 1967*]

2 volumes (16 ⅞ x 11 in.). (Vol. 1): Preface by U. N. Secretary General U Thant signed ("U Thant"), Thant's address welcoming Pope Paul VI to the United Nations 4 October 1965, Pope Paul VI's address signed ("Paulus P P. VI"), colophon; (Vol. 2): facsimile of Bodoni's *Oratio Dominica.* Both printed on specially commissioned Fabriano paper watermarked with the papal arms. Full tan morocco panelled gilt, papal arms stamped in gilt on upper covers, plain endpapers. Slipcase. Spines rubbed.

Limited edition, copy number 3, of a total edition of 700, commemorating the visit of His Holiness Pope Paul VI to the United Nations on 4 October 1965. This copy is an exemplaire nominatif, with a printed presentation leaf from the printer to Mrs. John F. Kennedy dated 30 January 1967, and bearing the signatures of both Pope Paul VI and U Thant.

$1,500–2,000

196 **Kunhardt, Philip B., Jr., et al.**

Lincoln. *New York: Knopf, 1992*

(10 ⅞ x 9¼ in.). Profusely illustrated. Publisher's maroon cloth, dust-jacket.

Presentation copy, inscribed and signed by Kunhardt on the front fly-leaf "For Jackie, Christmas 1992" and also signed by his collaborators Philip B. Kunhardt III and Peter W. Kunhardt. Loosely inserted is a copy print of a photograph of six Union officers, including Captain John Vernon Bouvier, taken near Culpeper, Virginia, on 6 October 1863. Accompanying the photograph is a note to Mrs. Onassis signed by Kunhardt, Jr.: "While doing the research for this book I came upon this picture of one of your ancestors."

$300–500

197 **Chiang Kai-Shek, Madame.**

Selected Speeches, 1958–1959. *Taipei, Taiwan: Office of the President, 1959.* — The Sure Victory. *Westwood, NJ: Fleming H. Revell, 1965.*

Together 2 volumes (9¼ x 6¼ in., the largest). Publisher's cloth, printed dust jackets; general wear.

An extraordinary set of presentations from the first lady of China to the former first lady, "Mrs. Jacqueline Kennedy...December 1964."

$600–800

198

198 **Kennedy, Jacqueline Bouvier.**

Daniel Rashall. *Portrait of a Valiant Lady*. Los Angeles: Research Craft Corp., 1964. Phono album in sleeve. Color photoreproduction of Jacqueline Kennedy on the cover. — Howard K. Smith, narrator. *Kennedy in Germany*. Chicago: Phillips Records, n.d. Phono album, in a special folding box gilt-stamped "Jacqueline Kennedy."

Together 2 phono albums.

$200–400

199 **De Andrea, Miguel.**

Pensamiento Cristiano y Democrático de Monseñor de Andrea. *Buenos Aires: Imprenta del Congreso de la Nacion, 1965.*

(9 ⅞ x 6 ⅞ in.). Color printed frontispiece, the Andrea arms, portrait and a few other illustrations in text, 1 folding diagram. Blue morocco, gilt, silk liners. In a folding box.

A fine presentation to Jacqueline Kennedy, "… esposa del gran Presidente" from the Vice President of Argentina, Carlos Perette, on the 5th of April, 1966.

$300–500

200 **Churchill, Winston S.**

Group of 4 volumes, various sizes. One illustrated. Publisher's cloth or wrappers, one with dust-jacket. Various places, various dates.

Randolph S. Churchill. *Winston S. Churchill*. Volume One. 1966. Inscribed by the author "To Jacqueline with my fondest love." — Randolph S. Churchill. — *The Fight for the Tory Leadership*. 1964. Inscribed by the author "Jacqueline with devotion from Randolph. P.S. I had so hoped that Jack would read this book. I did not write because I could not think of what to say. R." — Randolph S. Churchill. *The Six Day War*. 1967. Inscribed by the author to J. F. Walsh. — Richard Harrity & Ralph G. Martin. *Man of the Century*. 1962. Bookplate of Jacqueline Bouvier Kennedy.

$300–500

201 **The White House**

The White House: An Historic Guide. *Washington, D.C.: White House Historical Association, 1962*

(10 x 6 ⅞ in.). Numerous illustrations. Blue morocco, front cover gilt with the supralibros J.B.K., blue endpapers, top edge gilt, original pictorial paper covers bound in; extremities slightly rubbed.

MRS. KENNEDY'S COPY OF THE OFFICIAL WHITE HOUSE GUIDEBOOK, which she was instrumental in having prepared and published.

$700–1,000

202 **White House Guides**

A group of various editions, with successive revisions, of *The White House: An Historic Guide* (first published in the summer of 1962 at the request of the First Lady, Jacqueline Kennedy). Approximately 40 copies from the Kennedy years, 7 from Johnson's administration and 1 from Nixon's.

Together approximately 48 volumes, variously publisher's cloth and paper.

$300–500

204

203 **Biography and Literature**

A pair of biographical volumes inscribed by Father Joseph Leonard to Jacqueline Bouvier Kennedy, of which one bears her floral bookplate. Varying sizes and conditions.

Maurice Baring. *In My End is My Beginning. A Biography of Mary, Queen of Scots*. 1931. Inscribed by Father Joseph Leonard, October 1955: "This book was given to me by Lady La[?v]ey, who brought us together, and I know of no one better qualified in every way to have it than yourself, ..."; blind library stamp of Mill Hill, London, with Leonard's notation that he lived there for a year; floral bookplate of Jacqueline Bouvier Kennedy. — Penelope Chetwode. *Two Middle-aged Ladies in Andalusia*. 1963. Inscribed by the author: "To dear Father Leonard with love and blessings from Penelope (one of the middle-aged ladies)" and dated 19 November 1963; subsequently inscribed by Leonard: "To dearest Jacqueline, with love as ever, from her old and affectionate friend. J. L. Christmas, 1965."

$300–500

204 **Mugridge, Donald H.**

The Presidents of the United States 1789–1962: A Selected List of References. *Washington: Library of Congress, 1963*

(10⅝ x 8 in.). Brown morocco, covers with gilt-fillet border, front cover gilt with title, emblem of the Library of Congress, and the supralibros JACQUELINE BOUVIER KENNEDY, marbled endpapers.

Pages 145 and 146 list books by and about President Kennedy.

$1,000–1,500

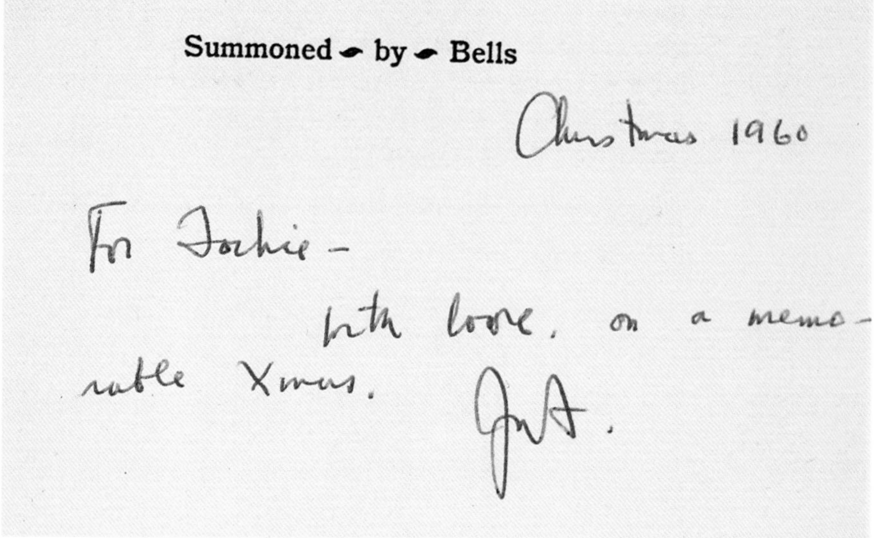

205

206

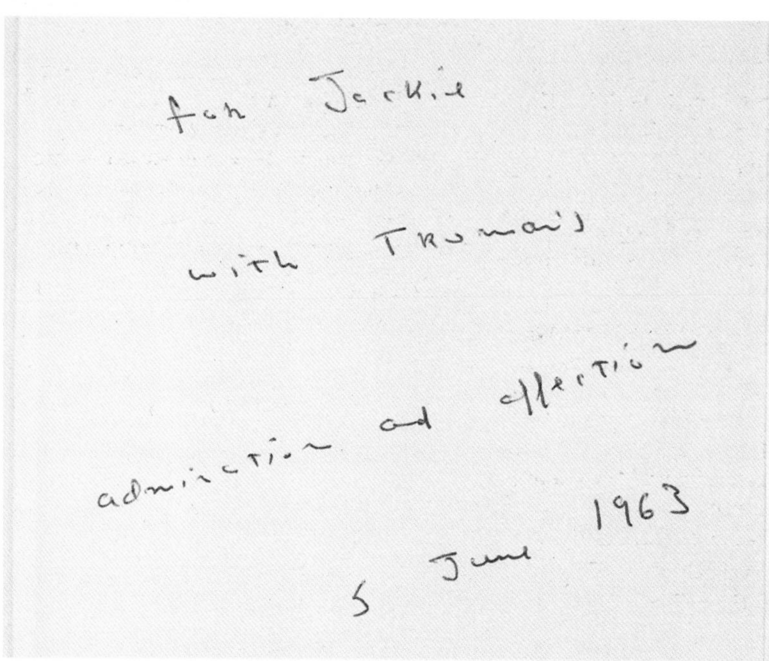

207

205 Betjeman, John

Summoned by Bells. *London: John Murray, 1960*

(9 x 6½ in.). Illustrated. Publisher's green cloth, blindstamped with repeating bell pattern, spine gilt-lettered, patterned endpapers, dust jacket; minor wear.

FIRST EDITION OF THE THEN-POET LAUREATE'S AUTOBIOGRAPHY IN VERSE, INSCRIBED BY HIM on the half-title, "Christmas 1960. For Jackie, with love on a memorable Xmas. John." With Mrs. Kennedy's engraved bookplate on the front pastedown.

$400–600

206 Lowell, Robert

A group of 5 PRESENTATION COPIES FROM THE AUTHOR of first editions and first English editions, each inscribed and signed on the free front endpaper or title-page, various sizes. Publisher's cloth and dust-jackets; some jackets chipped or darkened.

Imitations. London: Faber & Faber, (1962). Inscribed and signed: "For Jacqueline Kennedy with love & admiration from Robert Lowell, Christmas Eve, 1964. These all have the same inscription. But what can I say? I love and admire you as much as any man or woman I've ever met." — *Phaedra.* London: Faber & Faber, (1963). Inscribed and signed: "For Jacqueline Kennedy, with love & admiration from Robert Lowell, Christmas Eve 1964." — *For the Union Dead.* New York: Farrar Straus & Giroux, (1964). Inscribed and signed as above and dated: Christmas Eve, 1964. With an earlier inscription crossed out by Lowell. — *The Old Glory.* New York: Farrar Straus & Giroux, (1965). Inscribed and signed on the title-page: "For Jacqueline Kennedy with affection, as ever, Robert Lowell." — *Near the Ocean.* New York: Farrar Straus & Giroux, (1967). Inscribed and signed on the title-page: "For Jackie with all my love, as always, Cal. 1.19.67."

$1,200–1,800

207 Capote, Truman

Selected Writings. *New York: Random House, (1963)*

(7½ x 4⅝ in.). Publisher's yellow cloth, printed dust-jacket; front panel of jacket torn with adhesive residue from tape repair.

PRESENTATION COPY, inscribed and signed by the author on the front free endpaper: "for Jackie with Truman's admiration and affection, 5 June 1963." First edition of this collection from Capote's fiction and non-fiction, chosen by the author.

$600–800

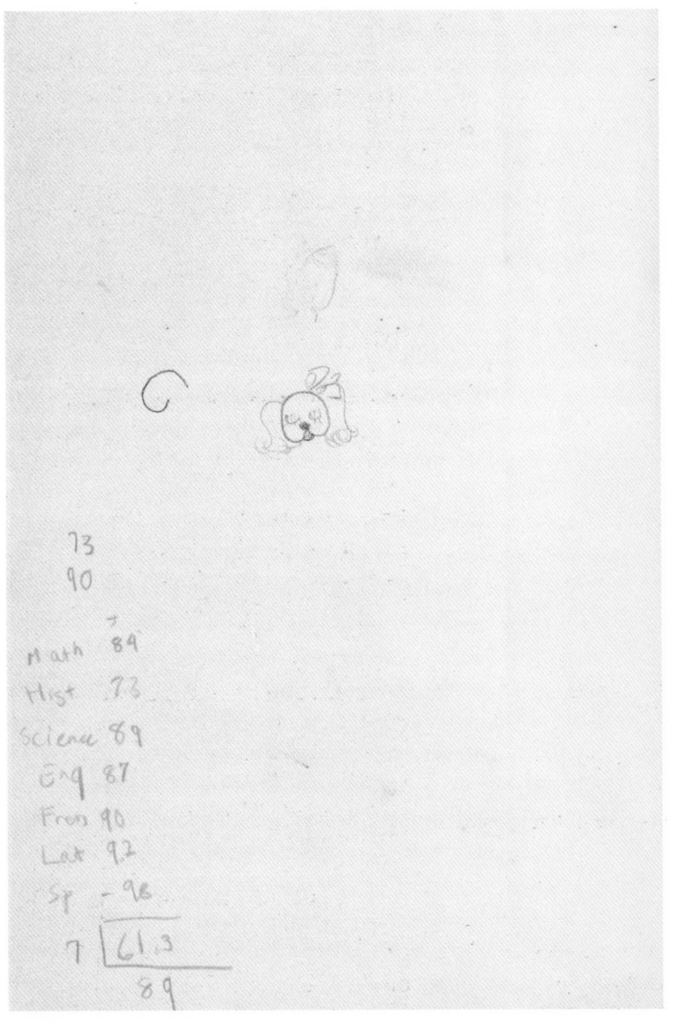

210

208 Cervantes Saavedra, Miguel de

The History and Adventures of the Renowned Don Quixote. Translated from the Spanish … by T[obias] Smollett. *London: Printed for A. Millar, et al., 1755*

2 volumes (11⅜ x 9 in.). Engraved frontispieces and plates after F. Hayman. Contemporary speckled calf; rebacked.

First edition of Smollett's translation. Inscribed on the front free endpaper: "To Jacqueline From her Man of La Mancha in the winter of our quest. D."

$250–350

209 Mahfouz, Naguib

Palace Walk. Cairo: The American University, 1989. — Palace of Desire. Cairo: The American University Press, 1991

Together 2 volumes (9¼ x 6 in.) Publisher's cloth. Printed dust-jackets; corners bumped, light wear.

SIGNED PRESENTATION COPIES FROM THE NOBEL PRIZE WINNING AUTHOR, MAHFOUZ, to "Mrs. Jacqueline K. Onassis, with my best wishes, 16–5–1991."

$200–300

210 Barker, Fred G.

Forty-Minute Plays from Shakespeare. *New York: Macmillan, 1939*

(7½ x 5 in.). Outline maps and photoreproductions in text. Publisher's green cloth, stamped in black. Endpapers with erasures and annotations.3

JACQUELINE BOUVIER'S SHAKESPEARE TEXT, SIGNED, "J. BOUVIER," in pencil. Passages from Katharina's role from the *Taming of the Shrew* (pp. 133-140) are marked. On the free endpaper at the back she has figured her grades, scoring 98 for Spanish, 90 for French and 89 for Science, yielding an 89 grade point average. She has also drawn a small cartoonish head of a poodle.

$600–800

211 Onassis, Jacqueline, editor

In the Russian Style. *New York: The Viking Press, (1976)*

(10¾ x 8¼ in.). Half maroon calf over marbled boards, spine gilt with title and editor's name, maroon endpapers, top edge gilt.

Evidently a publisher's presentation binding for Mrs. Onassis's history of Russian style from Peter I to Alexander III. Accompanied by two other copies of the work: one in the publisher's red cloth and dust-jacket, the other in publisher's wrappers.

$400–600

All Hallows College
Dublin, 9

215

212 **White House Guides**

A group of various editions, with successive revisions, of *The White House: An Historic Guide* (first published in the summer of 1962 at the request of the First Lady, Jacqueline Kennedy). Approximately 40 copies from the Kennedy years, 7 from Johnson's administration and 1 from Nixon's.

Together approximately 48 volumes, variously publisher's cloth and paper.

$300–500

213 **Advertising and Publishing**

Group of 5 volumes, various sizes. Publisher's cloth or wrappers, 3 with dust-jackets. Various places, various dates.

Cleveland Amory & Frederic Bradlee, eds., *Vanity Fair: A Cavalcade of the 1920s and 1930s*. 1960. INSCRIBED "To Jackie with much love Ben & Tony [Bradlee] Christmas 1960." — Norman Cousins. *Present Time. An American Editor's Odyssey*. 1967. INSCRIBED "For Jacqueline Kennedy, with profound respect and admiration. Norman Cousins. NY Dec. 1967." — Cass Canfield. *The Publishing Experience*. 1969. INSCRIBED "With affection from Cass." — Bryan Holme. *Advertising: Reflections of a Century*. 1982. INSCRIBED "For Dear Jackie—in memory of some golden days of publishing—Merry Christmas! Bryan." — Larry Goldman. *The Professional Photographer*. 1983. Signed by the author. 1960.

$600–900

214 **Health**

Group of 3 volumes, various sizes. Publisher's cloth, with dust-jackets. Various places, various dates.

Adele Davis. *Let's Eat Right to Keep Fit*. 1954. Bookplate of Jacqueline Bouvier Kennedy. — Hans Kraus, M.D. *Backache Stress and Tension*. 1965. INSCRIBED: "To Mrs Jacqueline Kennedy." — Janet Travell, M.D. *Office Hours: Day and Night*. 1968. INSCRIBED: "For Jackie, Always the first lady of my heart …" Dr. Travell was White House Physician to Presidents Kennedy and Johnson.

$300–500

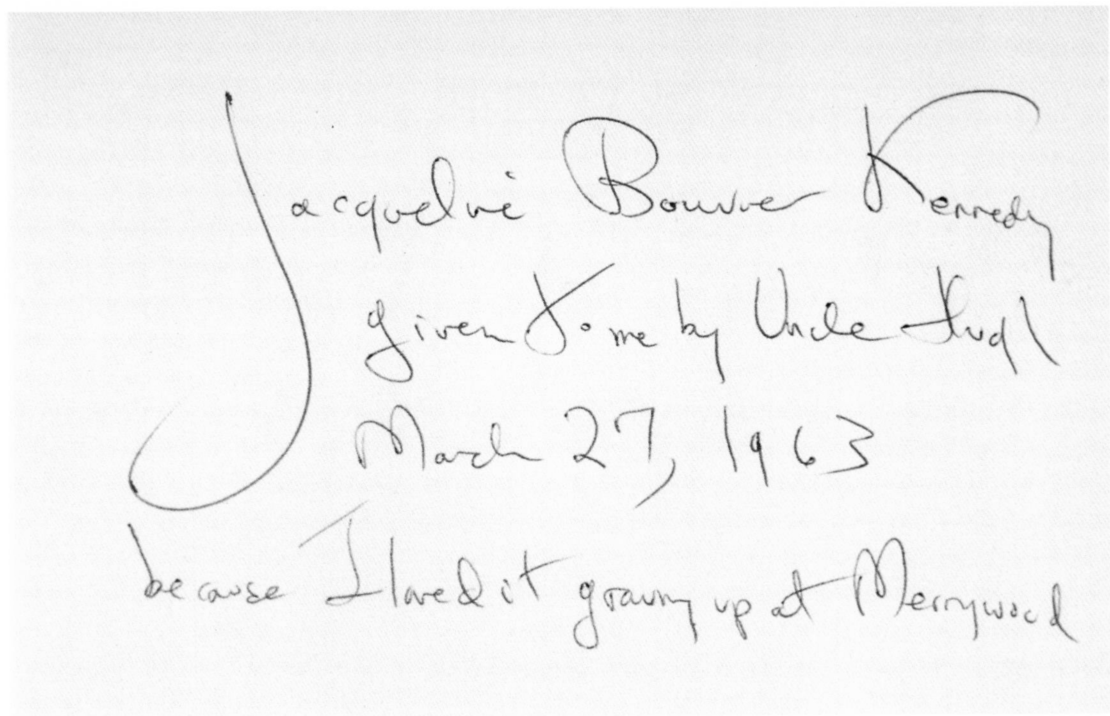

218

215 **Religion**

A group of 5 devotional texts inscribed by the Vincentian priest Joseph Leonard, of which 3 additionally contain the floral bookplate of Jacqueline Bouvier Kennedy. Publisher's cloth and wrappers. Varying sizes and conditions.

Henri Daniel-Rops. *Missa Est.* 1951. Inscribed "A ma très chère Jacqueline. Noël 1952. J. L."; bookplate. — Ronald Knox. *The Hidden Stream.* 1952. Inscribed "For Jacqueline Easter 1953. J. L." — Victor Giraud. *Saint Vincent de Paul* (trans. Joseph Leonard). 1955. Inscribed "To Jack and Jacqueline with love and admiration. J. L. 29 September-October 2, 1958"; bookplate. — Ronald Knox. *A Retreat for Lay People.* 1961. Fondly inscribed "To Jacqueline Kennedy with love, from her old, affectionate friend, J. L. Christmas 1967." — Ronald Knox. *The Layman and His Conscience.* 1961. Inscribed "To dearest Jacqueline with love on her birthday. From her old friend, J. L. 28 July 1962"; bookplate. Loosely laid in is an autograph lettered signed ("J. L."), 1 page on engraved stationery, All Hallows College, Dublin, 23 July 1962, to Jacqueline Kennedy, enclosing this book and a copy of a review on the same. Father Leonard warmly writes: "I remember yourself, Lee, the President, & all your children every day & whenever I say mass."

$800–1,200

216 **Religion and Philosophy**

A group of 17 volumes on Western religion and philosophy, of which 11 bear presentation inscriptions (ca. 1955-1980) and/or the floral bookplate of Jacqueline Bouvier Kennedy. Some illustrated; mostly publisher's cloth and wrappers. Varying sizes and conditions.

Mary Reed Newland. *We and Our Children; Molding the Child in Christian Living.* 1954. Bookplate. — *Letters from Vatican City; Vatican Council II.* 1963. Bookplate. — Pope John XXIII. *Peace on Earth.* 1964. Inscribed to Jacqueline Kennedy by Orville and Jane Freeman, Washington, D.C., December 15, 1964. — and others.

$500–700

217 **Religion and Philosophy**

A group of 18 volumes on Eastern religion and thought, of which 8 bear presentation inscriptions (ca. 1963–1989) and/or the floral bookplate of Jacqueline Bouvier Kennedy. Some illustrated; mostly in publisher's cloth and wrappers. Varying sizes and conditions.

Heinrich Zimmer. *Philosophies of India.* 1951. — G. F. Allen. *The Buddha's Philosophy.* 1959. — *The Bhagavad Gita.* 1960. Bookplate. — *The Brahma Sutra* (trans. S. Radhakrishnan). 1960. Inscribed by the translator and dated 6 October 1963; bookplate. — Muhammed Iqbal. *Shikwa & Jawab-i-Shikwa: Complaint and Answer. Iqbal's Dialogue with Allah.* 1981. — and others.

$500–700

218 **Munnings, A. J.**

Pictures of Horses and English Life. *London: Eyre and Spottiswoode, 1927*

(13¼ x 10¼ in.). 28 tipped-in color plates with lettered tissue-guards, numerous photographic plates and illustrations. Publisher's brown buckram lettered in black, brown endpapers, gilt edges; soiled, extremities rubbed, slightly shaken.

Association copy, signed and inscribed by Jacqueline Kennedy on the front flyleaf: "Jacqueline Bouvier Kennedy given to me by Uncle Hugh, March 27 1963 because I loved it growing up at Merrywood." Mrs. Kennedy referred to her stepfather, Hugh D. Auchincloss as "Uncle Hugh."

$1,500–2,500

THE ESTATE OF JACQUELINE KENNEDY ONASSIS

SESSION THREE

WEDNESDAY, APRIL 24,

2:00 P.M.

The Second Floor Oval Room, The White House, 1962, showing lots 15, 269, 286, 287, 303, 306, 338, 352, and 358.)

219

219

219

219

219 **Stefano Della Bella**

EXOTIC FIGURES ON HORSEBACK (Massar-de Vesme 270-280)

Six from the set of eleven, etchings, trimmed to the circular borderline, framed* (not examined out of frames)
Diameter 7 in. (17.8 cm.)

$1,500–2,000

220

220 **Louis Dupré**

L'ACROPOLIS, VUE DE LA MAISON DU CONSOL DE FRANCE, M. FAUVET

Hand-colored lithograph, c. 1850, framed* (not examined out of the frame)
Image: 21 by 27 in. (53.3 by 68.6 cm.)

$300–500

221 **Crepy (Engraver)**

THEATRICAL SETS AND DESIGNS

Six hand colored engravings, with margins, in generally good condition, framed* (not examined out of the frames) (6)
Each approximately 10 ¼ by 15 ¾ in. (26 by 40 cm.)

These prints were bought by Jacqueline Bouvier when she spent her Junior year in Paris at the Sorbonne.

$200–300

221

221

221

221

Each of the lots described above is subject to the Glossary of Terms printed at the back of this catalogue.

222

222

222

222 **Day and Son (Lithographers)**

SCENIC LANDSCAPES

Three hand colored lithographs printed with beige tone plates, by Charles Hague, with margins, defects, framed* (not examined out of the frames) (3)
Each approximately 11½ by 14½ in. (29.2 by 36.8 cm.)

$100–150

223 **G. Scotin (After)**

EXOTIC COSTUME DESIGNS: AFRIQUAINE, TCHINGUY, LE GRAND SEIGNEUR, and SOULAK

Four hand-colored engravings, 18th century (?), with margins, in apparently good condition, framed* (not examined out of frames) (4)
Each 14 by 10 in. (35.6 by 25.4 cm.)

$800–1,200

Each of the lots described above is subject to the Glossary of Terms printed at the back of this catalogue.

223

223

223

223

224 **Ravault, After Isabey and Percier**

L'EMPERATRICE EN PETIT COSTUME

Hand-colored engraving, c. 1840, with large margins, framed* (not examined out of the frame)
Image: 21 ½ by 13 in. (54.6 by 33 cm.)

These engravings were among the furnishings in Mrs. Kennedy's dressing room at the White House.

$150–250

224

225 **French Interior and Window Drapery Designs**

Two hand-colored engravings, c. 1840, with margins and in apparently good condition, framed* (not examined out of frames) (2)

These engravings were among the furnishings in Mrs. Kennedy's dressing room at the White House.

$100–125

Left: *Jacqueline Kennedy's Dressing Room at the White House, 1963, showing lots 72, 224, 225, 226, 227, 292, 348, 568, 569, 907.*

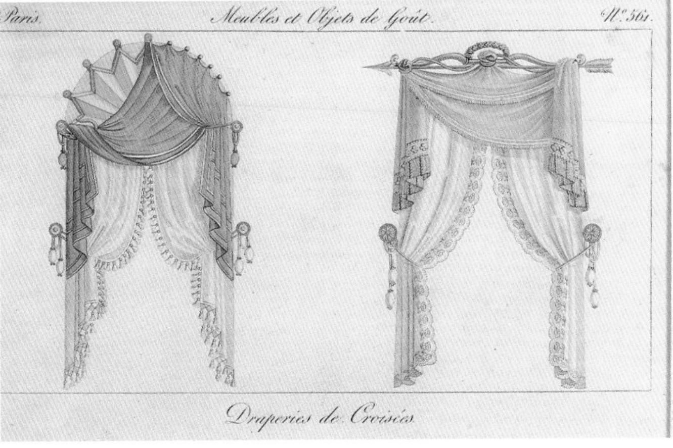

225

Each of the lots described above is subject to the Glossary of Terms printed at the back of this catalogue.

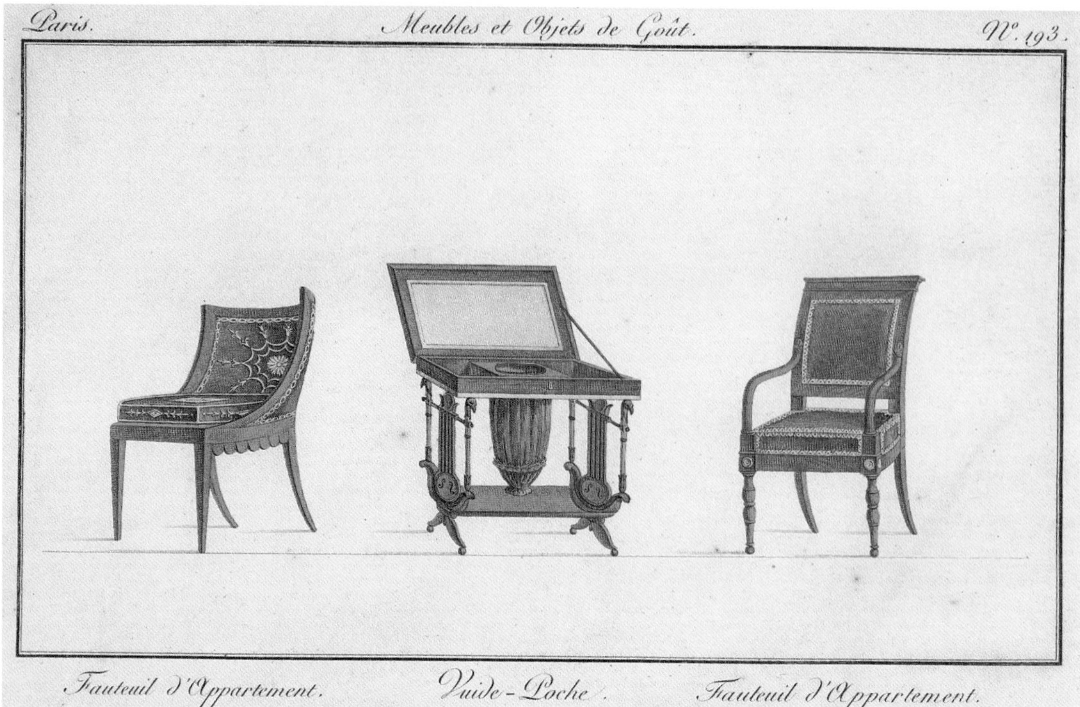

226

226

226 French Interior and Window Drapery Designs

Two hand-colored engravings, c. 1840, with margins and in apparently good condition, framed* (not examined out of frames) (2)

This engraving was among the furnishings in Mrs. Kennedy's dressing room at the White House.

$100–125

Each of the lots described above is subject to the Glossary of Terms printed at the back of this catalogue.

227

227

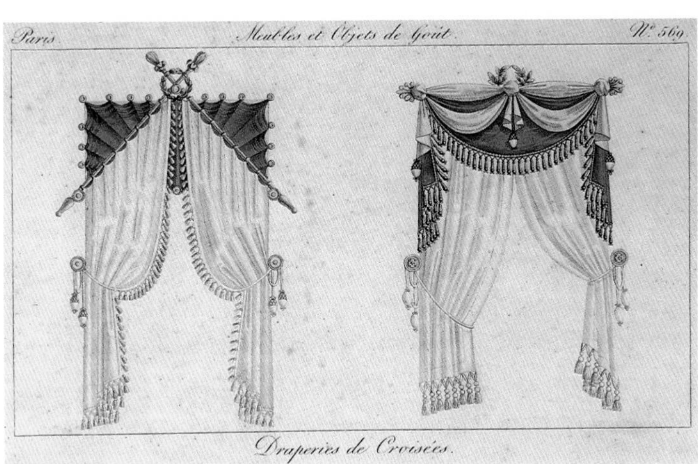

228

228

227 D. Guillmard

LE GARDE-MEUBLE: MANTLEPIECE AND CANOPIED BED

Two hand-colored lithographs by Midart, circa 1850 (one lightly foxed), framed* (not examined out of frame) (2)
Each: 12 by 8 in. (30.5 by 20.3 cm.)

$100–200

228 French Interior and Window Drapery Designs

Two hand-colored engravings, c. 1840, with margins and in apparently good condition, framed* (not examined out of frames) (2)

These engravings were among the furnishings in Mrs. Kennedy's dressing room at the White House.

$100–125

229

229 **Berthault(?) (Engraver)**

VIEW OF LA PLACE DE LOUIS XVI ET LA SALLE D'OPÉRA

Hand-colored engraving, c. 1800, with margins, framed* (not examined out of the frame)
Sight: 12 ½ by 9 in. (31.7 by 22.9 cm.)

$200–300

230

230 **Lemercier (Lithographer) After Provost**

LA GRANDE CASCADE DE LONGCHAMPS

Hand-colored lithograph printed with beige tone plate

Together with:

Tavernier (Engraver)

VUE GENERAL D'ERMENVIOLE

Hand-colored engraving

And:

Gamble (Engraver) After Bourgeois

LE PARC D'ERMENVIOLE

Hand-colored engraving
The largest, 10 ½ by 16 in. (26.7 by 40.6 cm.)

$200–300

Each of the lots described above is subject to the Glossary of Terms printed at the back of this catalogue.

A Prevost
A Prevost del
18
LA GRANDE CASCADE DE LONCHAMPS
au Bois de Boulogne

230

Pl. 29
Le PARC d'ERMENONVILLE, côté du Midi.
The PARK of ERMENONVILLE, from the South
Der PARK von ERMENONVILLE Mittagseite.

230

231

231

231

231

231 **Continental School, 19th Century**

BALLO IN MASCHERA-GIOCHI E PIACERI:
five designs

each ink and watercolor on paper
Each: 8 by 10 in. (20.3 by 25.4 cm.)

These drawings were bought by Jacqueline Bouvier when she spent her Junior year in Paris at the Sorbonne.

$2,000–3,000

231

232

232 Continental School, 19th Century

BALLO IN MASCHERA-GIOCHI E PIACERI:
four designs

each ink and watercolor on paper, one inscribed with title, another inscribed *Il calone in Utica*, another *Ballo Primo...*
Each: 8 by 10 in. (20.3 by 25.4 cm.)

See note to previous lot.

$2,000–3,000

232

232

232

233

233 **French School, 19th Century**

GARDEN FAÇADE OF A CHATEAU

watercolor over traces of pencil
5 ¾ by 7 ½ in. (14.6 by 19 cm.)

Provenance:
Shepherd Gallery, Inc., New York

$800–1,200

234 ***Federico Zuccaro (1540/1-1609)**

HALF-LENGTH PORTRAIT OF A MAN WITH WHITE RUFF AND CLOAK

black and red chalks
8 ¼ by 6 in. (21 by 15.2 cm.)

$6,000–8,000

234

**AUTHORSHIP: Ascribed to the named artist – subject to the qualifications set forth in the Glossary and Conditions of Sale, back of this Catalogue.*

235

235 **Attributed To Charles Parrocel (1688-1752)**

HUNTERS AND THEIR DOGS IN A LAND-SCAPE

brown and gray wash
12½ by 11 in. (31.7 by 27.9 cm.)

This portrait was among the furnishings of the White House during President and Mrs. Kennedy's residence, and, previously, of their house in Georgetown.

$1,000–1,500

236 **Flemish School, 17th Century**

STUDY OF A DOG

black chalk
11 by 8 in. (27.9 by 20.3 cm.)

Provenance:
Sale: Christie's, New York, May 31, 1990, lot 103, where acquired by present owner

$7,000–9,000

236

237

238

237 ***Jan de Bisschop (1628-1671)**

SOLDIERS IN AN ENCAMPMENT

pen and brown ink and brown wash
3 ½ by 5 in. (8.9 by 12.7 cm.)

Provenance:
Sale: Christie's, New York, May 31, 1990, lot 89, where acquired by present owner

$4,000–6,000

238 **Continental School, 18th Century**

A HUNT SERVANT WITH HOODED HAWKS ON A PORTABLE PERCH

pen and ink, and brown and gray wash on blue paper
10 by 8 in. (25.4 by 20.3 cm.)

This drawing was among the furnishings in Mrs. Kennedy's bedroom at the White House.

$2,000–3,000

**AUTHORSHIP: Ascribed to the named artist – subject to the qualifications set forth in the Glossary and Conditions of Sale, back of this Catalogue.*

239

240

239 **French School, 17th Century**

STUDY OF A YOUNG MAN IN AN ELABORATE COSTUME

red chalk on two joined sheets of paper
12 ¼ by 7 in. (31.1 by 17.8 cm.)

Provenance:
Herbert N. Bier, London, acquired May 23, 1959

This drawing was among the furnishings in the Second Floor Oval Room of the White House during President and Mrs. Kennedy's residence.

$2,500–3,500

240 **Studio of Jean Berain (1640-1711)**

DESIGN FOR A BALLET COSTUME

gouache and gold on vellum
12 by 8 ½ in. (30.5 by 21.6 cm.)

Berain was employed at the court of Louis XIV where he created festival designs and costumes. He was succeeded by his son, Jean II. Other costume designs in the same medium and of the same size as this one, and many from the Percy collection, are now in the collection of the Victoria and Albert Museum, London, catalogued as Berain.

Provenance:
Gilberte Cournand, Paris

$3,000–5,000

241

242

241 *Aert Schouman (1710-1792)

TWO ORNAMENTAL FOWL WITH BLACK PLUMAGE AND WHITE CRESTS IN A LANDSCAPE

watercolor over black chalk
10 by 15 in. (25.4 by 38.1 cm.)

Provenance:
Herbert N. Bier, London

This watercolor was among the furnishings in the Second Floor Main Hallway of the White House during President and Mrs. Kennedy's residence.

$5,000–7,000

242 *Jean-Baptiste Oudry (1686-1735)

STUDY OF A HOUND BAYING

oil and charcoal on paper
10 by 12½ in. (25.4 by 31.7 cm.)

There is a similar oil sketch in the Fitzwilliam Museum, Cambridge

Provenance:
Herbert N. Bier, London, acquired January 19, 1960

This painting was among the furnishings in the West Sitting Room of the White House during President and Mrs. Kennedy's residence.

$7,000–9,000

**AUTHORSHIP: Ascribed to the named artist – subject to the qualifications set forth in the Glossary and Conditions of Sale, back of this Catalogue.*

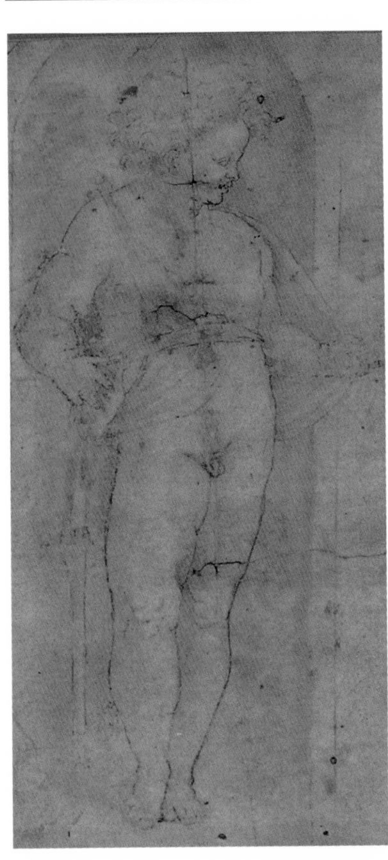

243

243 **Florentine School, 16th Century**

A YOUNG BOY STANDING IN A NICHE

pen and brown ink with brown wash, inscribed lower left ...*Rossi...*
7 ⅞ by 3 ¾ in. (20 by 9.5 cm.)

$1,000–1,500

244 **British School, 18th Century**

STUDY OF A GREYHOUND

pen and brown ink, dated lower left *1763 n2*
5 ½ by 4 ¾ in. (14 by 12.1 cm.)

$800–1,200

245 ***Aert Schouman (1710-1792)**

STUDY OF A WHITE MONKEY

pen and ink with wash and gouache on gray paper, inscribed, initialed and dated lower center verso *de Witt Aap. levend groot ald een Ordinare Kat. int Kabinet/von 2H. A.S. 1783/N346*
8 ½ by 6 in. (21.6 by 15.2 cm.)

Provenance:
K. J. Hewett, Bog Farm, Ashford, Kent, May 15, 1959
Herbert N. Bier, London, acquired September 30, 1960

This drawing was among the furnishings in the Second Floor Main Hall of the White House during President and Mrs. Kennedy's residence.

$2,000–3,000

244

245

**AUTHORSHIP: Ascribed to the named artist – subject to the qualifications set forth in the Glossary and Conditions of Sale, back of this Catalogue.*

246

246 **Italian School, 18th Century**

STUDY OF A YOUNG MAN IN A HAT AND CLOAK

pen and brown ink
8 by 5 ¼ in. (20.3 by 13.3 cm.)

Provenance:
Sir J. Reynolds (L.2364)
Dr. A. Ritter von Pfeiffer (1855-1913; L.20672)
F. Behrens (L.981)
H. M. Calman, London

$1,500–2,000

247

248

249

250

247 *Cajeton Roos, called Gaetano De Rosa (1690-1770)

STUDY OF BULL'S HEAD

signed lower left
red chalk
8 by 6½ in. (20.3 by 16.5 cm.)

$500–700

248 *Jean-Baptiste Oudry (1686-1755)

STUDY OF A SPANIEL BARKING

black chalk on gray paper
8 by 10 in. (20.3 by 25.4 cm.)

Provenance:
Herbert N. Bier, London, acquired May 23, 1961

$2,000–3,000

249 Studio of Jean-Antoine Watteau, (1684-1721)

THREE STUDIES OF A CAT

red chalk
5 by 5 in. (12.7 by 12.7 cm.)

$1,000–1,500

250 Circle of Giovanni Battista Tiepolo (1696-1770)

STUDY OF THREE PUCHINELLI GATHERED AROUND A BRAZIER

pen and brown ink over charcoal
6 by 12 in. (15.2 by 30.5 cm.)

Another version of this drawing, inscribed "Tiepolo," was in a private collection in Hampton Court Park, Surrey (see Los Angeles County Museum of Art, *Special Exhibition for the College Art Association*, January 18-April 16, 1965, illus.)

This drawing was among the furnishings in the West Sitting Room of the White House during President and Mrs. Kennedy's residence.

$2,000–3,000

*AUTHORSHIP: *Ascribed to the named artist – subject to the qualifications set forth in the Glossary and Conditions of Sale, back of this Catalogue.*

251

251

251

251

251 **English School, circa 1800**

CARICATURES OF MEN AND WOMEN: A SET OF TEN (one double-sided)

all pen and black ink over black chalk
Each: 11 13/16 in. by 9 1/16 in. (30 by 23 cm.)

This set of drawings was among the furnishings in Mrs. Kennedy's bedroom at the White House.

$3,000–5,000

252

253

254

252 *Rochus Van Veen (died 1709)

DUCK

pen and black ink with watercolor, signed and dated *G. V. Veen / fe. 1670 3/22 V.*, lower left
8 by 10¾ in. (20.3 by 27.3 cm.)

$600–800

253 *Rochus Van Veen (died 1709)

STUDY OF A DORMOUSE

pen and ink with watercolor, signed and dated *ROCHO VAN VEEN; 1680. bdz snot Muÿs*, lower left
4 by 6 in. (10.2 by 15.2 cm.)

$2,000–3,000

254 *P.*** H.***

STUDY OF AN OWL ON A STUMP

watercolor and gouache, initialed lower right *PH.* (in ligature) *fe.*
6¼ by 7¾ in. (15.9 by 19.7 cm.)

$700–900

**AUTHORSHIP: Ascribed to the named artist – subject to the qualifications set forth in the Glossary and Conditions of Sale, back of this Catalogue.*

255

255 **French School, late 18th Century**

PROFILE PORTRAIT OF A LADY

watercolor
Oval, height 4 ½ in. (11.4 cm.)

$300–500

256 ***Henry Singleton (British, 1766-1839)**

PORTRAIT OF A YOUNG GIRL, SAID TO BE MISS SIMPSON

pencil and watercolor on paper
9 ¼ by 5 ¾ in. (23.5 by 14.6 cm.)

The present work is said to be a study for an untraced portrait of Miss Simpson exhibited at the Royal Academy in 1809 as No. 414.

$500–700

257 **Continental School, possibly Dutch, 19th Century**

INTERIORS WITH FIGURES AND A LANDSCAPE WITH TWO EXHAUSTED MEN CONVERSING: A SET OF EIGHT

all watercolor and gouache
Each: 10 ⅝ by 7 ⅛ in. (27 by 18 cm.)

$3,000–4,000

256

**AUTHORSHIP: Ascribed to the named artist – subject to the qualifications set forth in the Glossary and Conditions of Sale, back of this Catalogue.*

257

257

257

257

258

258

258 **Neapolitan School, 19th Century**

A VIEW OF MOUNT VESUVIUS and A VIEW OF NAPLES: A PAIR OF WATERCOLORS

gouache on paper
Each: 17 ¼ by 26 ½ in. (43.8 by 67.3 cm.) (2)

Provenance:
M. C. Sestieri, Rome

$7,000–9,000

259

259

259 **French School, 19th Century**

TWO ARCHITECTURAL STUDIES

watercolor and gouache over traces of pencil on paper
20 ¼ by 29 in. (51.4 by 73.7 cm.) (2)

$4,000–6,000

260

261

260 ***Pierre Montani (French, 19th Century)**

THE EMPRESS EUGENIE VISITING THE BATHS OF THE IMPERIAL PALACE OF ÇIRAGAN

signed and inscribed *S. M. L'Impératrice Visite les bains du palais Impériale de Tcharagan*
gray wash over pencil on paper
9 ¼ by 14 in. (23.5 by 35.6 cm.)

Empress Eugénie (1826-1920), born Eugénia Maria de Montijo de Guzmán to a Spanish noble family, was wed to Napoleon III, Emperor of France, in 1853.

Maintaining an important influence on her husband's foreign policy, Empress Eugénie visited Egypt in 1869 for the opening of the Suez Canal. On route to Egypt "Empress Eugénie and Emperor Franz-Joseph first visited the head of the Ottoman Empire, Sultan Abd-el-Aziz, in Istanbul...The palace Çiragan Saray in Istanbul, depicted in the present drawing, was finished under Sultan Abd-el-Aziz in 1874. According to old descriptions, its decoration was dazzling. Obviously the Sultan wanted to show the Empress one of his major projects. The palace burnt to the ground in the first decade of the twentieth century" (Robert J. F. Kashey, *The Empress Eugenie's State Visit to the Opening of the Suez Canal*, n.p.).

Exhibited:
New York, Shepherd Gallery, *The Empress Eugenie's State Visit to the Opening of the Suez Canal*, Spring 1988, no. 1, illus.

$1,200–1,800

261 **Turkish School, 19th Century**

WOMEN OF THE HAREM

gouache and gold paint over traces of pencil
14 ½ by 19 in. (36.8 by 48.3 cm.)

Provenance:
Sale, The Collection of Kenneth J. Lane (Sotheby's, New York, October 21, 1977, Lot 651A)

$1,000–1,500

**AUTHORSHIP: Ascribed to the named artist – subject to the qualifications set forth in the Glossary and Conditions of Sale, back of this Catalogue.*

262

262 Manner of Jan Brueghel, the Elder (1568-1625), 18th/19th Century

A GATHERING OF BIRDS IN AN EXTENSIVE LANDSCAPE

oil on board
12 by 10½ in. (30.5 by 26.7 cm.)

The present painting repeats, with some differences, the left portion of a composition by Jan Brueghel, the Elder, *Allegory of Air*, now in the collection of the Musée du Louvre, Paris. The right side of Brueghel's composition includes the figure of Urania, muse of astronomy, painted by Hendrik van Balen.

$10,000–15,000

263

263 ****Scelles (active first quarter 18th Century)

EQUESTRIAN PORTRAIT OF A MEMBER OF THE HEBERT DE LA PLEIGNIÈRE FAMILY

signed lower left *Scelles pinx* and inscribed with a coat of arms upper left
oil on canvas
45 by 37 in. (114.3 by 94 cm.)

In an elaborately carved giltwood frame with coat of arms at top center.

The arms are those of the Hebert de la Pleignière family of France. The cross behind the shield indicates that the bearer of the arms was a Knight of the *Ordres de Saint Lazars de Jérusalem* and of *Nôtre Dame du Mont Carmel.* There were two members of this family who became Knights of these orders, Pierre Hebert de la Pleignière in 1698, and Paul Hebert de la Pleignière in 1723. Based on the date of the present picture, which is well into the 18th century, it is more likely to be the latter.

The artist is possibly Jean Scelles, a painter who is documented working in Caen circa 1728-1730 and who painted an altarpiece for the church of Saint-Gilles de Caen.

$25,000–35,000

**AUTHORSHIP: Ascribed to the named artist – subject to the qualifications set forth in the Glossary and Conditions of Sale, back of this Catalogue.*

264

264 *Johann Georg De Hamilton (1672-1737)

AN EQUESTRIAN PORTRAIT OF A NOBLEMAN, POSSIBLY A MEMBER OF THE THURN UND TAXIS FAMILY

oil on canvas
34 by 30¼ in. (86.4 by 76.8 cm.)

The horse's near hindquarter is branded with a princely crown and the initial 'T.' The only princely family of the period with this initial was Thurn und Taxis, but the head of a family might have used the initial of his Christian name. A 'T' within a wreath below a princely crown was used for Pinzgau horses bred in Thuringia.

Provenance:
Sotheby's, London, July 1, 1986, lot 264, illus.

$25,000–35,000

**AUTHORSHIP: Ascribed to the named artist – subject to the qualifications set forth in the Glossary and Conditions of Sale, back of this Catalogue.*

265 ***Nicolas-Louis-Albert Delerive (active 1773-1806)**

EQUESTRIAN PORTRAIT, SAID TO BE PETER THE GREAT

signed lower left *NL* (in ligature) *AD*(in ligature)*elerive*
oil on panel
22 by 15 ¾ in. (55.9 by 40 cm.)

$20,000–30,000

Delerive was born in Lille where he was a student at the *Ecole de Dessin* and the *Académie des Arts*. Primarily a history and genre painter, he exhibited a large number of paintings and drawings at the Salon in Lille between 1773 and 1788.

The present painting was formerly in the collection of Paul Delaroff (1852-1913) (see provenance below), and bears his wax seal on the reverse. Delaroff was the son of a general of the Russian army and had a successful career as a lawyer in St. Petersburg. His avocation was the study of art and he amassed a large collection of paintings, drawings and prints. After his death the collection was dispersed in a series of sales in Paris in 1914.

Provenance:
Paul Delaroff (sale: Hôtel Drouot, Paris, April 27, 1914, lot 101)

**AUTHORSHIP: Ascribed to the named artist – subject to the qualifications set forth in the Glossary and Conditions of Sale, back of this Catalogue.*

265

266 ***John Wootton (British, 1683-1764)**

LORD BATEMAN'S ARABIAN

signed, dated *Fecit 1733-34* and
inscribed with the title
oil on canvas
40 by 50 in. (101.6 by 127 cm.)

$80,000–120,000

"John Wootton's pre-eminent position in England in the first half of the Eighteenth century as a painter of sporting and landscape subjects was to go virtually unchallenged for almost four decades. His early years of service in a Beaufort-Coventry household gave him access to a formidable network of patronage whose support was unaffected by family or party loyalties. Among his royal patrons were George II and his estranged son, Frederick, Prince of Wales, and the same paintings commissioned by Sir Robert Walpole for Houghton Hall and for Downing Street also decorated the great houses of the Opposition. Besides these, his patrons included most of the leading families of the day: the Dukes of Beaufort, Devonshire, Newcastle and Bedford; Bolton, Rutland, Richmond, and Leeds; the munificent Edward Harley, 2nd Earl of Oxford; the influential banker, Henry Hoare; and many others. Wootton's career was formed by their benevolence and was assured by their complex web of intermarriages; he was successful largely because of the way in which his painting reflected the interests of the nobility and landed gentry, and securely identified them with country life and its pursuits" (Arline Meyer, *John Wootton 1682-1764, Landscapes and Sporting Art in Early Georgian England*, London, 1984, p.7).

According to Arline Meyer, the date inscribed, 1733-4, places this painting just shortly after Wootton painted the wonderful series of hunting scenes for Charles Spencer, 3rd Duke of Marlborough, that can still be seen decorating the entrance hall at Althorp. The painting is an extremely fine example of the innovative format John Wootton developed for the portraiture of distinguished bloodstock and which subsequently gained great currency.

At the time this work was painted, the current Lord Bateman was William, Baron Culmore (1695?-1744), of Shobdon Court, Herefordshire, MP for Leominster from 1721-22 and 1727-34. He succeeded to a great fortune and married, in 1720, Lady Anne Spencer, daughter of Charles, 3rd Earl of Sunderland, who was at that time Prime Minister.

Provenance:
Charles Spencer, 3rd Duke of Marlborough, Langley Park (commissioned directly from the artist)
Sir Robert Harvey (acquired with purchase of Langley Park in 1778)
Sir Robert Harvey, Bt., Langley Park, Slough (by descent from the above)
R.P.M.-Grenfell (1946)
Mrs. C. Denman
Arthur Ackermann & Son, Ltd., London

**AUTHORSHIP: Ascribed to the named artist – subject to the qualifications set forth in the Glossary and Conditions of Sale, back of this Catalogue.*

266

267 *Martin Drölling (1752-1817)

PORTRAIT OF BARTHÉLÉMY CHARLES, COMTE DE DREUX-NANCRÉ, STANDING AT A BALUSTRADE WITH A LANDSCAPE BEYOND

signed and dated lower left *Drölling.f./1797* and inscribed on the reverse in an old hand *Barthélémé Charles/Comte de Dreuse-/-Nancré/Peint par Drölling/en 1797*
oil on canvas
37 by 29½ in. (94 by 74.9 cm.)

$80,000–120,000

The Dreux-Nancré family, from Berry, France, were cousins of the better-known Dreux-Brézé family.

The sitter was a captain in the Royal Polish Cavalry. He was married to Marie-Louise-Aimée de Courcelles and their son, Hyacinthe-Louis-Ernest, born in Paris in 1787, had a long and eventful career in the French army, serving first under Napoléon and later under Louis XVIII. The last of the Dreux-Nancré line was Louis-Ernest, the sitter's grandson, who died in 1883.

This portrait was among the furnishings of the White House during President and Mrs. Kennedy's residence, and, previously, of their house in Georgetown.

Provenance:
Heim, Paris, by 1958

**AUTHORSHIP: Ascribed to the named artist – subject to the qualifications set forth in the Glossary and Conditions of Sale, back of this Catalogue.*

267

268

268 *Domenico Scianteschi (active first half 18th Century)**

ARCHITECTURAL CAPRICCIOS WITH FIGURES, ONE DEPICTING AN EPISODE IN THE LIFE OF SAINT MATTHEW: A PAIR OF PAINTINGS

both oil on canvas
Each: 77¼ by 65½ in. (196.2 by 166.4 cm.)

Count Domenico Scianteschi was originally from Borgo San Sepolcro, near Florence, and was a student of Francesco Bibiena (1659–1739).

The subject of the painting portraying figures terrorized by two dragons derives from the *Golden Legend*, and depicts an episode in the life of St. Matthew. The *Golden Legend (Legenda aurea)*, written in the 13th century by Jacobus da Voragine, is a devotional compilation of the lives of the saints in calendar format. Less concerned with historical and biographical accuracy, it presents fantastical stories of the saints and the ideals of saintly living. The work was immensely popular and early on was translated from Latin into the vernacular languages. The story related to St. Matthew is told on the saint's day, September 21st (English edition, 1941, vol. II, p. 562):

"Now a man came to say that the [two] sorcerers had come with two dragons, which belched forth sulphurous fire from mouth and nostrils and killed many peo-

268

ple. The apostle shielded himself with the sign of the cross and confidently went out to meet these beasts. The minute the dragons saw him, they fell asleep at his feet, and he said to the sorcerers: 'Where is your magical power now? Wake them up if you can! If I had not prayed to the Lord, I would have turned back upon you the harm you thought to inflict upon me.' And when all the people had gathered together, Matthew ordered the dragons in Jesus' name to go away, and off they went, harming no one."

The present pendant relates to a work by Domenico Scianteschi in the Collezioni Communali d'Arte, Bologna (see catalogue of the exhibition, Bibbiena, Palazzo Comunale, *Meravigliose scene Piacevoli inganni: Galli Bibiena*, March 28-May 23, 1992, p. 96, no. 41, illus.). That picture has the same horsedrawn carriage in the foreground, similar architectural elements, and would seem to represent the exact same subject. The meaning of this subject in both the Bologna picture and the present pendant remains obscure and, though it may be related to the story of St. Matthew, it does not seem to relate to the saint's life as told in the *Golden Legend*.

We are grateful to the Warburg Institute of the University of London for identifying the subject of the one painting.

$60,000–80,000

**AUTHORSHIP: Ascribed to the named artist – subject to the qualifications set forth in the Glossary and Conditions of Sale, back of this Catalogue.*

269

269 ***Judith Lewis (active mid-18th Century)**

ELEGANT FIGURES PREPARING FOR THE HUNT

oil on canvas
26 by 36 ¼ in. (66 by 92.1 cm.)

According to Ellis Waterhouse (see *Dictionary of British 18th Century Painters*, 1981, p. 223), Judith Lewis was probably a pupil of John Wootton. He lists a pair of paintings by Lewis (illus. of one), also hunting scenes, which are signed and dated *1755* and *1756*.

Provenance:
Arthur Ackermann & Son, Ltd., London, 1961

This painting was among the furnishings in the West Sitting Room of the White House during President and Mrs. Kennedy's residence.

$20,000–30,000

**AUTHORSHIP: Ascribed to the named artist – subject to the qualifications set forth in the Glossary and Conditions of Sale, back of this Catalogue.*

270

271

272

270 *J*** B*** (Continental School, 19th Century)

STILL LIFE WITH PINK ROSES RESTING ON A MARBLE LEDGE

signed with initials lower right *J.B.*
oil on canvas laid down on board
11 by 9 ¼ in. (27.9 by 23.5 cm.)

$10,000–15,000

271 **Venetian School, 18th Century**

STUDIES OF FIGURES IN PROCESSION

pen and brown ink
irregular: 5 ¼ by 11 ½ in. (13.3 by 29.2 cm.)

$1,500–2,000

272 **Eugene Berman**

THE COLUMNS OF NATHOR

signed with initials and dated *1964*
pen and ink, brown wash and watercolor
13 ⅛ by 9 ¼ in. (33.3 by 23.5 cm.)

$800–1,200

**AUTHORSHIP: Ascribed to the named artist – subject to the qualifications set forth in the Glossary and Conditions of Sale, back of this Catalogue.*

273

274

273 *George Chinnery, R.H.A. (British, 1774-1854)

AN OVERGROWN TOMB AT DUSK

watercolor over traces of pencil on paper
4 ¾ by 9 ⅛ in. (12.1 by 23.2 cm.)

"Chinnery became the leading artist of British India in the early 1800s...After a promising early career in England and Ireland, he spent the rest of his long life in the Far East - twenty-three years in India, and twenty-seven on the China coast, where he lies buried" (Conner, n.p.).

"Chinnery's [Indian landscapes are] a distinctive genre of intimate, informal views of village and countryside..." (pp. 135-136). Chinnery often "depicted the overgrown ruins of monuments in brick or stone [such as the remains of tombs and small mosques creating]...an eminently Picturesque composition" (Conner, p. 137).

Provenance:
Eyre & Hobhouse, Ltd., London (as *An Indian Temple at Sunset*)

Literature:
Patrick Conner, *George Chinnery 1774-1852, Artist of India and the China Coast*, Woodbridge, Suffolk, 1993, Pl. 43, illustrated p. 142

$3,000–4,000

274 Odilon Redon

STUDY OF TREES

monogrammed lower right *o.d.*
pencil on paper
8 by 11 in. (20.3 by 27.9 cm.)

Provenance:
Herbert N. Bier, London, January 16, 1962

Exhibited:
Municipal Museum, The Hague, *Odilon Redon*, 1957, no. 217

This drawing was among the furnishings in the West Sitting Room of the White House during President and Mrs. Kennedy's residence.

$3,000–5,000

**AUTHORSHIP: Ascribed to the named artist – subject to the qualifications set forth in the Glossary and Conditions of Sale, back of this Catalogue.*

275 **Chinese School, 19th Century**

NAPOLEON'S RESIDENCE, NEW HOUSE, LONGWOOD, ST. HELENA; THE SITE OF NAPOLEON'S TOMB, LONGWOOD, ST. HELENA; and NAPOLEON ON HIS DEATHBED, ST. HELENA: A GROUP OF THREE WATERCOLORS

watercolor heightened with white on pith paper
Each, sight: 4 1/8 by 6 1/8 in. (10.5 by 15.6 cm.) (3)

Executed circa 1825-40.

From October 15, 1815, until his death on May 5, 1821, Napoléon lived in exile on the remote island of St. Helena in the southern Atlantic. He was voluntarily accompanied into exile by General Henri-Gratien Bertrand, Grand Marshal of the palace, and his wife; General Gaspard Gourgaud; Emmanuel Las Cases, his former Chamberlain; and several servants. After a short initial stay at the house of a wealthy English merchant, Thomas H. Brooke, Esq., they moved to Longwood House, which had originally been built for the Lieutenant Governor. The British had intended Napoléon to reside during his exile in the residence, New House, which was built and shipped in prefabricated sections to St. Helena from England. Napoléon refused, however, to live there and moved instead to Longwood House.

This view of New House, Longwood, is undoubtedly based on the engraving by Danzil Ibbetson of the same subject reproduced in Thomas H. Brooke's *History of the Island of St. Helena* (2nd edition, 1824, p. 423).

Immediately after the death of Napoléon, his valet, Louis Marchand, bathed and dressed the Emperor's body before returning it to the death bed to await burial. Marchand executed an engraving of the Emperor on his death bed which was widely available and most likely the inspiration for the present watercolor.

The artist chose to illustrate the site of Napoléon's tomb immediately before his burial. In 1840, Napoléon's body was exhumed and returned to France accompanied by Louis Marchand.

These three watercolors are taken from an album inscribed: *J. Walter Canton Tenth & V Period, 1827.*

$1,000–1,500

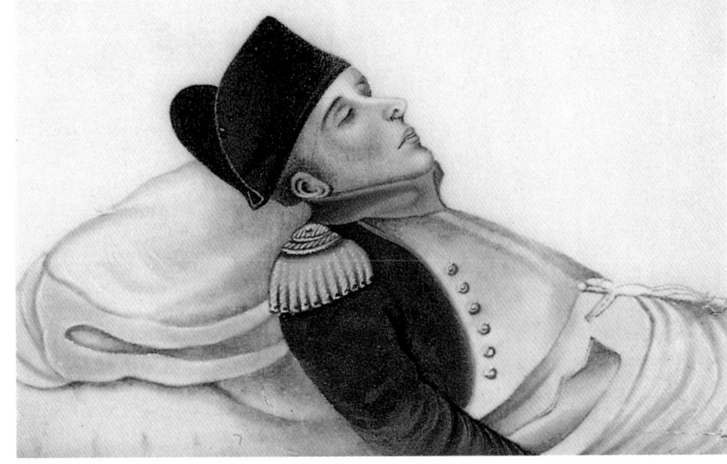

275

275

275

276

276 *John Ruskin (British, 1819-1900)

THE SPANISH STEPS, ROME

inscribed *Where Keats died*
watercolor over traces of pencil on paper
8 ⅛ by 4 ⅞ in. (20.6 by 12.4 cm.)

Executed *circa* 1841.

"John Ruskin, Victorian England's most brilliant and influential critic of the arts" was a prolific writer and draftsman (George P. Landow, "How to Read Ruskin: The Art Critic as Victorian Sage," *John Ruskin and the Victorian Eye*, New York, 1993, p. 52). "Throughout Ruskin's life...his subject was the visual world: the elements of nature framed by landscape, the human shaping of those elements into architecture, and the human response to them expressed in sculpture and painting" (Robert Hewison, "John Ruskin and the Argument of the Eye", *John Ruskin and the Victorian Eye*, p. 29). "For John Ruskin the very act of observing his physical surroundings was a stimulus to thought and a source of inspiration. To meditate upon the elements of nature of the works of man with a frank enjoyment of beauty, but also to understand intellectually the spiritual associations of landscape or architecture was, Ruskin came to believe, the highest form of appreciation" (Christopher Newall, "Ruskin and the Art of Drawing", *John Ruskin and the Victorian Eye*, p. 81). "During the 1840s and early 1850s, Ruskin...devoted much of his time to drawing architecture, which he considered 'an essential part of the landscape,' the study of which 'was one of the necessary functions of the landscape-painter'" (Newall, p. 96). "Ruskin's watercolors of the 1840s and 1850s are made delicious to the eye by his discovery of the power of light and color to give depth, volume and brilliance to architectural subjects" (Newall, p. 96). Ruskin's annotation to the present work supports the theory that "even in his earliest work on architecture, Ruskin has thought about buildings in terms of the historical evidence they provide" (Newall, p. 98).

Exhibited:
New York, Davis & Langdale Co., Inc., *American and British Works on Paper*, 1988, no. 31

$15,000–20,000

**AUTHORSHIP: Ascribed to the named artist – subject to the qualifications set forth in the Glossary and Conditions of Sale, back of this Catalogue.*

277

277 **A. D. (French School, 19th/20th Century)**

STILL LIFE WITH FLOWERS

signed with initials
oil on canvas
8 ½ by 5 ½ in. (21.6 by 12.7 cm.)

$500–700

278 **Augustus Edwin John (British, 1878-1961)**

PORTRAIT OF WILLIAM BUTLER YEATS

pen and ink and wash on paper
14 by 10 in. (35.6 by 25.4 cm.)

Executed circa 1907.

In 1907, John was commissioned to produce a portrait of the poet, William Butler Yeats (1865-1939) for the publication of Yeats' forthcoming *Collected Works*. The sittings took place at Coole Parks, County Galway, the home of the poet's patron, Lady Gregory. Lady Gregory's son, Robert, had recommended John for the commission.

Provenance:
Thomas Agnew & Sons, Ltd., London, (No. 29766)
Davis & Langdale Co., Inc., New York, (No. 1170)

$10,000–15,000

278

279

279 ***Isidore Alexandre Augustin Pils (French, 1813-75)**

"FONTAINEBLEAU"

signed, titled and dated *30 sept 1869*; also with the estate stamp on the *verso*
watercolor over pencil on paper
6 by 9½ in. (15.2 by 24.1 cm.)

Pils exhibited at the Paris Salon from 1846 to 1875. He was commissioned by Napoléon III to paint several works. It is of note that this watercolor is dated *30 Sept. 1869*, the eve of the Franco-Prussian War and the subsequent downfall of Napoléon III in 1870.

The Chateau of Fontainebleau is one of the largest residences built by the Kings of France. Originally a medieval royal hunting lodge enlarged by Louis IX in the thirteenth century, it was enlarged during the reigns of successive Kings. During the nineteenth century, the town of Fontainebleau became a popular resort for the Parisian bourgeoisie.

Provenance:
Estate of the artist
Shepherd Gallery, Inc., New York

$1,200–1,800

280

280 **Continental School, 19th Century**

AN ARAB HORSEMAN WITH RIFLE

watercolor over traces of pencil on paper laid down on board
8¼ by 10¼ in. (21 by 26 cm.)

$600–800

**AUTHORSHIP: Ascribed to the named artist – subject to the qualifications set forth in the Glossary and Conditions of Sale, back of this Catalogue.*

281

281 **Charles François Daubigny (French, 1817-78)**

LES BORDS DE L'OISE

signed and dated *1863*
oil on cradled panel
13 ½ by 25 ½ in. (34.3 by 64.8 cm.)

Charles Daubigny, the highly influential French painter, was born in Paris on February 15, 1817. He inherited his artistic talent from his father, Edme, and his uncle, Pierre, both painters, but independently developed a love of nature and specifically a lifelong admiration for the French rural landscape during a youth spent with an adopted family in the village of Valmondois, where he was sent as a child for his health.

Daubigny's study of nature produced "plein-air" landscapes, revolutionary in their emphasis on spontaneity and observations of season and climate. As early as the late 1840s and 1850s, Daubigny's entries to the Paris Salon drew the attention of critics for their break with landscape traditions of the past. Critics noted a "new revolution" (Henri Loyrette, "The Salon of 1859", *Origins of Impressionism*, New York, 1994, p. 15) in French landscape painting in works by Daubigny and other painters, such as his friends Corot and Rousseau.

In 1857, Daubigny, in the region of Auvers, northwest of Paris, began painting out-of-doors in a studio boat, the Botin, along the River Oise, where the present work was painted. The critic Théophile Gauthier wrote, after viewing Daubigny's entries to the 1859 salon, "His paintings are like pieces of nature cut out and set into a golden frame" (Loyrette, p. 15). This pervading reaction to Daubigny's works was echoed the same year by Baudelaire, who wrote "[Daubigny's landscapes] convey immediately to the viewer's soul the original feeling that pervaded them" (Gary Tinterow, "The Realist Landscape", *Origins of Impressionism*, New York, 1994, p. 59). Daubigny's revolutionary landscapes were not unnoticed: the young budding-Impressionist painter, Claude Monet, wrote in 1859, "*Les Daubigny sont pour moi quelque chose de bien beau*" (Loyrette, p. 25).

Robert Hellebranth has kindly confirmed the authenticity of this work.

This painting was among the furnishings of the White House during President and Mrs. Kennedy's residence.

$30,000–50,000

282, 283 (top center)

284

282 **A Spode Stone China 'Famille-Rose' Part Dinner Service, circa 1820**

Each piece transfer-printed in brown and painted in shades of rose, iron-red and yellow with a central peony medallion surrounded by three or four sprays of flowering peonies, chrysanthemums or hibiscus, the brown-edged rim (some flaking to the enamel) with a border of brown whorl-ground lappets superimposed with and surrounded by various blossoms and leaves, *SPODE Stone-China fret marks printed in brown, and pattern number 3144 and painter's marks in colored enamels*; comprising:

Oval soup tureen and cover with gilt-heightened foliate-scroll handles, *length 15 1/16 in. (38.3 cm.)*
Oval soup tureen stand, *length 16 3/4 in. (42.5 cm.)*
Square salad bowl, *width 9 1/2 in. (24.1 cm.)*
Twenty-one octagonal soup plates, *width 9 1/2 in. (24.1 cm.)*
Eighteen octagonal plates (worn, and one with a chip), *widths 9 1/2 to 9 5/8 in. (24.1 to 24.4 cm.)*
(42)

$2,500–3,500

285

283 **A Pair of Copeland and Garrett Stone China 'Famille-Rose' Octagonal Soup Plates, 1835-45**

Transfer-printed and painted in the same pattern as the preceding lot, *impressed* SPODES NEW•STONE *marks,* COPELAND & GARRETT LATE SPODE *circular marks printed in brown, and pattern number 3144 and painter's letter V in yellow enamel.* Together with an octagonal dinner plate, *en suite*, (chips), *similarly marked.* (3)
Widths 9 1/2 and 9 7/16 in. (24.1 and 24 cm.)

$200–300

284 **A Coalport-Type Porcelain Jardinière and Stand, circa 1810**

Each piece with a canary-yellow ground (discolored), the tapering cylindrical pot reserved on the front with a gilt-edged rectangular panel colorfully painted with a floral cluster, and molded on the sides with gilt integral-ring handles beneath the gilt-edged rim, and the stand also with a gilt-edged rim and footrim, (wear to the gilding).
Height 5 3/16 in. (13.2 cm.)

Provenance:
Navillus & Skull, Chelsea, London, April 5, 1959

$500–700

285 **A Pair of Coalport-Type Porcelain Jardinières and Stands, circa 1810**

Each tapering cylindrical pot with a chartreuse ground (discolored) reserved on the front and reverse with a gilt-edged octagonal panel painted in pale sepia and chartreuse with a landscape vignette, the sides molded with gilt integral-ring handles interrupting a gilt-edged and blue-dotted iron-red and chartreuse guilloche border repeated around the lower body and around the waisted cylindrical stands, and the upper rim of the pot (one chipped) with a gilt 'seaweed' border, (one stand with a central star crack).
Height 5 1/2 in. (14 cm.)

These jardinères were among the furnishings in the Second Floor Oval Room of the White House during President and Mrs. Kennedy's residence.

Provenance:
Mallett & Son, Ltd., London, purchased at the Antique Dealers' Fair at Grosvenor House, June 26, 1958

$600–900

286

287

286 **An Unusual Pair of Coalport Porcelain Meissen-Style Oval Dishes, circa 1810**

Each painted on the interior in predominant shades of brown, blue, green, iron-red and yellow with a scene of European figures, boats and buildings at the edge of an estuary within a quatrefoil panel edged in gilt, purple and iron-red scrolls, the rim with a border of gilt hatchwork and diapered panels, and the exterior with a tomato-red ground (slight wear) above a gilt-banded footrim, (some wear to the gilding).
Lengths 11 and 11 ⅛ in. (27.9 and 28.3 cm.)

These dishes were among the furnishings in the Second Floor Oval Room of the White House during President and Mrs. Kennedy's residence.

$500-700

287 **An Unusual Chinese Export Porcelain Oval Sugar Bowl and Cover, Teapot Stand and Spoon Tray, circa 1810**

After English porcelain originals, each decorated with a wide salmon-ground border edged with claret and gilt bands and painted in iron-red, blue, *grisaille*, white and rose with small figures of a traveller or a fisherman in a brown hilly terrain, the ends of the sugar bowl molded with gilt integral-ring handles, and the dome of the cover and oval knop (small chip) gilded, (general wear to the gilding, and the teapot stand damaged and repaired).

Lengths 5 13/16, 8 ½ and 6 ⅜ in. (14.8, 21.6 and 16.2 cm.)

This group of porcelain was among the furnishings in the Second Floor Oval Room of the White House during President and Mrs. Kennedy's residence.

$300–500

Grouped, left to right: 290, 288, 290

288 **A Canton Porcelain Famille-Rose Part Dinner Service, mid 19th Century**

Each piece brightly enamelled with exotic birds and butterflies amidst a profusion of floral and fruit sprigs within a gilt-edged rim (some wear); comprising:
Pair of oval soup tureens (both handles restored on one, one handle restored on the other) and covers, *length 14½ in. (36.8 cm.)*
Pair of oval sauce tureens (one with rim chips) and two covers (married), *length 8¼ in. (21 cm.)*
Six rectangular vegetable dishes and covers (three pine cone knops with a chip on the tip), *length 9¼ in. (23.5 cm.)*
Oval hot water dish and a cover (slightly large), *length 15 ⅞ in. (40.3 cm.)*
Oval open serving dish (two chips), *length 13½ in. (34.3 cm.)*
Square salad bowl, *width 10 in. (25.4 cm.)*
Large oval well-and-tree platter, *length 19 in. (48.3 cm.)*
Small oval well-and-tree platter, *length 15¾ in. (40 cm.)*
Pair of deep oval platters with pierced strainers, *length 16 in. (40.6 cm.)*
Large oval platter, *length 18 1/16 in. (45.9 cm.)*
Oval platter (slight wear), *length 15½ in. (39.4 cm.)*
Small oval platter (wear and chips), *length 11¾ in. (29.8 cm.)*
(22)

Provenance:
Sold at Christie's in New York City on June 2, 1990, lot 106, to benefit the Diplomatic Reception Rooms of the United States Department of State, Washington, D.C.

$9,000–12,000

289 **A Canton Porcelain Famille-Rose Soup Plate, mid 19th Century**

Similarly decorated to the preceding service with two Chinese pheasants, two large butterflies, a cricket and a beetle amongst sprigs and sprays of flowers and fruit, the rim (repaired and hair cracked) edged in worn gilding.
Diameter 9¾ in. (24.8 cm.)

$50–75

291

292

292

290 **A Set of Sixteen Canton Porcelain Famille-Rose Breakfast Cups and Fifteen Saucers, late 19th Century**

Each piece with a celadon ground vividly enamelled with exotic birds and butterflies amidst sprigs and clusters of flowers and fruit, the rim edged in gilding (slight wear, two cups hair cracked and two saucers with a chip). (31)
Diameters 4½ and 6½ in. (11.5 and 16.5 cm.)

Provenance:
Sold at Christie's in New York City on June 2, 1990, lot 106, to benefit the Diplomatic Reception Rooms of the United States Department of State, Washington, D.C.

$1,500–2,500

291 **A Set of Seventeen Sèvres Porcelain Dinner Plates, circa 1760**

Each colorfully painted with sprays and sprigs of flowers in the center and within three lobes of the hexafoil rim, the other three lobes lightly molded with a sprig of currants within foliate scrolls picked out in blue around the gilt edge (some wear to the gilding, and five with a chip), *interlaced L's, all but three with date letter H for 1760, and each with a painter's mark for Jacques Fontaine, mark for Charles-Louis (?) Méreaud, or unidentified letter H, in blue enamel, and most incised either CT or 60, one incised æ, and another* ε_o.
Diameters 10⅛ to 10¼ in. (25.7 to 26 cm.).

The model for plates of this form, *'assiette à groseilles'*, is recorded in the Sèvres (Vincennes) inventory of October 1752, and is still preserved at the factory.

$2,500–3,500

292 **A Pair of French Painted Tôle and Hard-Paste Porcelain Three-Light Candelabra**

Each foliate branch mounted with numerous porcelain flowers, on a marbleized base.
Height 10 in. (25.4 cm.)

Provenance:
Chrystian Aubusson, through Mrs. Henry Parish II, 1958

These candelabra were among the furnishings in Mrs. Kennedy's dressing room at the White House.

$600–800

293 **A Pair of Flemish Ivory Oval Bacchanalian Reliefs, after François Duquesnoy**

Both with dancing and music-playing, frolicking putti, one with a dog to the left, (losses). Upon blue velvet-covered boards.
Length 5¼ in. (13.3 cm.)

$3,000–5,000

294 An Unusual Charles X Ormolu and Patinated Bronze Mantel Clock, first quarter 19th Century

The chiselled ormolu dial inscribed *Caius Fraument à Paris*, set into a patinated bronze donkey and surmounted by the figure of an Arab rider, raised on a rectangular base cast with putti, foliate swags and birds.
Height 14 in. (35.6 cm.), width 10½ in. (26.7 cm.)

Caius Fraumont, recorded working in Paris at Marché Saint-Honoré in 1830.

$4,000–6,000

295 A Louis Philippe Gilt-Bronze Dog-Form Paper Clip, circa 1840

The realistically modelled seated spaniel with hinged mouth, raised on a rectangular velvet-covered base
Height 5 in. (12.7 cm.), width 3½ in. (8.9 cm.)

Provenance:
Leon Gruel, Paris

$500–700

294

295

296

296 A Fine Empire Ormolu and Cut-Glass 18-Light Chandelier, first quarter 19th Century

The ormolu rings cast with flower-heads, the lower tier with winged putti fitted with candle nozzles, flanked by flower-filled baskets, the curved candle branches cast with quatrefoil, the upper tier fitted with leafy mounts, the whole hung with cut-glass beaded chains and hung with pendants. *Height approximately 4 ft. 4 in. (132.1 cm.), width approximately 36 in. (91.4 cm.)*

$25,000–35,000

297

297 **A Pair of Continental Carved Ivory Covered Urns, 19th Century**

Each of baluster form with gadrooned flared upper rim, acanthus-carved domed covers, (lacking knops), the body carved with scenes of Venus and Cupid, and with handles in the form of Satyr's masks, acanthus below, resting on a spiral-fluted stemmed foot, mounted on wood octagonal plinth bases.
Height overall 10¾ in. (27.3 cm.)

$3,000–4,000

298 **A Pair of Napoleon III Ormolu and Patinated Bronze Six-Light Candelabra, second half 19th Century**

Each with a circular reeded support with ormolu bands of trellis enclosing quatrefoil and laurel leaves, fitted with three rope-twist molded curved candle arms interspaced by three leaf-cast candle arms centered by a flame finial, raised on a stepped circular base and paw feet.
Height 31 in. (78.7 cm.)

$10,000–15,000

298

299, 300, 301

299 **A Louis XVI Style Gilt and Tôle Peinte Brûle Parfum**

The urn-shaped body with leaf-cast finial flanked by rams' heads continuing to curved supports ending in hoof feet, raised on a circular pedestal and square base.
Height 13 ⅞ in. (35.2 cm.)

$500–700

300 **A Pair of Louis XVI Ormolu Cassollettes, last Quarter 18th Century**

Each of urn form with pine cone finial reversing to form a candle holder hung with ribbon-tied laurel swags, raised on a fluted columnar base above a stepped square base and bun feet.
Height 9 in. (22.9 cm.)

These cassollettes were among the furnishings in the Second Floor Oval Room of the White House during President and Mrs. Kennedy's residence.

$2,500–3,500

301 **A Pair of Louis XVI Style Ormolu-Mounted White Marble Small Candlesticks**

Each with a circular leaf-cast candle nozzle, the square base raised on *toupie* feet.
Height 6 in. (15.2 cm.)

Provenance:
Joan Briton, through Mrs. Henry Parish II, 1958

These candlesticks were among the furnishings in Mrs. Kennedy's bedroom at the White House.

$200–400

302

303

302 **A Louis XV Style Painted and Parcel-Gilt Mirror**

The arched divided plate contained within borders carved with floral garlands, the top rail centered by a shell, affixed to a rectangular backboard painted to simulate grey marble; painted gold highlighted with gilding. *Height 6 ft. (1.83 m.), width 33 in. (83.8 cm.)*

$1,500–2,500

303 **A Pair of French Aubusson Tapestry Covered Green Silk Cushions, the tapestry late 19th Century**

The tapestry with scenes from *Fables de la fontaine*, (extensive losses and wear), framed and backed by green silk, with gold-colored fringe border. *Each 14 in. by 18½ in. (35.6 by 47 cm.)*

Provenance:
Arditti & Mayorcas, London, 1961

These cushions were among the furnishings in the Second Floor Oval Room of the White House during President and Mrs. Kennedy's residence.

$150–250

304

305

304 **A Pair of Régence Style Patinated Bronze and Ormolu Chenets, 19th Century**

Each with a seated sphinx raised on a rectangular base centered by an espagnolette mask; together with a pair of fire tools with a stand. (4)
Height of chenets 16 in. (40.6 cm.)

Provenance:
Gerald Kerin, Ltd., London, July 1, 1958

$1,500–2,500

305 **A Louis XVI Style Giltwood Frame Fitted as a Mirror**

The rectangular frame carved with leaf tips and beading.
Height 4 ft. (121.9 cm.), width 30¾ in. (78.1 cm.)

$400–600

306

306 **A Pair of Régence Style Brass Candlesticks**

Each of octagonal knopped baluster form with foliate engraving, raised on a conforming stepped base with gadrooned bands, the center of each dished portion etched with indecipherable armorials.
Height 8 in. (20.3 cm.)

These candlesticks were among the furnishings in the Second Floor Oval Room of the White House during President and Mrs. Kennedy's residence.

$400–600

307

307 **A Neapolitan Tortoiseshell Box, mid 18th Century**

Of rectangular shape, the cover inlaid with mother-of-pearl and with gold, depicting figures before an architectural ruin, signed *Sarao F. a Nap*; each clasp in the form of a dolphin.
Length 6 ¾ in. (17.1 cm.)

$3,000–5,000

308 **A Pair of Unusual Ormolu-Mounted Japanese Porcelain and Marble Candlesticks**

Each with mythical beast supporting ormolu saddle cloth and candle nozzle on his back, resting on rockwork and supported on green quartz base.
Height 10 ½ in. (26.7 cm.), length 8 ⅜ in. (21.3 cm.)

$7,000–9,000

308

309 **A Fine Louis XV Gilt-Tooled Red Morocco Leather Small Casket, circa 1770**

The hinged rectangular top centered by the arms of Marie-Antoinette, surrounded by scrolling borders, the corners with ribbon-tied ovals, two enclosing a *fleur de lys*, two enclosing a bird; the front with an engraved gilt-bronze lock-plate, each side with a carrying handle, the underside with maker's (?) mark *L.L.* flanking a cockerel.
Height 6½ in. (16.5 cm.), width 17 in. (43.2 cm.)

$25,000–35,000

Sold with this lot is an envelope bearing the inscription *Cassette de la Reine Marie-Antoinette* in the hand of the fifth Earl of Rosebery.

This coffer belongs to a group of travelling caskets and trunks made for various members of the royal family. Similar examples of various sizes bearing the arms of Mesdames, Louis XV's daughters, are in the Louvre, the Musée Carnavalet and The Metropolitan Museum of Art, New York. Two more are in the Musée Cluny, one of which was no. 551 in the exhibition, *Louis XV un Moment de Perfection de l'Art Français,* Hotel de la Monnaie, Paris, 1974. The catalogue states that almost every year these caskets were delivered to the King's daughters for their travels.

Two similar coffers, one made for Marie-Leszcynska and one for the daughters of Louis XV, were sold from the Rosebery collection, Sothebys', Mentmore, May 18, 1977, lots 108 and 109. Another made for Marie-Josephine Louise de Savoie, later Comtesse de Provence, was sold from the Wildenstein and Ojjeh Collections, Sotheby's, Monaco, Monte-Carlo, June 25-26, 1979, lot 131. A smaller casket, again bearing the arms of the Comtesse de Provence, and with an identical cockerel underneath flanked by the initials LA, was sold, Sotheby's, London, December 9, 1994, lot 211, illustrated.

Provenance:
Queen Marie-Antoinette
The Earls of Rosebery, sold, Sotheby's, London, July 10, 1981, lot 95, illustrated in the *catalogue.*

309 detail

309

310

311

310 **A Louis XVI Brass-Mounted Mahogany Console Desserte, last Quarter 18th Century**

The rectangular white marble top with incurved sides and fitted with a three-quarter pierced gallery, the frieze with one drawer, raised on fluted supports, joined by a stretcher, above *toupie* feet ending in ormolu *sabots.*
Height 36 in. (91.4 cm.), width 38 in. (96.5 cm.), depth 14¼ in. (36.2 cm.)

This console desserte was among the furnishings in the Second Floor Oval Room of the White House during President and Mrs. Kennedy's residence, and previously, in their house in Georgetown.

$8,000–12,000

311 **A Pair of Régence Painted Chaises à la Reine, first quarter 18th Century**

Each cartouche-shaped upholstered backrest carved with a stylized shell and foliate motifs, the serpentine-fronted seat raised on cabriole legs; painted white.

Provenance:
Kraemer & Cie., Paris.

$8,000–12,000

312 **A Continental Rococo Style Ormolu-Mounted Fruitwood and Mahogany Commode, 19th Century, possibly Dutch**

The serpentine-fronted marble top above a pair of drawers veneered *sans traverse* with a basket of flowers, fitted with ormolu drawer handles, keyhole escutcheons and apron mount.
Height 32 in. (81.3 cm.), width 38½ in. (97.8 cm.), depth 21½ in. (54.6 cm.)

The underside of the marble top inscribed *J. Kennedy Wash. D.C.*

This commode was among the furnishings in Mrs. Kennedy's bedroom at the White House.

$5,000–7,000

312

313 **A Paris Style Porcelain Vase Mounted as a Lamp**

Height 22 in. (55.9 cm.)

This lamp was among the furnishings in the West Sitting Room of the White House during President and Mrs. Kennedy's residence.

$250–350

14 **An Italian Neoclassical Fruitwood Bouillotte Table**

The circular grey-mottled marble top with an ormolu gallery, the frieze with a pair of candle slides and a pair of drawers, raised on square tapered legs fitted with casters. *Restorations to carcass.*
Height 28½ in. (72.4 cm.), diameter 23 in. (58.4 cm.)

Provenance:
Chrystian Aubusson, New York, 1961

$2,500–3,500

15 **An Italian Neoclassical Painted and Parcel-Gilt Low Bergère, late 18th Century**

The tub-shaped backrest and armrests carved with twisted ribbon and flowerheads, the slightly serpentine-fronted seat raised on square tapered legs carved with bellflowers.

The back rail bearing a label stamped *1555.*

$5,000–7,000

313, 314, 315

316

316 **A Pair of Louis XV Painted Fauteuils à la Reine, mid-18th Century, signed N. Blanchard**

Each with a cartouche-shaped upholstered backrest carved with flowerheads and leaf tips, the padded armrests raised on voluted supports, the serpentine-fronted upholstered seat carved to match the backrest, raised on cabriole legs.

Nicolas-Sylvain Blanchard, *maître* in 1743

$15,000–25,000

317 **A Louis XV Style Painted Mirror**

The plate contained within a molded reeded frame carved with shell motifs; painted green and cream.
Height 4 ft. 4¾ in. (134 cm.), width 39¼ in. (99.7 cm.)

$800–1,000

317

319

318

318 **A Louis XVI Style Ormolu-Mounted Kingwood and Tulipwood Parquetry Table en Chiffonnière**

The rectangular crossbanded top above three drawers, raised on square tapered legs ending in ormolu *sabots*, fitted with ormolu keyhole escutcheons.
Height 26½ in. (67.3 cm.), width 17½ in. (44.4 cm.), depth 13¼ in. (33.7 cm.)

$800-1,200

319 **A Pair of Louis XV Style Grey-Painted Fauteuils en Cabriolet**

Each with a cartouche-shaped upholstered backrest carved with flowerheads, the padded armrests raised on voluted supports, the serpentine-fronted upholstered seat raised on cabriole legs.

$2,000–3,000

320

320 **A Pair of Louis XVI Style White- and Grey-Painted Tabourets**

Each with a rectangular upholstered top above guilloche-carved rails, raised on circular, tapered stop-fluted legs. One bearing a paper label inscribed *"Pair of Louis XVI banquettes, C.C. Paterson".*

$3,000–4,000

321 **A Louis XVI Style Giltwood Frame Mounted as a Mirror**

The rectangular mirror plate contained within a frame carved with leaf tips and beading.
Height 4 ft. 10 in. (10.2 cm.), width 38¾ in. (98.4 cm.)

$600–800

321

322

322 **A Pair of Louis XVI Style Caned Painted Fauteuils en Cabriolet**

Each with a molded oval caned backrest, wooden armrests raised on fluted supports, the serpentine-fronted seat raised on circular, tapered, fluted legs; with traces of green and cream paint.

$1,500–2,000

The John F. Kennedy Library

323 **A Pair of Louis XVI Ormolu-Mounted Black And White Marble Obelisks, last Quarter 18th Century**

Each obelisk surrounded by ormolu rope twist borders, centered by a lion's mask and pelt and surmounted by a pomegranate finial, raised on a rectangular pedestal fitted with an ormolu military trophy, surrounded by pylons linked by chains above a stepped white marble base and ormolu *toupie* feet.
Height 21 in. (53.3 cm.)

Provenance:
Vladimir Barjanasky, 1961

These obelisks were among the furnishings in the Red Room of the White House during President and Mrs. Kennedy's residence..

$10,000–15,000

The Red Room is one of the four state reception rooms in the White House. Furnished in the Late Federal and Empire style of 1810-1830, it contains several pieces of furniture from the New York workshop of the French-born cabinetmaker Charles-Honoré Lannuier. Benjamin Henry Latrobe's 1803 drawing of the principal floor of the White House with the rooms designated as Jefferson used them indicates that the Red Room served as "the President's Antechamber" for the Cabinet Room or President's Library next door. During the Madison Administration, the antechamber became the "Yellow Drawing Room" and the scene of Dolley Madison's fashionable Wednesday night receptions. This was the first room to be completely restored during the John F. Kennedy Administration, and the reception room decor instantly became the First Lady's favorite. The French neoclassical furniture design of Lannuier and the rectilinear shape and ornamental brass hardware characteristic of American Empire would set the tone of the decor. The elegance of the Red Room furniture derives from a combination of richly carved and finished woods with decorative hardware made of gilded bronze in characteristic designs and motifs such as dolphins, winged caryatids, acanthus leaves, lions' heads, paw feet, and sphinxes. Some pieces of furniture formerly belonging to Dolley Madison and Nellie Custis were acquired for the room; additional pieces were acquired under the supervision of the interior decorator Stephane Boudin. For the upholstery, walls, and window fabric, Boudin supplied a collection of early-nineteenth-century French Empire cerise and gold-colored silk lampas fragments that were reproduced by Scalamandré and woven in the United States. The walls were covered by a red twill satin fabric with a gold scroll design in the border.

For the windows Boudin provided draperies and drapery tie backs made of gold satin with tassel-trimmed red damask valances and handmade gold-and-red fringe. The beige, red, and gold rug is a reproduction of an early-nineteenth-century French Savonnerie rug in the White House Collection and was made for the room in 1965. The white marble mantel with caryatid figures is one of a pair ordered by Monroe that was originally installed in the State Dining Room. The French Empire chandelier was fashioned from carved and gilded wood about 1805. For the hanging of portraits and landscapes, Boudin followed his preference for full wall coverage like that of a gallery of paintings, placing the first tier at eye level and the second tier above door frame height. The Red Room decor instantly became Mrs. Kennedy's favorite and she admired this room so much that she loaned a pair of her own early-nineteenth century French Empire obelisks for mantel garniture during her husband's presidency.

323

324

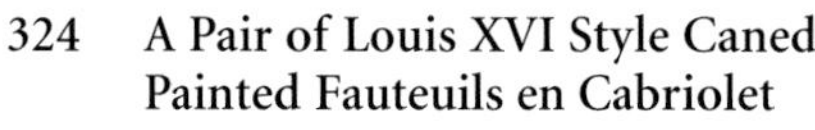

324 A Pair of Louis XVI Style Caned Painted Fauteuils en Cabriolet

Each with a molded oval caned back-rest, wooden armrests raised on fluted supports, the bow-fronted caned seat with loose cushion, raised on circular, tapered, fluted legs; painted cream and green.

$1,500–2,000

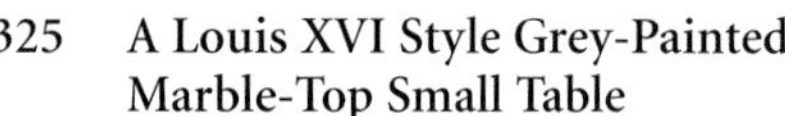

325 A Louis XVI Style Grey-Painted Marble-Top Small Table

The rectangular top with square outset corners and raised on fluted legs.
Height 15 in. (38.1 cm.), length 14 in. (35.6 cm.)

$400–600

325

326 A Louis XVI Style Mahogany Bureau Plat

The rectangular top inset with a brown leather writing surface, the frieze with two drawers, each side with a writing slide, raised on circular tapered legs.
Height 29½ in. (74.9 cm.), width 47 in. (119.4 cm.), depth 24¼ in. (61.6 cm.)

$700–900

327

326

328

327 **A Late George III Inlaid Mahogany Bedside Cupboard, 19th Century**

The rectangular crossbanded top above a case fitted with a hinged flap, supported on square tapering legs.
Height 29 in. (73.7 cm.), width 12 ¼ in. (31.1 cm.)

$1,000–1,500

328 **A Louis XV Style Giltwood Mirror**

The arched divided plate surrounded by molded borders, the top rail carved with a shell and scrolling foliage, the lower rail with flowerheads.
Height 5 ft. 10 in. (177.8 cm.), width 32 in. (81.3 cm.)

$4,000–6,000

330, 329, 331

329 **A Louis XVI Style Grey-Painted Writing Table**

The almost-square top lined with fabric, the serpentine-carved apron fitted with one large drawer at one side and one small drawer at the other, raised on circular tapered stop-fluted legs. *Height 28 in. (71.1 cm.), width 27 in. (68.6 cm.), depth 20 in. (50.8 cm.)*

This writing table was among the furnishings in Mrs. Kennedy's bedroom at the White House.

$1,000–1,500

330 **A Chinese Painted Leather Small Trunk**

The top and front painted with an overall scene of figures by a pavilion, in colors on a yellow ground. *Height 8 in. (20.3 cm.), length 17 in. (43.2 cm.), width 10 in. (25.4 cm.)*

$350–500

331 **A Louis XV Style Cream-Painted Bergère**

The tall tufted upholstered backrest continuing to padded armrests, the serpentine-fronted seat raised on cabriole legs.

$2,000–3,000

332

32 **A Set of Four Louis XVI Style Grey- and Blue-Painted Fauteuils en Cabriolet**

Each with a molded oval upholstered backrest, the padded armrests raised on voluted supports, the bow-fronted seat raised on circular tapered, fluted legs.

$4,000–6,000

33 **A Louis XVI Brass-Mounted Mahogany Console Desserte, last quarter 18th Century**

The rectangular white veined marble top fitted with a three-quarter gallery, the frieze fitted with a fruitwood-banded drawer, raised on vase-turned supports joined by two stretchers, above baluster-shaped legs ending in ormolu *sabots*.
Height 36½ in. (92.7 cm.), width 37½ in. (95.2 cm.), depth 13½ in. (34.3 cm.)

Provenance:
Gerald Kerin, Ltd., London, 1958.

This console desserte was among the furnishings in the Second Floor Oval Room of the White House during President and Mrs. Kennedy's residence.

$8,000–12,000

333

334

334 **A Biedermeier Walnut and Fruitwood Etagère**

The rectangular cornice fitted with finials, above five shelves joined by uprights upports surmounted by arrowheads, *incorporating 18th century elements.*
Height 7 ft. (2.13 m.), width 4 ft. 11 in. (1.5 m.), depth 16¼ in. (41.3 cm.)

$6,000–8,000

335 **A Louis XVI Grey-Painted Banquette**

The rectangular top upholstered in brown leather, the rails carved with twisted ribbon, raised on circular tapered stop-fluted legs headed by *paterae* and joined by an H-stretcher.
Height 18 in. (45.7 cm.), width 5 ft. (152.4 cm.), depth 14½ in. (36.8 cm.)

$6,000–8,000

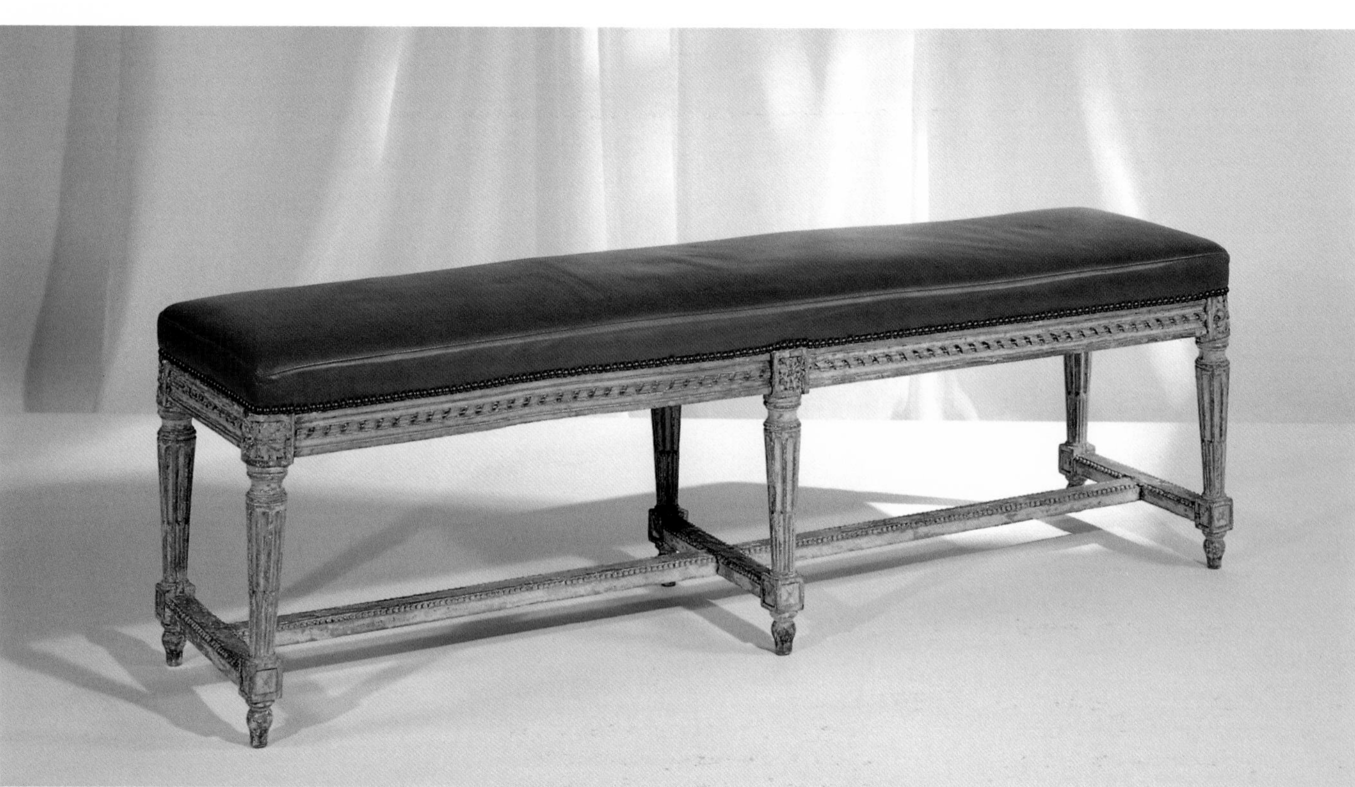

335

336

337, 340

36 **A Louis XV Painted Upholstered Banquette**

The shaped rectangular upholstered top with incurved sides, the rails carved with cabbage roses and leaf tips, raised on cabriole legs; painted green. *Partially of 18th century origin. Length 40 ½ in. (102.9 cm.)*

$1,500–2,500

337 **A Chinese Red-Lacquered Side Table, 18th/19th Century**

The rectangular top above a molded frieze and pierced apron on straight square-section legs, painted with flower and leaf sprays within a fret-work and floral border, (reduced in height).
Height 28 ½ in. (72.4 cm.), length 82 in. (208.3 cm.), width 29 in. (73.7 cm.)

$7,500–10,000

338

338 A Louis XV/XVI Style Ormolu-Mounted Fruitwood and Sycamore Parquetry Table Vide Poche

The rectangular top with rounded ends fitted with a wooden gallery hinged on one side, raised on lyre-form trestle supports joined by a stretcher, the whole inlaid with trellis parquetry marked at the interstices with dots.
Height 30 in. (76.2 cm.), width 28 in. (71.1 cm.), depth 14¾ in. (37.5 cm.)

This table is a copy of a model which was popularized during the Louis XV/XVI transitional period (circa 1770) by the *marchands-merciers,* and was interpreted by such leading 18th century *ébénistes* as Roger Vandercruse, called Lacroix, Martin Carlin, and Adam Weisweiler.

Exhibition:
The British Antique Dealers Association, Art Treasures Exhibition, Bath, 1958, Exhibition No. 154.

Provenance:
Collection of Viscount Furness.
Ayer & Co., Bath, 1958.

This table vide poche was among the furnishings in the Second Floor Oval Room of the White House during President and Mrs. Kennedy's residence.

$10,000–15,000

340

341

339

339 **A Louis XVI Style Beige-Painted Prie-Dieu**

With upholstered back and top rail and balloon-shaped seat, raised on turned and tapered stop-fluted legs.

$600–800

340 **A Bessarabian Kilim, late 19th Century**

The sand field with styled floral sprays overall, within a meandering flowering vine border, (small hole).
Approximately 8 ft. 7 in. by 5 ft. 9 in. (2.62 by 1.75 m.)

$2,000–3,000

341 **A Bessarabian Kilim, last quarter 19th Century**

The central cream wreath-filled roundel on a denim blue field of grape vines, (holes, rewoven areas).
Approximately 6 ft. 10 in. by 6 ft. 10 in. (2.08 by 2.08 m.)

$2,000–3,000

342 **A Victorian Needlepoint Rug, mid-19th Century**

The crimson ground with ivory floral cartouches overall with a cream scrollwork inner border with eagles at each corner and a floral garland border with mask rosettes at each corner, (small stains, minor losses). *Approximately 8 ft. by 7 ft. 1 in. (2.44 by 2.16 m.)*

This rug was among the furnishings in the Second Floor Oval Room of the White House during President and Mrs. Kennedy's residence.

$6,000–8,000

Below
Second Floor Oval Room, The White House, showing lots 3, 286, 303, 306, 342, 1014

342

The John F. Kennedy Library

343

343 **A Late Louis XVI Ormolu-Mounted Mahogany Secrétaire à Abattant, last quarter 18th Century**

The white marble top with outset rounded forecorners above a frieze drawer and a fall-front opening to form a leather-lined writing surface and to reveal an arrangement of seven small drawers beneath shelves, the lower part with a pair of cupboard doors raised on *toupie* feet; the whole outlined with brass banding.
Height 4 ft. 8 in. (142.2 cm.), width 37 in. (94 cm.), depth 15 in. (38.1 cm.)

Provenance:
Parke-Bernet, New York, March 30, 1963, Sale 2182, lot 150

$7,000–9,000

344

345

344 A Louis XVI Style White-Painted X-Form Upholstered Stool

The pale green upholstered seat with guilloche carseat rails on white-painted cruciform legs.
Height 20 in. (50.8 cm.), length 19½ in. (49.5 cm.), width 14½ in. (36.8 cm.)

$500–700

345 A Louis XV Style Painted Button-Tufted Upholstered Tabouret

With a rectangular top raised on short cabriole legs.
Length 37 in. (94 cm.)

$800–1,000

346 A Louis XVI Style Grey-Painted Canapé

The rectangular upholstered backrest with pine cone finials, the top rail carved with leaf tips, the downcurved armrests carved with overlapping discs, the bow-fronted upholstered seat with loose cushion, raised on spirally fluted, tapered legs; upholstered in dark red leather
Length 6 ft. 2 in. (188 cm.)

$8,000–12,000

347 A Pair of Louis XVI Grey-Painted Marquises, last quarter 18th Century, signed Tilliard

Each with a rectangular upholstered backrest with spherical finials, continuing to fluted downswept wooden armrests, the slightly bow-fronted seat carved with twisted ribbon, raised on circular tapered fluted legs headed by rosettes; upholstered in dark red leather. *Repairs to legs on one.*

Jean-Baptiste II Tilliard, *maître* in 1752.

$20,000–30,000

347

346

348, 349

350, 351, 29, 284, 1128

352

348 **An Italian Neoclassical Console Table, last quarter 18th Century**

The rectangular *brêche d'Alep* marble top with square outset corners above a frieze carved with scrolling foliage and beading, raised on circular tapered stop-fluted legs headed by rosettes, the underside of the marble marked in black crayon, *Kennedy Wash DC.*
Height 32½ in. (82.5 cm.), width 42½ in. (107.9 cm.), depth 20¾ in. (52.7 cm.)

This console table was among the furnishings in Mrs. Kennedy's dressing room at the White House.

$5,000–7,000

349 **A Louis XVI Style Grey-Painted Upholstered Tabouret, 19th Century**

The rectangular seat on stop-fluted short legs.
Height 10 in. (25.4 cm.), length 22 in. (55.9 cm.)

$1,500–2,000

350 **A Louis XVI Style Painted and Parcel-Gilt Voyeuse**

The shaped backrest with upholstered top rail, the horseshoe-shaped seat raised on circular tapered stop-fluted legs; painted grey highighted with gilding.

$200–300

351 **A Louis XVI Style Brass-Mounted Mahogany Table Vide Poche**

The octagonal top with a wooden gallery hinged at the front, raised on trestle supports joined by two elliptical stretchers.
Height 25½ in. (64.8 cm.), width 22¼ in. (56.5 cm.), depth 11 in. (27.9 cm.)

This table vide poche was among the furnishings in Mrs. Kennedy's bedroom at the White House.

$1,500–2,000

352 **An Italian Neoclassical Style Kingwood and Fruitwood Parquetry Games Table**

The rectangular top inlaid on one side with a checker board flanked by chevron banded borders, and on the other side with a baize playing surface; the interior veneered for backgammon, raised on circular, tapered stop-fluted legs.
Height 29 in. (73.7 cm.), width 43¼ in. (109.9 cm.), depth 21¾ in. (55.2 cm.)

This games table was among the furnishings in Second Floor Oval Room of the White House during President and Mrs. Kennedy's residence.

$5,000–7,000

353

354

353 **A Directoire Provincial Walnut Table Vide Poche, circa 1800**

The rectangular top with a wooden gallery, raised on baluster and columnar legs joined by a platform stretcher and an H-stretcher.
Height 29 in. (73.7 cm.), width 22 in. (55.9 cm.), depth 12¾ in. (32.4 cm.)

$1,200–1,800

354 **A Continental Fruitwood Hanging Shelf**

Of rectangular outline, with two shelves above a projecting pair of cupboard doors inlaid with ebonized stringing and Maltese crosses.
Height 31¾ in. (80.6 cm.), width 23 in. (58.4 cm.), depth 10 in. (25.4 cm.)

$800–1,200

355 **A Directoire Style Fruitwood Table Vide Poche**

The rectangular top with a wooden gallery and canted corners, raised on trestle supports joined by platform stretchers matching the top.
Height 28 in. (71.1 cm.), width 23¾ in. (60.3 cm.), depth 12½ in. (31.7 cm.)

$300–500

356, 355, 1103, 285

356 **Small Victorian Painted Satinwood Cane-Seat Side Chair, Late 19th Century**

The uprights, seat frame and legs painted with sprays of flowers

$200–300

357 **Directoire Painted Tabouret Mounted as a Low Table, late 18th Century**

The square grey marble top raised on circular tapering legs headed by cabochons.
Height 14½ in. (36.8 cm.), width 19 in. (48.3 cm.)

Please see illustration on page 318.

$1,500–2,500

The John F. Kennedy Library

358 **A Louis XVI Ormolu-Mounted Mahogany Bureau Plat and Cartonnier, signed E. Levasseur, JME**

The rectangular top with outset hexagonal corners inset with a gilt-tooled brown leather writing surface and surrounded by an ormolu border, the front with three frieze drawers, each side fitted with a leather-lined writing slide, the frieze fitted all around with ormolu beaded and leaf tip borders; the hexagonal corners inset with corrugated ormolu panels, raised on circular tapered fluted legs inset with ormolu flutes and *chandelles* ending in ormolu *sabots*, the cartonnier with a white marble top with hexagonal and rounded corners fitted with a three-quarter pierced ormolu gallery above four leather document boxes and four drawers flanking a niche, outlined with ormolu leaf tip borders. *Alterations, some restoration. Height 43 ¾ in. (111.1 cm.), width 5 ft. 2 ½ in. (158.7 cm.), depth 31 ¾ in. (80.6 cm.)*

$20,000–30,000

Etienne Levasseur, *maître* in 1766.

The middle drawer fitted with a brass plaque inscribed, *Desk on which Nuclear Test Ban Treaty was signed by President John Fitzgerald Kennedy Treaty Room - The White house August 5, 1963.*

The crisis of October 1962 between the United States of America and the Soviet Union over missiles in Cuba brought the world to the brink of nuclear war. "We have to remember," Secretary of State Dean Rusk later told President Kennedy, "that no one who went through the missile crisis came out the same as they went in." Indeed, the episode had rattled other world leaders besides the President of the United States: chiefly Nikita Khrushchev of the Soviet Union and Harold Macmillan of Great Britain. The latter had already discussed a nuclear test ban with Kennedy's predecessor, President Eisenhower, in 1959. Now, during the fall of 1962, the idea was revived. Macmillan was actually with Kennedy in the Bahamas when, on December 19, a letter arrived from Khrushchev declaring, "The period of maximum crisis and tension in the Caribbean is behind us. We are now free to consider other international matters, in particular a subject which has long been ripe for action—the cessation of nuclear tests... It seems to me, Mr. President, that the time has come now to put an end once and for all to nuclear tests..."

Letters between Washington and Moscow continued to be exchanged, until Chairman Khrushchev, in an otherwise belligerent reply, the tone of which was thought at the time to convey that he was under pressure from a Chinese Government hostile to his policies, agreed to President Kennedy and Prime Minister Macmillan's suggestion that they be allowed to send "highly placed" delegates to Russia to discuss details for a test ban treaty. The emissaries, including W. Averell Harriman for the United States and Lord Hailsham for the United Kingdom, set off for Moscow. Harriman subsequently recalled: "We argued about every word, every phrase, so that we could come to a thorough understanding as to the meaning of each word. So, on the afternoon of July 24, after ten days of most intensive negotiations, the representatives of the three governments initialed the limited test ban treaty." In spite of the tension, Khrushchev maintained his good humor thoughout, and after the talks, as he and Harriman walked across one of the Kremlin's courtyards, they found themselves among a group of Russian sightseers. Their Chairman introduced Harriman, saying that they had just signed the treaty and that they were off to have some dinner. "Do you think he deserves dinner?" Khrushchev shouted. The crowd cheered their approval.

With Harriman having flown home to report to Kennedy, the President broadcast his now historic address to the American people from the Oval Office on the evening of July 26, 1963. "I speak to you tonight in a spirit of hope," he began. "Eighteen years ago the advent of nuclear weapons changed the course of the world... Since that time, all mankind has been struggling to escape from the darkening prospect of mass destruction on earth. In an age when both sides have come to possess enough nuclear power to destroy the human race several times over, the world of communism and the world of free choice have been caught up in a vicious circle of conflicting ideology and interest... In these years, the United States and the Soviet Union have frequently communicated suspicion and warnings to each other, but ver rarely hope... Yesterday a shaft of light cut into the darkness. Negotiations were concluded in Moscow on a treaty to ban all nuclear rests in the atmosphere, in outer space and under water. For the first time, an agreement has been reached on bringing the forces of nuclear destruction under international control—a goal first sought in 1946..."

358

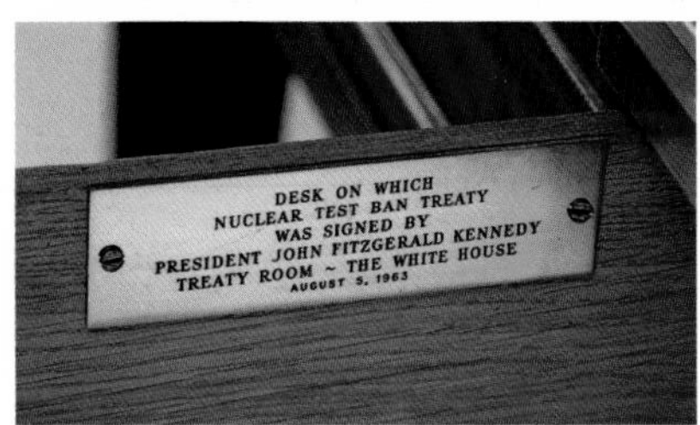

358 detail

The table in this lot was used by the President for the final signing of the Nuclear Test Ban Treaty of 1963, witnessed on 7th October that year by Vice President Lyndon B. Johnson, Secretary of State Dean Rusk, W. Averell Harriman, Senator J. W. Fulbright, Senator Hubert Humphrey and others.

Literature:
Illustrated, Nicolay, *L'Art et la Manière des Maîtres Ebénistes Français au XVIIIe Siècle,* 1956, p. 303, fig. D

Provenance:
Galerie Charpentier, Paris, 1951

A KING'S BOOK OF
THE LAKE REGIONS OF CENTRAL AFRICA VOL. 2
THE LAKE REGIONS OF CENTRAL AFRICA VOL. 1

JEWELRY FROM THE ESTATE OF JACQUELINE KENNEDY ONASSIS

SESSION FOUR

WEDNESDAY, APRIL 24,

6:00 P.M.

The Dining Room of Jacqueline Kennedy Onassis' New York City apartment, showing lots 3, 15, 79, 99, 122, 263, 273, 282, 299, 307, 323 and 332.

UPI / Bettmann

Left: *Jacqueline Kennedy and the President arriving at the National General Armory to attend a Democratic fund raising dinner on January 20, 1962.*

359 **Eighteen-Karat Gold Minaudière, Van Cleef & Arpels, France**

The rectangular case of basketweave design, the interior with fitted mirror, lipstick case, comb and two hinged compartments, gross weight approximately 300 dwts., *several dents on lid, signed Van Cleef & Arpels, numbered 77488.*
Length 6 ⅞ in. (17.5 cm.)

$2,000–3,000

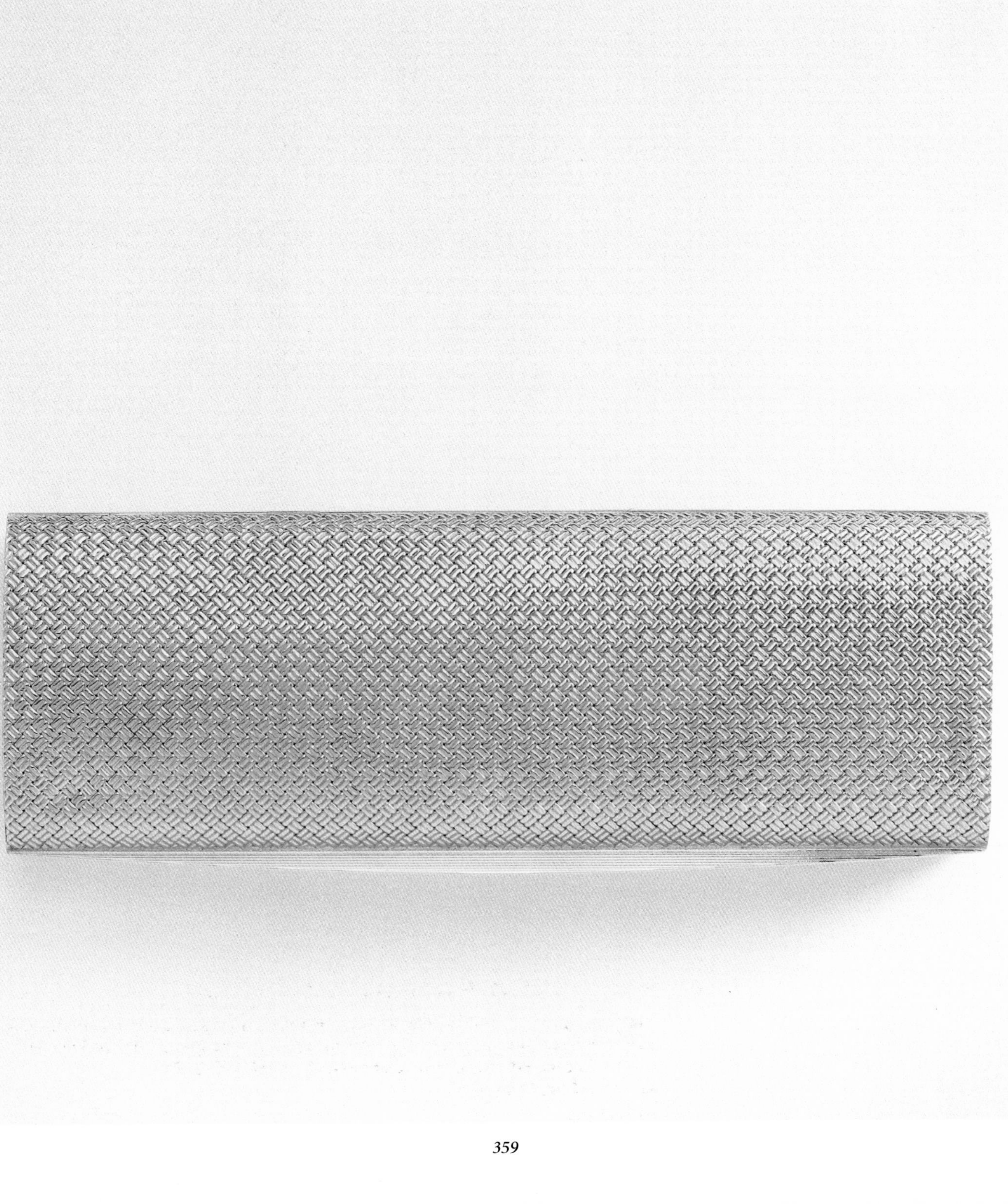

359

360 **Eighteen-Karat Gold Bracelet and a Gold and Diamond Brooch**

The wide strap decorated with diamond-shaped motifs engraved with stylized florets, weighing approximately 33 dwts, *length 7½ in. (19 cm.)*; the textured gold brooch designed as two slightly curved "twigs" accented with a single round diamond.

$700–900

361 **Group of Four Gold Rings**

Comprising two band rings of eighteen-karat gold, one enhanced with translucent red enamel, the other with green enamel; a coin ring, the Greek gold coin within a rope mounting of eighteen-karat gold, and a ring of gold rope, claw-set with a bluish-grey stone, *approximately sizes 5 to 7 1/2.*

$300–400

362 **Group of Miscellaneous Gold Jewelry**

Comprising an eighteen-karat gold hinged bangle-bracelet, *Lalaounis, Greece*; a ring set with a twenty-peso Mexican gold coin; a gold medallion depicting Menelik II of Ethiopia (1889-1913) mounted as a pendant within a gold bezel; a gold pen, *signed Waterman, made in France*; a yellow metal pen; a one-peso Mexican coin, *dated 1958*, a single gold earclip, the large hoop of hammered gold, *partially obliterated signature V.C.A., numbered 3V 587.24*, and an eighteen-karat gold arrow-head brooch with fourteen-karat gold brooch pin. (8)

$750–1,000

362
361
362
360
362
362
360

363 **Gold Charm Bracelet**

The gold link bracelet supporting 25 charms of various design, several accented with colorful hardstones and glass, including columns, fruits, a fish, a slipper, a padlock, a fan and an arm with a fist, the whole weighing approximately 104 dwts.
Length approximately 8 in. (20.3 cm.)

$1,500–2,000

364 **Gold and Black Enamel Lighter, Dupont, Paris**

The black enamel case with applied initial J., *signed Dupont, Paris, made in France, serial no. BLB516.* Together with a second gold lighter of cylindrical form and fluted design. (2)

$300–400

364

363

365 **Group of Gold Earclips**

Comprising a pair of hinged hoops of polished fourteen-karat gold; a pair of hoops of twisted rope design, in fourteen-karat gold with screw-back tops and pendant hooks at the base; a pair of pendant-earclips in ancient-revival style, the fan-shaped tops supporting crescent links graduating in size, decorated throughout with pendant fringes; three gold hoops of rope-twist design; and a pair of ivory hoops mounted in eighteen-karat gold. (11)

$1,000–1,200

366 **Two Gold Pendants and a Gilt Metal Charm Bracelet**

The first a pendant composed of a Byzantine Empire gold coin, *circa 11th/12th Century A.D.* (Histamenon Nomisma), within a gold bezel pendant mounting, supported on a long gilt-metal fancy link chain; the second a pendant-brooch of eighteen-karat gold depicting a pair of spiraling fish, *in ancient revival style, signed MMA*, engraved *JKO, from E & C.W.*; the chain link bracelet of "pink" gilt metal supporting a yellow metal charm decorated with a "teddy bear." (3)

$200–300

367 **Eighteen-Karat Gold Chain Necklace**

Of fancy baton links accented at intervals with carved ivory cylinders.
Length 38 in. (96.5 cm.)

$750–1,000

368 **Two Gold Commemorative Charms**

The first, *1967*, a polished gold disc engraved on one side with a trident entwined with the steering wheel of a boat, the top of the trident superimposed by two initials *N*, the reverse engraved *Launching John F. Kennedy, CVA-67 Mrs. John F. Kennedy, Matron of Honor, Newport News, Virginia, May 27, 1967*; the second applied with a ship against a blue enamel ground, engraved on the top border *Kennedy 60*, the lower border engraved with the Hebrew inscription for *Mazel Tov*.

$150–200

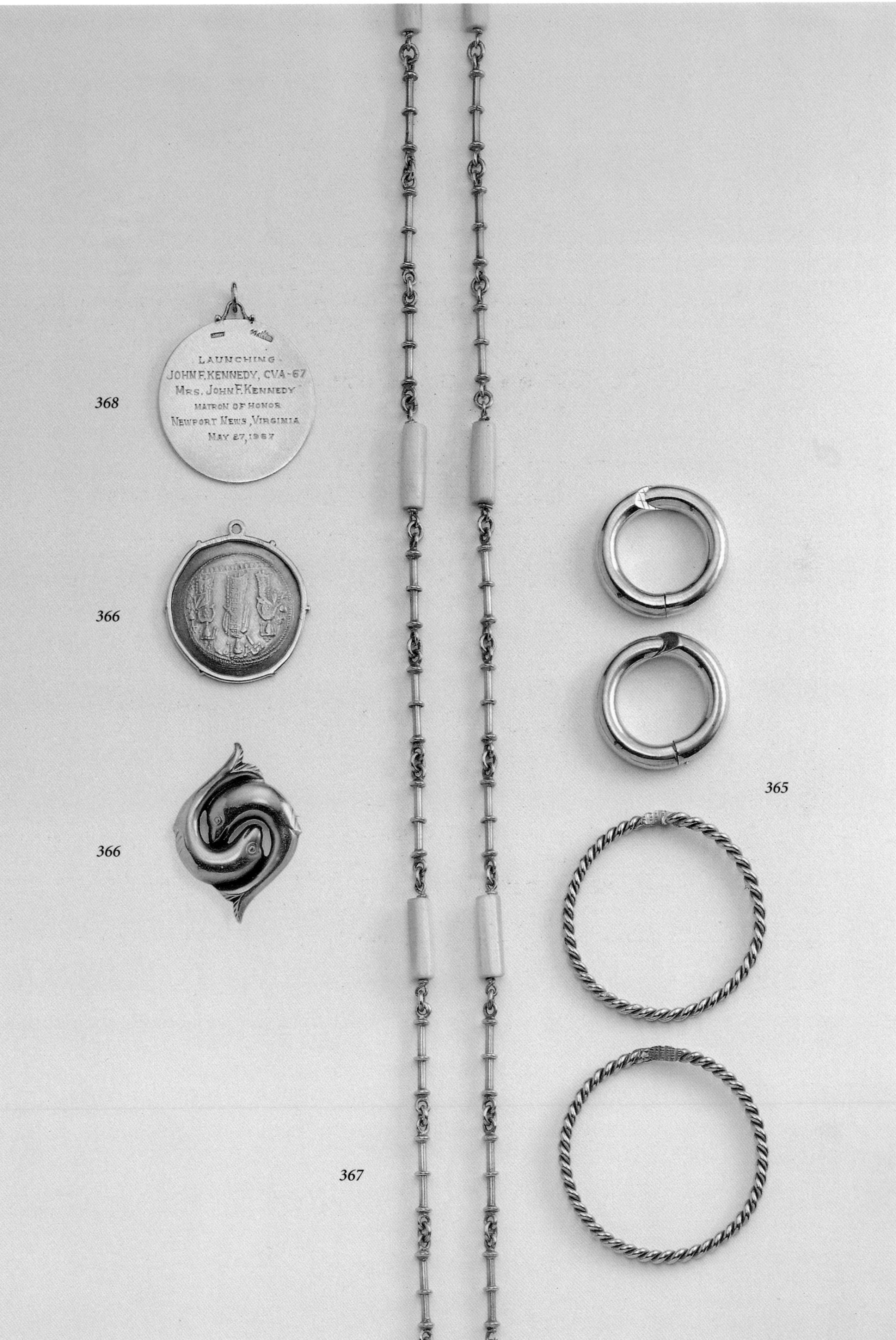
LAUNCHING
JOHN F. KENNEDY, CVA-67
MRS. JOHN F. KENNEDY
MATRON OF HONOR
NEWPORT NEWS, VIRGINIA
MAY 27, 1967
368
366
366
365
367

369 **Eighteen-Karat Gold Chain Necklace, David Webb**

Composed of elongated spiralling links of gold alternating with trios of spiral beads, weighing approximately 28 dwts., *signed Webb.*
Length 28 in. (71.1 cm.)

$600–800

370 **Two Gold Brooches, one by David Webb**

The first composed of a pale green hardstone carved as a seated abstract figure within an eighteen-karat gold rope cage supporting a cultured pearl drop, *signed Webb;* the second composed of a gold coin framed by a gold and emerald drop leaf-and-berry wreath.

$600–800

371 **A Pair of Gold Earclips, Van Cleef & Arpels**

Designed as Chinese masks, *signed VCA, numbered 3V501-2.*

$600–800

370

369

371

372 **Pair of Eighteen-Karat Gold and Diamond Earclips**

Designed as matte gold knots of square shape, each set in the center with a round diamond, together weighing approximately 1.20 carats.

$1,500–2,000

373 **Diamond Bar Brooch**

The bar of platinum and gold set in the center with a round diamond weighing approximately .90 carat and at either end with 2 triangular-shaped diamonds weighing .75 carat.

$2,000–3,000

374 **Diamond Bracelet**

The flexible strap decorated with 135 round diamonds set in three rows weighing approximately 8.00 carats, mounted in eighteen-karat gold.
Length 7 in. (17.8 cm.)

$6,000–8,000

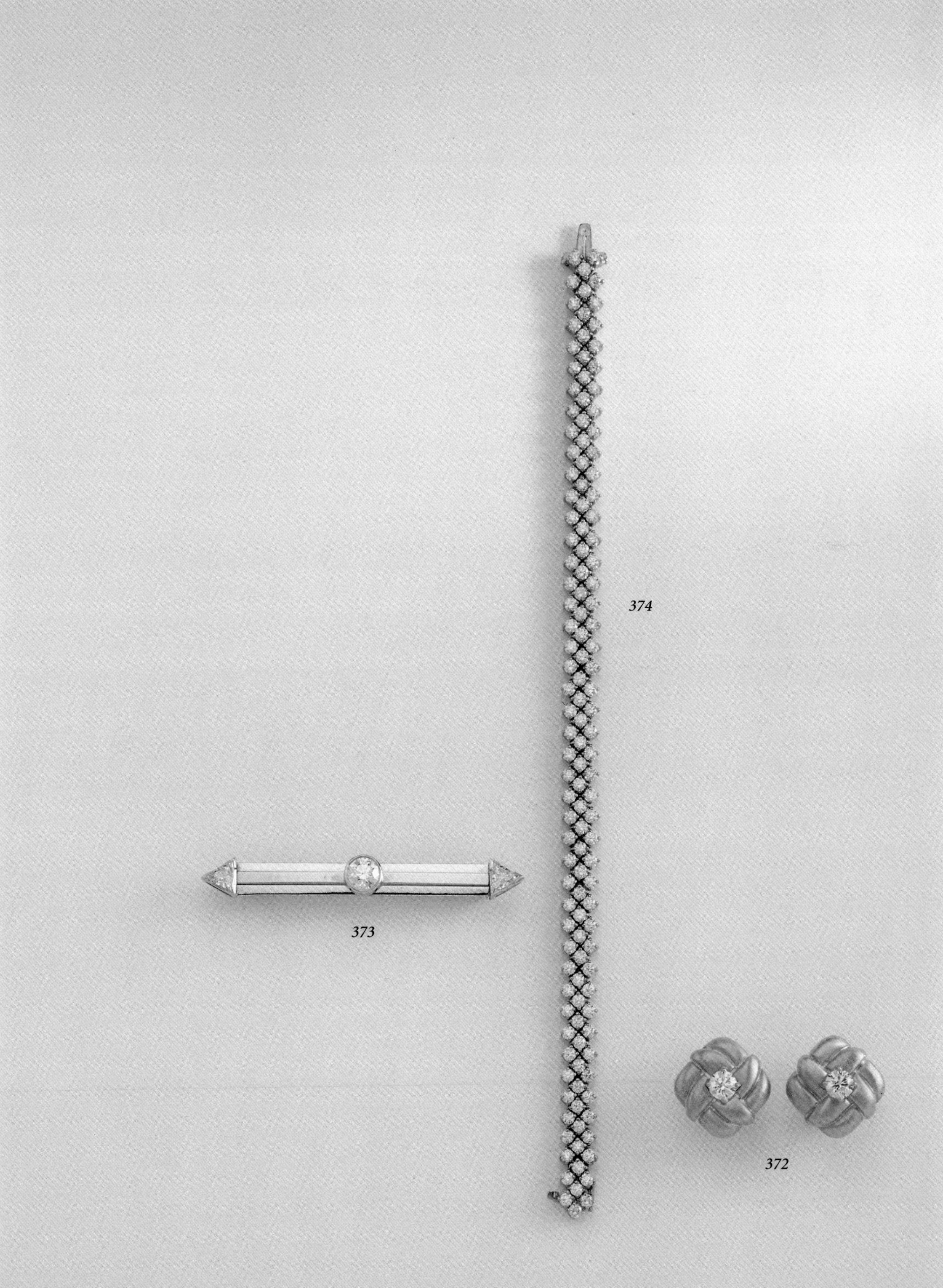
374
373
372

375 **Pair of Gold and Sapphire "Antelope Head" Bangle-Bracelets, Greece**

In Classical Revival style, the hinged bangles of openwork scroll and beadwork design accented with small round sapphires, each decorated with a pair of crossover antelopes' heads at the center, their eyes set with small round rubies, together weighing approximately 90 dwts., *maker's mark ZS and a Coptic cross.*

$2,000–3,000

376 **Group of Gold "Animal Head" Jewelry, Greece**

In Classical Revival style, comprising two pairs of earclips and three rings, the first pair of earclips designed as gold scrolls ending in antelopes' heads, in twenty-two karat gold, the second pair designed as large hoops of rope and beadwork design ending in bulls' heads; two of the rings decorated with rams' heads, one applied with red enamel, the other with blue enamel, each with ruby eyes and rose-cut diamond collars, in eighteen-karat gold, the third ring of textured eighteen-karat gold decorated with an antelope head. (7)

$1,200–1,500

376

375

377 **Twenty-Two Karat Gold Lion's-Head Collar, Lalaounis**

In Greek Revival style, the band-style collar with abstract rope design in relief, decorated at either end with a lion's head with filigree and beadwork decoration around the neck, weighing approximately 38 dwts., *signed Lalaounis.*

$750–1,000

378 **Two Gold Bangle-Bracelets, one by Zolotas, Greece**

In Greek Revival style, the first a tubular bangle with central hinge decorated at either end with confronting rams' heads, in eighteen-karat gold, *signed Zolotas*; the second of similar design, decorated with a pair of mythical dogs' heads at the terminals, *maker's mark ZS and Coptic cross*, together weighing approximately 60 dwts.

$1,000–1,500

377

378

Reuters / Bettmann

Right: *Jacqueline Kennedy Onassis, John F. Kennedy, Jr. and Caroline Kennedy with President Clinton at the rededication ceremony of the Kennedy Presidential Library in Boston in October 29, 1993.*

379 **Pair of Red Tourmaline and Amethyst Pendant-Earclips**

Composed of red tourmaline briolette drops supported by fancy-shaped amethysts within mountings of matte eighteen-karat gold.

These earclips were a gift from Artemis Garofalides, Aristotle Onassis' sister.

$800–1,000

380 **Pair of Eighteen-Karat Gold and Green Enamel Earclips, David Webb**

The slightly flared half hoops applied with gold lozenge-shaped motifs on an emerald green translucent enamel ground, *signed Webb.*

$2,000–3,000

381 **Pair of Eighteen-Karat Yellow and White Gold Earclips, Marina B.**

The heart-shaped motifs designed as interlocking fancy-shaped segments of yellow and white gold, *signed MB and Marina B.*

$3,000–4,000

382 **Pair of Diamond and Enamel Earclips, French**

The stylized cornucopiae of eighteen-karat gold applied with royal blue enamel, holding platinum spheres pavé-set with round diamonds weighing approximately 7.00 carats, *2 diamonds missing, signed made in France, maker's mark, numbered 30760.*

$7,500–10,000

379

382

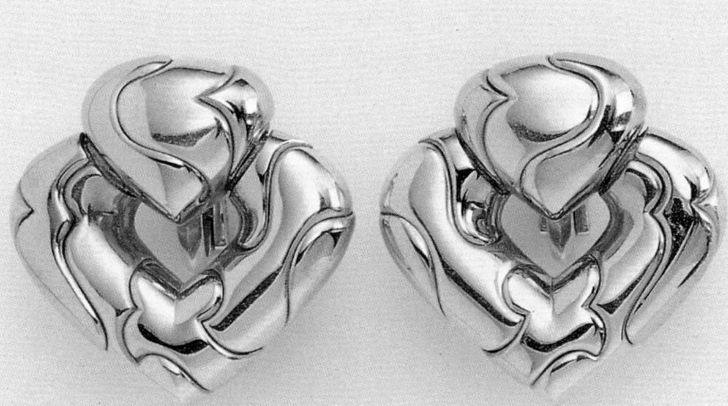

381

380

383 **Natural Baroque Pearl and Diamond Ring**

The floral motif composed of a baroque pearl measuring approximately 16.4 by 14.7 by 10.1 mm., bordered on one side by four leaves pavé-set with small round diamonds, mounted in gold, *accompanied by G.I.A. report no. 4262482.*

$750–1,000

384 **Eighteen-Karat Gold, Colored Stone and Diamond "Scarecrow" Brooch, Van Cleef & Arpels, France**

Wearing a ragged costume with top hat and scarf, decorated with cabochon rubies at the feet, cabochon sapphires and round diamonds on the jacket and pants, his head of dyed green chalcedony, *signed V.C.A. and made in France.*

$1,200–1,500

385 **Eighteen-Karat Gold, Diamond and Colored Stone Bracelet**

Composed of 9 textured gold links of oval form, alternately decorated with round diamonds, emeralds, rubies and sapphires, the diamonds weighing a total of approximately 15.00 carats, the colored stones approximately 13.00 carats, *numbered 6512. Length 8 in. (20.3 cm.)*

This bracelet was an Easter gift from Aristotle Onassis.

$15,000–20,000

384
383
385

386 **Lady's Gold Wristwatch, Cartier**

The bangle-watch of braided gold rope, the small square-shaped dial concealed by a hinged lid pavé-set with round diamonds, completed by an eighteen-karat gold deployant buckle, backwind, *case signed Cartier.*

$1,500–2,000

387 **Lady's Gold Wristwatch, Cartier**

Featuring a square-shaped dial with black Roman numerals and hands framed by round diamonds, the bracelet of woven gold, backwind, *dial signed Cartier, case numbered 3811N24, 139727 and O 22263, French import marks.*

Length 7 in. (17.8 cm.)

$1,500–2,000

388 **Lady's Eighteen-Karat Gold Wristwatch, Uri, France**

The rectangular dial inset within a woven strap of eighteen-karat gold, backwind, *dial signed Uri, France, case inscribed: "Merry Xmas Jackie, Francis, 12-25-64", numbered 55474.*

Length 6½ in. (16.5 cm.)

$1,000–1,500

386

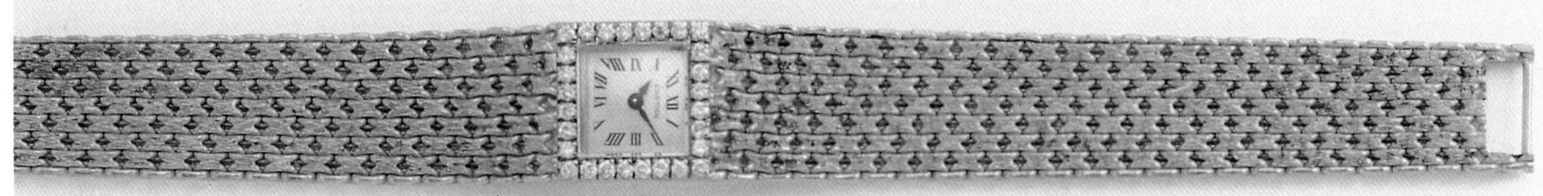

387

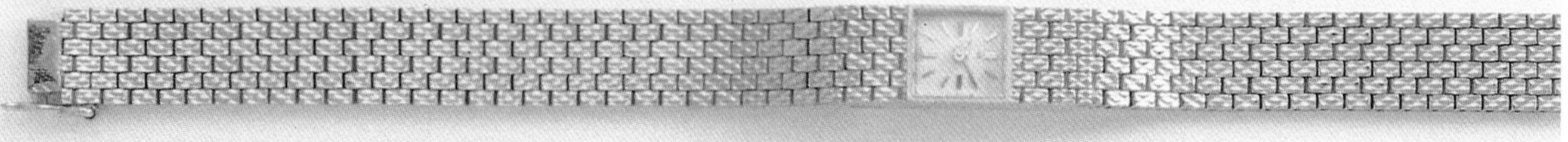

388

WWD / Fairchild Publications

Right: *Jacqueline Onassis with Rudolph Nureyev at a benefit for the American Ballet Theater, New York, May 7, 1992.*

389 **Lady's Eighteen-Karat Gold, Diamond and Emerald Wristwatch, Piaget**

The oval-shaped dial of nephrite jade framed by round diamonds weighing approximately 1.25 carats, accented with round emeralds at the quarters, completed by a textured gold strap, *dial signed Piaget, case numbered 9804A6 and 143186.*
Length 7 in. (17.8 cm.)

$2,000–3,000

390 **Emerald and Diamond Pendant-Brooch and Chain Necklace**

The lozenge-shaped brooch set with an emerald-cut emerald weighing approximately 18.00 carats bordered by rows of baguette diamonds and triangular segments of pavé-set round diamonds weighing a total of approximately 9.00 carats, the necklace of gold rectangular links interrupted by three-stone segments of round diamonds and emeralds, the diamonds weighing approximately 2.75 carats, mounted in gold.
Length 34 in. (86.4 cm.)

$10,000–12,000

391 **Eighteen-Karat Gold, Diamond and Green Glass Pendant**

The marine motif composed of a green glass plaque in the shape of Martha's Vineyard within a frame of polished gold decorated with starfish and a shell enhanced with round diamonds, the pendant loop collet-set with 2 larger diamonds.

$3,000–4,000

391

390

389

392 **Gold Rope "Lion's-Head" Necklace**

In Greek Revival style, designed as gold braided rope knotted in the center supporting two strands terminating in lions' heads and beads of aventurine quartz, weighing approximately 38 dwts.
Length 18 ½ in. (47 cm.)

An ancient prototype of this type of chain from Santa Eufemia (330-300 B.C.) is illustrated in the exhibition catalogue *Greek Gold: Jewelry of the Classical World*, Dyfri Williams and Jack Ogden, The Metropolitan Museum of Art, December 2, 1994-March 24, 1995, p. 207, no. 138.

$1,000–1,200

393 **Twenty-Two-Karat Gold Flower Brooch, Greece**

The large flowerhead with striated petals of sheet gold decorated in the center with a cluster of gold wire and seed-like motifs, weighing approximately 48 dwts., *maker's mark Z.*

A group of similarly designed flowers said to be from Matydos (330-300 B.C.) is illustrated in the exhibition catalogue *Greek Gold: Jewelry of the Classical World*, by Dyfri Williams and Jack Ogden, The Metropolitan Museum of Art, December 2-March 24, 1995, p. 115, no. 67.

This brooch was a gift from Alexander Onassis.

$1,000–1,200

393

392

394 **Fourteen-Karat Gold and Jade Brooch**

In Mixtec style, composed of a sun disc decorated with a gold and jade step motif pierced by four arrows at either side, supporting a fringe of gold dangles. With silver presentation box decorated with a mosaic of malachite and azur-malachite.

$1,000–1,500

395 **Carved Jade Pendant**

The pale green jadeite pendant carved on both sides with leaves and auspicious symbols including a bat and *lingzhi*.

$200–300

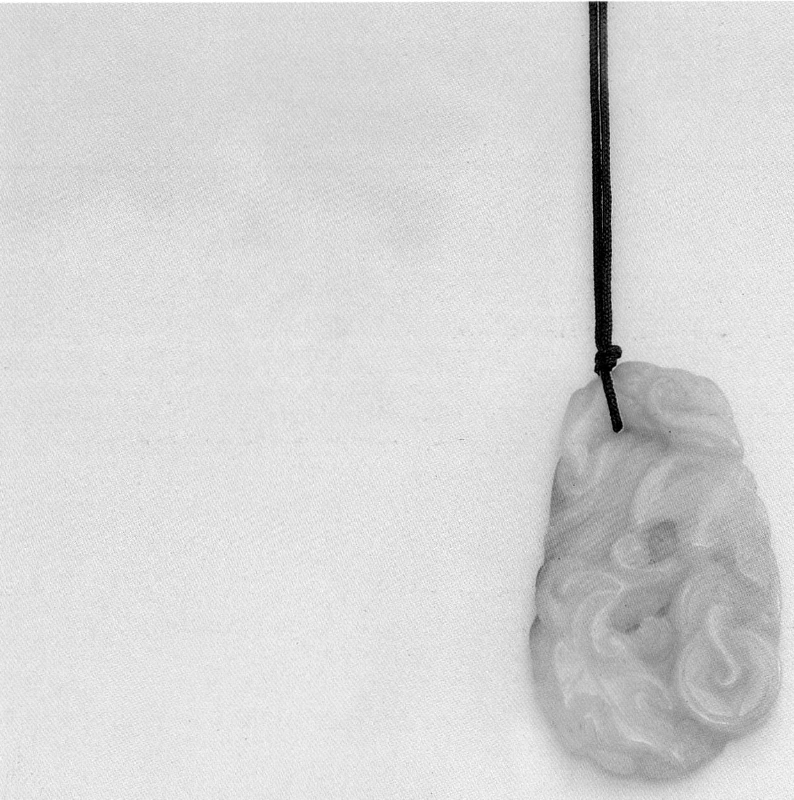

395

394

396 **Suite of Eighteen-Karat Gold Jewelry**

In Cambodian style, comprising a necklace, a bracelet and a brooch, the necklace composed of rectangular links decorated with dancing Apsaras, completed by navette-shaped links at the back, *length 17 in. (43.2 cm.)*; the bracelet composed of ten rectangular links decorated with dancing Apsaras against a bamboo background, *length 7 ¼ in. (18.4 cm.)*; the brooch designed as the head of Apsara, her headdress studded with rubies, the group weighing approximately 64 dwts., *signed Mek.* With red velvet presentation box.

$1,500–2,500

397 **Gold "Elephant" Bangle-Bracelet**

The rigid tapered cuff of gold filigree decorated with a procession of five elephants, weighing approximately 30 dwts.

$600–800

398 **Eighteen-Karat Gold Brooch, Zolotas, Greece**

Designed as the stylized figure of a young girl wearing an elaborate headdress of floral design, *signed Zolotas.*

$150–200

399 **Gold and Amber Worry Beads**

The gold chain loosely strung with 33 round and barrel-shaped amber beads, decorated with a gold slide link engraved "Jackie" on one side, the reverse with a motif of interlocked circles, ending in a golden colored silk tassel surmounted by a gold hoop and bead.
Length excluding tassel 29 in. (73.7 cm.)

$200–300

398

397

396

400 **Gold, Cabochon Emerald and Diamond Belt, Middle Eastern**

Composed of thirteen links of identical shape, one of larger size, each of trellis design enhanced with flowers and scrolls, set in the center with a cabochon emerald and accented throughout with rose-cut diamonds, the whole weighing approximately 168 dwts., *1 diamond missing.*
Length 27 in. (68.6 cm.)

$2,000–3,000

401 **Gold, Emerald and Diamond Belt**

Possibly Moroccan, designed as a wide band of hexagonal links arranged in a honeycomb design, decorated in the center with a starburst motif enhanced with round emeralds and round diamonds, the whole weighing approximately 260 dwts., *detachable segments at either side.*
Total length 26¾ in. (67.9 cm.)

$4,000–6,000

401

400

402 **Twenty-Two Karat Gold Collar, Lalaounis**

The rigid band decorated with square-shaped motifs of wave design within rope borders, weighing approximately 46 dwts., *signed Ilias Lalaounis.*

$1,000–1,200

403 **Pair of Twenty-Two Karat Gold Cuff Bangle-Bracelets, Greece**

The rigid cuffs embossed with wide bands of abstract floral motifs, weighing approximately 110 dwts.

$2,000–3,000

403

402

404 **Pair of Eighteen-Karat Gold, Colored Stone and Seed Pearl Pendant-Earclips, Lalaounis, Greece**

Designed as gold discs with seed pearl borders supporting curved segments of pentagonal shape, also bordered by seed pearls supporting chain and pearl fringes, decorated with various crystals including amethyst, carnelian and lapis lazuli, *signed Lalaounis, Greece.*

$1,000–1,500

405 **Pair of Gold, Cultured Pearl, Ruby and Sapphire Pendant-Earclips**

The tops designed as large gold filigree discs with beadwork borders accented with cultured pearls surrounding cabochon rubies, supporting openwork triangular pendants set with cultured pearls, all decorated with fringes of sapphire and ruby beads and seed pearls.

$1,000–1,500

404

405

406 **Gold And Cultured Pearl Pendant-Brooch**

In Indo-Islamic style, designed as a fan-shaped palmette supporting flexible fringes in various lengths, set throughout with button pearls in various sizes, mounted in gold; together with a fourteen-karat gold chain.

$1,500–2,500

407 **Emerald, Ruby and Cultured Pearl Brooch**

In Indo-Islamic style, designed as a fan of palmette motifs decorated with round emeralds, rubies and cultured pearls, supporting flexible fringes in various lengths, mounted in gold.

$3,000–4,000

406
407

408 Gold and Garnet Armlet, Greece

In Hellenistic style, the hinged bracelet composed of segments of sheet gold decorated with filigree and beadwork, the center featuring a Herakles knot enhanced with garnet-colored glass, a pin clasp at the side, the back later fitted with a curved sliding band on the interior, *some losses.*

$1,000–1,200

409 Pair of Gold Pendant-Earrings, Greece

In Hellenistic style, designed as flower-filled urns on pedestals supported on gold wires accented with heart-shaped links set with garnet-colored glass, suspended from later-added tops designed as rosettes of fourteen-karat gold with screw-back clasps.

$800–1,200

410 Garnet and Diamond Ring, mid-19th Century

The heart-shaped carbuncle garnet framed by old-mine diamonds, within a closed-back mounting of gold and silver.

$1,200–1,500

410

409

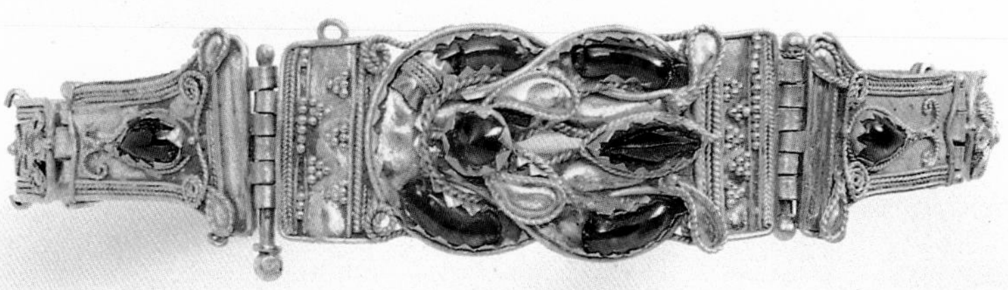

408

411 **Gold and Amethyst Bead Necklace**

The fringe of pear-shaped amethyst drops graduating in size from the center, strung on gold cord spaced by gold beads and rondels.
Length 21 in. (53.3 cm.)

$1,500–2,000

411

412 **Gold, Enamel and Diamond "Elephant-Head" Bangle-Bracelet, Indian, Benares**

The hinged bangle designed as confronting elephant heads decorated all over with polychrome enamel and set with rose-cut diamonds, *some losses.*

$3,000–5,000

413 **Gold, Enamel and Diamond Pendant, Indian**

The Mughal-style medallion with domed center applied with translucent red and green Jaipur enamel and decorated throughout with table-cut diamonds; together with a gilt-metal mesh chain necklace clasped by a link modeled as a gloved hand.

$400–600

414 **Enamel, Diamond and Simulated Pearl Torsade Bracelet**

Composed of confronting tigers' heads applied with yellow and black Jaipur enamel, and floral motifs of red, white and green enamel underneath, enhanced with table-cut diamonds, mounted in gold, *Indian*, fitted to a later multi-strand bracelet of simulated black pearls held by gilt metal caps.

$500–600

412
413
414

415 **Gold, Diamond and Enamel Pendant, late 19th Century**

In Renaissance style, designed as a starburst motif of square and triangular links set with square-cut and rose-cut diamonds against a background of scrollwork decorated with white and blue enamel, supporting three baroque pearl pendants, supported on a chain with jump ring. With leather box stamped A La Vielle Russie, 781 Fifth Avenue, New York.

$750–1,000

416 **Gold, Cameo, Enamel and Diamond Bracelet**

Composed of 9 oval-shaped cameos in various materials and colors including coral and soapstone, carved in classical style with heads of women and warriors, within gold frames decorated with sprays of florets applied with turquoise, red, white and blue enamel and set with small old-mine and rose-cut diamonds, *imperfections. Length 7 in. (17.8 cm.)*

$5,000–7,000

415

416

417 **Ruby, Diamond and Ivory Cruciform Pendant**

The carved ivory cross decorated with a central star motif set in the middle with an oval-shaped ruby and further decorated with single-cut diamonds, mounted in eighteen-karat gold.

This pendant was purchased in Capri in the 1970s.

$200–300

418 **Gold and Enamel Cross Pendant, Russian, early 20th Century**

With lobed edges, decorated in *champlevé* enamel with an orange cross and at the terminals with deep blue enamel letters "IC" and "XC" for Jesus Christ and motifs within a line border of white enamel, the reverse with a Russian inscription: "Preserve and Save".

$300–400

419 **Silver, Gold and Enamel Cruciform Pendant, late 19th Century**

Decorated with stylized floral and scroll motifs in blue, green, yellow, red and white champlevé enamel against a black enamel ground.

$600–800

420 **Gold and Hardstone Worry Beads**

The gold chain loosely strung with 25 beads in various hardstones including malachite, lapis lazuli, rose quartz, aventurine quartz and rhodochrosite, ending in a gold rope tassel surmounted by a bead and a slide link engraved *to Jackie* and *from Katrina.*

These worry beads were a gift from Caliroi Patronicolas, Aristotle Onassis' half-sister.

$400–600

417

419

420

418

421 **Diamond Bird Brooch, late 19th Century**

The bird with outstretched wings decorated with old-mine and rose-cut diamonds, the body set with a baroque pearl, further enhanced with two small pearls at the tail feathers, mounted in silver and gold.

$2,000–3,000

422 **Diamond and Enameled Miniature Brooch, late 19th Century**

The square-shaped panel decorated in multi-colored enamel with the scene of a setting sun within a landscape, the foreground with leafy branches accented with rose-cut diamonds, within a frame of old-mine and rose-cut diamonds and 2 small pearls, mounted in silver and gold, *the miniature signed LMR.*

$2,000–3,000

423 **Pair of Diamond Chandelier Earrings, 18th Century**

Designed as clusters of rosettes supported on flexible fringes, anchored at the base by a large scroll, set throughout with rose-cut diamonds within closed-back mountings of gold and silver, *later-added screw-back clasps.*

These earrings belonged to Annie Burr Auchincloss Lewis (Mrs. Wilmarth S. Lewis), Mrs. Onassis' aunt by marriage.

$3,000–4,000

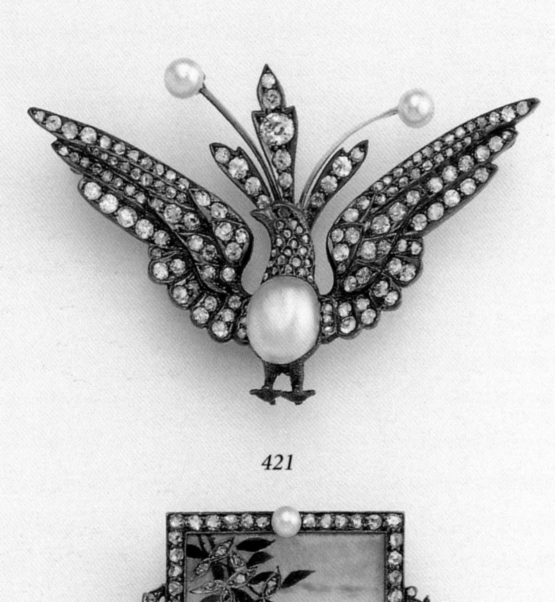

421

422

423

424 **Miniature of a Young Boy, possibly Louis, Dauphin of France (1727-65), French School, circa 1745**

Wearing a red jacket, contained in a gold frame with blue enamel border, the glazed back revealing the armorials and motto of the Dauphin.

Oval, height 1 ½ in. (3.8 cm.)

$800–1,200

425 **Fabergé Gold, Silver and Diamond Hair Ornament, Workmaster August Holmström, St. Petersburg, circa 1900**

Set with 11 old-mine diamonds weighing approximately 5.00 carats interspersed by ten rectangular forms set with numerous rose-cut diamonds, *marked with initials of workmaster and 56 standard (14 karat).* Contained in original fitted holly wood case, the silk lining stamped in Cyrillic, "Fabergé, St. Petersburg, Moscow, Odessa."
Width 4 in. (10.2 cm.)

$7,000–9,000

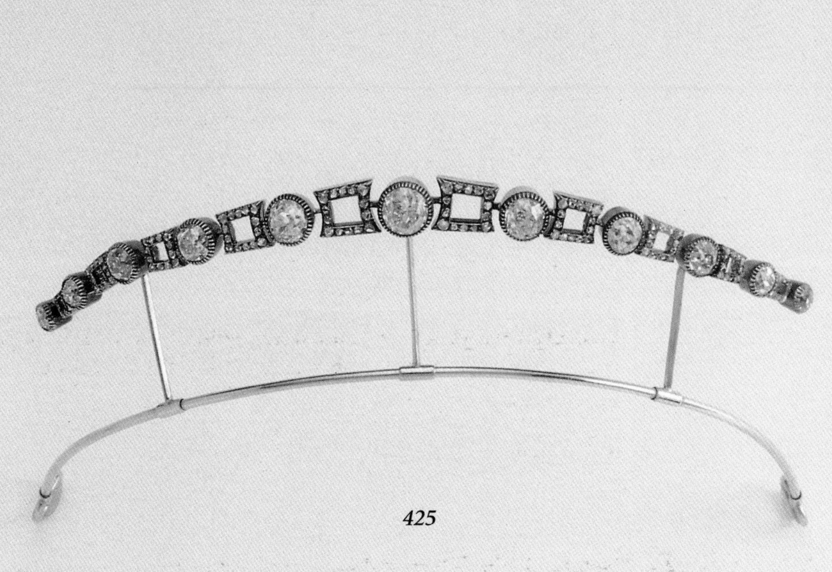

425

424

Gelman / Liason

Right: *Jacqueline Onassis with Brendan Gill at a party for The Municipal Arts Society, New York.*

426 **Cabochon Garnet and Diamond Flower Brooch, 19th Century**

Composed of a large flower with petals of elongated cabochon garnets decorated in the center with a spray of old-mine diamonds, bordered by pear-shaped cabochon garnet buds and leaves of old-mine and rose-cut diamonds, mounted in gold, the garnets in closed-back mountings. With fitted box stamped A La Vielle Russie, 781 Fifth Avenue, New York.

$12,000–15,000

426

427 **Gold, Enamel and Diamond Snake Bangle-Bracelet, mid 19th Century**

The multi-hinged coiling serpent applied with royal blue enamel, the head decorated with three full rose-cut diamonds, the eyes of cabochon garnets. With fitted box stamped A La Vielle Russie, 781 Fifth Avenue, New York.

$5,000–7,000

428 **Gold and Enamel Tiger Bangle-Bracelet, late 19th Century**

The hinged bangle decorated in the center with a tiger's head applied with shaded yellow and orange translucent enamel and black enamel, the eyes of small old-mine diamonds, the open mouth holding a pearl. With fitted box stamped A La Vielle Russie, 781 Fifth Avenue, New York.

$6,000–8,000

429 **Pair of Reverse-Tinted Crystal Intaglio Fox Cufflinks**

Each composed of a tinted crystal intaglio of a fox head, mounted in fourteen-karat gold. Together with a gilt metal riding crop bar brooch accented with a green "stone" riding cap. (3)

$300–400

428

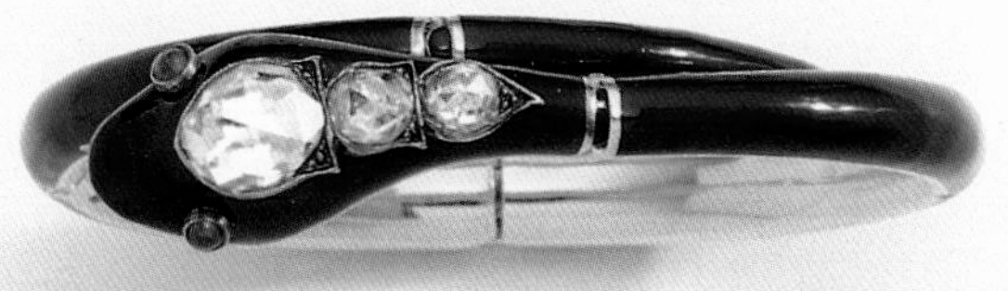

427

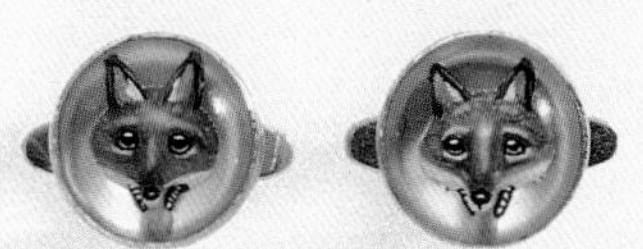

429

430 **Diamond and Plique-à-Jour Enamel Butterfly Brooch**

The wings set *en tremblant*, composed of blue, green and red *plique-à-jour* enamel and accented with old-mine and rose-cut diamonds, the body similarly decorated with a larger stone in the center, the eyes set with small cushion-shaped rubies, mounted in gold. With fitted box stamped A La Vielle Russie, 781 Fifth Avenue, New York, and presentation card stating: *English, circa 1910.*

$15,000–20,000

431 **Kunzite and Diamond Ring**

The cushion-shaped kunzite weighing approximately 47.00 carats, surrounded by 20 round diamonds weighing approximately 4.00 carats, mounted in eighteen-karat gold.

This ring was purchased by President Kennedy as a gift for his wife, but was never given to her.

$6,000-8,000

430

431

432 **Gold Key Pendant, Tiffany & Co.**

The top of the key enclosed within a polished gold circular jacket engraved "109" on both sides, *signed Tiffany on the pendant loop*. With fitted case stamped Tiffany & Co., New York.

This key was given to President Kennedy by Peter Tare, an organization of people who served on PT boats. Other gifts from this group are in the permanent collection of the John F. Kennedy Library Foundation.

Lieutenant John F. Kennedy became an instructor at the Melville Motor Torpedo Boat Squadron Training Center, Rhode Island, on December 3, 1942. After his own preparation there he had hoped to see immediate active service aboard a patrol torpedo (PT) boat, but was prevented from doing so in favor of remaining at Melville as a teacher. Kennedy managed to secure an interview with senator David I. Walsh, chairman of the Senate Naval Affairs Committee. Walsh promised to help him find a posting overseas. Less than three months later he received orders to join Motor Torpedo Boat Squadron Two and was soon on his way to the Solomon Islands in the southwest Pacific.

By the following August, Kennedy found himself in command of the PT 109, playing a small part in the sweeping counteraction that was to drive Japanese forces back from the area. He and his twelve-man crew were among a number whose function was to patrol the islands and coral islets to the east of New Georgia. According to an account written by John Hersey not long after the incident, the PT 109 was working one night forty miles from Rendova when disaster struck. "An officer named George ['Barney'] Ross was up on the bow, magnifying the void with binoculars. Kennedy was at the wheel, and he saw Ross turn and point into the darkness. The man in the forward machine-gun turret shouted, 'Ship at two o'clock!' Kennedy saw a shape and spun the wheel to turn for an attack, but the 109 answered sluggishly…The thirteen men on the PT hardly had time to brace themselves. Those who saw the Japanese ship coming were paralyzed by fear… Then the Japanese crashed into the 109 and cut her right in two… Kennedy was thrown hard to the left of the cockpit, and he thought, 'This is how it feels to be killed'…"

Hersey's detailed report of the events of the next few days makes harrowing reading. Two men vanished in the collision, others were wounded, and none survived without haunting memories. Kennedy's own part in the event was crucial to their eventual rescue. With Barney Ross he set out to explore nearby islands, the closest of which, Naru, was an hour's swim away. Along the way they found an abandoned Japanese canoe and in it they set off once more. "Soon the two could see a white line ahead and could hear a frightening roar—waves crashing on a reef. They had got out of the tidal current and were approaching the island all right, but now they realized that the wind and the waves were carrying them toward the reef."

Eventually Kennedy and Ross managed a painful crossing of the reef before finding dry land, where they instantly fell into a deep sleep. Awakening next morning they were surprised to find themselves surrounded by natives, one of whom handed over a letter which proved to be from the commander of a New Zealand infantry patrol operating nearby. Within hours, Kennedy, Ross and the other PT 109 survivors were with friendly forces and soon taken to the naval hospital at Tulagi. (Goddard Lieberson, editor, *John Fitzgerald Kennedy…As We Remember Him*, New York, 1965, pp. 39-45)

$200–300

432

433 **Coral and Diamond Flower Brooch and Matching Earclips, Van Cleef & Arpels, Paris**

Each designed as a flowerhead with scallop-edged petals, decorated with oval-shaped pink coral cabochons, the brooch set in the center with 7 round diamonds weighing approximately 1.75 carats and further decorated with additional round diamonds weighing approximately 6.25 carats, the earclips set with 104 round diamonds weighing approximately 7.25 carats, mounted in eighteen-karat gold, *signed Van Cleef & Arpels, numbered 19059 and 19083.*

This suite was a wedding gift from Artemis Garofalides, Aristotle Onassis' sister, in 1968.

An export permit may be required to remove this lot from the United States. For further information please inquire.

$15,000–20,000

433

434 **Pair of Eighteen-Karat Gold and Ruby "Moon" Earclips, Lalaounis, Greece, 1969**

Each anchored by a large moon of hammered gold, the textured surface indented with "craters" and studded with round rubies, supported by cone-shaped links designed as space capsules suspended from tops designed as rockets circling earth, weighing approximately 30 dwts., *signed Ilias Lalaounis.*

These earclips were a gift from Aristotle Onassis, made especially for Mrs. Onassis by Lalaounis in Greece to commemorate the first moon landing in 1969.

$1,000–1,200

434

UPI / Bettmann

Right: *Jacqueline Kennedy and Andre Meyer at the Wildenstein Gallery in New York to view the Eisenhower Collection on May 17, 1967.*

435 **Gold, Ruby and Diamond Pill Box**

The rectangular box decorated on the lid with a stylized floral and foliate motif set with old-mine diamonds and cushion-shaped rubies within a ruby border, the reverse engraved with foliate scrolls surrounding a central medallion, weighing approximately 80 dwts., *2 ¼ by 1 ⅜ in. (5.7 by 3.5 cm.).*

$3,000–4,000

436 **Cabochon Emerald, Ruby and Diamond Brooch, Van Cleef & Arpels, New York**

Designed as a palmette with a cabochon emerald in the center, framed by 13 round diamonds weighing approximately 3.00 carats, within an outer border of cabochon rubies, mounted in gold, *signed Van Cleef & Arpels, N.Y., numbered 34629.*

$5,000–7,000

437 **Pair of Cabochon Emerald and Diamond Pendants**

The pear-shaped cabochon emeralds weighing approximately 60.00 carats, framed by 48 round diamonds and decorated at the tops with 8 marquise-shaped and pear-shaped diamonds weighing approximately 11.00 carats, mounted in platinum.

$15,000–20,000

437

436

435

438 **Eighteen-Karat Gold, Sapphire and Diamond Table Clock, Van Cleef & Arpels, New York, circa 1956**

The rectangular panel of rock crystal fitted with a circular dial in a sunburst frame beneath a flowering tree bearing blossoms of round sapphires and diamonds, a pair of lovebirds perched on one of the branches, their heads, wings and tail feathers set with round and single-cut diamonds, upon a gold rectangular base, the whole edged in rope decoration, *dial signed Van Cleef & Arpels, case bezel stamped N.Y. and 34565.* With fitted presentation box stamped *Van Cleef & Arpels.*
Height 7 ¼ in. (18.4 cm.)

$7,500–10,000

438

439 **Pear-Shaped Diamond Ring**

Weighing 5.44 carats, within a simple white gold mounting.
Accompanied by G.I.A. report no. #8682605 stating that the diamond is D Color, SI1 clarity.

$60,000–70,000

440 **Ruby and Diamond Ring, Van Cleef & Arpels, New York, 1968**

The oval-shaped ruby weighing 17.68 carats, framed by round diamonds, the shoulders with additional small diamonds, weighing a total of approximately 5.50 carats, mounted in eighteen-karat gold and platinum, *signed VCA, numbered N.Y. 39075-3.*

This ring was a wedding present from Aristotle Onassis in 1968.

$20,000–30,000

441 **Group of Eleven Unmounted Round Diamonds**

Weighing a total of approximately 1.50 carats; together with three ruby beads. (14)

$500–700

439

440

WWD / Fairchild Publications

Right: *Mr. and Mrs. Aristotle S. Onassis at a party in New York, 1971.*

442 Diamond and Emerald Drop Necklace, Van Cleef & Arpels, New York, late 1960s

Designed as a slightly graduated row of flowerheads set with round diamonds, supporting a fringe of 5 pear-shaped emerald drops capped by diamonds, the back of the necklace composed of diamond-set foliate links within rope borders, the whole set with numerous round diamonds weighing approximately 35.00 carats, the emeralds weighing approximately 132.00 carats, mounted in eighteen-karat gold, *signed Van Cleef & Arpels, N.Y., numbered 39486, length 15½ in. (39.4 cm.), detachable in several places, all five drops also detach.* Together with three extra diamond-set links.

This necklace was an engagement present from Aristotle Onassis in 1968.

$100,000–125,000

443 Cabochon Emerald and Diamond Ring, Van Cleef & Arpels, New York, late 1960s,

The large oval-shaped cabochon emerald weighing 61.17 carats, within a frame of round diamonds, additional diamonds at the shoulders, weighing a total of approximately 4.00 carats, mounted in eighteen-karat gold, *signed Van Cleef & Arpels, numbered N.Y. 39387.*

This ring was a Christmas present from Aristotle Onassis in the early 1970s.

$10,000–15,000

443

442

Tony Palmieri / WWD / Fairchild Publications

Right: *Jacqueline Kennedy Onassis, at The Metropolitan Museum of Art's Costume Institute Gala for the opening of: Fashions of the Hapsburg Era: Austria-Hungary, December 4, 1979.*

444 Pair of Cabochon Ruby and Diamond Pendant-Earclips, Van Cleef & Arpels, France, 1968

The tops designed as large leaves set with round diamonds weighing approximately 14.00 carats, supporting pendants of pear-shaped cabochon rubies weighing approximately 76.00 carats within round diamond frames, mounted in eighteen-karat gold, *signed Van Cleef & Arpels and made in France, pendants detachable. These pendants were originally part of the necklace in lot* ***452.***

These earclips were a wedding gift from Aristotle Onassis in 1968.

$25,000–35,000

445 Cabochon Ruby and Diamond Ring, mid 1960s

The heart-shaped cabochon ruby surrounded by round diamonds, additional round diamonds at the shoulders, weighing a total of approximately 3.00 carats, mounted in gold.

$4,000–6,000

444

445

WWD / Fairchild Publications

Right: *Jacqueline Onassis fox hunting, December 30, 1972*

446 **Eighteen-Karat Gold, Carved Coral and Diamond Horse Bracelet, Van Cleef & Arpels, France**

Designed as a carved coral horse's head with cabochon emerald eyes and diamond-studded gold mane continuing to circular links of carved coral and gold joined by gold diamond-set bars, the total diamond weight approximately 8.00 carats, *1 diamond missing, signed Van Cleef and Arpels and made in France, numbered 40280. Length 8 ½ in. (21.6 cm.)*

An export permit may be required to remove this lot from the United States. For further information please inquire.

$10,000–15,000

446

UPI / Bettmann

Jacqueline Kennedy at the Metropolitan Opera, New York City on December 16, 1967.

447 Ruby and Emerald Bead and Diamond Necklace, Van Cleef & Arpels, Paris, 1960s

Strung with 5 fluted emerald beads and 44 smaller ruby beads spaced by rondels of round diamonds within eighteen-karat gold beadwork borders, the total diamond weight approximately 34.00 carats, *signed VCA, numbered 99508.*
Length 25 in. (63.5 cm.)

$60,000–80,000

448 Pair of Emerald Bead, Cabochon Ruby, Diamond and Cultured Pearl Pendant-Earclips, David Webb

Of modified girandole style, decorated with fluted emerald beads and oval-shaped cabochon rubies within borders of round diamonds weighing approximately 9.00 carats, each supporting a baroque cultured pearl drop, the pearls and emeralds capped by small diamonds, mounted in eighteen-karat gold, *signed David Webb and Webb.*

$20,000–30,000

448
447

449 **Eighteen-Karat Gold and Coral Mythical Figure Sculpture, David Webb, 1966**

Designed as a mythical beast with lion's head and paws, the body formed of a V-shaped branch of buff-colored coral completed by a fish tail, the eyes of pear-shaped cabochon emeralds, upon a coral mound base within a border of clusters of faceted gold "pebbles", *signed David Webb, 1966.* With fitted presentation box signed *David Webb, Inc.*
Height 3 in. (7.6 cm.), length 6 in. (15.2 cm.)

While she was First Lady, Jacqueline Kennedy commissioned the jeweler David Webb to design individual paperweights made of different American minerals to be given as gifts to visiting heads of state. For example, King Hassan of Morocco was given a gold figure of an American eagle inset with American topaz. The coral in this piece was presented to President John F. Kennedy at the White House by Robert Donovan, author of the book PT 109. The coral, which is from the South Pacific island where Kennedy was shipwrecked, was then given to David Webb for mounting; he designed the present mythical figure especially for the Kennedys.

An export permit may be required to remove this lot from the United States. For further information please inquire.

$8,000–12,000

449

450 **Ruby and Diamond Necklace, Van Cleef & Arpels, New York, 1967**

Designed as a slightly graduated row of floral motifs alternately-set with cabochon rubies and small round faceted rubies, the petals set with round diamonds, supporting a fringe of tumbled ruby drops surmounted by foliate motifs of round diamonds and rubies, the drops anchored by round diamonds, the total diamond weight approximately 35.00 carats, mounted in eighteen-karat gold, *signed Van Cleef & Arpels, numbered N.Y. 38552, detachable in several places.*
Length 16 in. (40.6 cm.)

$75,000–100,000

450

UPI / Bettmann

451 **Pair of Gold Cuff Bangle-Bracelets, Van Cleef & Arpels**

The rigid cuffs of hammered free-form design weighing approximately 100 dwts., *one signed VCA and numbered 2V702-50.*

$1,500–2,000

Above: *Jacqueline Kennedy Onassis and Muhammad Ali at the pre-game celebration on August 26, 1977 for the annual Robert F. Kennedy Pro-Celebrity Tennis Tournament held in Forest Hills, N.Y.*

451

452 **Cabochon Colored Stone and Diamond Pendant-Necklace, Van Cleef & Arpels, New York, 1967**

The pendant designed as a large palmette set with a heart-shaped cabochon ruby within a border of round diamonds further decorated with cabochon emeralds and a single cabochon sapphire at the top, supported on a necklace designed as floral medallions set with cabochon rubies, emeralds and sapphires within borders of round diamonds and with ruby beads flanked by gold and diamond caps, the total diamond weight approximately 47.00 carats, the heart-shaped ruby in the pendant weighing 56.76 carats, mounted in eighteen-karat gold, *signed Van Cleef & Arpels, and V.C.A., numbered N.Y. 37729, pendant detachable, one section detaches to shorten. Length 17½ in. (44.4 cm.)*

This pendant-necklace was a wedding gift from Aristotle Onassis in 1968.

$75,000–100,000

452

WWD / Fairchild Publications

Above: *Jacqueline Kennedy Onassis leaving La Côte Basque in New York.*

453 **The Lesotho III Diamond, Harry Winston**

The marquise-shaped diamond weighing 40.42 carats, flanked by tapered baguette diamonds weighing approximately 1.50 carats, mounted in platinum, *signed Winston.* Together with a brooch attachment (diamond detaches from ring mounting). (2)

Accompanied by G.I.A. report no. 8682475 stating that the diamond is L color (Faint Brown), VS2 clarity; together with original working diagram stating that the stone may be potentially flawless.

This ring was an engagement present from Aristotle Onassis.

$500,000–600,000

The history of this famous diamond begins in Lesotho, South Africa, in May of 1967 when a large brownish rough of irregular shape was found by Mrs. Ernestine Ramaboa, wife of digger Petrus Ramaboa. Mrs. Ramaboa was certain that the object she found at the Letseng-la-Terai diggings was a diamond although the rough was dull and cloudy. She placed it in her pocket for safekeeping and made her way back to her hut to await her husband's return.

Without a word to their colleagues, the Ramaboas made their way on foot to Maseru, the capital of Lesotho, where they hoped to find a buyer. They were rewarded for their efforts and the stone was sold to Eugene Serafini, a South African dealer, who, in turn, sold it to a dealer from Europe. According to Ian Balfour in his book *Famous Diamonds*, the 601-carat rough is the eleventh largest of gem quality on record and the largest ever to be discovered by a woman.

In October of 1967, the Lesotho, like many other notable rough diamonds, made its way into the hands of Harry Winston. Mr. Winston invited the Ramaboas to New York to participate in a press conference in which the stone was introduced to the American public. Later, it was exhibited at the Smithsonian Institution in Washington, D.C. and the Museum of Natural History in New York. In March of 1968, after weeks of deliberation, the Lesotho was cleaved by Pastor Colon, one of Winston's master cutters; the event was broadcast live on television. Soon after, the polishing of the Lesotho was completed, resulting in eighteen gems totaling 242.50 carats, all noticeably lighter in color than the original rough.

The present stone, a marquise-shape of 40.42 carats, was the third in size to be cut from the rough; the two larger stones, weighing 71.73 and 60.67 carats, are both emerald cut. All three diamonds were sold individually as rings to private buyers by 1970.

Literature:

Ian Balfour, *Famous Diamonds*, London: William Collins Sons & Co., Ltd., 1987, pp. 200-203.
Laurence S. Krashes, *Harry Winston: The Ultimate Jeweler*, Harry Winston Inc. and the Gemological Institute of America, New York: 1988 (Third Revised Edition), p. 100.
Diamond Promotion Service, *Notable Diamonds of the World*, edited by Barbara Gleason, pp. 25-26.

453

Osbert Sitwell QUEEN MARY

FASHION JEWELRY FROM THE ESTATE OF JACQUELINE KENNEDY ONASSIS

SESSION FIVE

THURSDAY, APRIL 25,

10:00 A.M.

The Living Room of Jacqueline Kennedy Onassis' New York City apartment, showing lots 13, 72, 76, 102, 120, 159, 238, 241, 242, 245, 248, 287, 288, 306, 310, 316, 338, 340, 357, 565, 566, 568 and 569.

The John F. Kennedy Library

454 **Simulated Pearl Necklace**

The triple strand of "pearls" with silver Art Deco style clasp set with single rows of "diamonds".
Length approximately 19 in. (48.3 cm.)

This triple strand of "pearls" is one of those worn by Jacqueline Kennedy while in residence at the White House.

$500–700

Above: *Mrs. Kennedy and John F. Kennedy, Jr., upstairs in the White House, August 1962.*

454

455

455 **Simulated Ruby and Emerald Bead and Pearl Torsade Necklace**

The necklace formed by four strands of tumbled "ruby", "emerald" and "pearl" beads separated by two large pairs of emerald-set roundels separating to form two choker necklaces (of short length), *stone missing.*
Length approximately 26 in. (66 cm.)

$300–400

56 Pair of Gilt Metal and Simulated Emerald Earclips and Two Green Glass Bead Necklaces

The earrings consisting of three overlapping metal circles applied with leaf-shaped "emeralds", the necklaces formed with melon-shaped "emerald" beads, with hook closures.
Lengths approximately 21 in. (53.3 cm.).

$300–400

457 **Gilt Metal Station Necklace, Chanel**

Composed of facing rams' heads centering gilt metal oval links connected by multi-strand gilt metal chains; *hook closure stamped Chanel. Length approximately 46 in. (116.8 cm.)*

$300–400

458 **Pair of Gilt Metal and Simulated Pearl Button Earclips, Chanel**

Each with a large simulated golden pearl centered within a framework of confronting peacock heads alternating with simulated golden pearl beads, *backs stamped Chanel.*

$200–300

459 **Two Yellow Metal Necklaces and a Pair of Earclips**

The first designed as a flat band of "braided" links; *length 15 ½ in. (39.4 cm.)*, the second a chain of large circular links and bands, *tarnished, length 18 in. (45.7 cm.)*; the earclips composed of paired interlocking links. (4)

$100–150

Mark Shaw Collection/Photo Researchers

Jacqueline Kennedy giving a campaign speech in Wheeling, West Virginia, 1960.

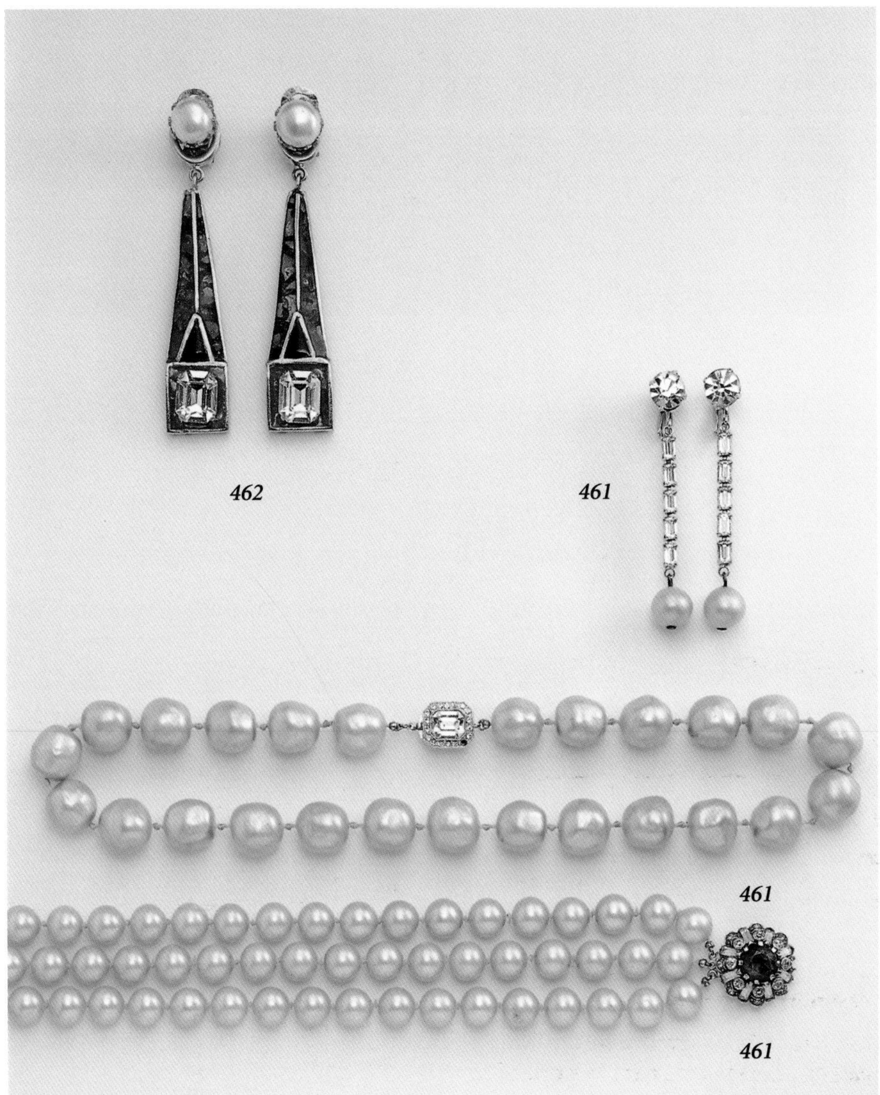

460 **Four Bangle Bracelets**

The first a plain hoop of low-content gold, *marked 12 K.G.F.*; the second, gilt metal decorated with a continuous row of chevrons; the last, a pair of square hinged form.

$200–300

461 **Two Simulated Pearl Necklaces and a Pair of Simulated Diamond and Pearl Earclips**

The triple-strand necklace of "pearls" with an "emerald" and "diamond" Sterling silver clasp, the single strand of champagne-colored "pearls" with "diamond"-set Sterling silver clasp, and the earclips with "diamond"-set chain and "pearl" drops, *"diamonds" missing.*
Lengths approximately 18 and 16 in. (45.7 and 40.6 cm.)

The triple-strand "pearls" were worn by Mrs. Kennedy while in residence at the White House and on a state visit to Colombia.

$250–350

462 **Simulated Pearl Necklace and Two Pairs of Earclips**

The necklace composed of a simple strand of creamy-colored "pearls", the first pair of earclips set with a large golden pearl and simulated "diamonds", the second pair of pearl earclips dropping triangular pendants set with emerald-cut "diamonds" in aqua-colored resin.

$150–250

463 **Group of Five Bead Necklaces**

Three of identical design, strung with silvered metal beads, *length 31 in. (78.7 cm.)*; one strung with glass beads of mottled red and black color, *length 17 in. (43.2 cm.)*; and the last a long strand of red beads simulating coral connected by gilt metal links, *length 53 in. (134.6 cm.).*

$300–400

UPI / Bettmann

Right: *Jacqueline and Caroline Kennedy look at the carrier U.S.S. John F. Kennedy after it was christened by Caroline on May 27, 1967.*

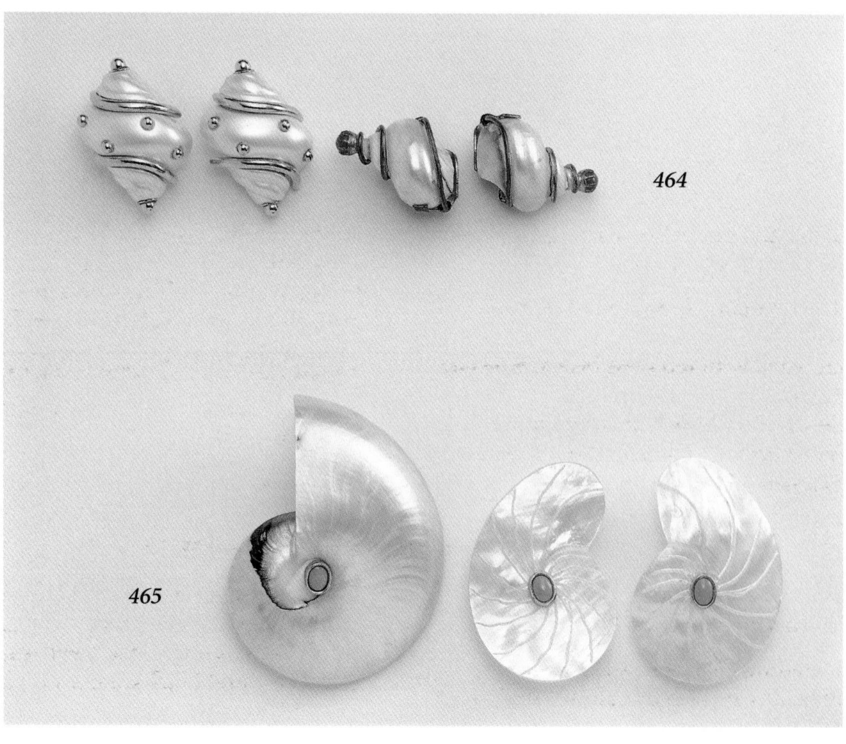

464

465

464 **Two Pairs of Shell-Form Earclips, one Kenneth Jay Lane**

The first pair composed of natural shells held by gilt metal cages and crowned with red glass beads, *probably French*, the second pair of earclips designed as "pearl" shells with gilt metal accents, *the second marked Kenneth Jay Lane.*

$400–600

465 **Group of Simulated Turquoise and Mother-of-Pearl Jewelry**

Including a pair of earclips and matching brooch of nautilus design applied with "turquoise" accents and three "mother-of-pearl" bangle-bracelets, two applied with similar accents; together with three bangle-bracelets of varying widths applied with "mother-of-pearl" tinted with shades of aqua, lavender and salmon, *Philippines.* (9)

$150–250

466 **Group of Four Wristwatches**

The first two, *by Timex*, with round white metal cases and black straps; the third, *by Pulsar*, with rectangular gilt-metal case and black leather strap; and the fourth, *Swiss Army*, with round blackened metal case and black strap.

$400–500

467 **Dramatic Simulated Colored Stone Bib Necklace**

Of stylized floral design, decorated with four mother-of-pearl ovals surrounded by clusters of marquise-shaped "agates" and larger "moonstones", round faceted "jet" and pear-shaped cabochon "emeralds", mounted in gilt metal, *one stone missing. Length approximately 17 in. (43.2 cm.)*

$400–500

468 **Two Gilt Metal Necklaces**

The first designed as a mesh bib of gilt metal scroll links, the second a long chain composed of links of bearded gentlemen spaced by textured gold links, supporting a double-row fringe in the center.
Length of second necklace without fringe approximately 20 in. (50.8 cm.)

$300–400

469 **Two Pairs of Gilt Metal Earrings**

The first of trefoil design formed by three interlocking gilt metal twisted wires, the second pair with "lapis" beads centering a basket formed as well with gilt metal twisted wires, *the second marked ELFE Italy.*

$150–250

70 **Five Pairs of Gilt Metal Hoop Earclips, one by Lanvin, one by Napier**

The first designed as large plain hoops of polished gilt metal, *signed Lanvin, Paris*; the second designed as gilt metal wire hoops, each accented with a bead and supported by a bead clip-on top, *signed Napier*; the third formed of concentric rings supported by button tops; the fourth composed of hammered gilt metal concentric ring pendants supported by similar tops of smaller size; the last designed as rope hoops supported on button clip-on tops, *one tarnished.* (10)

$300–400

71 **Gilt Metal Cuff Bracelet and Bangle Bracelet, the cuff by Kenneth Jay Lane**

The hinged cuff with four rows of abstract rope design, and the bangle of perforated bombé form, *the cuff marked Kenneth Lane.*

$150–200

72 **Group of Four Choker-Necklaces**

The first a multi-strand collar of gilt metal wire, the remaining three of similar design, the flexible tubular chokers of yellow metal, white metal and mixed yellow and white metal respectively.

$150–200

73 **Four Tribal-Style Necklaces**

The first two with confronting horns set in silver and silver gilt mountings, *one stamped Made in Kenya, lengths approximately 14 and 15 in. (35.6 and 38.1 cm.)*; the third designed with brass beads strung on a leather cord, *length approximately 15 in. (38.1 cm.)*; and the last *in Ivory Coast style* designed as a crescent pendant centered with a mask hung on a gilt metal chain, *length approximately 19 in. (48.3 cm.).*

$350–450

74 **A Gilt Metal Pectoral and a Silver-Gilt Armlet**

The pectoral, *Baule style, Ivory Coast,* cast with two opposing figures of lizards, supported on a black cord, the crossover armlet, *Islamic style,* decorated with patterns of flowers and scales, the ends with bead dangles.

$250–350

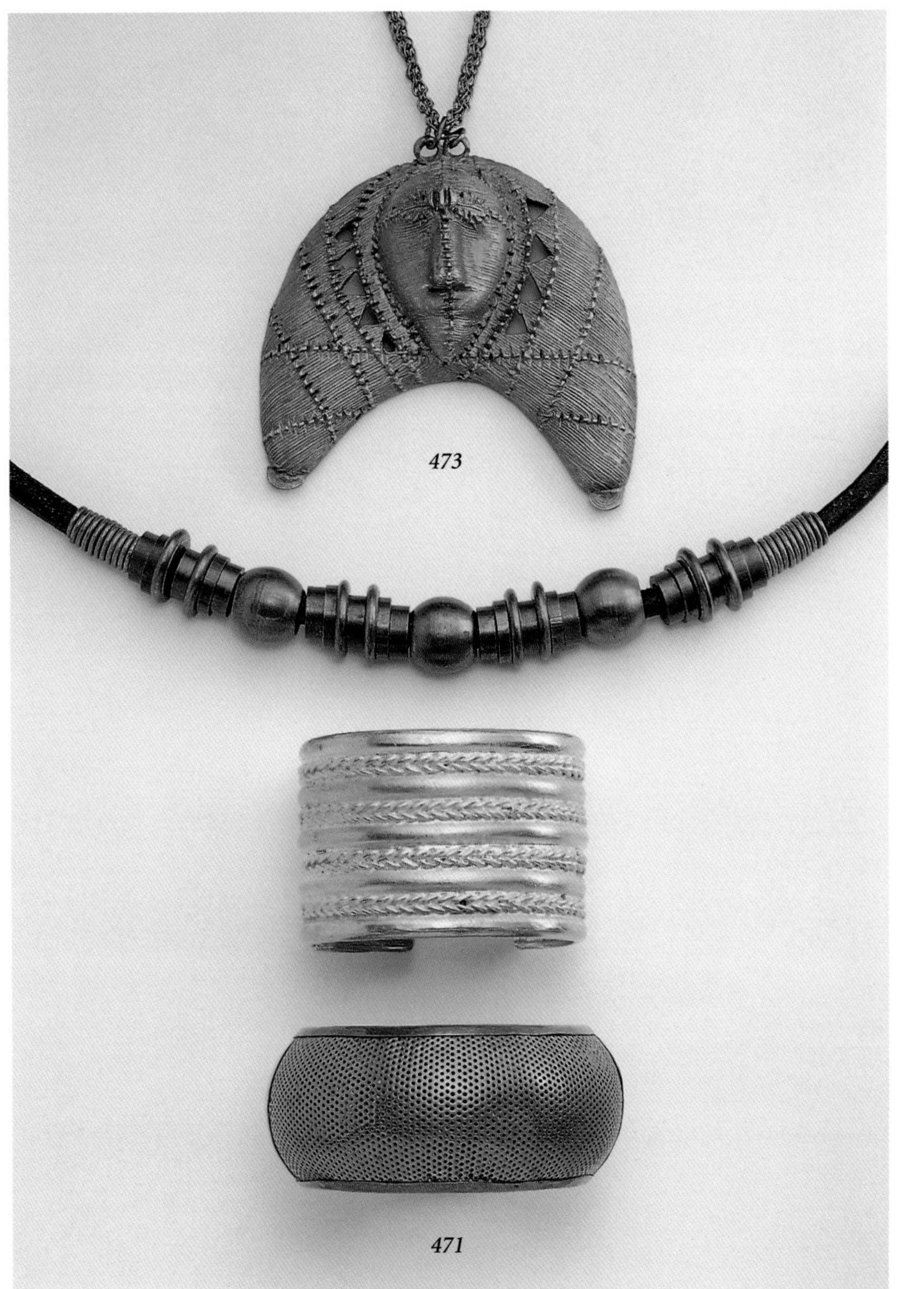

Jacqueline Kennedy at Expo '67 in Montreal.

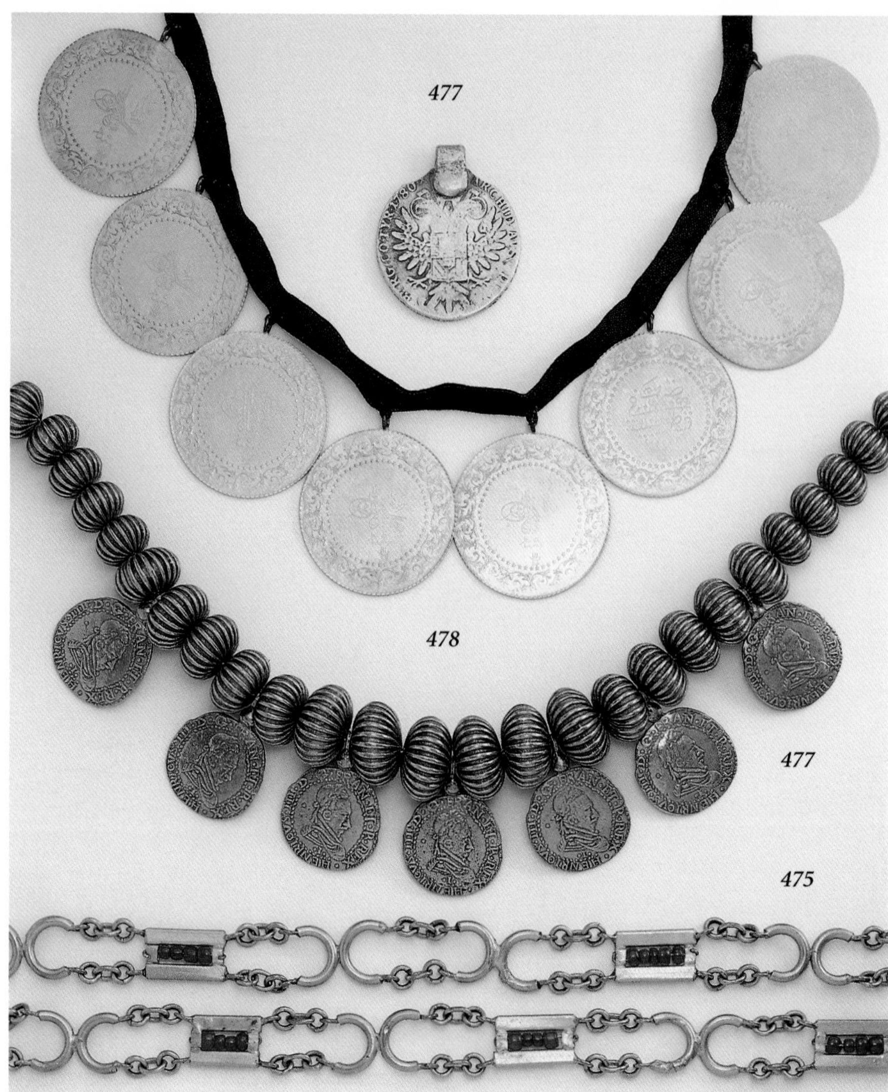

475 **Two Gilt Metal Chain Belts, one by Yves Saint Laurent**

The first formed with double rows of oval links attached to round link stations, one dropping an oval "carnelian" pendant; the second formed with rectangular stations accented with "ruby" beads alternating with chain and C-link stations, dropping a heavy coin pendant in antique taste. *Lengths approximately 31 and 32 in. (78.7 and 81.3 cm.)*

See illustration of first in above left photograph.

$300–400

476 **Gilt Metal Belt**

The large navette-shaped hinged links cast in a rope design.

$250–350

477 **Coin Necklace and a Coin Pendant, necklace by Yves Saint Laurent**

The necklace with gilt metal ribbed beads dropping a row of pendant faux "Ecu d'or" coins of Henry III of France and the pendant a Maria Theresa Thaler with a loop, *the first necklace with tag marked YSL. Length approximately 17 in. (43.2 cm.)*

$150–250

478 **Gold Coin Necklace**

The black ribbon supporting eight gold Turkish 100-Piastre coins. *Length 22 in. (55.9 cm.)*

$1,200–1,500

479 **Group of Silver and Hardstone Jewelry**

Comprising a necklace, the double strand snake chain interrupted at intervals by oval-shaped orange and white agate cabochons, *length 30 in. (76.2 cm.)*; a pair of earclips, the large silver hoops supported by oval-shaped carnelians; and a fringe necklace, strung with brownish-orange beads of barrel shape simulating carnelian and spherical beads of blackened silver, ending in a silver fringe with bell cap, *length 29 in. (73.7 cm.)*. (3)

$600–800

480 **Four Silver Pendants and Three Metal Bead Necklaces**

The first pendant designed as an endless knot, the next two of cross form and the last of pendent-medallion form with blackened decoration; the three necklaces consisting of barrel-shaped metal beads strung on cord. *Lengths approximately 28, 29 and 25 in. (71.1, 73.7 and 63.5 cm.)*

$350–450

481 **Three Multi-Color Bead Necklaces**

The first a long strand of multi-shaped beads in shades of semi-precious stones centering a gilt-metal disc ornament, *length approximately 70 in. (177.8 cm.)*; the second a choker with "carved jade", "amber", "sodalite" and "ivory" beads, *length approximately 15 in. (38.1 cm.)*; and a multi-strand speckled blue bead necklace, *marked Made in France, length approximately 15 in. (38.1 cm.)*. Together with a brown and grey mottled stone pendant suspended on a macrame cord, *length approximately 14½ in. (36.8 cm.)*. (4)

$300–400

482

483

482 **A Silver Belt, probably Nepal or Tibet**

The belt designed as a triple rope held together with silver gilt ornaments formed at the buckle with ornate fittings decorated with flowers and masks, *weight 300 dwts.* *Length approximately 30 in. (76.2 cm.)*

$400–500

483 **Two Hinged Bangle-Bracelets, India or North Africa**

The first silver with beaded borders, the second, possibly horn, decorated with hammered silvered-metal mounts.

$300–400

484 **Sterling Silver St. Christopher Medal**

The obverse depicting the saint, the reverse inscribed *J.F.K.* and *J.L.W.J.C.* and dated *3-15-53*, supported on a silver chain bracelet of child's length, *4 in. (10.2 cm.).*

$150–200

485 **Group of Bedouin Jewelry**

The first ornament designed as a large hinged plate decorated with chains and accented with "sapphires", "rubies" and "emeralds"; the second ornament designed with an articulated band supporting a large fringe, accented with "rubies", "emeralds" and a "sapphire", all held on a velvet cord; and the last a silver ring of stylized conical form. Together with a Bedouin-style necklace *by Kenneth Jay Lane* with a silvered metal pendant hung from multi-strands of blue, orange and red beads, *marked KJL, length approximately 15 in. (38.1 cm.)* (4)

$400–600

486 **Group of Bangle-Bracelets**

All designed as circular hoops, the first three of gold and black striped resin, *one broken*; the next pair with applied gilt-metal decoration; the single bangle with alternating "silver", black and white stripes; and the last resin with "gold" wash and painted silver and red spots. (7)

$150–200

487 **Group of Ivory and Ebony Jewelry**

Comprising a necklace of ebony and ivory beads, supporting five long fringes, the central fringe decorated with larger ivory beads and an oval-shaped bead strung on black silk cord, *length approximately 47 in. (119.4 cm.)*; two carved ivory bangles, one a cuff, the other a circular hoop; and a pair of earclips set with oval-shaped ivory cabochons, mounted in silver. (5)

$500–700

487

488 **Group of Four Bead Necklaces**

The first a double strand composed of tubular beads simulating carved bone spaced by dark blue glass beads, the clasp a carved ram's head, *length 17 in. (43.2 cm.)*; the second a long strand of reddish-orange beads simulating coral, interrupted at intervals by larger brass beads with three large red beads in the center, *length approximately 33 in. (83.8 cm.)*; the third a strand of ebony beads with a barrel-shaped fluted bead in the center, *length 15 in. (38.1 cm.)*; the fourth a silver bead and shell necklace, strung with shell discs decorated with two silver rods and a circular bead, *length 22 in. (55.9 cm.)*. Together with a strand of taupe-colored stone "worry beads". (5)

$200–250

489 **Two Gilt Metal Pendants and a Belt Buckle, the buckle by Mary McFadden**

The two pendants *in Pre-Columbian taste*, the first a Mixtec-Style zoomorphic bell and the second a Sinu-style figure; the large circular cut-out belt buckle of gilt metal, *stamped handcrafted and, indistinctly, Mary McFadden*. Together with a pair of Indian-style gold hoop earrings with fringe, *pieces missing*. (5)

$250–350

490 **Pair of Gilt Metal Earclips and Two Gilt Metal Chain Necklaces, the earclips by Yves Saint Laurent**

The first necklace composed of textured gilt metal oval-shaped links, *length 16½ in. (41.9 cm.)*; the second composed of circular and bar links, *length 26 in. (66 cm.)*; the earclips designed as buttons and triangles of hammered gilt metal, *signed Yves Saint Laurent, Rive Gauche, Made in France*. (4)

$300-400

491 **Group of Three Bead Necklaces**

The first a five-strand necklace of mottled coral-colored glass beads graduating in size, *signed made in France, lengths 15 to 19 in. (38.1 to 48.3 cm.)*; the second a triple-strand of honey-colored beads simulating amber, *length 16 in. (40.6 cm.)*; the last a long single strand of mottled brown and tan beads graduated in size, *length 35 in. (88.9 cm.)*.

$300–400

492 **Two Simulated Ivory Bead Necklaces and a Pair of Simulated Ivory Earclips**

The first necklace strung with "ivory" beads spaced by yellow metal roundels and decorated at intervals with faceted "crystals" of oval and square shape, *length approximately 34 in. (86.4 cm.)*; the second a single-strand necklace of graduated "ivory" beads, a large honey-colored bead in the center, *length approximately 29 in. (73.7 cm.)*; the hoop earclips of honey-colored "ivory". (4)

$400–500

494

493 **Group of Five Necklaces**

The first with large mottled blue oval beads suspending a large blue silk tassel, *length approximately 13 in. (33 cm.)*; a cork bead necklace painted with "silver" and "gold" decoration, *length approximately 18 in. (45.7 cm.)*; two bead rope necklaces in shades of green, yellow, orange and blue, *lengths approximately 56 and 64 in. (142.2 and 162.6 cm.)*; and a maroon silk cord open-ended necklace, *length approximately 27 in. (68.6 cm.)*

$250–350

494 **Simulated Black Pearl, Rock Crystal and Gold Bead Multi-Strand Necklace and Simulated Pearl Earclips**

The four-strand necklace composed of alternating beads with hook closure, the button earclips with large pearl beads surrounded by a nest of gilt metal chain.
Length approximately 16 in. (40.6 cm.)

$150–250

495 **Two Simulated Pearl Necklaces and a Pair of Simulated Diamond Earclips, the Earclips Kenneth Jay Lane**

The triple-strand "pearl" necklace with diamond hook closure, the single strand of South Sea baroque "pearls" with pavé "diamond" ball closure and the earrings of half hoop design pavé-set with "diamonds", *earclips marked Kenneth Lane.*
Lengths approximately 16 and 31 in. (40.6 and 78.7 cm.)

$400–500

496
495

496 **Pair of Simulated Pearl and Diamond Earclips and Two Pendants**

The earclips set with clusters of marquise-shaped "diamonds" dropping one grey and one cream-colored baroque "pearl"; the first pendant designed with a baroque drop "pearl" set in a simulated diamond-covered cap, and the second pendant with a gold bezel holding an irregularly shaped white coral, both pendants held on an olive green velvet ribbon, *"diamond" missing.*

$250–350

497 **Simulated Pearl and Emerald Brooch, probably French**

The oval cluster of "pearls" of button and circular form accented with four simulated emeralds, sporting a pearl drop, *one pearl missing.*

$250–350

498 **A Coral and Mother-of-Pearl Brooch**

The branch coral naturalistically set in silvered metal with mother-of-pearl and jet, *stamped Italy.*

An export permit may be required to remove this lot from the United States. For further information please inquire.

$200–300

499 **Group of Animal and Insect Jewelry, one by Valentino, one by Coro**

Comprising a crab brooch, set with a large simulated topaz and enhanced with pavé-set simulated diamonds, *signed Valentino*; a cricket brooch, of gilt metal; a bee brooch, of Sterling silver, *signed Coro*; a lion-head clip; and a snake ring, of braided yellow metal. (5)

$400–500

500 **Gilt Metal and Simulated Diamond Necklace and a Pair of Dress Clips, the necklace by Brookraft**

The gilt metal choker *in 1940s style*, with snake chain necklace holding a flower spray ornament with diamond accents, the dress clips *in Art Deco style*, with silvered metal decorations set with "diamonds" applied to "amber" resin mounts, *necklace clasp marked Brookraft, "diamonds" missing.*

$200–300

498

497

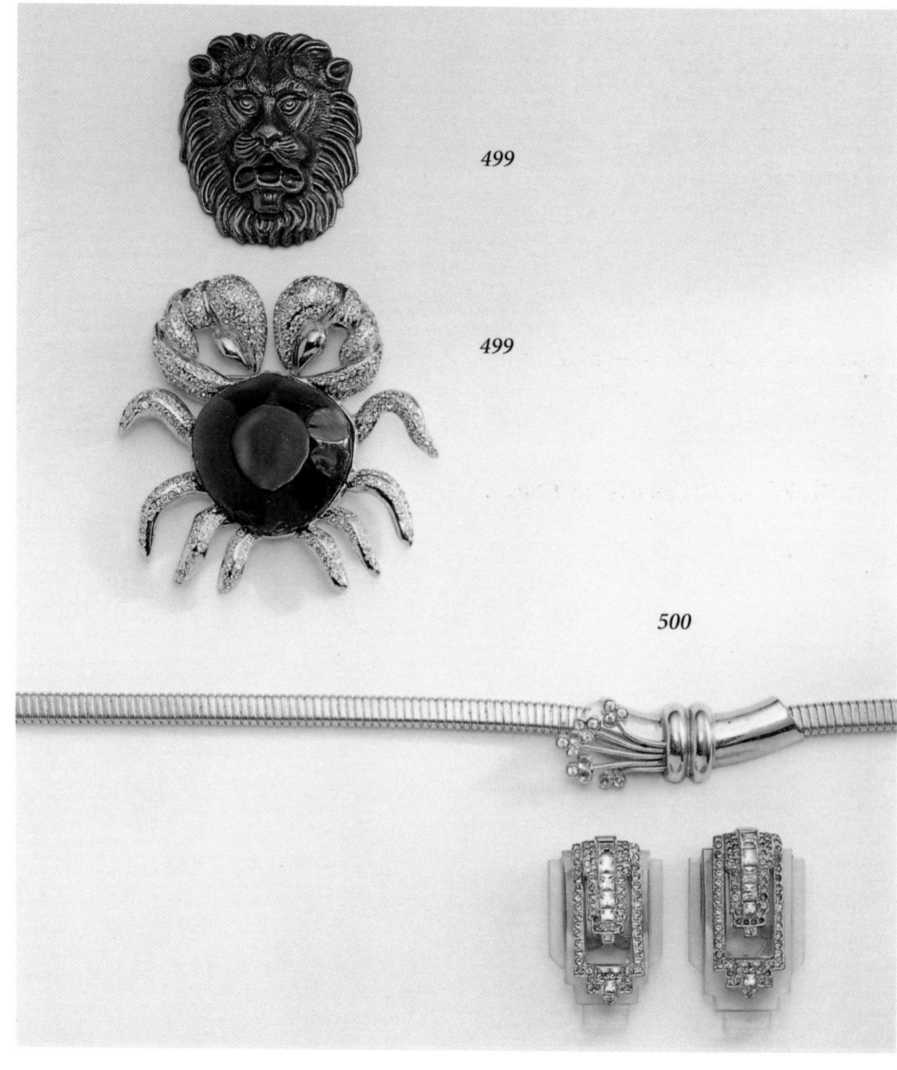

499

499

500

501 **Gilt Metal and Simulated Coral Bead Chain Necklace and Simulated Pearl Earclips, the necklace Christian Dior, the earclips Kenneth Jay Lane**

The multi-strand graduated necklace interspersed with fluted "coral" beads, the earclips with baroque "pearls" set in gilt metal branches; *the necklace with Christian Dior tag marked 1973, Germany, the earclips marked K.J.L.*
Length of necklace 23 to 39 in. (58.4 to 99.1 cm.)

$400–500

502 **Gilt Metal and White Bead Necklace, Kenneth Jay Lane**

The sautoir of white beads supporting a gilt metal plaque of reverse pear shape decorated with filigree and beadwork, and supporting a bead fringe, *small losses, signed Kenneth Lane.*
Length 31 in. (78.7 cm.)

$200–300

503 **Gilt Metal and Simulated Colored Stone Choker-Necklace, Kenneth Jay Lane**

The flexible band decorated with cabochons imitating emeralds, topazes and amethysts within borders of "diamonds," supporting a fringe of faceted "crystal" beads, completed by gilt metal chain at the back, *signed Kenneth Lane, several stones missing.*
Total length 15½ in. (39.4 cm.)

$300–400

504 **Three Pairs of Gilt Metal Earclips, one by Kenneth Jay Lane and one by Christian Lacroix**

The first designed as curved leaves of matte "gold", *signed Kenneth Jay Lane*; the second of trefoil shape designed as trees, *signed Christian Lacroix*, and the last a pair of "bamboo" hoops.

$300–400

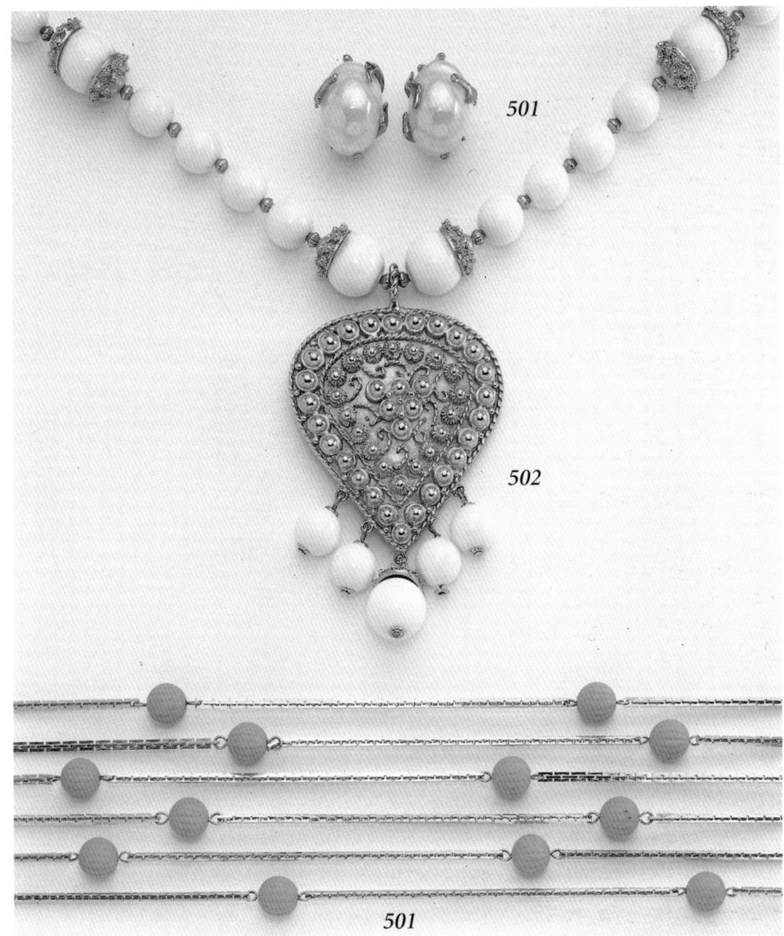

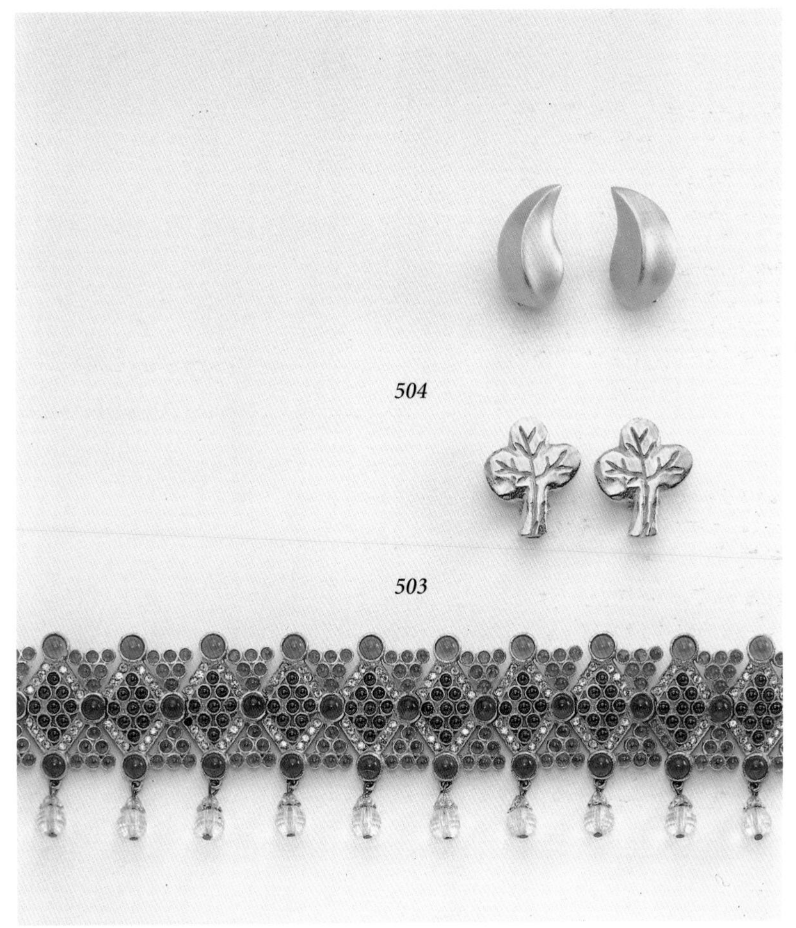

506
505
506

505 Black and Grey Bead Multi-Strand Choker

The multi strands of black and grey bugle beads looped at center and held by caps of pavé-set simulated diamonds continuing to large beads of silver-blue color and faceted black beads spaced by diamond roundels.

$100–150

506 Simulated Diamond and Jet Brooch and Two Pairs of Earclips, one pair by Kenneth Jay Lane

The brooch set with triangular-shaped "diamonds" and "jet", the first pair of earclips designed in half-hoop form set with alternating "diamonds" and "jet" ending in teardrop-shaped "diamonds", and the second pair of earclips consisting of large cushion-shaped "diamonds" set in black lacquered frames, *the last pair marked KJL, brooch missing pin.*

$300–400

Above: *Jacqueline Kennedy Onassis, September 22, 1983.*

507 **A Black Bead Necklace and a Pair of Simulated Diamond Earclips**

The multi-strand faceted "jet" bead necklace with silvered metal filigree stations and end caps, the earclips with large round simulated diamonds set in a black bezel.
Length approximately 16 in. (40.6 cm.)

$300–400

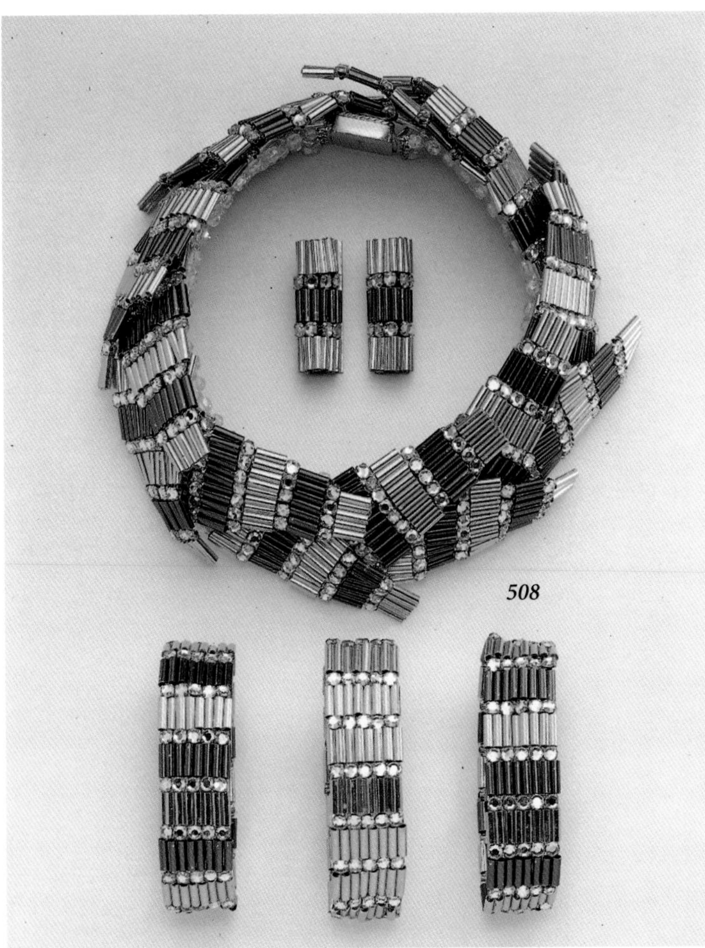

508 **A Suite of Gilt Metal Bead and Simulated Diamond Jewelry, Coppola & Toppo, Italy**

Comprising a collar-necklace, three bracelets and a pair of earclips, composed of cylindrical "gold" and "copper" beads spaced by rows of simulated diamonds, the partly flexible necklace backed by "crystal" beads, *signed Coppola & Toppo, made in Italy.* (6)

$500–700

509 **Miscellaneous Group of Jewelry**

Comprising a silver wire choker with hook and bead closure; a fringe necklace in American Indian style, strung with irregularly shaped "turquoise" beads, cylindrical "coral" beads and lantern-shaped and baton beads of white metal, *length 22 in. (55.9 cm.)*; a thin necklace of small turquoise-colored beads with gold hook clasp, *length 15 in. (38.1 cm.)*; and a silver pendant of drop shape. (4)

$150–200

510 **Two Pairs of Silvered Metal Earclips, the first Yves Saint Laurent, the other Kenneth Jay Lane**

The first pair designed as silver balls, the second as simple silver hoops; *the first marked YSL and the second Kenneth Lane.*

$200–300

511 **Simulated Hematite Bead Necklace**

The single strand of beads interspersed with gilt-metal roundels. *Length approximately 35 in. (88.9 cm.).*

$150–250

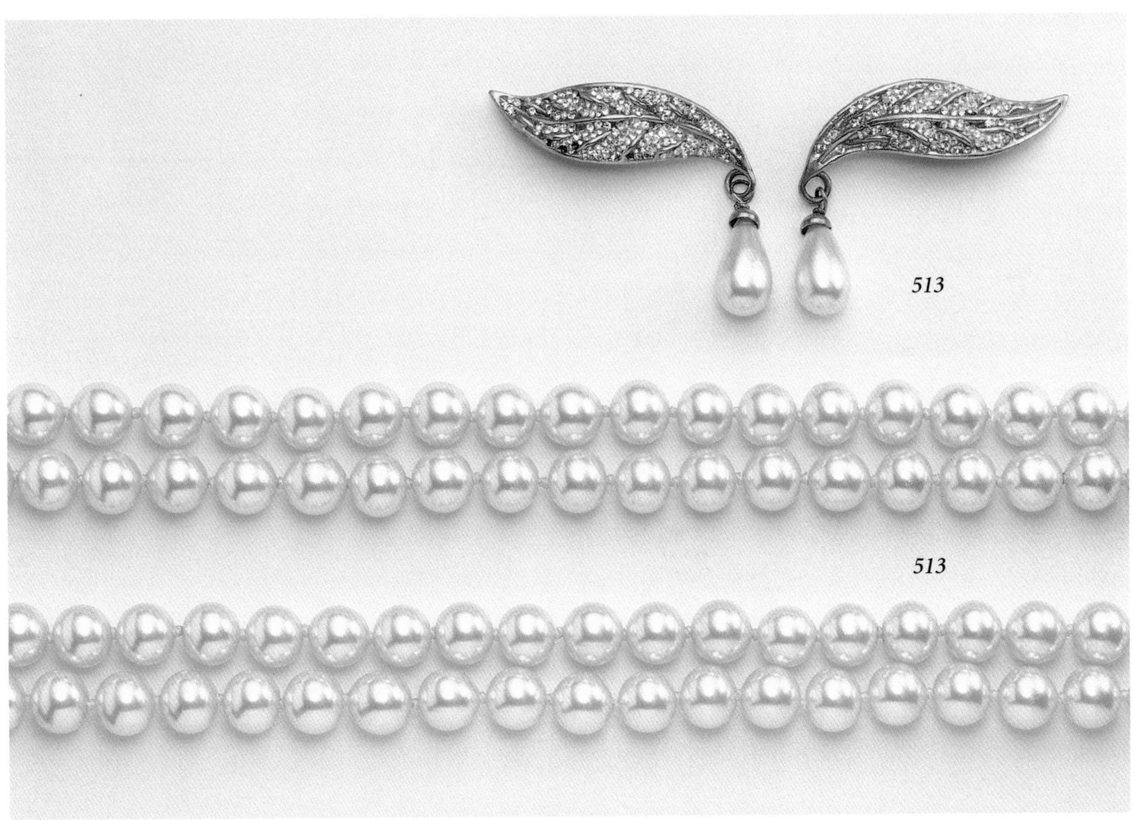

512 **Group of Three Necklaces**

The first a three-row snake chain necklace of silver interrupted at intervals by oval-shaped black onyx cabochons, *length 29 inches*; the second a seven-row necklace of "onyx" beads, *length approximately 16 in. (40.6 cm.)*; the third decorated with hemispheres and roundels of black plastic simulating onyx, joined by multi rows of white metal chain, *length 36 in. (91.4 cm.)*.

$400–600

513 **Simulated Pearl Necklace and a Pair of Simulated Diamond and Pearl Earclips**

The "pearls" a long single strand and the earclips of leaf design pavé-set with "diamonds" suspending a teardrop pearl.
Length of necklace approximately 60 in. (152.4 cm.).

$400–500

Left: *Jacqueline Kennedy Onassis at a party for Diana Vreeland in New York, October 15, 1980.*

514 **Simulated Pearl and Crystal Bead Tassel Necklace, France**

The beads of openwork form set allover with "crystal" stones, each suspending a "pearl" tassel, alternating with pearl beads centered by gilt metal filigree caps, *clasp indistinctly marked France.*
Length approximately 30 in. (76.2 cm.)

$150–250

515 **Two Pairs of Gilt Metal Pendant-Earclips**

The first pair *in antique style*, set with smoky "topazes", "diamonds" and "pearls"; the second pair *in Indian style*, decorated with "moonstones" and "pearls", *parts missing.*

$150–250

516 **Three Gilt Bead Necklaces and Gilt Metal Earclips, Kenneth Jay Lane**

Two necklaces formed by double strands of gilt beads, with hook closures; the third necklace a single strand of graduated gilt-metal beads and the pair of earclips of abstract trefoil form, *necklaces marked K.J.L. or Kenneth Lane.*
Lengths approximately 16, 16 and 36 in. (40.6, 40.6 and 91.4 cm.) respectively.

$200–300

517 **Two Pairs of Gilt Metal Earclips and a Pendant-Necklace, the earclips by Kenneth Jay Lane and Liz Claiborne**

The first pair of earclips designed as silvered metal pyramids within textured gilt metal frames, *signed Kenneth Lane*; the second designed as polished gilt metal ovals of domed form, *post backs with clasps missing, signed Liz Claiborne*; the gilt metal chain necklace supporting a large dramatic pendant, the elongated plaque of slightly flaring shape enhanced with two black stripes. (5)

$300–400

515

514

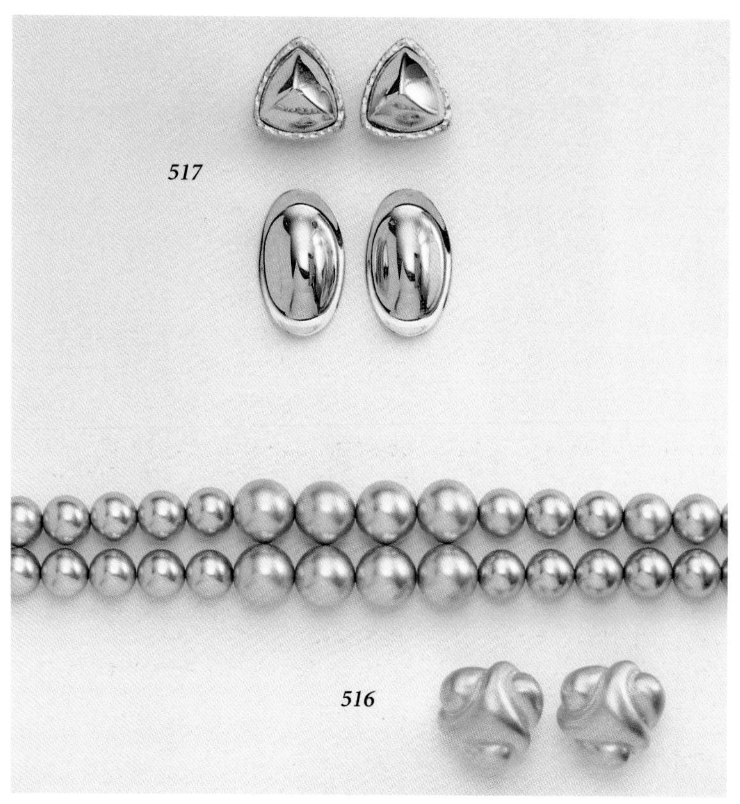

517

516

18 **Silk Rope and Simulated Stone Necklace and Matching Earclips, Essege Design**

The blackened metal pendant with half roundels of baguette "diamonds" and red "tourmalines", hung from a braided black silk cord, the hoop earrings of blackened metal set with baguette "diamonds", *necklace marked Essege Design.*
Length approximately 16 in. (40.6 cm.).

$500–600

519 **Two Silk Rope and Simulated Stone Necklaces, probably Essege Design**

The gilt and blackened metal ornaments set with pink and yellow "topazes", "aquamarines" and "diamonds", both hung on grey braided silk cords.
Lengths approximately 16 in. (40.6 cm.)

$500–600

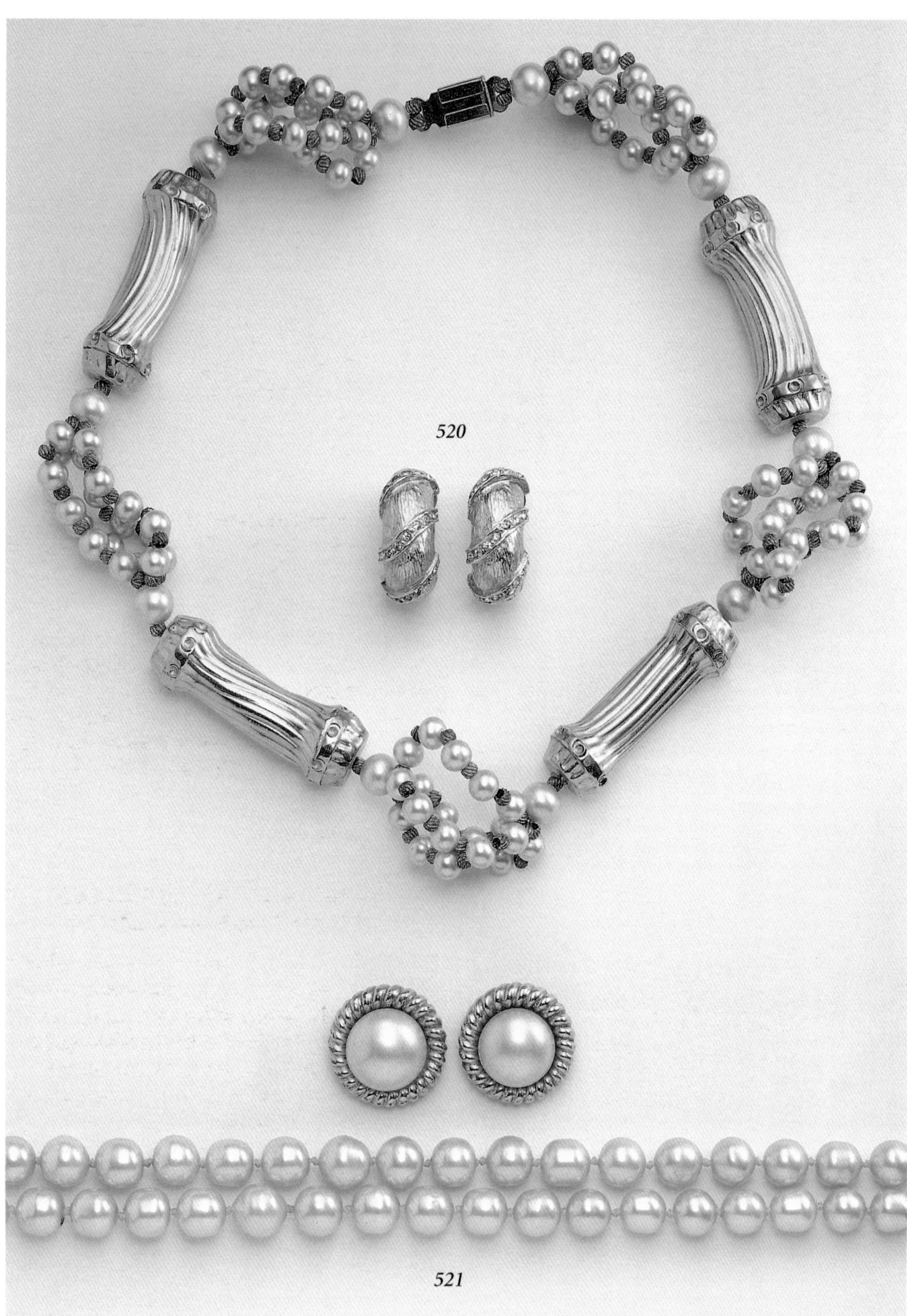

520

521

520 **Gilt Metal and Simulated Pearl Necklace and Gilt Metal and Simulated Diamond Earclips, the earclips by Kenneth Jay Lane**

The necklace designed as sections of bamboo alternating with multi-strand "pearls" and gilt beads, the earclips designed as bamboo half hoops accented with curved rows of "diamonds", *earrings marked KJL.*
Length of necklace approximately 20 in. (50.8 cm.)

$200–300

521 **Two Simulated Pearl Necklaces and Two Pairs of Gilt Metal Earclips**

The triple strand of "pearls" with simple "gold" button closure ("pearl" missing), the double strand of "pearls" with similar "pearl" button closure, and the first pair of earclips of button form with "pearl" centers, the second pair of simple shell form, *"pearl" button earclips marked Jomaz.*
Lengths approximately 17 and 16 in. (43.2 cm.).

$400–500

UPI / Bettmann

Left: *President and Mrs. Kennedy attending a celebration of the second anniversary of the President's inauguration on January 21, 1963.*

522 **Simulated Turquoise, Emerald and Diamond Necklace**

The collar crossing over in the front, decorated with green glass cabochons and beads simulating emeralds, and brilliant-cut pastes simulating diamonds, the front suspending a fringe of "turquoise" drops, mounted in white metal, *some losses and loose stones.*

$100–150

523 **Simulated Diamond Bangle Bracelet and Two Pairs of Earclips, the bracelet by Lanvin**

The thin silvered metal bracelet set with a continuous row of diamonds, the first pair of earrings designed as "gypsy" hoops set in silvered metal with a row of baguette "diamonds", the second pair of bombé hoop form set in resin with "diamond" sequins, *the bracelet stamped Lanvin Paris.*

$200–300

524 **Silver Buckle Belt and Simulated Diamond and Ruby Buckle Belt**

The first with large rectangular silver buckle with oval insert, attached to a black elasticized belt, *weight approximately 82 dwts.*, the second designed as "diamond" studded confronting eagles with "ruby" eyes; attached to a black velvet belt.
Lengths approximately 26 and 27 in. (66 and 68.6 cm.)

$400–500

525 **Simulated Pearl and Diamond Earclips and Simulated Grey Baroque Pearl Necklace, the earclips by Chanel**

The button earrings centering simulated pearls surrounded by two rows of "diamonds", *ear pad stamped Chanel, diamonds missing,* the simulated pearl necklace with carved "emerald" clasp.
Length approximately 16 in. (40.6 cm.)

$200–300

526 **Two Pairs of Simulated Diamond and Emerald Earclips, Kenneth Jay Lane**

The first with sugarloaf cabochon top suspending a similar "emerald" drop surrounded by a double row hoop of "diamonds"; the next with a feathered diamond cap holding teardrop-shaped "emeralds", *the first with earclip marked Kenneth Lane, the second stamped Kenneth Lane.*

$300–400

527 **Two Pairs of Gilt Metal and Simulated Diamond Earclips, one by Kenneth Jay Lane**

The first designed as flowerheads pavé-set with simulated diamonds, the next flower-form with ribbon-shaped petals centering light "canary" emerald-cut simulated diamonds, the second pair with earclips marked *K.J.L., missing stones.*

$200–300

528 **Simulated Diamond and Sapphire Earclips and Dress Clip, Kenneth Jay Lane**

The earclips consisting of clusters of marquise-shaped "sapphires" surrounded by single rows of "diamonds", the dress clip in Art Deco style with a single row of channel-set "sapphires" flanked by pavé-set diamonds, *all pieces marked Kenneth Lane.*

$250–350

529 **Pair of Simulated Diamond Cluster Earclips and a Flower Brooch, the earclips by Valentino**

The circular earclips of domed form decorated with large round simulated diamonds in the center, surrounded by concentric rows of smaller round stones, mounted in gilt metal, *one stone missing, signed Valentino*; the flower brooch composed of red glass beads surrounding a central cluster of simulated diamonds, "seed pearls", "coral" and "emerald" beads, *signed France.* (3)

$400–500

530 **Pair of Simulated Turquoise, Amethyst and Diamond Dress Clips**

Each dome-shaped clip centering a cushion-shaped "amethyst" surrounded by a single row of "diamonds" and three rows of round "turquoise" stones, all set in gilt-metal mounts.

$300–400

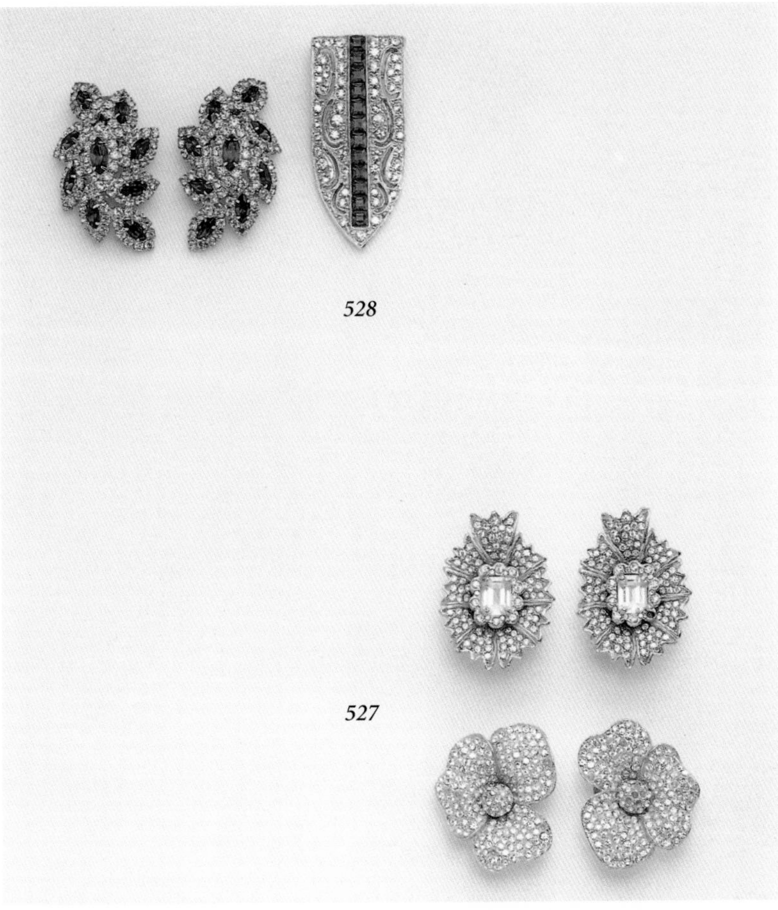

528

527

530

529

532

531

531 **Caucasian Silver and Niello Belt, circa 1880**

Composed of twelve links of lobed shape and floral design joined by two rows of chain, completed by a two-part buckle with sabre closure, *bearing a Russian inscription: Cavkaz,* the whole weighing approximately 120 dwts.
Length approximately 33 in. (83.8 cm.).

$500–700

532 **Silver Belt**

Composed of rectangular-shaped plaques of embossed silver alternately decorated with bird and floral motifs, completed by a circular buckle similarly decorated with a flower and scrolls, weighing approximately 110 dwts.
Length 34 in. (86.4 cm.).

$400–600

533 **Two Simulated Colored Stone and Gilt Metal Pendants, one made in France**

The first, *French, in Renaissance style,* set with sugarloaf "rubies", "sapphires" and "pearls" surrounding a central cabochon "emerald", with brooch clip; the second with cabochon "rubies", "turquoise", and "moonstones" set in a filigree mounting accented with enamelling, *the second missing brooch pin.*

$250–350

534 **Two Gilt Metal and Colored Bead Station Necklaces**

Both necklaces formed by blue or red glass beads flanked by filigree stations. *Lengths approximately 66 in. (167.6 cm.)*

$100–200

535 **Three Metal Chain Necklaces**

The first in Indian style, a multi-strand faceted bead necklace with S-form closure, the second a long cable-link chain necklace and the last a gilt metal double-chain necklace with pendant charms and carved "stone" pendant with metal tassel.
Lengths 45, 66 and 30 in. (114.3, 167.6 and 76.2 cm.)

$250–350

536 **Four Cross Pendants**

Each pendant designed as a cross wrapped in heavy silvered metal wire, one cross pendant from a silvered metal choker with gilt metal accents, two crosses held on leather cording.

$400–500

537 **Four Cross Pendants**

The first designed as a wide silver cross depicting the crucifixion of Christ, the second designed as a silver cruciform bezel holding a false scyphate of the Byzantine Emperor Michael with Constantine, the third a white metal circular charm cast with a stippled cross design and the last a gilt metal cross with glass mosaic decoration.

$400–500

538 **Silver Cross Necklace**

The chain necklace with cruciform links alternating with silver beads, holding an ornate pendant centering a winged heart dropping three silver orbs and three crosses applied with tiny hearts, weight approximately 60 dwts.
Length approximately 27 in. (68.6 cm.)

$400–600

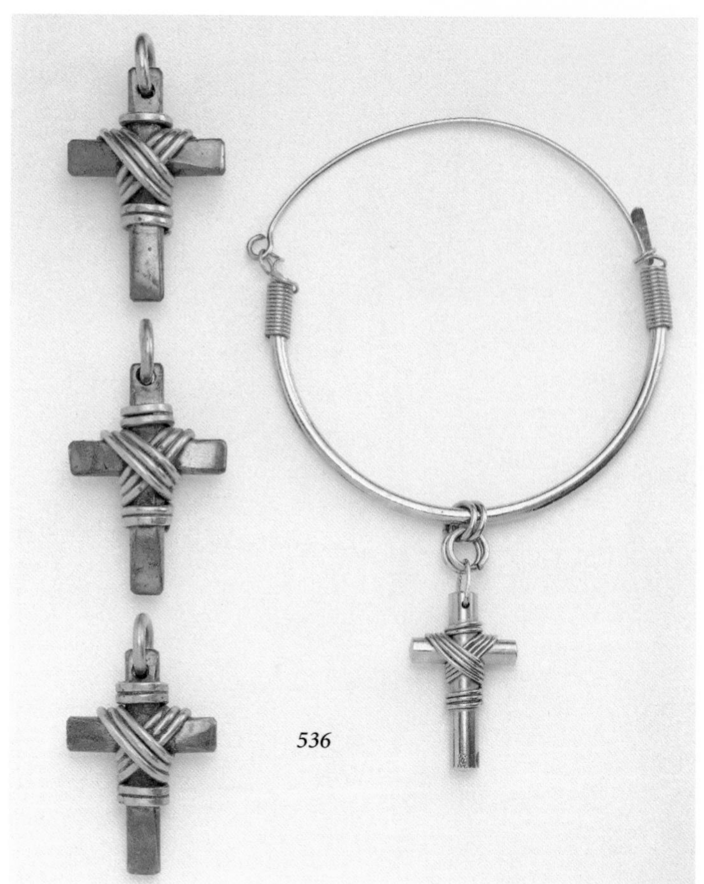

536

538

537

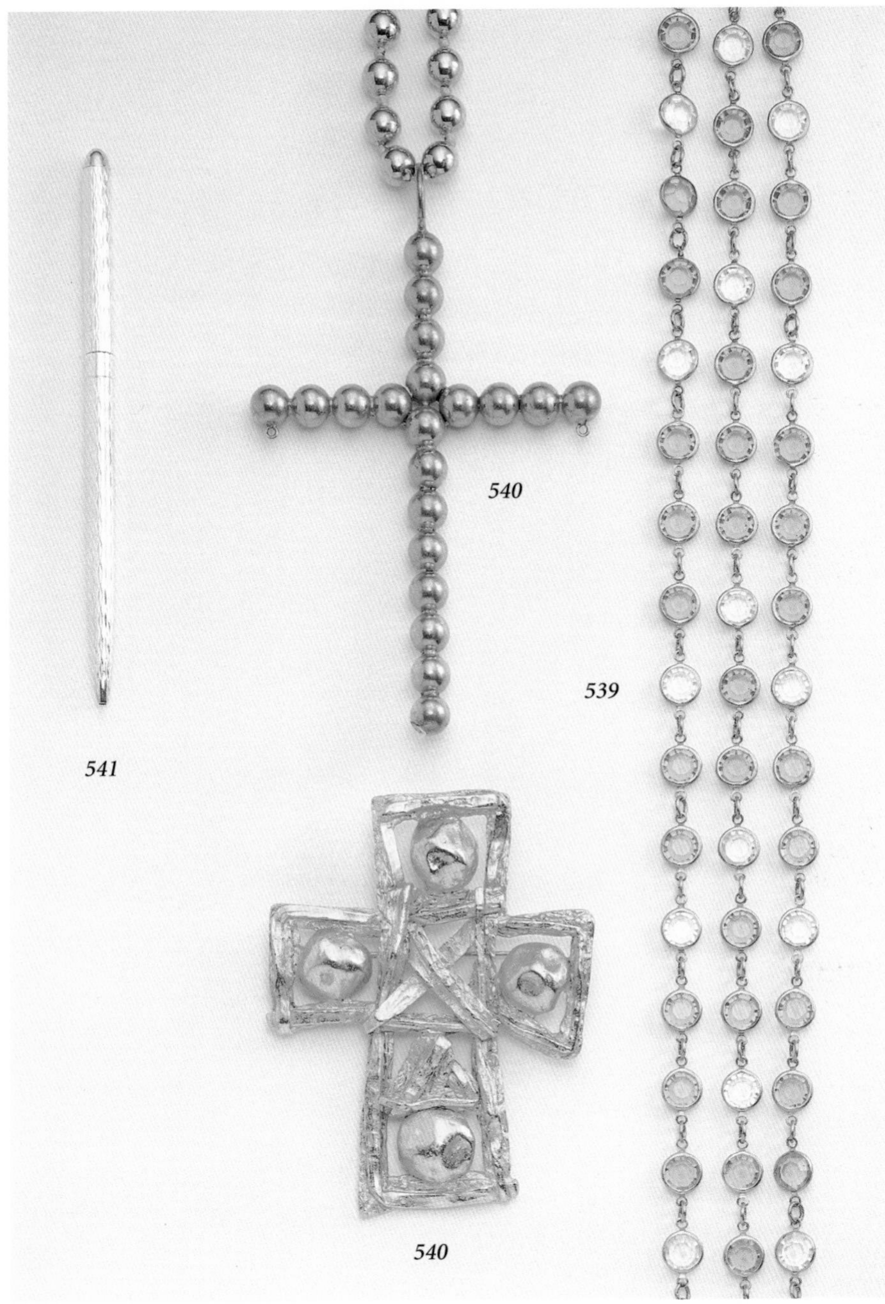

Above: *Jacqueline Kennedy Onassis, December 3, 1993*

539 **Three Simulated Gem-Set Chains**

The first with faceted round "amber" and "crystal" stones; the second with faceted "crystal" stones and the last with faceted "crystal" stones alternating with gilt metal filigree stations, *stone missing.*
Lengths approximately 60, 55 and 36 in. (152.4, 139.7 and 91.4 cm.) respectively

$150–250

540 **Gilt Metal Cross Brooch and Pendant Cross Necklace, the brooch Christian LaCroix**

The brooch of whimsical cross design, the necklace with gilt metal cross pendent from a gilt bead chain, *the brooch marked Christian Lacroix, made in France.*
Length approximately 36 in. (91.4 cm.)

$200–300

541 **Sterling Silver Ballpoint Pen and Silver Cigarette Holder, the pen by Tiffany & Co.**

The pen decorated in a vertical wave motif, signed *Tiffany & Co., W. Germany*; the cigarette holder of tapering form chased and engraved with birds, flowers and foliage; together with another cigarette holder of simulated coral, *top segment missing.* (3)

$75–100

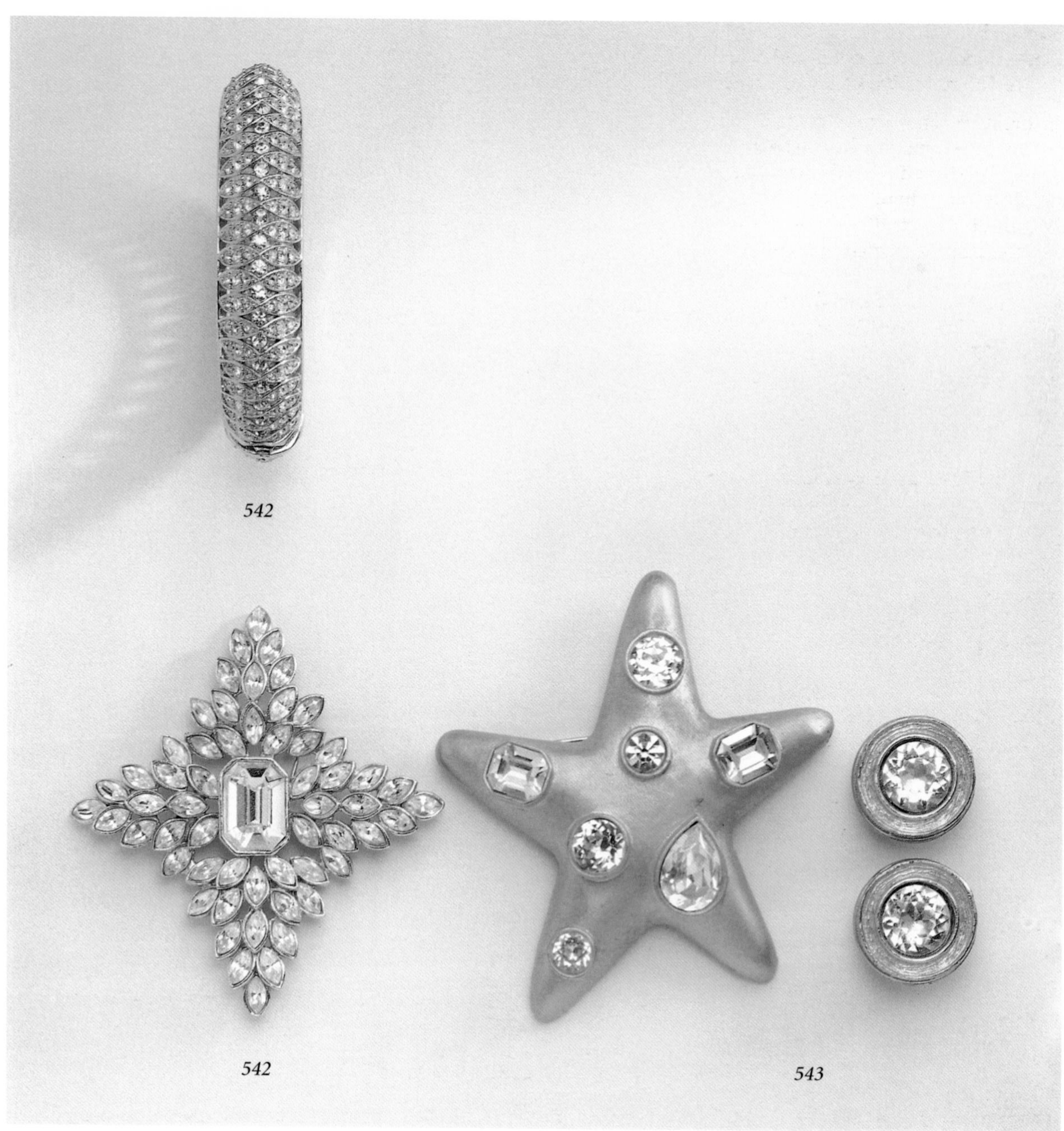

542

542

543

542 **Simulated Diamond Brooch and Bangle-Bracelet, Kenneth Jay Lane**

The cruciform brooch composed of a central step-cut "diamond", centering sprays of marquise-shaped "diamonds", the hinged silvered metal bangle-bracelet covered with an openwork pattern of pavé-set "diamonds", *both marked Kenneth Jay Lane.*

$400–600

543 **Group of Gilt Metal and Simulated Diamond Jewelry, two by Kenneth Lane**

Comprising a star brooch, the gilt metal motif inset with fancy shaped simulated diamonds **by Kenneth J. Lane**, a pair of earclips set with circular "diamonds" within textured gilt metal frames, *signed Kenneth Lane*, and a bangle-bracelet of simulated rock crystal inset with round "diamonds" in gilt metal bezels. (4)

$400–500

44 Simulated Diamond and Crystal Necklace and Two Pairs of Simulated Diamond Earclips, Yves Saint Laurent

The necklace composed of faceted "crystal" cubes and beads centering a rectangular-shaped faceted "diamond", with silver metal hook closure, the first pair of "diamond" earrings with large teardrop-shape diamond pendants, the second of faceted rectangular form set in silver metal frames, *necklace with YSL tag, the earclips marked YSL.*
Length approximately 17 in. (43.2 cm.)

$500–600

45 Simulated Black Pearl Torsade Necklace and Earclips, Mimi di Niscemi and Kenneth Jay Lane

The necklace composed of multi strands of simulated black seed pearls clasped by gilt metal foliate motifs studded with simulated diamonds, *signed Mimi di N., length 18 in. (45.7 cm.)*; the earclips set with black baroque "pearls" topped by gilt metal foliate motifs pavé-set with simulated diamonds, *signed K.J.L.*

$400–500

46 Simulated Seed Pearl and Diamond Bracelet and a Pair of Simulated Diamond and Colored Stone Earclips, the bracelet by Mimi di Niscemi

The multi-strand torsade bracelet of simulated seed pearls clasped by gilt metal links of foliate design studded with simulated diamonds, *signed Mimi di N., length 9 in. (22.9 cm.)*; the hoop earclips decorated with cabochon and faceted "stones" simulating emeralds, rubies and sapphires against a pavé-set ground of "diamonds", in gilt metal.

$300–400

547 **Two Pairs of Simulated Diamond and Colored Stone Earclips, Kenneth Jay Lane**

The round "ruby" and "emerald" cabochon tops suspending oval cabochon drops surrounded by a single row of "diamonds", *marked K.J.L.*

$300–400

548 **Two Pairs of Simulated Diamond and Colored Stone Earclips, Kenneth Jay Lane**

Both with "diamond" X tops suspending "ruby" and "emerald" pendants with diamond-encrusted bellflower-shaped caps, *marked K.J.L.*

$300–400

549 **Silver Gilt Belt, Cartier**

The belt formed with abstract coin medallion links, *marked Cartier, Sterling; 240 dwts.*
Length approximately 29 in. (73.7 cm.)

$500–700

548

547

549

WWD / Fairchild Publications

Above: *Jacqueline Kennedy Onassis at a party for The Municipal Art Society, February 27, 1991, wearing a "Chanel" necklace similar to the one in lot 551.*

550 **Gilt Metal and Simulated Colored Stone Chain Necklace, Chanel**

The tumbled "emerald" and "ruby" beads joined by sections of gilt metal chain, *with tag stamped Chanel, 1984. Length approximately 72 in. (182.9 cm.)*

$400–600

551 **Gilt Metal Filigree and Simulated Pearl and Colored Stone Pendant-Necklace, Chanel**

In Indian style, composed of large "emerald" beads capped by gilt metal filigree and joined by sections of multi strand chain, suspending a large "ruby" bead and simulated pearl drop; *with tag stamped Chanel.*
Length approximately 22 in. (55.9 cm.)

$600–800

Wide World Photos

Right: *Jacqueline Kennedy and President Charles de Gaulle meeting during the President and Mrs. Kennedy's trip to Paris. May-June, 1961.*

552 **Black "Stone" Bead Double-Strand Necklace**

Strung with black-colored beads of baroque and spherical form, completed by a cluster clasp, mounted in white metal, *some losses to clasp,* together with a single earclip, *en suite.* (2)
Length 17 in. (43.2 cm.)

Jacqueline Kennedy wore this necklace when her husband announced his candidacy for President, later during the campaign and while he was in office..

$200–300

552

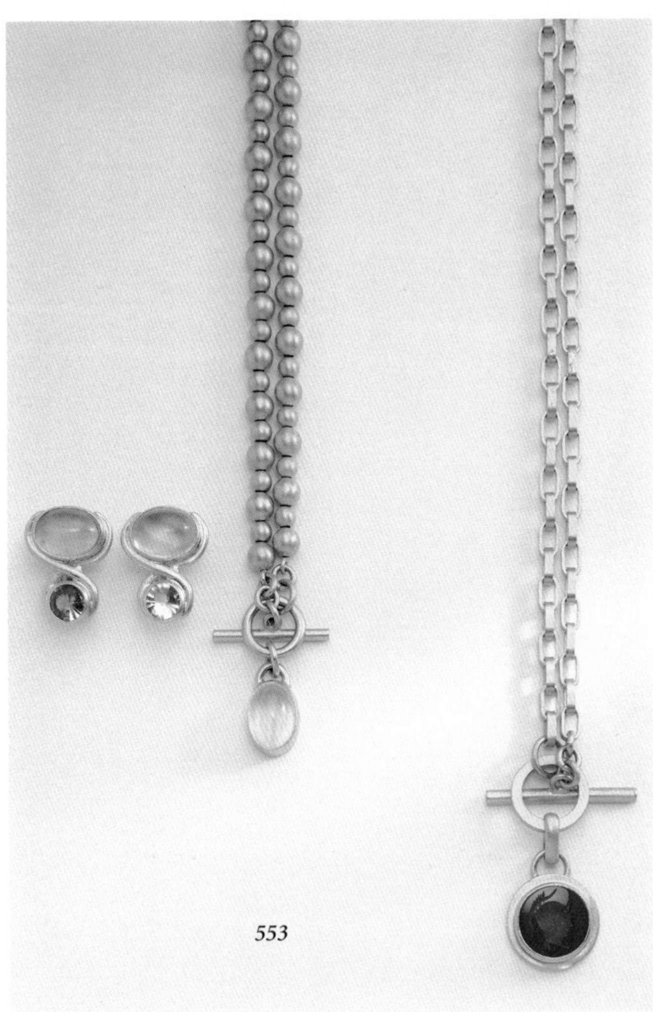

553

554

553 **Vermeil and Pale Green Stone Necklace and Matching Earclips, Mark Spirito**

The vermeil bead necklace with ring and bar clasp supporting a cabochon stone of pale green color, *length 16 in. (40.6 cm.)*; the earclips set with similar pale green stone cabochons of oval shape and colorless circular cabochons, *signed Mark Spirito*; together with a gilt-metal and hardstone intaglio necklace, the long chain of oval links ending in a carnelian intaglio carved in classical taste in the head of a soldier, *length 35 in. (88.9 cm.)*.

$600–800

554 **Simulated Turquoise, Diamond and Ruby Necklace-Bracelet Combination and Matching Brooch, Chanel**

The necklace pendent with multiple "turquoise" and "diamond" flowers separating to form two bracelets (one of shorter length), the brooch formed with "turquoise" petals accented by "rubies" and "diamonds", *the brooch marked Chanel.*
Length approximately 14 in. (35.6 cm.).

$500–700

555

555 **Simulated Pearl and Diamond Bead Necklace and Matching Earclips**

The "South Sea pearl" necklace with three beads covered in "diamond" sequins, the earclips designed as matching sequin-covered balls. *Length approximately 16 in. (40.6 cm.)*

$400–500

556 **Pair of Yellow Metal "Gypsy" Bangle-Bracelets**

The rigid cuffs of polished yellow metal applied with large beads flexibly attached by circular links.

$300–500

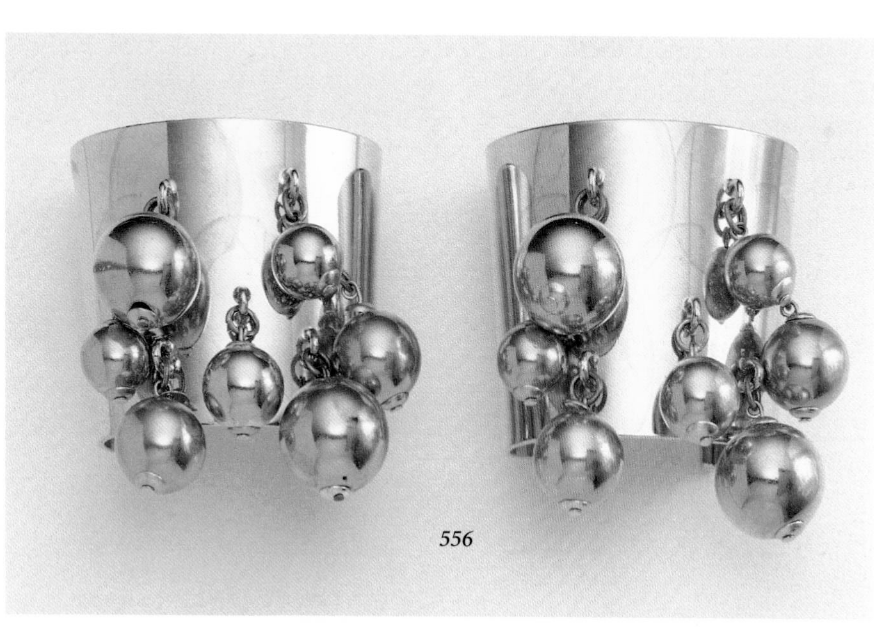

556

557 **Two Pairs of Simulated Diamond and Colored Stone Earclips, Kenneth Jay Lane**

The first with "diamond" encrusted foliate tops suspending "ruby" drops, the next with "diamond" feathered caps holding teardrop-shaped "emeralds", *the first with earclip marked Kenneth Lane, the second marked K.J.L.*

$300–400

558 **Two Pairs of Simulated Diamond and Colored Stone Earclips, Kenneth Jay Lane**

The first with "diamond" encrusted foliate tops suspending "emerald" drops, the second with "diamond" feathered caps holding "rubies"; *the first marked Kenneth Lane, the second marked K.J.L.*

$300–400

559 **Simulated Diamond and Colored Stone Necklace and Matching Earclips, Kenneth Jay Lane**

In Indian style, the necklace composed of floral medallions centered with cabochon "rubies", "emeralds" and "sapphires", the center supporting a large palmette set with "rubies" and "diamonds", the earclips designed with large foliate tops encrusted with "diamonds" supporting large "ruby" pendants, *necklace and earclips stamped Kenneth Lane, some losses.*

This necklace and pair of earclips are near replicas of the necklace and earclips made in colored stones and diamonds by Van Cleef & Arpels, lots 452 and 444, respectively.

$1,000–1,500

"Jackie had been wearing my jewelry since the middle 60's—often visiting my showroom, where she was like a kid in a candy shop—but buying pieces at Saks as well.

When one day she asked me if I would do her a favor, I of course said yes. The "favor" was to make a *near* replica of a wonderful Van Cleef necklace that Ari had given her.

I went to tea at 1040, where Jackie had taken it out of the bank to show to me. Basically it consisted of five motifs set with diamonds and cabochon colored gems.

We discussed the price of making the model and Jackie gave a sweet little gasp. I suggested that if she gave permission for me to include the necklace in my collection that we would absorb the model-making cost.

With her blessing, I have produced the necklace and used the motifs in every possible manner for the past twenty-five years.

One day Jackie said to me in her wonderful whisper, "Kenny, I saw our necklace again on Dynasty."

—*Kenneth J. Lane*

559

THE ESTATE OF JACQUELINE KENNEDY ONASSIS

SESSION SIX

THURSDAY, APRIL 25,

2:00 P.M.

The Entrance Hall of Jacqueline Kennedy Onassis' New York City apartment, showing lots 36, 258, 259, 268, 285, 337, 347 and 631.

560 **A Russian Silver-Gilt Bonbonnière, Late 18th Century**

The slip-on cover mounted with a medallion of the Empress Catherine depicted as Minerva, signed *Waechter*.
Diameter 3¼ in. (8.3 cm.)

$700–900

561 **A Russian Silver-Gilt and Niello Vodka Cup, Moscow, 1882**

Decorated with strapwork on a stippled ground, the lower part decorated with scalework.
Height 2 in. (5.1 cm.)

$500–700

560

561, 562, 563, 564

562 **A Gold-Mounted Bloodstone Bonbonnière, 19th Century**

Of egg shape, the gold mounts decorated with neo-rococo scrolls and foliage, the border with a French inscription on a white enamel ground. With a stand in the form of three silver-gilt arrows.
Height 4⅜ in. (11.1 cm.)

$2,000–3,000

563 **A Twenty-Two Karat Gold and Enamel Byzantine Style Icon Roundel, 20th Century**

Depicting St. John the Baptist, his robes enameled blue, with blue halo, filigree gold border and gold strut.
Diameter 2¼ in. (5.7 cm.)

$700–900

564 **A Swiss Gold and Enamel Zarf, Geneva, circa 1830**

Enameled with swirling panels of flowers on a red ground.
Height 2½ in. (6.3 cm.)

$2,500–3,500

568, 569

565, 566, 567

565 **A German Enamel Snuff Box, circa 1765**

Of rectangular shape, the cover decorated with a courting couple in a landscape, the shaped sides decorated with flowers, with gilt-metal mounts, with inscribed note.
Length 3 ⅛ in. (7.9 cm.)

$700–900

566 **A French Gold-Mounted Agate Snuff Box, Gabriel Gallois, Paris, 1743**

Of rectangular shape, mounted *en cage*, with brown moss agate panels, the gold mounts with wavy borders.
Length 3 ⅛ in. (7.9 cm.)

$4,000–6,000

567 **A Greek Icon Triptych, 18th Century**

With a silver mounting, depicting St. George, St. Dimitri and The Virgin of the Passion.
2 ½ by 7 ½ in. (6.3 by 19 cm.)

$1,200–1,500

568 **An Austrian Silver and Translucent Enamel Table Clock, early 20th Century**

Of urn shape, enameled translucent pink over a *guilloché* ground, with revolving chapter ring, with octagonal hardstone base.
Height 4 ½ in. (11.4 cm.)

This table clock was among the furnishings in Mrs. Kennedy's dressing room at the White House.

$1,000–1,500

569 **An Austrian Silver and Translucent Enamel Table Clock, early 20th Century**

Of urn shape, enameled translucent lilac over a *guilloché* ground, and also painted with *en plein* reserves.
Height 4 ½ in. (11.4 cm.)

This table clock was among the furnishings in Mrs. Kennedy's dressing room at the White House.

$1,000–1,500

570 **Two Matching French Silver-Gilt Beakers, one Théodore Tonnellier, 1819-38, the other maker's mark badly struck, possibly the same, Paris**

Each on a domed circular base with die-stamped stiff foliate border, the bell-shaped bowls punched or milled in low relief with foliate and floral motifs between formal borders.
Height 4 in. (10.2 cm.)

$250–450

570, 571, 571, 570

left to right: 572, 572, 572, 573, 573, 573, 573, 572

571 **A Pair of Silver-Gilt Salt Cellars and a Pair of Russian Silver-Gilt Liners to Fit, the salts unmarked, mid 19th Century, the liners Carl Johann Berg, St. Petersburg, 1796**

Oval, the salts in English style of the 1770s, pierced sides above cast and pierced panel supports, waved gadroon lips, the liners each with a central division, respectively engraved "No. 6" and "No. 7", together with a Pair of American Silver Salt Spoons, pointed terminals, *Dominick & Haff, Inc., Newark and New York, early 20th Century.* (4)
Width of salts 4 in. (10.2 cm.)

$500–700

572 **A Pair of American Silver Salt Cellars and a Pair of English Electroplate Pepperettes, respectively Gorham Mfg. Co., Providence, Rhode Island, and Barker Brothers, Ltd., of Birmingham, all early 20th Century**

The salts of compressed circular form, lightly gilt interiors, *stamped "A4070"*, the baluster pepperettes each on four curved supports.
Diameter of salts 1½ in. (3.8 cm.), height of pepperettes 3 in. (7.6 cm.)

$80–120

573 **Three English Electroplate Salt Cellars, Barker Brothers Silversmiths, Ltd., of Birmingham, early 20th Century**

Of plain compressed oblong form, each on three curved supports below waved lips, with blue glass liners; together with a Small Silver-Plated Cream Jug, *Reed & Barton.* (4)
Width of salt cellars 2½ in. (6.3 cm.)

$50–80

574

575-579

74 **A Victorian Silver Ewer, J. Smyth, Dublin, 1867**

The domed circular foot and baluster body richly chased with foliage, flowers and diaperwork surrounding two scroll cartouches, one engraved with a demi-maiden crest, scroll handle and hinged lid.
Height 14 in. (35.6 cm.)

$1,500–2,500

75 **An American Silver Trophy Two-Handled Cup, Gorham Mfg. Co., Providence, Rhode Island, 1933**

The inscribed vase-shaped body with applied die-stamped laurel leaf and berry borders, angular handles, stamped "11974."
Height 15 in. (38.1 cm.)

The inscription on one side reads "East Hampton Riding Club Horse Show 1936 Harry L. Hamlin Memorial Challenge Cup Ladies Hunters To be Won Three Times by Same Owner Before Becoming Property of Winner."

The inscription on the other reads: "Won By / 1936 - Mrs J.V. Bouvier III's Stepaside / 1937 - Rolling Rock Farms Rector / 1938 - Mr. and Mrs. A. Biddle Duke's 'Because'."

$1,200–1,500

576 **An American Silver Two-Handled Trophy Cup, Gorham Mfg. Co., Providence, Rhode Island, circa 1929**

On spreading pedestal foot, the inscribed bell-shaped body with applied scroll handles.
Height 12½ in. (31.7 cm.)

The inscription on one side reads "East Hampton Riding Club Horse Show The Harry L. Hamlin Challenge Cup Ladies Hunters".

The inscription on the other reads: "Won By / 1929 - Miss Marjorie E. Simonds - Ace of Hearts / 1930 - Mrs. John C. Loud - Curry Sauce / 1931 - Miss Carolyn Roberts - Nancy / 1932 - Mrs. John V. Bouvier III - Danseuse"

$1,500–2,000

577 **An American Silver Two-Handled Trophy Cup, International Silver Co., Meriden, Connecticut, circa 1931**

Of plain tapered cylindrical outline, with waisted shoulder and angular handles, engraved with an inscription.
Height 10½ in. (26.7 cm.)

The inscription reads "The Southampton Cup 2½ Miles Suffolk Hounds 1931 Presented by Little Gunpowder Farm Won by J.V. Bouvier III Joe Marshall."

$650–850

580, and 581-587

578 **A George III Silver Dinner Plate, Paul Crespin, London, 1732**

Shaped circular, applied gadroon border above armorials, the underside engraved "No.1" and scratch weight "30=5".
Diameter 11 in. (27.9 cm.)

The arms are apparently those of Cavendish.

$500–700

579 **An American Silver Waiter, The Randahl Shop, Chicago, Illinois, early 20th Century**

Circular, applied molded border, the centre engraved with the initials JLB (Janet Lee Bouvier).
Diameter 7½ in. (19 cm.)

$75–150

580 **An American Silver Trophy Bowl, circa 1933**

Of plain circular form, the deep bowl engraved with an inscription and stamped "Heather Mathews 118 Sterling."
Diameter 10¾ in. (27.3 cm.)

The inscription reads "Brookville Horse Show 1933 Thoroughbred Hunters Won by Mrs J.V. Bouvier III's Danseuse."

$250–500

581 **An American Silver Trophy Goblet, International Silver Co., Meriden, Connecticut, circa 1934**

On spreading pedestal foot, the bell-shaped body inscribed, stamped "P 664"
Height 6½ in. (16.5 cm.)

The inscription reads "East Hampton Riding Club, Horse Show, Aug. 18, 1934, Lightweight Hunters, Won by" (inscription not completed).

$100–150

582 **An American Silver Trophy Goblet, International Silver Co., Meriden, Connecticut, circa 1934**

On spreading foot, the bell-shaped body inscribed, stamped "P 664".
Height 6½ in. (16.5 cm.)

The inscription reads "East Hampton Riding Club, Horse Show, Aug. 18, 1934, Champion Hunter, Won by" (inscription not completed).

$100–150

583 **An American Silver Trophy Goblet, International Silver Co., Meriden, Connecticut, circa 1933**

On spreading foot, the bell-shaped body inscribed, stamped "P 664".
Height 6½ in. (16.5 cm.)

The inscription reads "East Hampton Riding Club, Horse Show, Aug. 19, 1933, Lightweight Hunters, Won by" (incomplete inscription).

$100–150

584 **An American Silver Trophy Goblet, International Silver Co., Meriden, Connecticut, circa 1933**

On spreading foot, inscribed bell-shaped body, stamped "P 664".
Height 6⅝ in. (16.8 cm.)

The inscription reads "East Hampton Riding Club, Horse Show, Aug. 19, 1933, Hunt Teams, Won by" (inscription not completed).

$100–150

585 **An American Silver Trophy Goblet, International Silver Co., Meriden, Connecticut, circa 1934**

On spreading foot, inscribed bell-shaped body, stamped "P 664".
Height 6½ in. (16.5 cm.)

The inscription reads "East Hampton Riding Club, Horse Show, Aug. 18, 1934. Hunt Teams, Won by" (inscription not completed).

$100–150

586 **An American Silver Trophy Goblet, International Silver Co., Meriden, Connecticut, circa 1933**

On spreading pedestal foot, the bell-shaped body engraved with an inscription, stamped "P 664".
Height 6⅝ in. (16.8 cm.)

The inscription reads "East Hampton Riding Club, Horse Show, Aug. 19, 1933, Champion Hunter, Won by" (inscription not completed).

$100–150

587 **An American Silver Trophy Goblet, International Silver Co., Meriden, Connecticut, circa 1934**

On spreading pedestal foot, the bell-shaped body engraved with an inscription, stamped "P 664".
Height 6½ in. (16.5 cm.)

The inscription reads "East Hampton Riding Club, Horse Show, Aug. 18, 1934, Local Hunters, Won by" (inscription not completed).

$100–150

588

589

588 **An Electroplate Dressing Table Mirror, 20th Century**

The rectangular base on four paw supports, swivel oval mirror with reeded supports and milled stiff leaf borders. *Height 20½ in. (52.1 cm.)*

$400–600

589 **A Silver-Gilt and Cut-Glass Dresser Set, Continental, 19th Century**

Comprising four stoppered bottles, a rectangular jar with locking cover, and a rectangular clothes brush; each foliate-chased cover engraved with crest, the glass bodies deeply cut with pointed arches.

$1,800–2,200

590 **A George III Silver Old English Pattern Soup Ladle, Eley & Fearn, London, 1800**

The terminal engraved with the initial H.
Length 12½ in. (31.7 cm).

William Eley and William Fearn, originally silver buckle makers, changed the emphasis of their business towards the close of the eighteenth century when buckles for gentlemen's shoes became less fashionable. The firm subseqently grew to become one of London's most prolific producers of silver spoons and forks.

$500–600

591 **A Pair of English Electroplate Berry Spoons, circa 1890**

Old English pattern, flat-chased scrolling foliage and embossed fruit and leaves.
Length 9 in. (22.9 cm.)

$40–80

592 **A Victorian Silver Paper Knife, George Unite & Sons, Birmingham; the blade, 1888; the handle, 1889**

Plain blade, the handle repoussé with scrolls and a shield-form cartouche, blade detached.
Length 14¼ in. (36.2 cm.)

$300–400

590, 592, 591

595, 594, 596, 597, 593, 594

598

599

593 **An American Silver Ash Tray, makers' mark B&M, 1956/57**

Circular, inset with a 1956 quarter, inscribed "N.G.A. 6.8.57 J.B.K".

$150–200

594 **Four American Silver Ash Trays, unmarked, mid 20th Century**

Gadroon bordered circular, the centers engraved with the initial K.
Diameter 3¼ in. (8.3 cm.)

Together with:

A Set of Ten American Silver Ashtrays, Matthews Company, Newark, New Jersey, mid 20th Century

Plain circular, molded borders.
Diameter 3⅝ in. (9.2 cm.)

$400–600

595 **Twelve American Silver Ash Trays, makers' mark a monogram, circa 1950**

Rectangular with cut corners, die-stamped borders, the centers engraved with the initials JBK (Jacqueline Bouvier Kennedy).
Length 3 in. (8 cm.)

$150–200

596 **An American Silver Cigarette Lighter, Fisher Silversmiths Inc., New Jersey and New York, mid 20th Century**

Compressed vase-shaped, plain, electroplated mechanism, stamped "2531 'Paul Revere' 1768 Reproduction".
Height 3 in. (7.5 cm.)

$150–200

597 **An American Silver Candy Dish, Gorham Mfg. Co., Providence, Rhode Island, mid 20th Century**

Heart-shaped, pierced and embossed, on three ball supports, stamped "966".
Length 5 in. (12.5 cm.)

$150–200

598 **An Electroplate Vegetable Dish, Liner and Covers, unmarked, English, circa 1950**

Gadroon bordered oblong, the detachable liner with two depressions, each with a detachable cover.
Length 13 in. (33 cm.)

$50–100

599 **An Indian Enameled Gold Box, Jaipur, late 19th/early 20th Century**

Of rectangular form with cover hinged on one side, enameled in red, blue, white and green on the gold ground, the top decorated with a tiger attacking a gazelle, the underside with an elephant, scrolling foliate vine in the field.
2¼ by 3¼ in. (5.7 by 8.3 cm.)

$2,000–3,000

600

600

600 **Four Engraved Aquatints from *Select Views of India* by William Hodges (1744-1797), 1783-87**

Aquatint on European paper, each inscribed with titles including "A View of the S. Well Side of Chunar Gur, 1783"; "A View of Part of the Palace of the Late Nawals Suja al Dowla at Fizabad"; "A View of the Bridge at Honpoor over the River Goonity, 1787"; and "A View of Part of the Palace of the Late Nawals Suja al Dowla at Fizabad."
12 ¼ by 18 in. (31.1 by 45.7 cm.)

William Hodges, an artist trained in the classical tradition of his mentor Richard Wilson, was the official artist on Captain Cook's second voyage to the Pacific from 1772 to 1775. After this tour and the death of his wife in 1777, he decided to visit India, arriving there in 1780. He traveled extensively through the country and painted productively under the patronage of Warren Hastings and later Augustus Cleveland.

Professional artists began to record views of the famous Indian monuments and countryside by the end of the 18th century. Not only was the British public eager for pictures of the exotic land, but the large numbers of

600

600

citizens working for the East India Company wanted records of India and its peoples.

Hodges developed a very individual vision of India, his landscapes were spontaneous and often included monuments of seemingly little historical importance. They reflected a personal style that Mildred Archer and Ronald Lightbrown describe as follows: "The impressionistic style of Hodges' pictures was as novel as his subject matter. He conveyed the towering bulk of many Indian monuments by exaggerated proportions and foreshortened perspective. The countryside is shown rough with stunted shrubs and windswept trees; paint is vigorously applied—a contemporary critic in fact complained of the 'ragged' mode of colouring; all his pictures appear as if they were unfinished, and as if the colours were laid on the canvas with a skewer" (Archer and Lightbrown, *India Observed, India as Viewed by British Artists 1760-1860*, exhibition catalogue, Victoria and Albert Museum, London, 1980, p. 10).

$4,000–6,000

601

601 **An Architectural Study of the Private Audience Hall (Diwan I Khass) in the Red Fort of Delhi, Company School, circa 1820-30**

Inscribed in Persian nasta'liq script "A picture of the Diwan I Khass of the Qil 'ah-i Mubarak (Blessed Fort) of Shah Jahanabad", watercolor on paper.
12 ¼ by 18 ½ in. (31.1 by 47 cm.)

Provenance:
Eyre & Hobhouse, London

For a comparison see S. C. Welch, *Room for Wonder, Indian Paintings during the British Period 1760-1880*, exhibition catalogue, The American Federation of Arts, New York, 1978, no. 50.

$2,500–3,500

602

603

602 **A Small Architectural Study of a Lake Pavilion, Company School, 19th Century**

Watercolor on European paper, inscribed "Bassi Bagh".
4 ½ by 7 ½ in. (11.4 by 19 cm.)

$700–1,000

603 **An Illustrated Folio from a Manuscript of the *Khamsa* by Amir Khusrau Dihvali, Deccan, Sultanate School, circa 15th Century**

A turbaned man kneeling before another man on horseback, stylized colored rocks in the background; *four columns of Persian nasta'liq text above, gouache on paper.*
Folio: 11 ¼ by 8 ½ in. (28.6 by 21.6 cm.)

Provenance:
Prince Sadruddin Aga Khan Collection, Geneva (inscribed on the reverse of frame "from Sadri, Geneva airport - Feb of 1966")

Compare:
Edwin Binney, 3rd, *Indian Miniature Painting from the Collection of Edwin Binney, 3rd, I, The Mughal and Deccani Schools*, exhibition catalogue, Portland Art Museum, Portland, Oregon, nos. 1 a-b, illus. (detail)

Other dispersed leaves from this manuscript are in the Nelson-Atkins Museum, the Los Angeles County Museum of Art, the Seattle Art Museum, the Arthur M. Sackler Gallery (Vever Collection), and the Freer Gallery.

$2,500–3,500

Two Illustrations from the 'Victoria And Albert Museum' *Akbarnama*

The *Akbarnama* is the most prestigious and informative of the historical texts written for the Mughal emperor Akbar (1556-1605) and illustrated by his court artists. In the tradition adhered to by his grandfather Babur, Akbar commissioned a comprehensive memoir of the events of his reign. He gave the task to Abul Fazl, his Prime Minister and biographer, who completed several volumes of the *Akbarnama* before his death in 1602. Akbar ordered manuscript copies of this significant contemporary text, with illustrations provided by the artists of his great atelier. Of the two surviving illustrated copies, the one now in the Victoria and Albert Museum, London is generally acknowledged as the earliest and grandest. (A somewhat later illustrated *Akbarnama* is the manuscript known as the 'Chester Beatty' *Akbarnama*, datable towards the end of Akbar's reign, and of which one volume is in the Chester Beatty Library, Dublin, and another is in the British Library, London.) The Victoria and Albert Museum's volume covers the years 1560-1578 and contains 116 illustrations, representing the zenith of the Mughal historical style of Akbar's atelier. As with the present two illustrations, almost all of the few stray pages from this *Akbarnama* depict incidents from before the period covered by the Victoria and Albert volume.

These two pages illustrate events from the period prior to Akbar's accession, while he was still a small child. They illustrate events which appear very close to each other in the narrative, perhaps reflecting the fact that they are from a common former collection. Both pages are mounted with the loss of any artist ascriptions of the type which typically are written in the bottom margins of the Victoria and Albert examples. There is nevertheless no reason to suppose they are not by artists represented in the Victoria and Albert series.

The text of the *Akbarnama* has been translated into English by H. Beveridge, *The Akbar Nama of Abu-i-Fazl* (originally published in Calcutta, 1898-1910, reprinted Delhi, 1972-3). Illustrations from the Victoria and Albert Museum *Akbarnama* are published in most books on Mughal painting, of which a selection is quoted here:

Beach, M.C., *The Imperial Image. Paintings for the Mughal Court*, Washington, 1981, no. 9, pp. 83-91

Brand, M. and Lowry, G. D., *Akbar's India: Art from the Mughal City of Victory*, New York, 1985, nos. 4, 14, 15, 16, 17 and 32

Sen, G., *Paintings from the Akbar Nama*, Varanasi, 1984 (with reproductions of over 40 *Akbarnama* illustrations)

604 An Illustration from the *Akbarnama*: The child Akbar wrestling with his cousin Ibrahim Mirza for possession of a drum, Mughal (royal atelier), circa 1590

The scene taking place at a garden pavilion, the two-year-old Akbar getting the better of his cousin before his uncle Mirza Kamran, his wet-nurse and numerous courtiers watching in amazement, a pair of kettle-drums with drum-sticks, the origin of the dispute, lying at the side of the dais; *illustration with four lines of* Akbarnama *text in nasta'liq calligraphy in two panels, slight discoloration and minor surface defects, mounted with blue border, inventory notes in Persian at outer edge.*
13 by 7¾ in. (33 by 19.7 cm.)

When the child Akbar, not yet three years old, was at Kabul in 1544-5 during the return to India, an incident took place which was later acclaimed as a significant omen of his imperial destiny. Humayun's younger brother Mirza Kamran had a son, Ibrahim Mirza, for whom he had hopes as successor to the Mughal throne, should Akbar not survive. The incident is described in the *Akbarnama* in terms of a glorious omen of Akbar's predestined superiority: "It chanced that on the occasion of Shab-i-Barat they had, according to the custom, brought a decorated kettle-drum for his [Mirza Kamran's] son Ibrahim Mirza. His Majesty the Shahinshah [Akbar] took a fancy to it, in accordance with the principle that the orchestra of world conquest must strike up in his name...[Mirza Kamran] made the taking of the drum a pretext for a trial of strength and a wrestling-match. Whoever conquered was to have the drum. His Majesty who was aided by heaven...rejoiced on hearing the condition. Despite his tender years, which made such actions very surprising, he, by Divine inspiration, and celestial teaching, without hesitation girt up his loins, and rolled up his sleeves, and with strong arm, which was strengthened by eternal power, stepped bravely forward. He grappled with Ibrahim Mirza...and flung him on the ground...This was the beginning of the beating of that drum of victory and conquest of his Majesty the Shahinshah, the Shadow of God, which came to be beaten above the loftiest pinnacles of earth" (Beveridge, *The Akbarnama*, Biblioteca Indica, Calcutta, 1898-1910 [reprinted Delhi, 1972-73], I, 455-6).

An interesting comparison can be made between this picture and the illustration of the same subject painted for the slightly later *Akbarnama* manuscript referred to above (Chester Beatty Library, Dublin, and British Library, London). The miniature was formerly in the Rothschild Collection and is now in the Art and History Trust Collection (T. Falk, "Rothschild Collection of Mughal Miniatures," *Persian and Mughal Art*, Colnaghi, 1976, no. 86; A. Soudavar, *Art of the Persian Courts*, New York, 1992, no. 135; M. Brand and G. Lowry, *Akbar's India*, Asia Society Galleries, New York, 1985, no. 1). In this slightly later version the pair of drums are shown attached to the back of a page-boy and in use, in contrast to the present miniature in which they are shown cast aside.

$15,000–20,000

که غریو از مجلس برخاست و از نزدیک و دور نعره آفرین بلند شد این اول نقاره فتح و نصرت حضرت شاهنشاهی بود
که بر سطح تمه عنبر او زیر قبه سپهر خضرا نواخته شد میرزا کامران که این جنگ کشتی را جهت امتحان مآل صحبت
کارزار خود با حضرت جهانبانی در ضمیر گرفته بود از مشاهده این صورت سکون بدگرفته بخود فرو رفت
و هواخواهان و نزدیکان حضرت شاهنشاهی گل گل شگفته فالهای خجسته فرا گرفتند و آنحضرت نقاره را

605 **An Illustration from the *Akbarnama*: The Mughal Emperor Humayun watching hockey and wolf-running at Tabriz in 1544, Mughal (royal atelier), circa 1590**

Humayun seated at an upper balcony watching an active scene taking place in the courtyard below, several young men wielding hockey-sticks while others flee in apparent terror from a wolf which is being restrained on a long red lead held by one of Humayun's men, many others watching and gesticulating from the sides; *illustration with panel of five lines of* Akbarnama *text in nasta'liq calligraphy, some discoloration and minor defects, mounted with narrow yellow border, an illuminated quatrain on the reverse in nasta'liq calligraphy by Abd al-Rahman, with inventory notes in Persian on border.*
12½ by 7½ in. (31.7 by 19 cm.)

$15,000–20,000

In this illustration Humayun has reached Tabriz during his exile from India, prior to his return to regain his empire there. He has spent the preceding weeks traveling in Persia and being well received by Shah Tahmasp, who had arranged various festivities and hunting parties for him in the region of Qazwin. More significantly, he furnished Humayun with a force of troops to assist him in the reconquest of northern India. Humayun set off via Ardebil and Tabriz, where "in accordance with the Shah's orders the governor put the city in fete, and decked her for his Majesty's enlightened gaze, and himself performed the rites of hospitality. The games of hockey and wolf-running for which Tabriz was famous, but which had been interdicted on account of riots, were revived by the Shah's orders for his Majesty's delectation. His Majesty visited the splendid buildings, the memorials of ancient kings—and the pleasure-parks of the city" (Beveridge, *op. cit.*, I, 443-4).

In the light of the succeeding development of painting at the Mughal court, Humayun's visit to Tabriz is now remembered for the contact he made there with the artists Mir Sayyid Ali and Abd al-Samad. These two Persian masters had been employed under the brilliant art-patronage of Shah Tahmasp, both of them contributing illustrations to the famous *Shahnama* manuscript which has received continuing recognition in this century in the ownership of the Rothschild and Houghton families. The two artists were destined to become joint founders of the new Mughal school of painting in the employ of Humayun and his son Akbar. The beginning of the passage telling of Humayun's employment of Abd al-Samad appears at the bottom of the text of this illustration: "The exquisite and magical Khwaja 'Abdu-s-Samad Shirinqalam (sweet pen) also entered into service in this city, and was much esteemed by that connoisseur of excellence. But from the hindrances of fate he could not accompany him" (Beveridge, *op. cit.*, I, 444-5). The last comment refers to the fact that Abd al-Samad did not travel immediately with Humayun to India but followed subsequently.

605

606 **Two Ladies in Discussion on a Palace Terrace, Provincial Mughal, possibly Oudh School, late 18th Century**

With flowering plants, a meadow and a lake in the background; *gouache on paper.*
7 by 6 in. (17.8 by 15.2 cm.)

$1,500–2,500

607 **A Princess Entertained by Two Female Musicians, Provincial Mughal, possibly Oudh School, circa 1760**

The princess dressed in an orange sari, seated on a floral carpet spread over a palace terrace, and holding the nozzle of a hookah pipe, a maidservant holding a flywhisk standing behind her; *gouache with gold on paper.*
10½ by 8 in. (26.7 by 20.3 cm.)

$2,000–3,000

606

607

608 Portrait of a Stallion with His Groom, Mewar School, circa 1760

The chestnut-brown horse wearing a green saddle, his groom wearing a white jama, orange patka and turban; *red borders with black nagari inscriptions at the top, gouache on paper.*
8 ¾ by 10 in. (22.2 by 25.4 cm.)

$1,500–2,000

609 Baz Bahadur and Rupmati Hunting in a Landscape, Bundi School, circa 1770

The heroic couple astride horses galloping to left along a riverbank, hunting gazelle with bows and arrows; *gouache on paper.*
6 ⅞ by 10 in. (17.5 by 25.4 cm.)

$2,500–3,500

608

609

610

610 **Maharana Ari Singh and a Nobleman Hunting Wild Boar, Rajasthan, Mewar School, circa 1760**

Each on horseback holding a sword and lance respectively, two hounds and a man holding a flywhisk in the field; *red borders with nagari inscriptions in black above, gouache on paper. 13 ⅝ by 19 in. (34.6 by 48.3 cm.)*

$2,000–3,000

611 **A Portrait of Maharaja Pratap Singh of Jaipur (1779-1803), Jaipur School, late 18th Century**

Standing and facing to right, wearing a gold jama, jewelry and turban, a gold nimbus radiating around his head; *gouache on gold paper. 8 by 5 ½ in. (20.3 by 14 cm.)*

$500–700

612 **A Lady on a Terrace Feeding a Parakeet, Guler School, circa 1770**

Dressed in a green sari and smoking a hookah pipe, seated on a floral summer carpet spread over a terrace, a maidservant seated behind her, a landscape with rolling hills in the background; *oval format with white spandrels, speckled pink outer borders, gouache with use of gold on paper. 8 ⅝ by 5 ⅞ in. (21.9 by 14.9 cm.)*

Published:
Stuart Cary Welch and Milo Cleveland Beach, *Gods, Thrones and Peacocks, Northern Indian Painting from Two Traditions: Fifteenth to Nineteenth Centuries*, exhibition catalogue, The Asia Society, Inc., New York, 1965, no. 48, illus.

$7,000–10,000

611

612

613 **A Ruler and His Mistress Strolling by a Pool in a Garden Enclosure, Guler School, circa 1800-10**

The young man holding the nozzle of a hookah pipe carried by a maidservant, two ladies bearing his bow, quiver of arrows, and sword in front of the couple, four ladies in the background with their reflections seen in the water, a red tented wall beyond; *dark blue inner border, speckled pink and white outer border decorated with ogival medallions, gouache with gold on paper.*
Image: 6 ⅜ by 4 in. (16.2 by 10.2 cm.)

$20,000–30,000

Published:
Stuart Cary Welch and Milo Cleveland Beach, *Gods, Thrones and Peacocks, Northern Indian Painting from Two Traditions: Fifteenth to Nineteenth Centuries*, exhibition catalogue, The Asia Society, Inc., New York, 1965, no. 46, color illus. (p. 38).

The ruler depicted in this painting is most likely Raja Bhup Singh of Guler (c. 1775-1826), who took charge of state affairs at Guler in 1790, following the retirement of his father Raja Prakash Chand. During his youth he is thought to have supported numerous zenana, giving rise to a genre of Guler paintings of romantic or even mildly erotic subjects, often showing him with one of his Ranis. Compare W. G. Archer, *Indian Paintings from the Punjab Hills*, London, 1973, II, p. 115, nos. 57-59. For a closely related painting of Bhup Singh strolling in a garden with a Rani, see Sotheby's, New York, June 2, 1992, no. 158.

613

614

614 **Two Women Celebrating the Festival of Holi on a Palace Terrace, Kangra School, circa 1830**

One lady dressed in off-white throwing orange henna on her companion, a canopied courtyard in the background with a group of women spraying colored dyes in several directions; *oval format with red and white spandrels, dark blue inner border with scrolling vine, speckled pink outer border, gouache on paper.*
Image: 7⅜ by 4⅝ in. (18.7 by 11.7 cm.)

Published:
Stuart Cary Welch and Milo Cleveland Beach, *Gods, Thrones and Peacocks, Northern Indian Painting from Two Traditions: Fifteenth to Nineteenth Centuries*, exhibition catalogue, The Asia Society, Inc., New York, 1965, no. 71, illus.

$3,000–5,000

615 **A Lady Playing with a Peacock on a Terrace, Garhwal School, early 19th Century**

Dressed in orange robes and dangling a strand of pearl beads above the bird's head, a man watching the lady from a balcony at upper left; *blue and red borders, gouache on paper.*
9⅛ by 6⅜ in. (23.2 by 16.2 cm.)

$1,500–2,500

616 **A Lady Enticing a Peacock with a Strand of Pearls, Kangra School, circa 1800**

The lady striding to left across a palace within a lakeside pavilion, rolling green hills in the background; *dark blue inner border, orange outer border decorated with gold, gouache with gold on paper.*
Image: 7 by 4½ in. (17.8 by 11.4 cm.)

Published:
Stuart Cary Welch and Milo Cleveland Beach, *Gods, Thrones and Peacocks, Northern Indian Painting from Two Traditions: Fifteenth to Nineteenth Centuries*, exhibition catalogue, The Asia Society, Inc., New York, 1965, no. 47, illus.

$15,000–20,000

615

616

617 **A South Indian Reverse Glass Painting, Tanjore, 19th Century**

Depicting a ruler seated in a European chair facing left, a dog beneath him and an inscription at the top.
19 by 13 in. (48.3 by 33 cm.)

$300–500

618 **Eight Reverse-Glass Paintings of Dancing Courtesans, Tanjore, 19th Century**

Including two larger paintings and six smaller works, each depicting one or two ladies in lively attitudes, dancing or seated and holding floral sprays or fans.
19¼ by 13⅝ in. (48.9 by 34.6 cm.), 9⅜ by 7¼ in. (23.8 by 18.4 cm.), and smaller

$3,000–5,000

617

618

618

619

620

619 **The Mughal Emperor Aurangzeb as a Prince Spearing a Raging Elephant before His Father Shah Jahan, Delhi School, 20th Century**

Aurangzeb on horseback prancing before the enraged bull elephant and checking his advance with the thrust of a spear, watched from left by his father and brothers; *gouache on paper. 12⅝ by 18½ in. (32.1 by 47 cm.)*

$700–1,000

620 **An Illustration from a Manuscript of Poetry, Persia, early 20th Century**

Depicting an enthroned ruler receiving courtiers on a terrace; *four columns of nasta'liq script above and below, gouache and black ink on paper. 12 by 6 in. (30.5 by 15.2 cm.)*

$500–700

621 **A Warrior on Horseback, Deccan, 18th/19th Century**

The white horse facing left and rearing up on its rider, the man dressed in a jama and turban, a saluki hound running alongside; *gouache on paper.*
8 ½ by 6 in. (21.6 by 15.2 cm.)

$500–750

622 **A Princely Couple on a Terrace, Delhi, late 19th/early 20th Century**

Painted on ivory, in leather case.
5 by 4 in. (12.7 by 10.2 cm.)

$2,500–3,500

621

622

3 **A Thai Clay Votive Tablet, Lopburi Region, circa 13th Century**

Of triangular form, molded in relief with a central image of Buddha seated in *dhyanasana*, his hands poised in *dhyana* and *bhumisparsa* mudras, surrounded by an elaborate throne with repeated diminutive images of Buddha.
Height 4 ⅛ in. (10.5 cm.)

$500–700

4 **An Indian Polychrome Wood Figure of a Maharaja, 19th Century**

Seated on a separately carved throne, wearing green floral robes, thick ribbed patka around his waist, and a jeweled turban.
Height 11 ½ in. (29.2 cm.)

$1,000–1,500

623

624

625 **A Thai Gold Jar, Ratanakosin Period, Ayutthaya or Bangkok, 18th Century**

Of ovoid form, with attached base and flaring rim, each finely embossed in relief with a stylized foliate frieze.
Height 4 ⅛ in. (10.5 cm.)

Provenance:
J. J. Klejman, New York

$3,000–4,000

626 **A Thai Gold Spice Box and Cover, Bangkok, 19th Century**

Of compressed spherical form, embossed with stylized foliate motifs, and surmounted by a tiered top enameled in red and green. Together with two similarly decorated spice box finials. (3)
Height of first 3 in. (7.6 cm.)

$400–600

627 **An Italian Marble Medallion Relief, 19th Century**

Carved with the head of a goddess facing right, her wavy hair bound in a sakkos, two long spiral curls escaping in front of the ear.
15 by 11 ½ in. (38.1 by 29.2 cm.)

$12,000–18,000

625

626

627

628

629

628 **A Hellenistic Marble Head of a Goddess, circa 2nd/1st Century B.C.**

Turned slightly to her right, with long straight nose, large eyes, and centrally parted hair bound in a diadem of rosettes and tied in a spiral chignon behind.
Height 3 in. (7.6 cm.)

Provenance:
J. J. Klejman, New York, 1962

$2,000–3,000

629 **A Roman Marble Head of a Man, circa mid 3rd Century A.D.**

From a high relief, his vigorously carved head turned sharply to his left, his face with long unruly beard and moustache, eyes with incised irises and dotted pupils, and strong prominent brows, his hair parted in the center and swept back in flowing wavy curls, the beard, moustache, and hair deeply drilled.
Height 7¾ in. (19.7 cm.)

$7,000–10,000

630 **A Roman Marble Torso of a God or Hero, circa 2nd Century A.D.**

From a high relief, with powerfully delineated musculature, tooled leather or chain-mail guards bound with straps to the arms.
Height 13¼ in. (33.7 cm.)

$10,000–15,000

630

631 **A Roman Marble Hekateion Finial, circa 2nd Century A.D.**

Inspired by a Greek prototype, in the form of the triple-headed Hekate, each face with full lips and straight nose and brow, the long centrally parted hair surmounted by a crested and crenellated diadem, a central polos with a moon crescent behind them.
Height 3½ in. (8.9 cm.)

Provenance:
J. J. Klejman, New York

Compare Comstock and Vermeule, *Sculpture in Stone, The Greek, Roman and Etruscan Collections of the Museum of Fine Arts Boston*, 1976, p. 125, no. 192.

As in the present example Hekate was usually represented by three figures standing back to back, each holding her own special attributes. The goddess, only daughter of the Titan Perses and Asteria, sister of Leto, had a celebrated temple near Stratonicea in Caria. The last day of the month was especially sacred to her, and young dogs, black ewes, honey, eggs, fish, and onions were offered and sacrificed. All enchanters and enchantresses were the goddess's disciples and protégés, and Medea was particularly regarded as her votary.

$3,000–5,000

631

632 **A Greek Terracotta Figure of Dionysos, Tarentine, 1st half of the 4th Century B.C.**

Molded in relief with the young god reclining on the back of a goat in the pose of a banqueteer, and wearing a long himation and high pilos surmounting the long coiffure, a phiale mesomphalos in his right hand, the goat with long tapering horns and head turned slightly to the right; traces of blue and red pigment over white gesso.
Height 6¼ in. (15.9 cm.)

Compare *Catalogue Raisonné des Figurines et Reliefs en Terre-cuite Grecs Étrusques et Romains, Musée du Louvre*, Paris, 1954, pl. XIII, no. C43, a figure of Dionysos resting on a mule.

$3,000–5,000

632

633

633 **A Greek Terracotta Figure of a Youth, Boeotia, 3rd Century B.C.**

Seated on a rocky outcrop with his right foot advanced, his left hand held up to his chest, and wearing an enveloping himation and hat with large rolled brim, a large rectangular vent-hole behind; traces of pigment remaining.
Height: 5½ in. (14 cm.)

$2,000–3,000

634

635

634 **A Roman Bronze Figure of Hygeia, circa 1st Century A.D.**

The goddess of health and daughter of Asklepios standing in a graceful attitude on a high turned pedestal with her weight on the right leg, a serpent coiled around her left arm, a fragmentary attribute in her right hand, and wearing a long chiton and Egyptian mantle falling from the left shoulder, her finely engraved coiffure parted in the center, bound in a chignon behind, and surmounted by a crescentic diadem and high polos.
Height with pedestal 6½ in. (16.5 cm.)

Regarding the example in the Fleischman Collection (*A Passion for Antiquities*, Malibu, 1994, no. 156), Ariel Herrmann notes: "Small images of the healing gods must frequently have been votive offerings or objects of household devotion for people acknowledging or hoping for cures from illness as well as for physicians."

$6,000–9,000

635 **A Roman Bronze Figure of Aphrodite, circa 1st/2nd Century A.D.**

Inspired by a Hellenistic statue of the late 4th Century B.C., perhaps the Capitoline Aphrodite, of slender form, standing with her weight on the left leg and holding her right hand to her breast, the engraved centrally parted coiffure surmounted by a high crested diadem and swept back into a chignon above the nape of the neck, a gold wire bracelet remaining on the right forearm.
Height 5 in. (12.7 cm.)

Compare Robert Fleischer, *Die römischen Bronzen aus Österreich*, Mainz, 1967, no. 78.

$4,000–6,000

636

636 **A Roman Bronze Figure of a Horse, circa 3rd Century A.D.**

Stepping forward in a lively attitude on a rectangular base, with the head turned to the left and the left front hoof raised and resting on a *tabula ansata*, and with short erect tail and open mouth, the details of the neck and mane engraved, a loop positioned behind the right hind leg.
Length 2 3/8 in. (6 cm.)

$1,500–2,500

637

637 **A Roman Bronze Handle, circa 1st Century A.D.**

Perhaps from a knife or dagger, in the form of a lion springing from acanthus leaves and devouring the head of a wild boar clasped in his paws, the details finely engraved.
Length 3 1/2 in. (8.9 cm.)

Compare David Gordon Mitten, *Classical Bronzes, Catalogue of the Collection, Museum of Art, Rhode Island School of Design*, Providence, 1975, p. 155, no. 43, a similar handle with a panther attacking a fawn.

$2,000–3,000

638 Two Pottery Vessels

Comprising a Greek gray-ware trefoil oinochoe, *5th/4th Century B.C.*, with low foot, ovoid body, and cylindrical handle, a grayish-brown slip overall, and a Hellenistic red-ware jug, *circa 2nd/1st Century B.C.*, of slender tapering form with flaring mouth and ribbed handle.
Heights 7 and 7¼ in. (17.8 and 18.4 cm.)

$500–800

639 An Egyptian Bronze Figure of Nefertum, Late Period, 716-30 B.C.

Striding on a rectangular base rounded at the corners, his arms held to his sides, and wearing a striated kilt and his tall composite lotus crown, a fragmentary pendant loop behind.
Height 3⅜ in. (8.6 cm.)

Compare W. M. Flinders Petrie, *Amulets*, London, 1914, pl. XXX, no. 175e.

$200–300

640 An Egyptian Bronze Figure of Osiris, Late Period, 716-30 B.C.

Standing and holding the crook and flail, and wearing a short beard and the *atef*-crown with uraeus.
Height 3¾ in. (9.5 cm.)

$200–300

641 An Egyptian Banded Alabaster Jar, Old Kingdom, 6th Dynasty, 2360-2195 B.C.

With everted rounded rim and slender ovoid body tapering to a small flat base.
Height 14½ in. (36.8 cm.)

Compare W. M. Flinders Petrie, *The Funeral Furniture of Egypt with Stone and Metal Vases*, London, 1937, pl. XXVIII, no. 577.

This jar was given to Jacqueline Kennedy Onassis by Anwar Sadat in 1974.

$6,000–9,000

638

639, 640

641

642

642 **A Greek Terracotta Figure of a Woman, Boeotia, circa 3rd Century B.C.**

Leaning in a contemplative attitude against a column with her weight on the right leg and head turned to the left, and wearing a long chiton and himation falling in graceful folds and leaving the right shoulder bare, her right hand crossing her breasts and gathering the folds of her garment, her wavy hair swept back into a large chignon; traces of pink and gray pigment over white gesso, an old German exhibition label underneath.
Height 9¼ in. (23.5 cm.)

$6,000–9,000

643

643 A Greek Terracotta Figure of Aphrodite, circa late 4th Century B.C.

Standing on an oval base with her weight on the left leg, and wearing a long himation gathered into folds in her left hand and held up behind her head in the right hand, the breasts left bare, her coiffure parted in the center and swept back in spiral braids; remains of pigment, an old German exhibition label underneath.
Height 9¾ in. (24.8 cm.)

$4,000–6,000

644 No Lot

645

646

647

645 A Fragmentary Persian Luster-ware Cup, Seljuk, early 13th Century A.D.

With splayed foot, the flaring sides reserved in white against the brown luster ground with a frieze of spotted hounds running against a scrolling tendril ground.
Height 2½ in. (6.3 cm.)

$400–600

646 A Small Painted Neolithic Jar, Machang Type, Yangshao Culture

Thinly potted, the compressed ovoid body freely painted in reddish-brown and black with a wide striated band, the neck decorated with cross-hatch-infilled lozenges and set with loop handles, *four apertures on mouth, chips.*
Height 3½ in. (8.9 cm.)

$300–350

647 A Group of Five Pieces of Ethnographic Jewelry

Including two Naga necklaces composed of single strands of coral beads interrupted by boar's teeth and turquoise beads, a Naga choker composed of four boar's tusks joined by steel and red beads, a Turkoman silver cuff inset with amber-color glass oval sections, and a Naga necklace composed of multiple strands of cinnabar cylindrical glass beads terminating in strands with turquoise, orange, indigo, white and yellow beads, with a clasp of an Indian coin dated *1941* and a Burmese(?) coin. Contained in an M. Lafleur brass-mounted leather small trunk.

The trunk 8 by 9½ in. (20.3 by 24.1 cm.)

$1,000–1,500

648

649

648 Oliver Smith

DECOR DESIGN FOR CAMELOT

gouache and pencil on artist's board, signed, titled, inscribed *Outside Camelot* and dedicated *For Jackie, with love—Merry Christmas 1966*; inscribed *Painting elevation: opening of Act I* on reverse
18 by 26 in. (45.7 by 66 cm.)

Jacqueline Kennedy Onassis was a great lover of ballet and a frequent patron of American Ballet Theatre, of which Oliver Smith was the co-director from 1945-1980.

$1,000–1,500

649 Oliver Smith

DECOR DESIGN FOR "THE EMBASSY" IN MY FAIR LADY

watercolor and pencil on paper, signed, titled and dated '76
Sight 6½ by 10½ in. (16.5 by 26.7 cm.)

Provenance:
The Touchstone Gallery, Inc., New York

$1,000–1,500

651

650

650 **British School, 20th Century**

GENTLEMAN ON HORSEBACK BY A GOTHIC FOLLY

watercolor and ink on paper
14 by 10 in. (35.6 by 25.4 cm.)

The watercolor depicts the Gothic Octagon created by the Hon. Charles Hamilton in 1775 for his extensive landscape garden at Pain's Hill in Surrey. Hamilton was a noted amateur of the Picturesque and modeled his landscape garden after the Italianate images found in the paintings of Poussin.

A series of ink sketches of characters drawn in the style of various artists (for example, Dufy and Van Dongen) appears on the *verso*

$200–300

651 **Oliver Smith**

DECOR DESIGN FOR THE SLEEPING BEAUTY

watercolor on artist's board, signed and dated '74
13 ¾ by 17 ½ in. (34.9 by 44.4 cm.)

Provenance:
The Touchstone Gallery, Inc., New York

$1,000–1,500

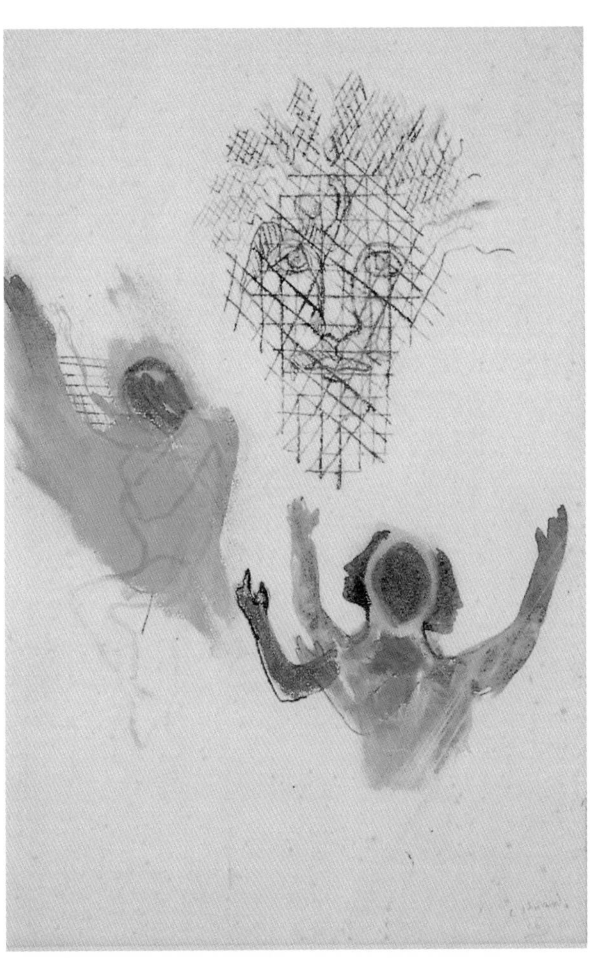

652

652 **Christian Berard**

ETUDE

gouache on paper laid down on board, signed and dated '26
17 by 11 ½ in. (43.2 by 29.2 cm.)

Provenance:
Alexandre Iolas, New York

$1,000–1,500

653 **Madeline Hewes (20th Century)**

ARAB IN DESERT SEATED ON CARPET WITH TIGER

signed *M. Hewes*, l.r.; also inscribed *Proverb: Chapter 2, verse 19; "It is better to dwell in the wilderness, than with a contentious and angry woman"* on the reverse
tempera on masonite
17 by 20 in. (43.2 by 50.8 cm.)

Painted in 1961.

This painting was among the furnishings in the West Sitting Room of the White House during President and Mrs. Kennedy's residence.

$300–400

653

654

655

654 Madeline Hewes (20th Century)

CATFISH CREEK

signed *M. Hewes*, l.r.
tempera on masonite
17 by 23 in. (43.2 by 58.4 cm.)

Painted in 1961.

Provenance:
Maynard Walker Gallery, New York, 1961

$300–500

655 Sorines Mentor

SANS TITRE

oil on masonite
24 by 16 in. (61 by 40.6 cm.)

Painted circa 1960.

$600–800

656 Philomé Obin

PARADIS TERRESTRE APRÈS JE PÉCHÉ

signed and titled
oil on masonite
10 ¼ by 24 ¼ in. (26 by 61.6 cm.)

Painted circa 1960.

$5,000–7,000

656

657 **Charles Baskerville (b. 1896)**

GUARDIANS OF THE PORTAL OF THE TEMPLE, RAJASTHAN, INDIA

signed *Charles Baskerville*, l.l.
watercolor on paper
17 by 14 in. (43.2 by 35.6 cm.)

Exhibited:
Palm Beach, Florida, Palm Beach Galleries, n.d.

$800–1,200

658 **Préfète Duffaut**

SANS TITRE

signed and inscribed *Jecmel, Haiti*
oil on masonite
28 by 30 in. (71.1 by 76.2 cm.)

Painted circa 1960.

Provenance:
Sale: New York, Parke Bernet Eighty-Four, May 7, 1980, Sale 757, lot 23, illustrated

Exhibited:
Alpena, Jane Besser Museum, *Haitian Painting—The Bold and the Beautiful*, 1976

$800–1,200

658

657

659 **Indian Art, History and Culture**

A group of 36 volumes. Illustrated, chiefly in publisher's cloth and wrappers. Varying sizes and conditions.

Louis Rousselet. *India and its Native Princes.* 1878. — Heinrich Zimmer. *The Art of Indian Asia.* 1955. 2 vols. — Toby Falk and Mildred Archer. *Indian Miniatures in the India Office Library.* 1981. — *Krishna, The Divine Lover. Myth and Legend through Indian Art.* 1982. — Pratapaditya Pal. *Court Paintings of India 16th-19th Centuries.* 1983. — Pramod Chandra. *The Sculpture of India 3000 B. C.-1300 A. D.* 1985. Naveen Patnaik. *A Second Paradise. Indian Courtly Life 1590-1947.* 1985. — Virginia Fass. *The Forts of India.* 1986. — and others.

$700–1,000

660 **Indian Art**

A group of 29 volumes, chiefly on Indian miniatures, drawing, and painting. Illustrated; most in publisher's cloth and wrappers. Varying sizes and conditions.

M. S. Randhawa. *Kangra Valley Painting.* 1954. — Eric Dickinson. *Kishangarh Painting.* 1959. — M. S. Randhawa. *Basohli Painting.* 1959. — W. G. Archer. *Indian Miniatures.* 1960. — Lubor Hajek. *Indische Miniaturen der Lokalen Schulen.* 1960. 2 copies (one English translation). — M. S. Randhawa. *Kangra Paintings of the Bhagavata Purana.* 1960. — Idem. *Kangra Paintings of the Gita Govinda.* 1963. — Stuart Cary Welch. *Indian Drawings and Painted Sketches.* 1976. — Francis Wacziarg and Aman Nath. *Rajasthan; The Painted Walls of Shekhavati.* 1982. — Mark Zebrowski. *Deccani Painting.* 1983. — and others.

$700–1,000

661 **Jackson, A. V. Williams, ed.**

History of India. *London: The Grolier Society, (1906–1907)*

9 volumes (9⅛ x 6¼ in.). Hand- tinted photogravure frontispieces, plates and text illustrations. Publisher's rust buckram, printed spine labels, top edges gilt; extremities of a few volumes bumped.

The Baroda Edition of this once-standard history of India.

$400–600

662 **India**

A group of 17 volumes, various sizes. Some illustrated. Publisher's cloth.

H. Beveridge. *The Akbarnama.* 1904. — Jahangir. *The Tuzuk-i-Jahangeri.* 1909. — W.G. Archer. *The Loves of Krishna.* 1957. — Jawaharlal Nehru. *Toward Freedom.* 1958. 2 copies. — Vitold de Golish. *Splendeur et Crépuscule des Naharajha.* 1963. — Yasuf Husain. *The First Nizam.* 1963. — William Plomer. *The Diamond of Jannina.* 1970. — Maharani of Jaipur. *A Princess Remembers.* 1976. — Rumer Godden. *Gulbadan.* 1980. — Percival Spear. *The Nabobs.* 1980. — and others.

$500–700

663 **West, Edward W., ed.**

Diary of the late Rajah of Kolhapoor, during his Visit to Europe in 1870. *London: Smith, Elder, 1872*

(8⅝ x 6½ in.). Additional lithographed title-page with tinted vignette, handcolored engraved frontispiece portrait of the Rajah, engraved portrait plate of the Rajah on India paper mounted, mounted albumen photograph portrait of Narrain Rao, successor to the Kolhapoor Gadee. Contemporary green morocco gilt, slate brown endpapers, all edges gilt; extremities a bit rubbed.

Presentation copy, with an accomplished presentation leaf forwarding the volume to Mrs. Borthwick from the family of the late Rajah of Kolhapoor.

$400–600

664 **Indian Art**

Group of 9 volumes, various sizes. Illustrated. Publisher's cloth, some with dust-jackets. Various places, various dates.

C. S. H. Jhabvala. *Delhi Stones and Streets.* 1990. Signed by the author. — Stuart Cary Welch. *Gods, Thrones and Peacocks.* 1965. Inscribed by the author "For Jackie who deserves one of these." — Elizabeth B. Moynihan. *Paradise as a Garden.* 1979. Signed "Jacqueline Kennedy Onassis." — Stuart Cary Welch. *Room for Wonder.* 1978. Signed "Jacqueline Kennedy Onassis." — Stuart Cary Welch. *A Flower from Every Meadow.* 1973. Signed "Jacqueline Kennedy Onassis." — Rudolf von Leyden. Ganjifa. *The Playing Cards of India.* 1981. Signed "Jacqueline Kennedy Onassis." — Pratapaditya Pal. *Elephants and Ivories in South Asia.* 1981. Signed "Jacqueline Kennedy Onassis." — Philip S. Rawson. *Indian Painting.* 1961. Bookplate of Jacqueline Bouvier Kennedy. — and another.

$600–900

665 **Indian Philosophy and Culture**

Group of 10 volumes, various sizes. Mostly publisher's cloth or wrappers, some with dust-jackets. Various places, various dates.

Radhakrishnan. *Indian Philosophy.* Volumes I and II. 1962 and 1958. Signed by the author. Bookplates of Jacqueline Bouvier Kennedy. — Radhakrishnan. *Religion and Society.* 1959. Signed by the author. Bookplate of Jacqueline Bouvier Kennedy. — Radhakrishnan. *East and West.* 1954. Inscribed by the author "Mrs & Mr Kennedy Best wishes." — Radhakrishnan. *An Idealist View of Life.* 1957. Inscribed by the author "Mrs & Mr Kennedy with cordial good wishes for the future." — Radhakrishnan. *My Search for Truth.* Signed by the author. Bookplate of Jacqueline Bouvier Kennedy. — John Brough. *Poems from the Sanskrit.* 1982. Signed "J.K.O." — M. N. Das. *The Political Philosophy of Jawaharlal Nehru.* 1961. Bookplate of Jacqueline Kennedy. — and 2 others.

$400–600

66 **Indian Art**

Group of 14 volumes, various sizes. All/most illustrated. Publisher's cloth or wrappers, some with dust-jackets . Various places, various dates.

Jules Hermes. *The Children of India.* 1993. Inscribed by the author "For Jackie, Thanks for your encouragement." — Naveen Patnaik. *A Second Paradise.* 1985. Inscribed by the author "To dear Jackie–traditionally people come to India in search of their gurus. It was my good fortune that my guru came to India. In every sense this book is a tribute to you." — Bedrich Forman. *Borobudur.* 1980. Inscribed. — Andrew Robinson. *Maharaja.* 1988. Inscribed. — Mildred Archer. *Early Views of India.* 1980. Signed "Jacqueline Kennedy." — Ray Desmond. *Victorian India in Focus.* 1982. Signed "Jacqueline Kennedy Onassis." — Robert Bussabarger. *The Everyday Art of India.* 1968. Signed "Jacqueline Kennedy Onassis." — W. G. Archer. *Visions of Courtly India.* 1976. Signed "J.K.O." —*Rabindranath Tagore: A Centenary Volume 1861-1961.* 1961. Bookplate of Jacqueline Bouvier Kennedy. — Roderick Cameron. *Shadows from India.* 1958. Bookplate of Jacqueline Bouvier Kennedy. — Jean Filliozat. *Inde.* 1961. Bookplate of Jacqueline Bouvier Kennedy. — Ananda K. Coomaraswamy. *The Dance of Shiva.* Bookplate of Jacqueline Bouvier Kennedy. — and 2 others.

$500–700

67 **Indian Art**

Group of 15 volumes, various sizes. Illustrated. Publisher's cloth or wrappers, some with dust-jackets. Various places, various dates.

Judith Gutman. *Through Indian Eyes.* 1982. Inscribed "For Jacqueline Kennedy Onassis with respect and admiration." — Ghika. *India.* 1959. Inscribed "for Jacky en souvenir." — Richard Ettinghausen. *Paintings of the Sultans and Emperors.* 1961. With inscribed card of the author. — Basil Gray. *The Arts of India.* 1981. Signed "Jacqueline Kennedy Onassis." — Pradumna Tana and Rosalba Tana. *Traditional Designs from India.* 1981. Signed "Jacqueline Kennedy Onassis." — *The Imperial Image : Paintings for the Mughal Court.* 1981. Signed "Jacqueline Kennedy Onassis." — Rai Krishnadasa. *Mughal Miniatures.* 1955. Bookplate of Jacqueline Bouvier Kennedy. — W. G. Archer. *Indian Painting.* 1965. Bookplate of Jacqueline Bouvier Kennedy. — Pramod Chandra. *Bundi Painting.* 1959. Bookplate of Jacqueline Bouvier Kennedy. — M. S. Randhawa. *Kangra Valley Painting.* 1954. Bookplate of Jacqueline Bouvier Kennedy. — and 5 others.

$400–600

668 **Layard, Austin Henry**

The Monuments of Nineveh. *London: John Murray, 1849*

Broadsheets (22 x 14½ in.). 100 Engraved plates of which 4 are hand-colored and mounted on heavier stock, a few others tinted; light dampstaining. Contemporary half morocco over marbled boards; a little worn.

$600–800

669 **Alsop, Joseph**

From the Silent Earth: A Report on the Greek Bronze Age. *New York: Harper & Row, 1964*

(8¼ x 6 in.). Blue cloth, dust-jacket.

Two copies, both very warmly INSCRIBED; the first, undated, presumably from 1964: "For dearest Jackie—The one thing I've ever written I used to hope the President would read—with more admiration & more love than I can possibly express—Joe Alsop." The second: "For darling Jackie, One of the women I've most admired in my life ... Joseph Alsop, 9/7/86."

$500–800

670 **Middle Eastern Art**

A group of 14 illustrated volumes. Publisher's cloth and wrappers. Varying sizes and conditions.

Richard Ettinghausen. *Arab Painting.* 1962. — Alberto Arbasino. *I Turchi. Codex Vindobonensis 8626.* Deluxe edition, boxed. 1971. — Esin Atil. *Art of the Arab World.* 1975. — Metin Aud. *Turkish Miniature Painting.* 1982. — Franco Maria Ricci. *Qajar. La pittura di corte in Persia.* Deluxe edition, boxed. 1982. — Oleg Grabar and others. *Treasures of Islam.* 1985. — and others.

$300–500

671 **Antiquity: Egyptian, Greek, Roman, and Early Byzantine Art**

A group of 44 illustrated volumes (some duplicates), various sizes. Publisher's cloth with dust jackets. Various places, various dates.

Gisela Richter. *A Handbook of Greek Art.* 1959. — Edward L. B. Terrace. *Egyptian Paintings of the Middle Kingdom.* [1967]. — Giuseppe Bovini. *Ravenna.* 1971. — Nicholas Platon. *Zakros; The Discovery of a Lost Palace of Ancient Crete.* 1971. — John Travlos. *Pictorial Dictionary of Ancient Athens.* 1971. — S. M. Pelekanidis and others. *The Treasures of Mount Athos: Illuminated Manuscripts.* 1974. 1 vol. only. Manolis Andronicos. *Vergina: The Royal Tombs.* 1984. — Athanasios D. Kominis, ed. *Patmos, Treasures of the Monastery.* 1988. — *Thera and the Aegean World.* 3 vols. 1990. — Christos Doumans. *The Wall-Paintings of Thera.* 1992. — and others.

$1,000–1,500

672 **The Ancient World**

A group of 32 volumes, various sizes. some illustrated. Publisher's cloth and wrappers.

Henry Salt. *Essay on Dr. Young's and M. Champollion's Phonetic System of Hieroglyphics.* 1825. — Ivan Lissner. *The Caesars: Might and Madness.* 1958. — Nelson Glueck. *Rivers in the Desert.* 1959. — Paul MacKendrick. *The Greek Stones Speak.* 1962. — Joseph Alsop. *From the Silent Earth.* 1964. — Stringfellow Barr. *The Will of Zeus.* 1965. — C. W. Ceram. *Hands on the Past.* 1966. — Aubrey de Sélincourt. *The World of Herodotus.* 1982. — and others.

$300–500

675

673 **The Ancient World**

Group of 9 volumes, various sizes. All illustrated. Publisher's cloth or wrappers, some with dust jackets. Various places, various dates.

Edward Bacon. *Digging for History*. 1960. — André Parrot. *Sumer*. 1960. — Bernard Ashmole. *Architect & Sculptor in Classical Greece*. 1972. Printed "compliments" note of Charles and Jayne Wrightsman. — Champollion. *Principes généraux de l'écriture sacrée égyptienne*. 1984. — *Cleopatra's Egypt: Age of the Ptolemies*. Brooklyn Museum, 1988. Inscribed: "For JKO, Thanks for coming, 'Dr. Bob' Bianchi, 6 Oct 88." — and 4 others.

$400–600

674 **Asian Art**

A group of 21 illustrated volumes. Publisher's cloth and wrappers. Various places, various dates.

Daniel Sheets Dye. *A Grammar of Chinese Lattice*. 2 vols. 1937. — Malcolm MacDonald. *Angkor*. 1960. — Hugh Honour. *Chinoiserie*. 1962. — J. Boisselier. *Le Cambodge*. 1966. — Bernard Groslier and Jacques Arthaud. *Angkor: Art and Civilization*. 1966. — and others.

$1,000–1,500

675 **Parks, Fanny**

Wanderings of a Pilgrim, in Search of the Picturesque, during Four-and-Twenty Years in the East; with Revelations of Life in the Zenana. *London: Pelham Richardson, 1850*

2 volumes (10½ x 7⅛ in.). 49 (of 50) lithographed plates, some tinted, some handcolored. Contemporary brown morocco gilt, marbled endpapers, gilt edges.

$300–400

676 **The Mediterranean and Near East**

Group of 8 volumes, various sizes. All illustrated. Publisher's cloth or wrappers, some with dust-jackets. Various places, various dates.

Stringfellow Barr. *The Will of Zeus*. 1961. BOOKPLATE of Jacqueline Bouvier Kennedy. — Roloff Beny. *A Time of Gods*. 1962. BOOKPLATE of Jacqueline Bouvier Kennedy. — J. D. S. Pendlebury. *The Archaeology of Crete*. 1963. — John Lloyd Stephens. *Incidents of Travel in Egypt, Arabia Petraea, and the Holy Land*. 1970. Warmly INSCRIBED "For Jackie, To travel with some snowy midnight, Ruth, Christmas '77". — Charles M. Doughty. *Arabia Deserta, New Illustrated Edition*. 1989. Warmly inscribed by the editor: "for Jacqueline Kennedy Onassis—who always believed in this book ..." — and 3 others.

$400–600

677 **Asia**

A group of 6 volumes, various sizes. Most illustrated. Publisher's cloth.

George Coedes. *Angkor*. 1963. — Jorgen Bisch. *Why Buddha Smiles*. 1964. — George Coedes. *The Making of South East Asia*. 1966. — Jonathan D. Spence. *Emperor of China*. 1974. — Jonathan D. Spence. *The Gate of Heavenly Peace*. 1981. — Syed Amjad Ali. *Prints and Imprints*. 1983.

$100–150

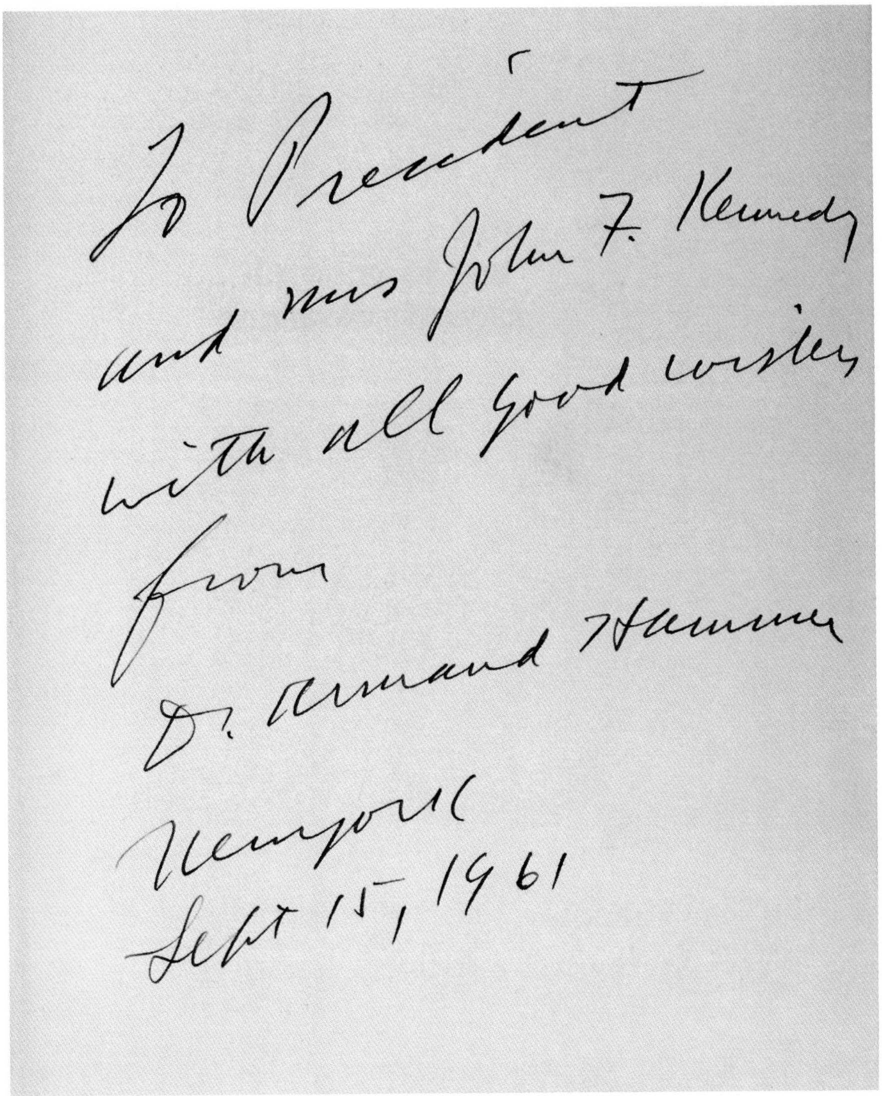
To President
and Mrs John F. Kennedy
with all good wishes
from
Dr. Armand Hammer
Newyork
Sept 15, 1961

679

678 **Oriental Art**

Group of 10 volumes, various sizes. Most illustrated. Publisher's cloth. Various places, various dates.

Yashiro Yukio. *Art Treasures of Japan.* 2 vols., 1960. INSCRIBED "to Mrs. John F. Kennedy with the compliments of Howard P. Jones, Chancellor, East-West Center, July 22, 1966." — Lynne Thornton. *The Orientalists, Painters-Travellers 1828-1908.* 1983. Signed "Jacqueline Kennedy Onassis." — Chou ta-Kuan. *Notes on the Customs of Cambodia.* 1967. INSCRIBED "To Mrs. Kennedy with best wishes from Chou ta-Kuan and the collaborators. Xmas 1967." — Chinese National Palace Museum. *Chinese Art Treasures.* 1961. Bookplate of Jacqueline Bouvier Kennedy. — and 5 other volumes inscribed to Mrs. Onassis or with her bookplate.

$600–900

679 **Hammer, Armand**

The Quest of the Romanoff Treasure. *New York: Paisley Press, 1936*

(8⅛ x 5½ in.). Photographic plates. Publisher's white cloth gilt, dust-jacket.

PRESENTATION COPY, inscribed and signed by the author on the front free endpaper: "To President and Mrs. John F. Kennedy with all good wishes from Dr. Armand Hammer, New York, Sept. 15, 1961."

$500–700

680 **Renaissance Art**

A group of 25 illustrated volumes (some duplicates), various sizes. Publisher's cloth and wrappers. Various places, various dates.

Guido Piovene. *Italie.* 1958. — Angela Ottino della Chiesa. *Botticelli and His Contemporaries.* 1960. — James Lees-Milne, intro. *Renaissance Europe.* 1961. — John Pope-Hennessy. *The Portrait in the Renaissance.* 1966 (2 copies). — Desmond Seward. *Prince of the Renaissance: The Golden Life of François I.* 1973. — Jan Bialostocki. *The Art of the Renaissance in Eastern Europe.* 1976. — Glenn Andres and others. *The Art of Florence.* 2 vols. 1988. — Lionello Venturi. *Italian Painting & the Renaissance.* [n.d.]. — and others.

$1,200–1,800

681 **Art and Art Appreciation**

A group of 14 volumes, various sizes (including 3 small paperbacks). Publisher's cloth. Various places and dates. Most with bookplate or signed by the author.

John Rewald. *History of Impressionism.* 1961. With the bookplate of Jacqueline Bouvier Kennedy. — *A Civil War Album of Paintings by the Prince of Joinville.* 1964. Signed by one of the contributors, James Gavin, to Jacqueline Kennedy, and with a letter laid-in. — Colta Ives. *The Great Wave: The Influence of Japanese Woodcuts on French Prints.* 1974. Signed by the author. — James Henry Rubin. *Eighteenth Century French Life-Drawing: Selections from the Collection of Mathias Polakovits.* 1977. Signed presentation copy from Polakovits. — Robert Fagles. *I, Vincent: Poems from the Pictures of Van Gogh.* 1978. Presentation copy to Jacqueline Kennedy Onassis "with her fine eye for color" from the author.

$400–600

682 **Art Exhibitions and Collections**

Group of 17 volumes, various sizes. Illustrated. Publisher's cloth or paper. Various places and dates. All with bookplate or presentations.

The National Gallery of Canada. *Catalogue of Paintings and Sculpture.* 1961. Presentation copy, "For Mrs. John Fitzgerald Kennedy a memento of her visit to the National Gallery of Canada, Ottawa 17th May 1961 Charles Y. Comfort, Director." — Victoria and Albert Museum. *Third International Art Treasures Exhibition.* 1962. With Jacqueline Bouvier Kennedy bookplate. — National Gallery of Art. *Treasures from the National Gallery of Art.* 1962. Signed by Jacqueline Kennedy. — Sotheby's *Art at Auction.* 9 volumes. 1970-1979, 1984-1987. — and 5 others.

$500–700

683 **Art History, Spanish and Dutch**

A group of 9 books, various sizes mostly folio. Publisher's cloth (one with publisher's wrappers). Various places and dates. Most with signature, or presentation and/or bookplate.

M.H. Grant. *Jan van Huysum, 1682–1749.* 1954. Signed, "Jacqueline Kennedy." Limited edition. — Jean Leymarie. *Dutch Painting.* 1956. Presentation copy, "To the President and Mrs. Kennedy In Remembrance of my visit to Washington, Beatrix, April 18th, 1963." — Jacques Lassaigne. *Spanish Painting from Velázquez to Picasso.* 1953. With an initialed note from Joseph Leonard, laid in, "To dearest Jacqueline – and John– wishing you peace, prosperity and happiness throughout the coming years, J.L., Eng. 1953."

$800–1,200

684 **Modern Artists**

Group of 4 volumes, various sizes, illustrated. Publisher's cloth or wrappers, 4 with dust-jackets. Various places, various dates.

Louise Nevelson. *Dawns + Dusks.* 1976. INSCRIBED to Mrs. Onassis, 12 December 1976: "This is not an autobiography. This is not a biography. This is a gift. L.N." — Saul Steinberg. *The Inspector.* 1973. INSCRIBED: "To Jacqueline O. With Affection. Saul Steinberg." — Saul Steinberg & John Hollander. *The Passport.* 1979. Signed by both. — Lucien Clergue. *Picasso mon ami.* 1993. INSCRIBED by the author: "… en souvenir de déja longue et fidèle amitié …"

$300–500

685 **Modern Painters**

Group of 5 volumes, various sizes, illustrated. Publisher's cloth or wrappers. Various places, various dates.

Jean de Botton: Retrospective. (California Palace of the Legion of Honor), 1944. INSCRIBED to "Madame J. Kennedy" by the artist, December 1960. — Elizabeth Mongan. *Berthe Morisot.* [1960]. Bookplate of Jacqueline Bouvier Kennedy. — Willy Eisenhart. *The World of Donald Evans.* 1980. INSCRIBED: "for Jackie With love and friendship from Willy + Siri(?), as ever, Oct. 81." — *Francesco Clemente pinxit.* London & Rome, 1981. INSCRIBED on separate letter, laid in: "JO dear, Happy^2 Love^3 Liz & Karl." — Ellen G. D'Oench & Hilarie Faberman. *Silvia Plimack Mangold. Works on Paper 1968–1991.* INSCRIBED: "For dearest Jackie, with love, Puffin."

$300–500

686 **Modern Photography**

Group of 4 volumes, various sizes, illustrated, 3 with presentation inscriptions. Publisher's or wrappers, two with dust-jackets. Various places, various dates.

Judith Turner. *Annotations on Ambiguity: Photographs of Architecture.* 1986. INSCRIBED: "For Jackie, Judith Turner, with love, 1987." — Alexander Liberman. *The Artist in his Studio.* 1988. INSCRIBED in silver ink: "to Jackie—Happy holidays and love, Ruth." — Hayden Herrera. *Mary Frank.* 1990. With laid in postcard to Mrs. Onassis from Mary Frank, 12 February 1994: "I was so struck [with] what you said about memorizing poetry …" — Richard Avedon. *Evidence 1944–1994.* 1994. INSCRIBED: "For Jackie with affection from Dick, 1994."

$400–600

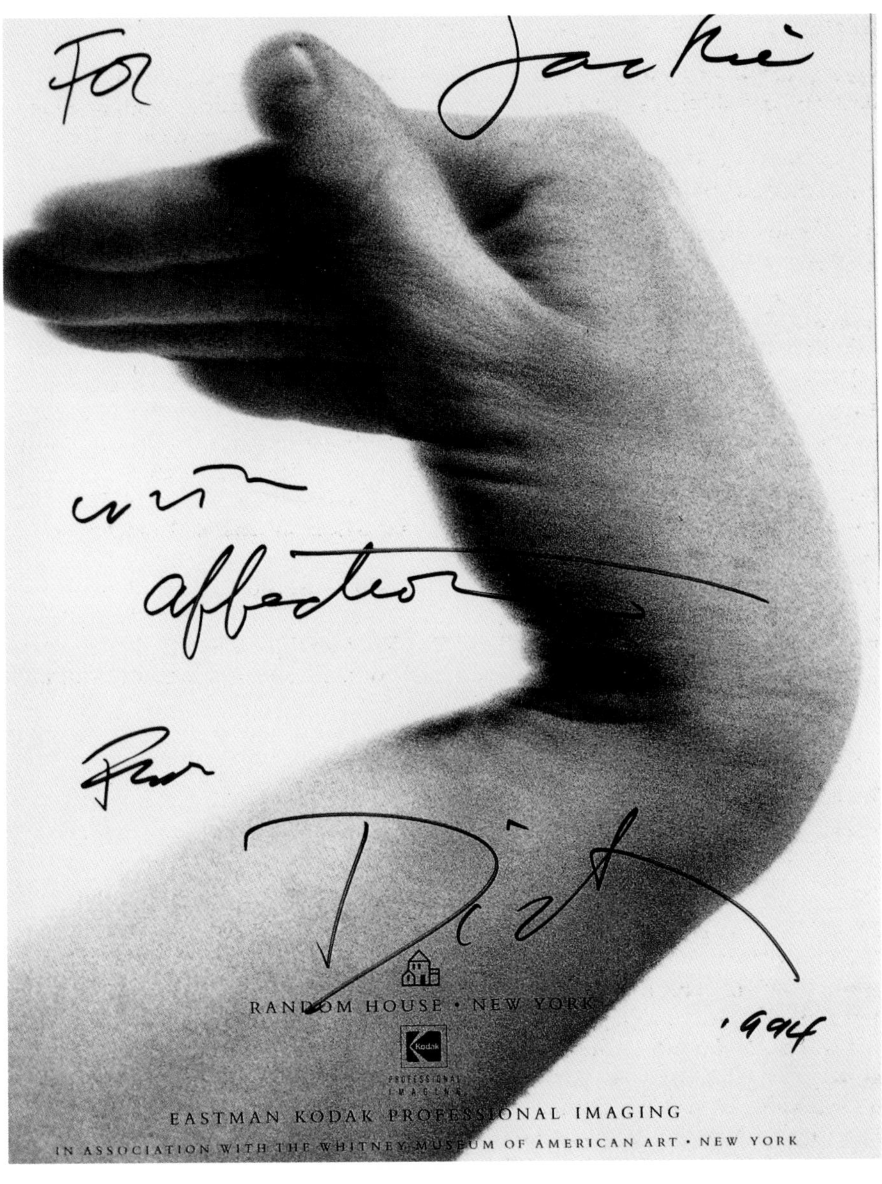

686

687 **American Art and Artists**

Group of 6 volumes, various sizes. All illustrated. Publisher's cloth. Various places, various dates.

David Douglas Duncan. *Yankee Nomad, a Photographic Odyssey*. 1966. INSCRIBED "For Jacqueline Kennedy. — There should have been another very special book before this one. Saludos, David Duncan." (Duncan refers to the project he planned in 1962 with Mrs. Kennedy, which to his lasting regret he eventually declined, to make a photographic book to be called *The White House*. The story of this project forms the final chapter of the present book, titled "With Regret.") — *The Water Colors of Dong Kingman and How the Artist Works*. 1958. INSCRIBED "To our first Lady Mrs. Jacqueline Kennedy with respects & best wishes. Dong Kingman. Feb. 61." — and 4 others.

$400–600

688 **Photography**

A group of 21 volumes, varous sizes. Mostly publisher's cloth. Various places, various dates.

Truman Capote and Richard Avedon. *Observations*. 1959. Publisher's slipcase. — Marcel Proust and Eugène Atget. *A Vision of Paris*. 1963. — J. H. Lartigue. *Boyhood Photos of J. H. Lartigue: The Family Album of the Gilded Age*. 1966. — William Howard Adams. *Atget's Gardens*. Introduction by Jacqueline Onassis. 1979 (3 copies). — Sarah Greenough and Juan Hamilton. *Alfred Stieglitz: Photographs and Writings*. 1983. — and others.

$400–600

689 **Modern Photography**

A group of 4 modern photography books, various sizes. All illustrated. Publisher's cloth. New York and Paris. All are signed by the photographers.

Ruth Orkin. *A Photo Journal*. 1981. Signed presentation, "To Jacqueline Kennedy From one photographer to another… All my best wishes. Ruth Orkin." — François-Marie Banier. *Photographies*. 1991. Signed presentation in French from the photographer, "Pour Jackie …" — Robert Farber. *Nudes*. 1984. Signed presentation copy from the photographer to "Jackie – Thank you for the support + the great interest you have shown in my work…" — Marc Riboud. *Journal*. 1986. Signed presentation from the photographer, "Pour Jacky …"

$500–800

690 **Rodin, Auguste**

A la Vénus de Milo. *Paris: La Jeune Parque, 1945*

(9¾ x 7¾ in.) 5 color reproductions of watercolor drawings by Rodin. Original wrappers, printed in red and black; some minor wear and soiling.

No. 805 of 2,500 numbered copies.

$300–500

692

691 **Photography**

A group of 5 modern photography books, various sizes. All illustrated. Publisher's cloth, and one in wrappers. Various places and dates. One each printed in German and Italian.

Christopher Simon Sykes. *Country House Camera*. 1980. Inscribed to, "Mrs Onassis" from Ruth Ansul. — Ann Novotny. *Alice's World*. 1976. Inscribed to "Mrs. Jacqueline Onassis" from the "Friends of the Alice Austen House." — David Robinson. *Reflections*. 1979. Signed presentation from the photographer. — Herlinde Koelbl. *Jüdische Porträts*. 1989. Signed by the photographer to "J. Onassis." — Beni Montresor. *La Magica di Montresor*. 1990. Signed presentation from Beni Montresor, "Pour Jackie ..."

$400–600

692 **Canaletto, Antonio**

Prospectus Magni Canalis Venetiarum. *London: Joseph Smith, 1735*

Broadsheets (15 x 21 in.). Handcolored engraved title-page, frontispiece, and 38 plates after Canaletto by Antonio Visentini (numbered I–XIV; 1–12; I–XII), letterpress list of plates; title, frontispiece, and first series of plates lightly browned, some marginal chipping and soiling. Modern replica of a painted Venetian panel binding by F. Ongania, brown calf, front cover and spine painted in black, red, and gold, central panel of front cover with supralibros of Mrs. Kennedy's stepfather, H. D. Auchincloss; extremities rubbed.

An attractive copy of Canaletto's complete engravings of Venice.

$2,000–3,000

920 **Alain-Fournier, Henri**

Le Grand Meaulnes. *Paris: Éditions Michèle Trinckvel, (1972)*

Unbound as issued (15 x 11½ in.). 12 color lithographs by Brasilier. Original printed wrappers. Yellow silk folding-case; faded, frayed.

One of 200 numbered copies on vélin d'Arches, with an extra lithograph signed by the artist (of an entire edition of 920).

$300–500

694 American Art

A group of 21 illustrated volumes (some duplicates), various sizes. Publisher's cloth and wrappers. Various places, various dates.

Metropolitan Museum of Art. *Life in America*. 1939. — Edgar P. Richardson. *American Romantic Painting*. 1944. — *America's Arts and Skills*. 1957. — Lloyd Goodrich and John I. H. Baur. *American Art of Our Century*. 1961. — Frederic G. Renner. *Paper Talk: Illustrated Letters of Charles M. Russell*. 1962. — Arnold Nicholson. *American Houses in History*. 1965. — George Catlin. *Drawings of the North American Indians*. 1984 (2 copies). — and others.

$800–1,200

695 Nineteenth-Century Art

A group of 11 illustrated volumes, various sizes. Publisher's cloth and wrappers. Various places, various dates.

Marcel Brion. *Romantic Art*. 1960. — Henry & Sidney Berry-Hill. *George Chinnery, 1774-1852: Artist of the China Coast*. 1963. — Raymond Escholier. *Eugène Delacroix*. 1963. — John Baskett. *Constable Oil Sketches*. 1966. — Hans Naef. *Ingres in Rome*. 1971. — Martin Butlin and others. *Turner at Petworth*. 1989. — and others.

$400–600

696 Old Master Paintings and Drawings

A group of 35 illustrated volumes, various sizes. Publisher's cloth and wrappers. Various places, various dates.

Das Bruegelbuch. 1936. — Ludwig von Baldass. *Hieronymus Bosch*. 1943. — Anthony Blunt. *The Drawings of G. B. Castiglione and Stefano della Bella*. 1954. — Carl Linfert. *Hieronymus Bosch*. 1943. — Decio Gioseffi. *Canaletto and His Contemporaries*. — J. Bryan Shaw. *The Drawings of Domenico Tiepolo*. 1962. — *Old Master Drawings from Chatsworth*. 1962. — Vittorio Moschini. *Francesco Guardi*. [n.d.]. — Lajos Vayer. *Master Drawings from the Collection of the Budapest Museum of Fine Arts*. [n.d.]. — and others.

$1,500–2,000

697 Russian Art and History

A group of 15 volumes, various sizes. Mostly illustrated. Publisher's cloth and paper. Some in Cyrillic. Various places, various dates.

George Heald Hamilton. *The Art and Architecture of Russia*. 1975. Slipcase. — Jacqueline Onassis, ed. *In the Russian Style*. 1976. — Chloe Obolensky. *The Russian Empire*. 1979. — *Valentin Sirov: Painting, Graphic Works, Stage Designs*. 1982. — Mikhail P. Iroshnikov et al. *Before the Revolution: St. Petersburg in Photographs*. 1991. — Suzanne Massie. *Pavlovsk: Life of a Russian Palace*. 1991. — and others.

$300–500

698 Russian Art and Style

A group of 29 volumes and approximately 22 pamphlets, various sizes. Mostly illustrated in color. Some books in Cyrillic. Various places, various dates.

G.-K. Loukomski. *Mobilier et décoration des anciens palais impériaux russes*. 1928. — Charles Sterling. *Great French Painting in the Hermitage*. 1958. — K. M. Malitskaya. *Great Paintings from the Pushkin Museum*. 1964. — Victor and Audrey Kennet. *The Palaces of Leningrad*. 1973. — Jacqueline Onassis. *In the Russian Style*. 1976 (2 copies). — and others.

$300–500

699 Nineteenth- and Twentieth-Century Art

A group of 33 volumes, various sizes. Publisher's cloth and wrappers.

Francis Carco. *Vertès*. 1950. — Walter Pach. *Renoir*. 1950. — Marcel Brion. *Léonor Fini*. 1955. — W. Somerset Maugham. *Purely for My Pleasure*. 1963. — Rodolfo Pallucchini. *Pericle Fazzini*. 1963. — Alan Solomon. *New York: The New Art Scene*. 1967. — and others.

$800–1,200

700 Art History

A group of 49 volumes of treatises, and museum monographs, guides, reports, and catalogues. Illustrated; mostly in publisher's cloth and wrappers. Varying sizes and conditions.

Library of Congress. *Catalog of the Gardiner Greene Hubbard Collection of Engravings*. 1905. — Museum of Fine Arts, Boston. *M. and M. Karolik Collection of American Paintings 1815 to 1865*. 1949. — Arno Schonberger and Halldor Soehner. *The Rococo Age*. 1960. — John Walker. *Self-Portrait with Donors*. 1974. — Réunion des musées nationaux. *Cinq années d'enrichissement du Patrimoine national 1975-1980*. 1980. — Bernard Berenson. *The Letters of Bernard Berenson and Isabella Stewart Gardner 1887-1924*. 1987. — and others.

$600–800

701

701 Costume

The Military Costume of Turkey. *London: Thomas McLean, 1818*

(18⅛ x 12⅝ in.). Handcolored engraved frontispiece, additional title, and 30 plates; frontispiece creased, some marginal soiling. Contemporary black morocco gilt, top edges gilt; scuffed, extremities worn, front cover detached.

ASSOCIATION COPY, with Mrs. Kennedy's bookplate. Also with the bookplate of John Birley.

$800–1,200

702 Fashion, Costume, Jewelry, and Style

A group of 40 volumes, various sizes, including a few pamphlets, one presentation copy and one book with the floral bookplate of Jacqueline Bouvier Kennedy. All illustrated; a few books in Cyrillic. Mostly publisher's cloth. Various places and dates.

Petit Courrier des dames: Journal des Modes. 1834-1835. Handcolored plates. — *John Perona's El Morocco Family Album*. 1937. — N. Wooster. *Semi-Precious Stones*. 1952. Bookplate. — Cecil Beaton. *Cecil Beaton Diaries: The Wandering Years*. 1961. — V. B. Neen and A. D. Tushingham. *Crown Jewels of Iran*. 1968. — Diana Vreeland. *Allure*. 1980 (5 copies). — Richard de Combray. *Armani*. 1982. — Gilberte Gautier. *Cartier: The Legend*. 1983. — Caroline Rennolds Milbank. *Couture: The Great Designers*. 1985. — Suzy Menkes. *The Windsor Style*. 1987. — John Loring. *The Tiffany Wedding*. 1988 (2 copies). — Diana Vreeland. *Bijoux de Jean Schlumberger; Objets de Jean Schlumberger*. 2 vols. 1976. — Geoffrey Munn and Charlotte Gere. *Artist's Jewelry*. 1989. PRESENTATION COPY from Geoffrey Munn. — and others.

$800–1,200

703 Ballet, Dance, and Theatre

A group of 23 illustrated volumes, various sizes. Mostly in publisher's cloth and wrappers. Various places, various dates.

Salvatore Cabasino. *Il Figurino nel teatro italiano contemporaneo*. 1945. — S. L. Grigoriev. *The Diaghilev Ballet 1909-1929*. 1953. — Margaret Crosland. *Jean Cocteau*. 1955. — Stephen Orgel and Roy Strong. *Inigo Jones: The Theatre of the Stuart Court*. 2 vols. 1973. — M. N. Pozharskaya. *The Russian Seasons in Paris*. 1988. Russian-English text. — Margaret M. McGowan. *The Court Ballet of Louis XIII; A Collection of Working Designs for Costumes*. [n.d.]. — and others.

$400–600

704 Costume and Fashion

Group of 9 volumes, various sizes. Illustrated. Publisher's cloth, some with dust-jackets. Various places, various dates.

Doreen Yarwood. *English Costume*. 1952. Bookplate of Jacqueline Bouvier Kennedy. — David Mathew. *The Courtiers of Henry VIII*. 1970. Inscribed by author "For Jacqueline Onassis." — *The Imperial Style: Fashions of the Hapsburg Era*. 1980. With engraved card of Diana Vreeland. — Nirad C. Chaudhuri. *Culture in the Vanity Bag*. 1976. Inscribed by author "To Mrs. Jacqueline Kennedy Onassis." — Charles Fabri. *A History of Indian Dress*. 1960. Bookplate of Jacqueline Bouvier Kennedy and inscribed by author "To Mrs. Kennedy." — *Historical Russian Costumes XIV-XVIII Century*. [1903]. Bookplate of Le Prince Leon Ouroussoff (Ambassador to Russia). — Susan Bean. *Costumes from India*. [n. d.]. Letter from Stephen Jamail of the Metropolitan Museum, noting "this essay ... is fascinating—the only thing I've read on Indian costume that didn't put me to sleep!" — George F. Collie. *Highland Dress*. 1948. Two copies. Bookplates of Jacqueline Bouvier Kennedy.

$600–800

705 **History and Travel**

Group of 13 volumes, various sizes, 6 of which signed by Mrs. Onassis "Jacqueline Kennedy 1960," "Jacqueline Kennedy Onassis," and "J." Publisher's cloth, most with dust jackets. Various places, various dates.

Martin F. Herz. *A Short History of Cambodia.* 1958. — Freya Stark. *Alexander's Path.* 1958. — Simon Leys. *Chinese Shadows.* 1977. — Daniel J. Boorstin. *The Creators.* 1992. With chronological notes by Mrs. Onassis on flyleaf. — and 9 others, 3 with the bookplate of Jacqueline Bouvier Kennedy.

$600–900

706 **Art and Art Appreciation**

A group of 5 volumes. Mostly illustrated. Publisher's cloth. Various places and dates. Most with Jacqueline Bouvier Kennedy's bookplate.

Bertrand Russell. *Wisdom of the West.* 1959. Inscribed, "To Jackie and Jack with the belief that this book will give both a few hours of pleasant reading. Geoffrey T. McHugh." — Bernard Berenson. *One Year's Reading for Fun (1942.)* 1960. — Bernard Berenson. *The Passionate Sightseer; from the Diaries 1947 to 1956.* — Maurice Rheims. *The Strange Life of Objects.* 1961. — Francis Haskell. *Patrons and Painters.* 1963.

$200–400

707 **Art History and Appreciation**

A group of 10 volumes, various sizes (several folios). All illustrated. Mostly publisher's cloth. Various places and dates. All inscribed or with the Jacqueline Bouvier Kennedy bookplate.

Filippo Rossi. *The Uffizi, Florence.* 1957. — John Canaday. *Metropolitan Seminars in Art. Portfolio 1: What is a Painting?* 1958. — Jerzego Szablowskiego. *Arrasy Flamandzkie w Zamku Królewskim na Wawelu.* 1975. Inscribed in Polish to Jacqueline Kennedy Onassis from Edward Grabowski, bookseller. In slipcase. — Michel de Grèce. *Portrait et Séduction.* Inscribed, "For Jackie with much appreciation and the hommages de Michel, April '94."

$400–600

708 **Decorative Arts, French**

A group of 17 volumes, various sizes. Mostly French texts, illustrated. Publisher's cloth and wrappers. Various places, various dates.

H. Clouzot and Ch. Follot. *Histoire du papier peint en France.* 1935. Uncut. — Frits Lugt. *Marques de collections.* 2 vols. Reprint, 1956. — François de Salverte. *Les ébénistes du XVIIIe siècle.* 1962. — Mario Praz. *L'ameublement.* 1964. — Emile Molinier. *Le mobilier au XVIIe et XVIIIe siècle.* — *Styles de France; objets de collection de 1610 à 1920.* 2 vols. [n.d.] — and others.

$800–1,200

709 **Wrightsman Collection**

Watson, F. J. B. The Wrightsman Collection. *New York: Metropolitan Museum of Art, (1966–1973)*

5 volumes (11 x 9½ in.). Numerous color plates and halftone illustrations. Publisher's red cloth gilt. Dust-jackets; some wear. 3 slipcases.

$400–600

710 **American Architecture**

A group of 19 volumes, various sizes. All illustrated. Mostly publisher's cloth. Various places and dates.

William H. Adams, ed. *The Eye of Thomas Jefferson.* 1981. — Fiske Kimball. *Thomas Jefferson, Architect.* 1981. — Mills Lane. *Architecture of the Old South:* (1) *South Carolina*; (2) *North Carolina*; (3) *Georgia*; (4) *Virginia*. 4 vols. 1984-1987. — Bates Lowry. *Building a National Image.* 1985. — Philip Johnson. *The Glass House.* 1993. — and others.

$400–600

VANISHED CIVILIZATIONS
China
RICHELIEU

THE ESTATE OF JACQUELINE KENNEDY ONASSIS

SESSION SEVEN
THURSDAY, APRIL 25,
6:00 P.M.

The Dining Room in Jacqueline Kennedy Onassis' New York City apartment, showing lots 14, 264, 265, 282, 303, 314, 332 and 968.

711 *British School, 19th Century

"TRUMPET HONEYSUCKLE"

titled and dated *Nov. 1834*
tempera on paper
7 ¾ by 9 ¾ in. (19.7 by 24.8 cm.)

This painting was among the furnishings in the White House during President and Mrs. Kennedy's residence.

$600–800

712 Camilla Gandolfi

OWL ON A ROCK

pen and brown ink and wash, inscribed lower center *A. Iocco*
8 ¾ by 6 ¼ in. (22.2 by 15.9 cm.)

This drawing was among the furnishings in the Second Floor Oval Room of the White House during President and Mrs. Kennedy's residence.

$500–700

711

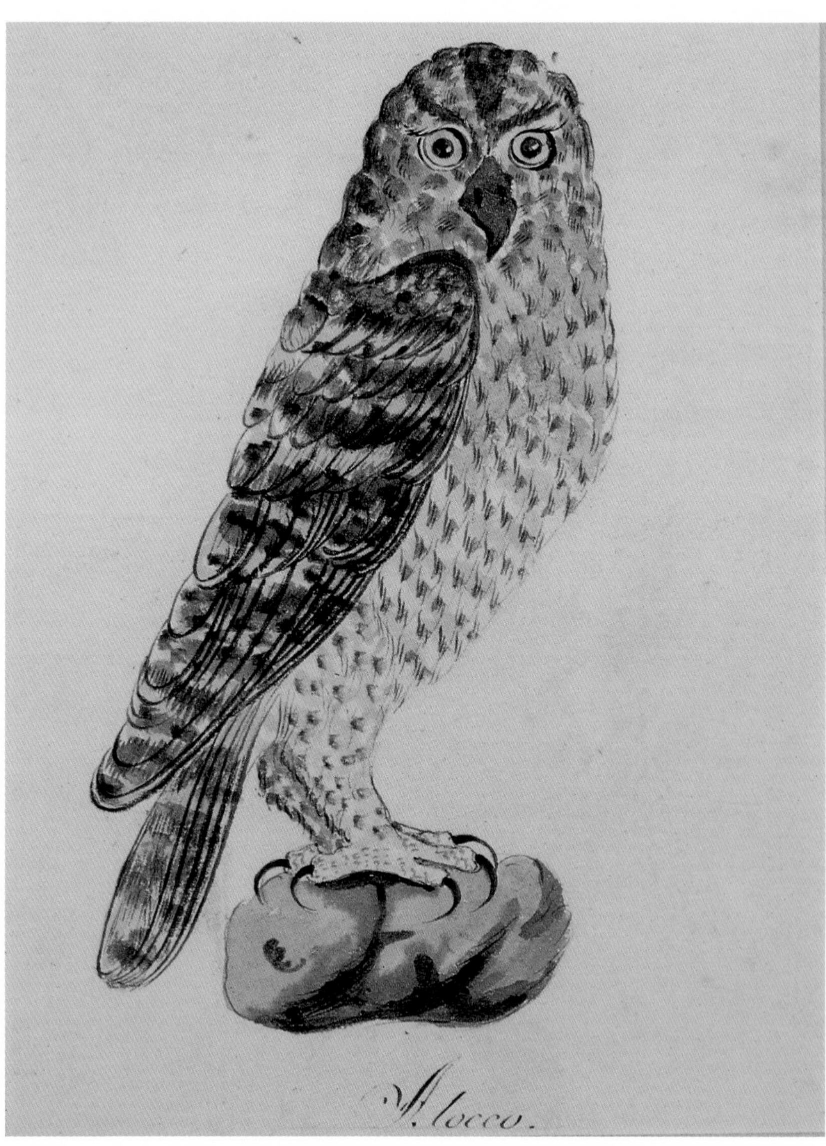

712

**AUTHORSHIP: Ascribed to the named artist – subject to the qualifications set forth in the Glossary and Conditions of Sale, back of this Catalogue.*

713

714

713 **William Huggins (British, 1820-84)**

STUDY OF A LEOPARD

signed and dated *1880*
colored chalks and pencil on paper
laid down on board
6 ¾ by 10 ¼ in. (17.1 by 26 cm.)

Huggins is regarded as one of Victorian England's greatest painters of animals and, in particular, wild game. A Liverpool native, he became a member of the Liverpool Academy in 1850. Huggins "developed a penchant for painting lions, tigers and other members of the cat family at Chester Zoo, and at Wombwell's menagerie whenever it happened to stop near Merseyside. From 1857 onwards he exhibited at the Liverpool Institute of Fine Arts and at the Royal Academy" (Jeremy Maas, *Victorian Painters*, London, 1978, pp. 82-82).

$1,800–2,500

714 **Attributed to Daniel Maclise**

A STUDY OF A LEOPARD

pencil and charcoal on paper
4 ⅛ by 6 in. (10.5 by 15.2 cm.)

$500–600

715

715 **Charles Baskerville (American, b. 1896)**

TIGER

signed *Charlie Baskerville* and inscribed *Especially made for Jackie*, l.r.
watercolor and pencil on paper
7½ by 11 in. (19 by 27.9 cm.)

$500–700

716 **A Painted Leather Three-Fold Screen**

each panel with arched top painted with a fox hunting scene.
Height 5 ft. 8 in. (1.73 m.), width of each panel 18 in. (45.7 cm.)

$1,500–2,000

716

717

717 **American School, 19th Century**

THE YELLOW HORSE: A WATERCOLOR DRAWING

gouache on paper
6 by 8 in. (15.2 by 20.3 cm.)

Executed circa 1820, Shenandoah Valley, Virginia; in what appears to be the original frame.

$600–800

718 **Charles Parrocel**

STUDY OF A SOLDIER ON HORSEBACK AND ANOTHER ON FOOT

watercolor and black chalk, inscribed lower center *Parrocel* and upper right *cacon / c peau / verte jaune*
12 by 8½ in. (30.5 by 21.6 cm.)

Provenance:
H. M. Calmann, London, 1958

$2,000–3,000

718

719 *James Seymour (British, 1702-52)

THE GALLOP TO THE RIGHT HAND

pencil on paper
5 ½ by 6 ¼ in. (14 by 15.9 cm.)

"The rider is training his horse to gallop upon a volte, *i.e.* in a sideways circular direction, thus powerfully exercising the shoulders" (Drummond, n.p.).

Exhibited:
London, William Drummond, Covent Garden Gallery, Ltd., *'The Ingenius Mr. Seymour', James Seymour 1702-1752*, 1978, No. 38, Pl. 6, illustrated

$800–1,200

719

720 *James Seymour (British, 1702-52)

A RACEHORSE WITH JOCKEY UP

pencil on paper
6 ½ by 8 in. (16.5 by 20.3 cm.)

Exhibited:
London, William Drummond, Covent Garden Gallery, Ltd., *'The Ingenius Mr. Seymour', James Seymour 1702-1752*, 1978, No. 13

$800–1,200

720

721 *James Seymour (British, 1702-52)

A GROOM WATERING A HORSE AT A TROUGH

pencil on paper
5 ¼ by 7 in. (13.3 by 17.8 cm.)

Exhibited:
London, William Drummond, Covent Garden Gallery, Ltd., *'The Ingenius Mr. Seymour', James Seymour 1702-1752*, 1978, No. 48, Pl. 8, illustrated

$800–1,200

721

**AUTHORSHIP: Ascribed to the named artist – subject to the qualifications set forth in the Glossary and Conditions of Sale, back of this Catalogue.*

722

722 *James Seymour (British, 1702-52)

A CANTER ALONG THE WALL OF A RIDING-HOUSE

dated *1740* and inscribed *This riding house was built by J.S.*
gouache over traces of charcoal on paper
5½ by 5½ in. (14 by 14 cm.)

The present drawing "was evidently made from life at one or other of the London riding-schools, where the scholar of horsemanship (then considered as much a part of a gentleman's education as fencing or dancing, and now called *haute école*) learnt to manage his horse in successive exercises or 'airs', from a mannered walk forwards, sideways and in a circle ('upon a volte') to the 'higher airs' such as the *Levade* and the spectacular *Capriole.* The classic text-book on the subject was the Duke of Newcastle's *A General System of Horsemanship*, illustrated with forty-three sumptuous plates after Abraham van Diepenbecke; first published in 1658 in a French translation, and widely circulated in this form, it was published in its original English in 1743. Seymour would certainly have been familiar with this classic treatise" (Drummond, n.p.).

According to Sally Mitchell, "An interesting plaque on the wall of a *manège* in a picture of *haute école* by Seymour quite plainly states 'This riding house was built by J.S. 1740.' One feels that this must have referred to himself and that maybe one of his interests was, as for many of the gentry of his time, the study of horsemanship as an art" (*The Dictionary of British Equestrian Artists*, Woodbridge, Suffolk, 1985, p. 384).

"There are group of drawings by Seymour in the collections of Her Majesty the Queen (purchased in 1803 by the then Prince of Wales) and the British Museum...and there are over eighty drawings and fourteen paintings in the Mellon Collection" (Drummond, n.p.).

Exhibited:
London, William Drummond, Covent Garden Gallery, Ltd., *'The Ingenius Mr. Seymour', James Seymour 1702-1752*, 1978, No. 37, cover illustration

$4,000–6,000

**AUTHORSHIP: Ascribed to the named artist – subject to the qualifications set forth in the Glossary and Conditions of Sale, back of this Catalogue.*

723

724

725

723 **G. B. Foggini**

HORSE SEEN FROM THE REAR

charcoal and gray wash, signed lower right *Gio Ba: Foggini F.* and inscribed lower left *10*
7½ by 9½ in. (19 by 24.1 cm.)

$3,000–4,000

724 **Circle of Carle Vernet**

A GROOM MOUNTED ON A HORSE IN A LANDSCAPE

black chalk on paper
7 9/16 by 10¾ in. (19.2 by 27.3 cm.)

Provenance:
The Shepherd Gallery, New York

$700–1,000

725 ***Dutch School, 19th Century**

A GRAY STALLION IN A LANDSCAPE

indistinctly signed and dated *1841*
charcoal on paper
12¾ by 18 in. (32.4 by 45.7 cm.)

$800–1,200

**AUTHORSHIP: Ascribed to the named artist – subject to the qualifications set forth in the Glossary and Conditions of Sale, back of this Catalogue.*

726

726 **Reverse-Painting on Glass, probably Continental**

Depicting a military figure on horseback with sword raised, cracked
Sight 18 by 14½ in. (45.7 by 36.8 cm.)

$200–400

727 ***John Nost Sartorius (British, 1759-1828)**

"FLOSS", A SADDLED BAY HUNTER TIED TO A TREE IN A LANDSCAPE

signed and dated *pinx 1789*
oil on canvas
20 by 24 in. (50.8 by 61 cm.)

'Floss' was a hunter owned by Sir Harbord Harbord, 1st Lord Suffield (1734-1810), MP Norwich (1756-86) of Gunton Hall, Norfolk. He married, in 1760, Mary, daughter of Sir Ralph Assheton, 3rd Bt., of Middleton, Lancashire.

$8,000–12,000

727

**AUTHORSHIP: Ascribed to the named artist – subject to the qualifications set forth in the Glossary and Conditions of Sale, back of this Catalogue.*

728

728 **Attributed to Clifton Tomson**

TWO BAYS AND A GREY IN A LANDSCAPE

oil on canvas
34 by 44 in. (86.4 by 111.8 cm.)

$5,000–7,000

729

729 **Circle of John Wootton**

A BAY HORSE IN A LANDSCAPE WITH GROOM, SAID TO BE 'FLYING CHILDERS'

inscribed *This representation of Flying Childers (1715), many others exist, was done by John Wootton (1685-1765), ca. 1721./ before he went to Italy to study, whence he returned a good painter, said Horace Walpole. By the exercise/ of his art he acquired a house in Cavendish Square. in which he died.*
oil on canvas
40 by 49½ in. (101.6 by 125.7 cm.)

" 'Flying Childers' is generally recognized as the first supreme thoroughbred racehorse. Bred by Colonel Leonard Childers [of Carr House] at Doncaster, he was known in his own day as 'Childers', or 'The Childers'; the prefix 'Flying' was a soubriquet added later as the racing performances of this unbeaten champion grew into legend, such as that he had averaged a mile a minute. 'Flying Childers' was a bay foaled in 1715, by the 'Darley Arabian' out of 'Betty Leedes'. The blood of both the Darley and the Leedes Arabians was thus in his veins; and his forebears included 'Careless' and 'Spanker', famous racehorses of the late seventeenth century. The Duke of Devonshire bought him from Colonel Childers as a yearling" (Judy Egerton, *British Sporting and Animal Paintings 1655-1867*, London, 1978, pp. 45-46).

Provenance:
Robin Symes, Ltd., London

$30,000–40,000

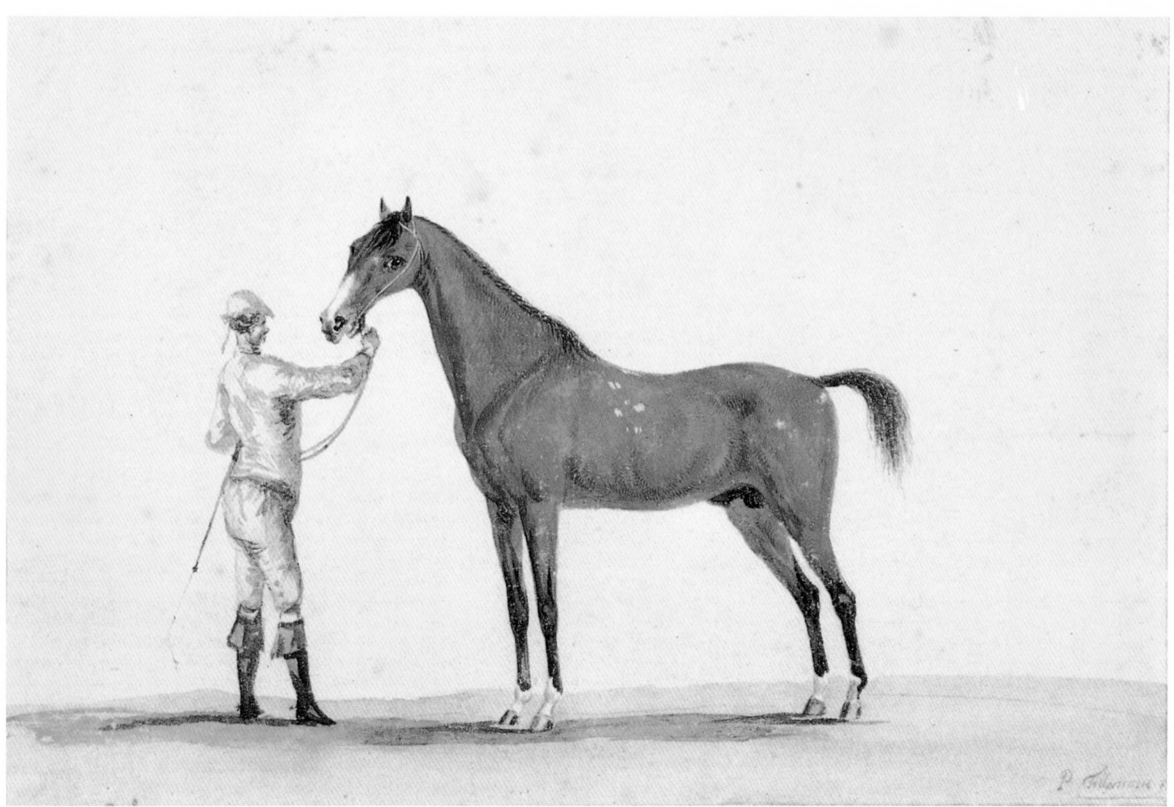

730

730 *Peter Tillemans (1684-1734)

A JOCKEY STANDING WITH A BAY HORSE

signed
watercolor and gouache over traces of pencil on paper laid down on paper
7 by 10 ¼ in. (17.8 by 26 cm.)

Tillemans was a "painter of portraits of country houses, sporting scenes, battle pieces and decorative land-scape" (Judy Egerton, *British Sporting and Animal Paintings 1655-1867*, London, 1978, p. 29). After arriving on English shores in 1708 from his native Antwerp, Tillemans painted *Queen Anne in the House of Lords* (in the collection of Her Majesty the Queen) and *Interior of the House of Commons* (in the collection of the House of Commons). His patronage later broadened with his popular views of gentlemen's country seats. Tillemans learned to add interest to these "topographical panoramas [by]...enlivening them with strings of horses" (Egerton, p. 29). He was "a friendly associate of...John Wootton at Newmarket...[and learnt much about drawing horses] from Wootton's por-traiture of horses" (Egerton, p. 29).

This watercolor was in the collection of Richard Cavendish, the second son of William, 4th Duke of Devonshire. Upon his death this work was bequeathed to his brother, George Augustus Henry, 1st Earl of Burlington.

Provenance:
Richard Cavendish (d. 1781)
George Augustus Henry, 1st Earl of Burlington (1754-1834) (by descent from the above)

Exhibited:
London, Herbert N. Bier, Ltd., August 17, 1959

$1,200–1,800

731

731 British School, 20th Century

A BAY HORSE WITH P. EDGLEY UP

inscribed *Golden...P. Edgley up* on the stretcher
oil on canvas
20 by 24 in. (50.8 by 61 cm.)

$600–800

**AUTHORSHIP: Ascribed to the named artist – subject to the qualifications set forth in the Glossary and Conditions of Sale, back of this Catalogue.*

732

732 **Manner of Sir Edwin Landseer**

A WHIPPET AND A KING CHARLES SPANIEL ON A RED CUSHION

oil on canvas
25 by 20 in. (63.5 by 50.8 cm.)

This painting was among the furnishings in the West Sitting Room of the White House during President and Mrs. Kennedy's residence.

$2,000–4,000

733 **After Sir Edwin Henry Landseer**

"THE CAVALIER'S PETS"

oil on canvas
12 by 15½ in. (30.5 by 39.4 cm.)

This work repeats the composition with some variations of Landseer's famed painting of the same title, now in the collection of The Tate Gallery, London.

This painting was among the furnishings in the West Sitting Room of the White House during President and Mrs. Kennedy's residence.

$700– 900

733

734 **A Leather Hunting Saddle, Stübben Riding Equipment, Switzerland**

With stirrups.
Height approximately 17 in. (43.2 cm.)

$300–500

735 **A Leather Hunting Saddle, A. Pariani, Milan**

Height approximately 16 in. (40.6 cm.)

$300–500

736 **A Leather Hunting Saddle, London Harness Co., Boston**

Height approximately 20 in. (50.8cm.)

$300–500

John F. Kennedy Library

Previous page: *Jacqueline Kennedy at Merrywood, her Mother and Stepfather's Virginia Farm.* Photo credit: The Mark Shaw Collection / Photo Researchers
Right: *Jacqueline Kennedy riding "Sadar," a horse given to her by Ayub Khan, President of Pakistan, who is standing in the background, at Glen Ora, Middleburg, Virginia, September 1962.*

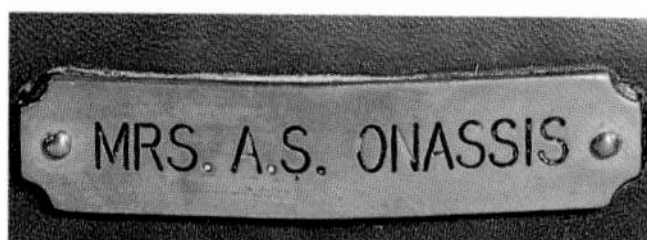

734

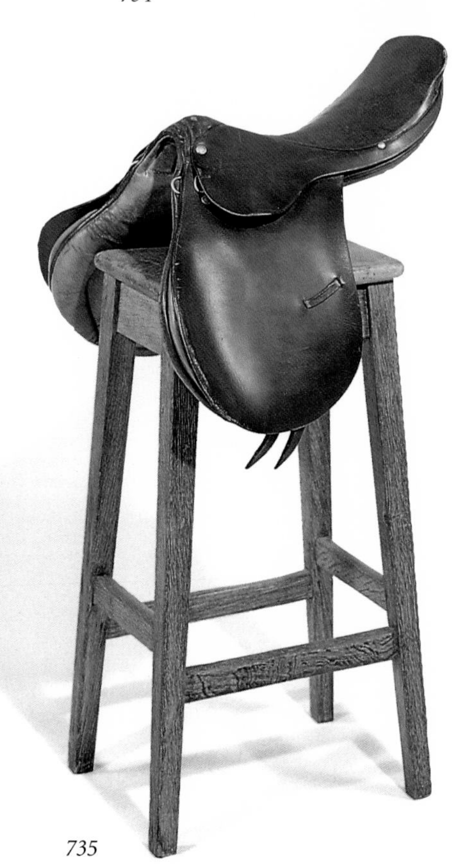

735

734

737

737 **John James Audubon (after)**

THE GREAT BLUE HERON (Plate CCXL)

Hand colored etching, engraving and aquatint, a fine, fresh impression, by R. Havell, on J. Whatman paper, with margins, in apparently good condition apart from very minor soiling, framed* (not examined out of the frame)
Sheet 37 by 24½ in. (94 by 62.2 cm.)

$30,000–50,000

738 **John James Audubon (after)**

HERRING GULL (Plate CCXCI)

Hand colored etching, engraving and aquatint, a fine, fresh impression, by R. Havell, on J. Whatman paper, with large margins, in apparently good condition, framed* (not examined out of the frame)
Sheet 36½ by 24 in. (92.7 by 61 cm.)

$3,500–4,500

739 **John James Audubon (after)**

THE VIOLET GREEN CORMORANT AND TOWNSEND'S CORMORANT (Plate CCCXII)

Hand colored etching, engraving and aquatint, a fine, fresh impression, by R. Havell, on J. Whatman paper, with large margins, in apparently good condition apart from a few slight handling creases, framed* (not examined out of the frame)
Sheet 25 by 38 in. (63.5 by 96.5 cm.)

$1,800–2,400

738

739

Each of the lots described above is subject to the Glossary of Terms printed at the back of this catalogue.

740

741

740 **John James Audubon (after)**

ARCTIC TERN (Plate CCL)

Hand colored etching, engraving and aquatint, a fine, fresh impression, by R. Havell, on J. Whatman paper, with large margins, in apparently good condition apart from a few slight handling creases, framed* (not examined out of the frame)
Sheet 37 by 26 in. (94 by 66 cm.)

$3,000–5,000

741 **John James Audubon (after)**

MARSH TERN (Plate CCCX)

Hand colored etching, engraving and aquatint, a fine, fresh impression, by R. Havell, on J. Whatman paper, with large margins, in apparently good condition apart from a soft diagonal crease in the left margin, a few slight handling creases, framed* (not examined out of the frame)
Sheet 37 by 26 in. (94 by 66 cm.)

$1,500–2,000

742

742

742 **Anonymous**

FISH SPECIMENS

Two hand-colored engravings, c. 1825, with ink inscriptions, with margins, framed* (not examined out of frames) (2 pieces)
Each approximately 11 by 19 in. (27.9 by 48.3 cm.)

$500–600

743 **Currier & Ives (Publishers)**

AMERICAN THOROUGHBREDS

Hand-colored lithograph, c. 1855, with margins, in apparently good condition, framed* (not examined out of the frame)
Image size 8 by 12½ in. (20.3 by 31.7 cm.)

$300–400

743

744

744

744

744

744 **J. G. Warnicke and Alexander Lawson (Engravers)**

SEVEN ORNITHOLOGICAL SUBJECTS: SPOTTED GROUS, CURLEW, WHOOPING CRANE, GREAT HERON, AND OTHERS

Seven hand-colored engravings, after Ryder and Wilson, with margins and in apparently good condition, framed* (not examined out of the frames) (7)

$1,200–1,600

745 **American School, 19th/20th Century**

STILL LIFE

watercolor on linen
17 ¾ by 21 ½ in. (45.1 by 54.6 cm.)

$300–500

746 **Victorian Needlework Picture, second half 19th Century**

A PARROT ON A FRUIT BRANCH

in giltwood frame
12 by 12 in. (30.5 by 30.5 cm.)

This picture was among the furnishings in the White House during President and Mrs. Kennedy's residence.

$300–500

747 **American School, 19th Century**

CALLIGRAPHIC SPECIMEN PICTURE OF A BIRD

signed *Chas.*, framed
8 ¼ by 6 ¼ in. (21 by 15.9 cm.)

$200–400

745

746

747

748

749

748 **American School, 19th Century**

SHIP ON ROUGH SEAS

indistincly inscribed on the reverse
watercolor on paper
7 ¾ by 9 ¾ in. (19.7 by 24.8 cm.)

$150–300

749 **Junius B. Stearns (American, 1810-1885)**

DISBROW COTTAGE IN MAMARONECK

inscribed *Disbrow Cottage in / Mamaroneck / Painted & Presented by / J. Stearns as a / token of friendship / N.Y. 1838* on the reverse
oil on panel
22 by 27 ½ in. (55.9 by 69.8 cm.)

$1,500–2,500

750

750 **American School, 19th/20th Century**

VIEW ON THE HUDSON TOWARD BEAR MOUNTAIN, WITH A PADDLEWHEELER AT THE CENTER

oil on canvas
23 ½ by 32 in. (59.7 by 81.3 cm.)

$300–500

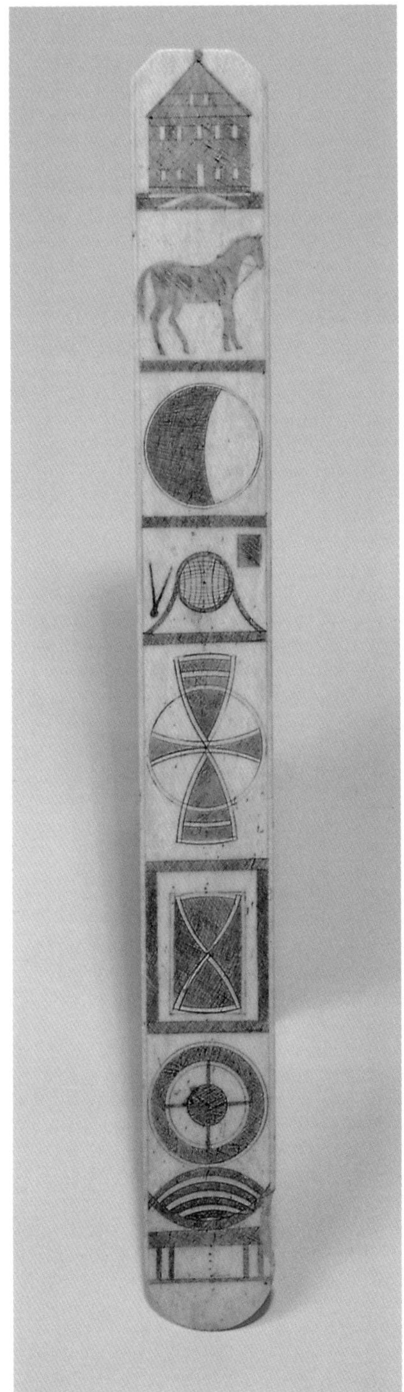

752

751

751 **American School, 19th Century**

HOUSE BY A LAKE

dated *April 8, 1896* on the reverse
oil on board
18½ by 24½ in. (47 by 62.2 cm.)

$100–200

752 **Engraved Scrimshaw Whalebone Busk, New England, 19th Century**

Of rectangular outline, engraved with a house, a horse and a variety of geometric devices, (chipped).
Length 12¾ in. (32.4 cm.)

$700–900

753 **A Carved and Painted Wood Half-Hull Model of the "Wianno, Sr."**

Built by Robert P. Frazee, Osterville, Massachusetts, 1977, (one design knockabout)
Painted blue with copper and mahogany backplate, bearing paper label on the reverse
Overall length 32 in. (81.3 cm.)

$800–1,200

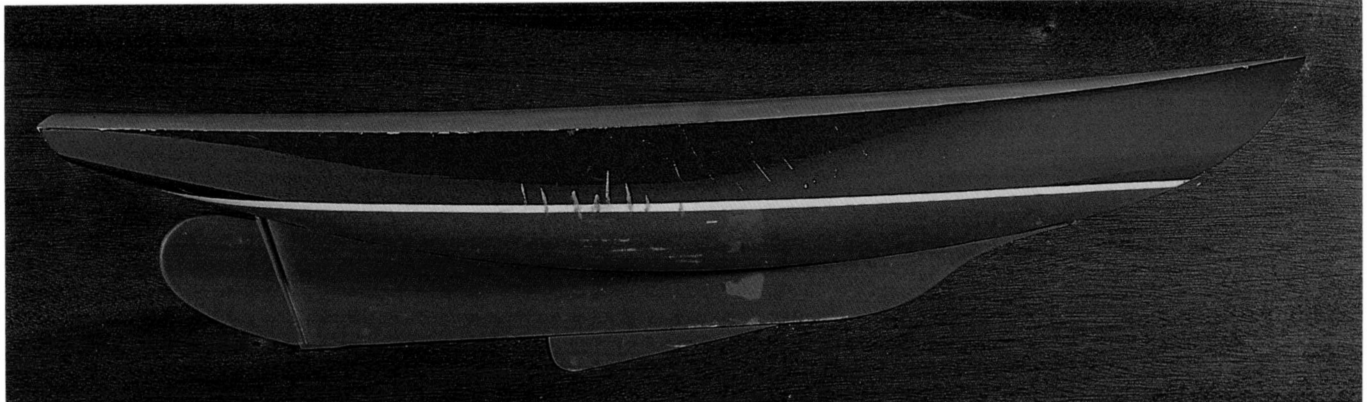

753

4
4

754

754 **A Set of Ben Hogan Power Thrust Irons**

Comprising irons 2 through 9, a wedge and a sand wedge; together with a black leather MacGregor tourney bag inscribed *JFK Washington, D.C.* (11)

$700–900

755 **A Set of MacGregor Woods**

Comprising a driver and woods 2 through 4; together with a Wilson 2 wood and a red and black golf bag inscribed *JFK Washington, D.C.* (7)

$700–900

756 **A MacGregor 147 Putter, "The Krook"**

$200–300

757 **A Robot K-44 Putter**

$200–300

758 **A Swiss "Golf-Sport" Stroke Counter**

The square gilt-metal face with two numerical dials.

$50–100

The John F. Kennedy Library

Previous page: *President Kennedy golfing with Benjamin Bradley, accompanied by their wives, at Newport, Rhode Island, September 13, 1963.*
Photo credit: The John F. Kennedy Library

Above: *President Kennedy golfing at Hyannisport, Massachusetts, July 27, 1963.*

755

756, 757

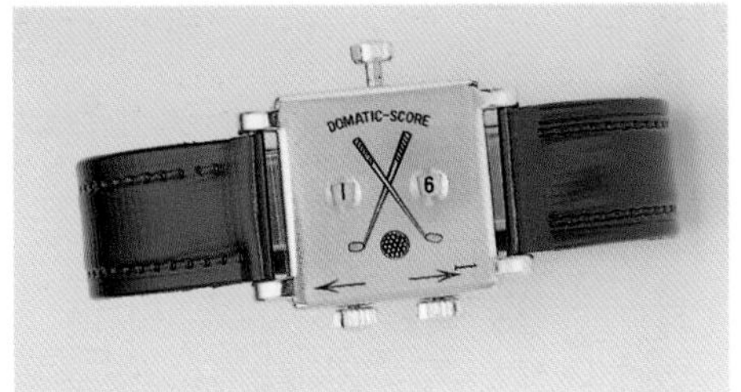

758

759

760

759 **Elaine De Kooning (American, 1919-1989)**

PORTRAIT OF JOHN F. KENNEDY

signed with initials and dated *1/3/63*; signed and dated *1963* on the reverse
charcoal on paper
17 by 14½ in. (43.2 by 36.8 cm.)

See note to lot 55.

Provenance:
Graham Gallery, New York

$1,500–2,500

760 **Elaine De Kooning (American, 1919-1989)**

PORTRAIT OF JOHN F. KENNEDY

signed with initials and dated *1/3/63*; signed and dated *1963* on reverse
charcoal on paper
16½ by 13½ in. (41.9 by 34.3 cm.)

See note to lot 55.

Provenance:
Graham Gallery, New York

$1,500–2,500

Eddie Johnson

Above: *Elaine De Kooning drawing President Kennedy in Palm Beach.*

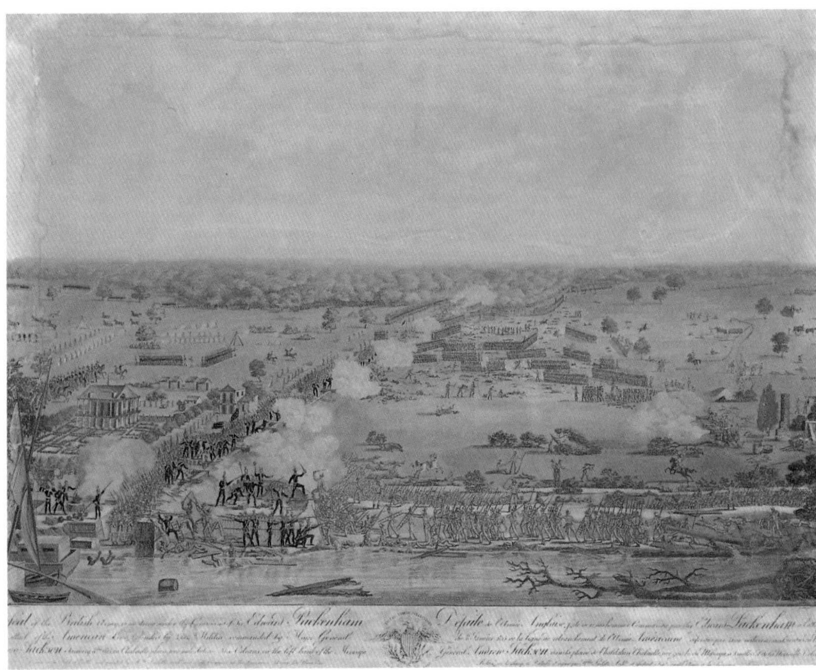

761

763

762

761 **Handcolored Lithograph**

BATTLE OF NEW ORLEANS 1815

Hand-colored engraving, c. 1815, discolored, some tears, framed* (not examined out of frame)

19⅜ in. (49.2 cm.), by 26¼ in. (66.7 cm.)

$300–400

762 **Dahl, Frank**

"The Next Democratic Convention 'Now is there anyone here whose name isn't John F. Kennedy?'"

(7 x 10 in.). Sight. Cartoon ink and wash drawing with white highlights. Inscribed "With best wishes to the real John F. Kennedy" by Dahl. Framed, matted and glazed.

$500–700

763 **Apollo 10**

Color photograph of the earth (13⅝ x 10¾ in.) taken from the capsule of Apollo 10, 19 May 1969. Matted, framed and glazed.

INSCRIBED AND SIGNED BY THE CREW OF APOLLO 10 to Aristotle Onassis. Alan Shepard has inscribed, signed, and dated the mat "to Ari Onassis—Scorpios, with lesser important islands." The mat is also signed by crew members Gene Cernan, Tom Stafford, and John Young. Apollo 10 (18 May–26 May 1969) was a dress rehearsal for a United States manned lunar landing and explored the surface of the moon for potential landing spots for Apollo 11.

$500–700

764 **Lapel Pins representing 29 countries**

Mounted on silk, (16½ x 12½ in.) with calligraphic labels identifying the country. Framed and glazed.

A group of 30 lapel pins representing various countries, (2 for Japan) including Afghanistan, Bolivia, Cyprus, Iran, Ireland, Korea, Morocco, Somalia, Senegal and others.

$200–300

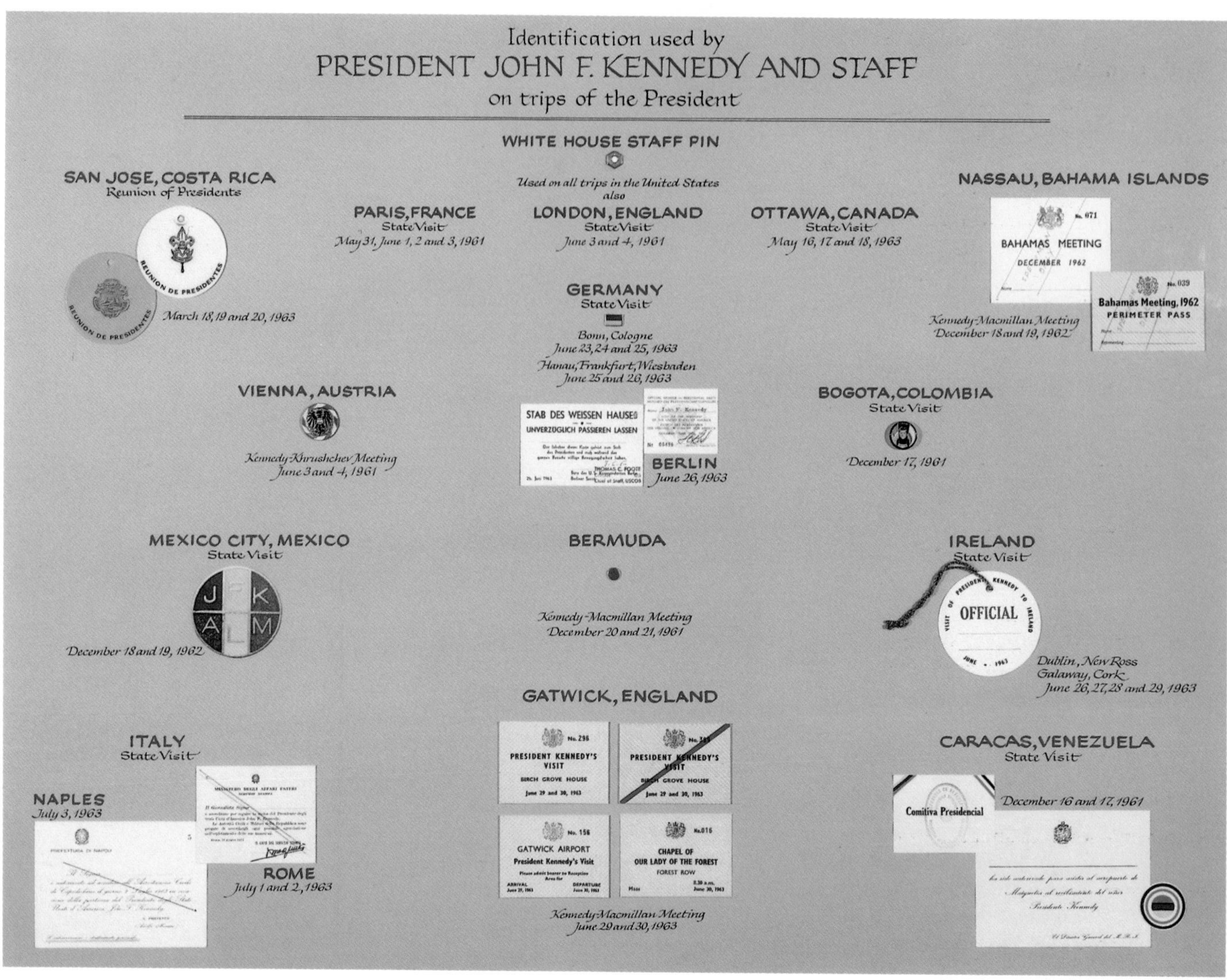

765

765 **Kennedy, John F.**

Identification used by President John F. Kennedy and Staff on trips of the President. *N.p., (ca. 1963)*

Approximately (31 x 41 in.), framed and glazed. Calligraphic manuscript mount incorporating some of the printed ephemera and lapel pins or buttons (5) used on all of JFK's state visits.

A fine group of label pins and official printed ephemera, passes, etc., from the official visits of JFK, including Costa Rica, Vienna (button), Nassau Bahamas, Bermuda (pin), Colombia (button with JFK portrait), England, Italy, Germany (pin), and Argentina. Also included is a White House staff pin.

$2,000–3,000

766 **Group of Eleven Kennedy Half Dollars**

Nine dating from 1967 and two from 1964. (11)

$200–300

767 **(Salinger, Pierre.) Thomas Jefferson.** [Facsimile autograph letter to Mr. Norvell, Washington, June 11, 1807]

(9½ x 15¼ in.), sight. Framed, matted and glazed. Signed on the mat.

PRESENTATION FROM PRESS SECRETARY PIERRE SALINGER, "To the President, Anytime you get mad at the Press, this will remind you that Jefferson got madder."

$300–500

768 **Virginia.** [Photo-facsimile of deed of Virginia land. *Dated 1728*]

(20 x 8½ in.), sight. Framed, matted and glazed. Typed transcript on the frame verso.

A Christmas present from Lady Bird Johnson and the President, 1963. On the back of the frame is written in Mrs. Kennedy's hand, "Christmas Present Dec. 1963 from Lyndon & Lady Bird."

$200–300

769 **Cleveland, Grover.** [Engraved wedding announcement. *June, 1886*]

(10½ x 4¼ in.), sight. Framed, matted with envelope and glazed.

The wedding announcement for Grover Cleveland. The envelope is made out to Judge & Mrs. Merrick. On the back of the frame is written, "From Wyckliffe Wyse, April 19, 1961, Jacqueline Kennedy."

$200–300

770 **Lincoln, Abraham**

A group of 7 volumes about Lincoln, various sizes, several inscribed. Some illustrated. Publisher's cloth and wrappers.

George Bancroft. *Memorial Address on the Life and Character of Abraham Lincoln*. 1866. INSCRIBED by C. M. Clay to Grand Duke Alexander of Russia, 1866. — F. B. Carpenter. *Six Months in the White House with Lincoln*. 1867. Bookplates of Victor S. Frankenstein and W. A. Tope, M. D. — Abraham Lincoln. *Lincoln Letters*. 1913. — Stefan Lorant. *Lincoln: His Life in Photographs*. 1941. — Benjamin Barondess. *Three Lincoln Masterpieces*. 1954. — C. Vann Woodward. *Reunion and Reaction*. 1956. — David S. Sparks, ed. *Inside Lincoln's Army*. 1964.

$300–500

767

767

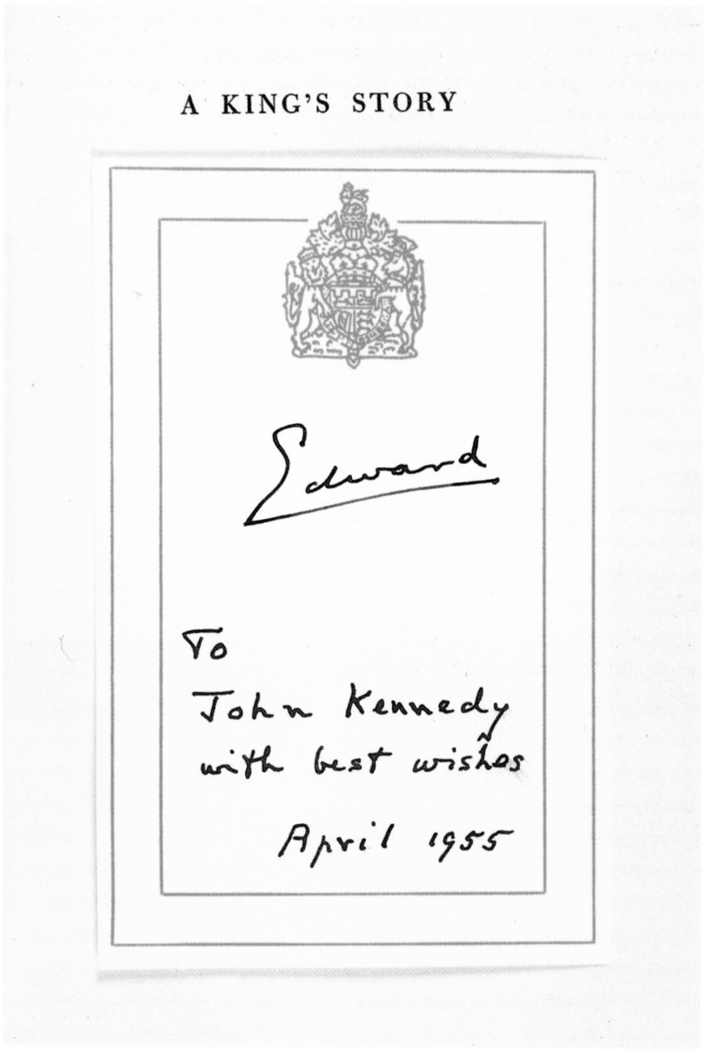

771

771 **Edward, Duke of Windsor**

A King's Story: The Memoirs of the Duke of Windsor. *New York: G. P. Putnam's Sons, (1951)*

(8⅜ x 5⅝ in.). Photographic frontispiece and plates; pages 104–105 discolored from inserted 1957 newsclippings about the 1960 Democratic presidential contest. Publisher's black cloth gilt, cartographic endpapers, top edges stained red, pictorial dust-jacket; jacket a bit worn.

FIRST EDITION, PRESENTATION COPY, with an inserted card inscribed "To John Kennedy with best wishes, April 1955" signed by the author ("Edward"). The volume also bears the presidential bookplate of John F. Kennedy.

$1,000–1,500

772 **The Cambridge Modern History**

The Cambridge Modern History. *Cambridge: The University Press, 1904–1925.*

11 volumes only (9⅛ x 6⅜ in.); lacking vols. IX and XI. Publisher's blue cloth, top edges gilt; several spines frayed and faded to brown.

ASSOCIATION SET, each volume bearing the presidential bookplate of John F. Kennedy.

$1,000–1,500

773 **World War I**

George Aston. *The Biography of the Late Marshal Foch.* New York, 1929. — R. H. Mottram, et al. *Three Personal Records of the War.* London, 1929. — Charles F. Horne, ed. *Source Records of the Great War.* (Np, 1923). Volumes 1, 4, and 7 only.

Together 5 volumes, various sizes. Various publisher's cloth; a bit worn.

ASSOCIATION COPIES, each bearing the presidential bookplate of John F. Kennedy.

$600–800

774 **Politics and Policy: European**

Norman Angell. *The Defence of the Empire.* London, (1937). — M. K. Dziewanowski. *The Communist Party of Poland: An Outline of History.* Cambridge, Massachusetts, 1959. — Carlton J. H. Hayes. *A Political and Cultural History of Modern Europe. Volume 1: Three Centuries of Predominately Agricultural Society, 1500–1830.* New York, 1937.

Together 3 volumes, various sizes. Various publisher's cloth, second title with dust-jacket; some wear.

ASSOCIATION COPIES, each bearing the presidential bookplate of John F. Kennedy. Dziewanowski's book is also inscribed by the author on the front free endpaper: "To Senator John F. Kennedy as a small token of admiration for his work … Cambridge, 5.II.1959." The volume by Angell has extensive marginal rulings and checkmarks in pencil.

$800–1,200

775 **Modern Warfare and Armament**

Ronald Adam and Charles Judd. *Assault at Arms: A Policy for Disarmament.* London, (1960). — Eugene Burdick and Harvey Wheeler. *Fail-Safe.* New York (1960). — Harold B. Hinton. *Air Victory: The Men and the Machines.* New York (1948). — Franklin Mark Osanka, ed. *Modern Guerrilla Warfare: Fighting Communist Guerrilla Movements, 1941–1961.* (New York, 1962)

Together 4 volumes, various sizes. Various publisher's cloth and half-cloth, dust-jackets; slight rubbing, jackets rather worn.

ASSOCIATION COPIES, each bearing the presidential bookplate of John F. Kennedy. *Air Victory* is also inscribed on the front free endpaper to President Kennedy by the author's wife, Eva Hinton, evidently shortly after the 1960 election: "Another Navy man, James Forrestal, found this useful for reference when he had to cope with the Air Force. Hope you may find it useful too. I know Harold would want you to have it. All best wishes & congratulations … to Jack Kennedy." *Fail-Safe* is inscribed on the front free endpaper to President Kennedy "with all good will in the essential cause of world peace and security" by Dag E. Hinkley.

$1,500–2,500

776 **Politics and Policy: European**

Geoffrey Bailey (pseudonym of George Varsilchikov. *The Conspirators.* New York (1960). — Friedrich A. Hayek. *The Road to Serfdom.* Chicago (1944). — Salvador de Madariaga. *Englishmen, Frenchmen, Spaniards: An Essay in Comparative Psychology.* London, (1949)

Together 3 volumes, various sizes. Various publisher's cloth, first and third title with dust-jackets; slight rubbing and chipping.

ASSOCIATION COPIES, each bearing the presidential bookplate of John F. Kennedy. *The Conspirators* is cryptically inscribed by the author on the front free endpaper: "In memory & thanks for the Nina Steers, September in Hyannis, memorial head-cold. XO, 9/27/60"; on the title-page, Varsilchikov has ruled through the printed pseudonym and signed his own name. Hayek's volume has several marginal pencil rules throughout.

$800–1,200

777 **Bourrienne, Louis Antoine Fauvelet de**

Memoirs of Napoleon Bonaparte. *London: Richard Bentley, 1885*

3 volumes (8⅜ x 5⅜ in.). Title-pages printed in red and black, engraved frontispiece portraits and numerous portrait plates, folding map depicting Napoleon's conquests. Half purple morocco, spines gilt with Napoleonic emblems, marbled endpapers, top edges gilt; spines uniformly faded to brown, extremities rubbed, rear cover of first volume detached.

ASSOCIATION COPY, the first two volumes with the presidential bookplate of John F. Kennedy; the third volume with an earlier juvenile bookplate and Kennedy's inkstamp.

$400–600

778 **United States Constitution**

The Constitution of the United States of America: Analysis and Interpretation; Annotations of Cases decided by the Supreme Court of the United States to June 30, 1952. *Washington, D.C.: Government Printing Office, 1953*

(11⅛ x 7⅝ in.). Blue cloth gilt, front cover blind-stamped with the seal of the United States; extremities rubbed.

JFK'S COPY OF THE FEDERAL CONSTITUTION, bearing his Presidential bookplate. This copy is one of 800 copies printed for the use of the Senate (as Senate Document 170 of the eighty-second congress), of a total edition of 3,000. The volume had previously been in the Library of Congress, and has ink and perforated stamps from that institution.

$800–1,200

779 **Sport**

Group of 6 volumes, various sizes, most illustrated. Publisher's cloth or boards (one full red morocco). Various places, various dates.

Gene Schoor. *Red Grange: Football's Greatest Halfback.* 1962. INSCRIBED: "To President John F. Kennedy. Best Personal Wishes. Gene Schoor." — Jerome E. Brooks. *The $30,000,000 Cup.* 1958. INSCRIBED: "for Mrs. John F. Kennedy with the deep respect, admiration, and good wishes of the author ... September 1963." — [Willy Schaeffler]. *The Sports Illustrated Book of Skiing.* 1957. INSCRIBED: "To Jackie, hope this contributes to your skiing success ... First of 1965. Willy Schaeffler" with flyleaf note at end in Mrs. Onassis's hand listing names, perhaps for a social occasion. — and 3 others.

$500–800

780 **Encyclopædia Britannica**

Encyclopædia Britannica. *London, 1937*

24 (of 25) volumes (11 x 8½ in.). Volume 3 not present. Publisher's blue cloth, spines gilt-decorated; slightly rubbed.

ASSOCIATION COPY, with the presidential bookplate of John F. Kennedy in each volume.

$500–700

781

781

781 **Abernon, Viscount d'**

The Eighteenth Decisive Battle of the World: Warsaw 1920. *London: Hodder and Stoughton, 1931*

(8¼ x 5⅜ in.). Photographic portrait plate of General Weygand, text maps, 3 large folding maps in pocket on rear pastedown. Publisher's purple cloth; faded, scuffed.

ASSOCIATION COPY, SIGNED BY JOHN F. KENNEDY, with his presidential bookplate and ink-stamp on the rear pastedown. Also with the bookplate of the Bibliotheca Arcis Pomorzanensis.

$1,000–1,500

782 **Congress of the United States**

Together, 3 volumes, various sizes. Various publisher's cloth, dust-jackets; slight wear. The volumes comprise:

James MacGregor Burns. *The Deadlock of Democracy.* Englewood Cliffs, N.J., 1963. — Franklin Burdette. *Filibustering in the Senate.* Princeton, 1940. — Andrew Tully. *Capitol Hill.* New York, 1962.

ASSOCIATION COPIES, each with the presidential bookplate of John F. Kennedy. Tully's novel is also inscribed by him on the front flyleaf: "For President Kennedy, who's showing my president how it's done." Burns's study of the conflict between the executive and legislative branches of government discusses Kennedy as Congressman, Senator and President.

$800–1,200

783 **Atlas**

Encyclopædia Britannica World Atlas (ed.: G. Donald Hudson). *Chicago: Encyclopædia Britannica, 1961*

(14½ x 11 in.). Numerous maps, charts and tables. Red morocco gilt, moiré endleaves, edges gilt; upper hinge cracked, extremities somewhat worn.

PRESENTATION COPY FROM THE PUBLISHER, WILLIAM BENTON, with an elaborate illuminated presentation leaf incorporating a calligraphic inscription to President Kennedy. Also with the presidential bookplate of John F. Kennedy on the front flyleaf.

$400–600

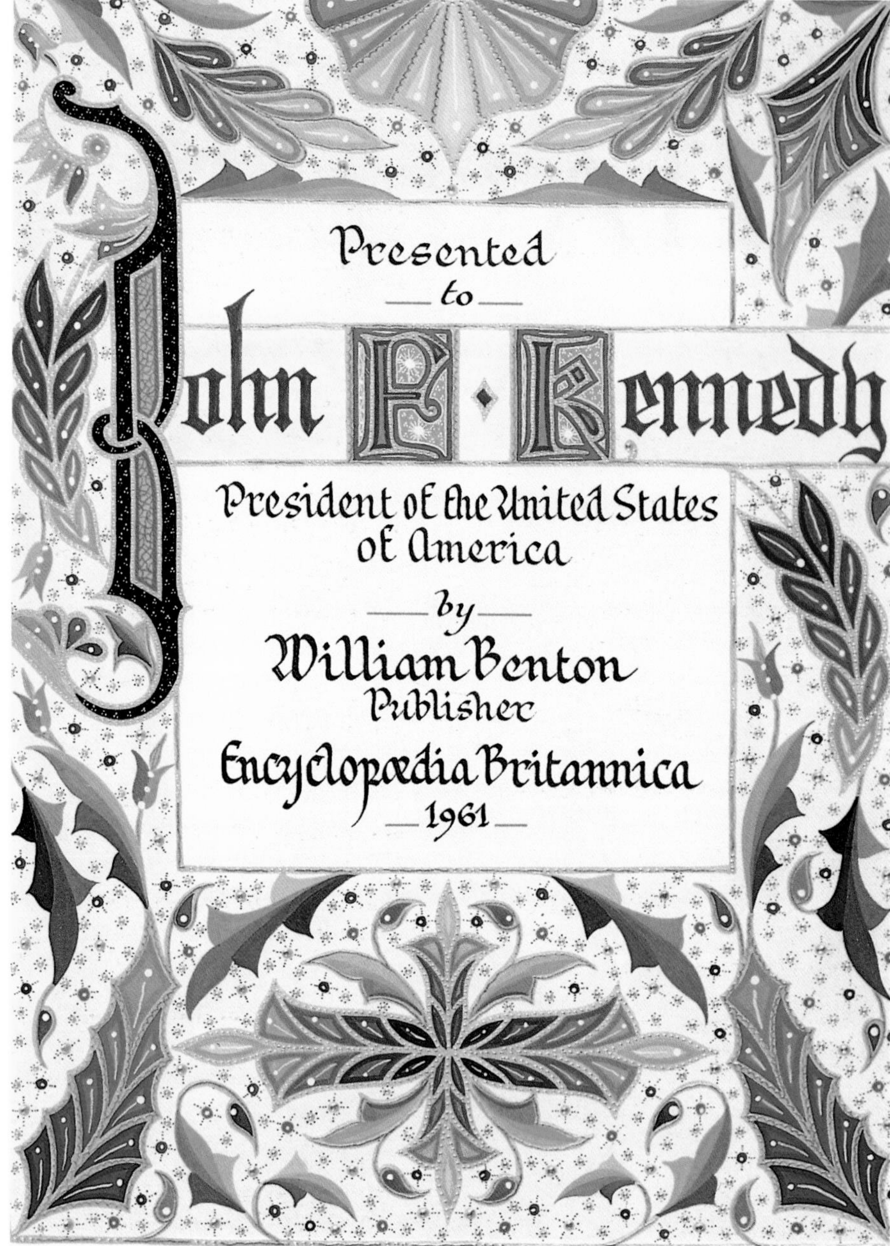

783

784 **Philosophy and Religion**

Henry Edward, Archbishop of Westminster. *The Vatican Decrees in their Bearing on Civil Allegiance.* New York, 1875. — Walter Farrell & Martin J. Healy. *My Way of Life, Pocket Edition of St. Thomas: The Summa Simplified for Everyone.* Brooklyn, 1952. — Charles A. Fecher. *The Philosophy of Jacques Maritain.* Westminster, Maryland, 1953. — Niccolò Machiavelli. *The Prince and The Discourses.* New York, [n.d.]. — Norah Willis Michener. *Maritain on the Nature of Man in a Christian Democracy.* Hull, Quebec, 1955. — Josef Pieper. *Fortitude and Temperance.* London, (1955).

Together 6 volumes, various sizes. Various bindings, the last two titles with printed dust-jackets.

ASSOCIATION COPIES, each bearing the presidential bookplate of John F. Kennedy (with the exception of the Machiavelli, which bears his ink-stamp). Michener has also inscribed her book to Kennedy, writing on the front free endpaper: "For the President of the United States, on the occasion of his visit to Canada ... Speakers Chambers, Ottawa, May 1, 1961."

$1,000–1,500

785 **American History**

A group of 10 volumes chiefly about or by American presidents, most bearing presentation inscriptions to Jacqueline Bouvier Kennedy or joint inscriptions to the President and Mrs. Kennedy. Mostly publisher's cloth and wrappers. Varying sizes and conditions.

John Quincy Adams. *Lectures on Rhetoric and Oratory.* 1st ed. 2 vols.; contemporary half calf. Cambridge, 1810. Ownership stamp of Gustav Tuckerman. — Benson J. Lossing. *The Home of Washington.* 1871. Inscribed by D.Warren, Boston, 7 June 1962: "For the library of two latter-day Washingtonians of whom I am certain George and Martha would be proud." — William Dorsheimer. *Life and Public Services of Hon. Grover Cleveland … the Unanimous Nominee of the Democratic Party for the President of the United States* [and] W. U. Hensel. *A Biographical Sketch of …Thomas A. Hendricks, Democratic Nominee for Vice-President.* 1884. Inscribed "To Jackie, With love from Molly." — Lucius Wilmerding, Jr. *James Monroe: Public Claimant.*1960. Inscribed by the author to Mrs. Kennedy. Cloth chemise and slipcase, morocco spine. — Richard D. Heffner. *A Documentary History of the United States.* November 1963. Paperback. Inscribed by the author: " 2 September 1965. To Mrs. John F. Kennedy. With great admiration and compassion." — Philip Wayne Powell. *Tree of Hate.* 1971. Inscribed by the author, with a further inscription by Stewart Udall, former Secretary of the Interior under President Kennedy, and his wife: "For Jackie. Brought from the West with affection by two couriers. Stew and Lee. With the compliments of the author [Powell's signature]. April 1, 1985." — and others.

$500–700

786 **The White House and the Presidency**

Group of 16 volumes, various sizes. Mostly illustrated. Publisher's cloth and wrappers, many with dust-jackets. Various places, various dates.

Laura C. Holloway. *The Ladies of the White House; or, In the Houses of the Presidents.* Philadelphia, 1881. — Hugo Ziemann and Mrs. F. L. Gillette. *The White House Cook Book.* Chicago, (1900). — Amy La Follette Jensen. *The White House and its Thirty-Two Families.* New York, (1958); *…and its Thirty-Three Families.* (1962); *…and its Thirty-Four Families* (1965). — Cranston Jones. *Homes of the American Presidents.* New York, (1962). — *Pennsylvania Avenue: Report of the President's Council on Pennsylvania Avenue.* (Washington, D.C., 1964). — *The White House Library: A Short-Title List.* Washington, D.C., 1967. — Kenneth W. Leish. *The White House.* New York, (1977). — Carl Sferrazza Anthony. *First Ladies.* 2 volumes. New York, (1990–1991). — and others.

$300–500

787 **The White House**

Group of 12 volumes, various sizes. Mostly illustrated. Publisher's cloth and wrappers, many with dust-jackets. Various places, various dates.

Ruth Montgomery. *Flowers at the White House: An Informal Tour of the Home of the Presidents of the United States.* New York, 1967, PRESENTATION COPY, inscribed by the author to Mrs. Kennedy, February 1967. — Frederick L. Kramer, et al. *The White House Gardens: A History and Pictorial Record.* New York, (1973), number 26 of 1,000 copies signed by Kramer and artist Harold Sterner. — Susan G. Detweiler. *American Presidential China.* Washington, D.C., 1975, housed in a buckram slipcase with the gilt supralibros JACQUELINE KENNEDY ONASSIS; Mrs. Onassis was a lender to this exhibition. — Elsie K. Kirk. *Music at the White House: A History of the American Spirit.* Urbana, Illinois, (1986), PRESENTATION COPY, inscribed by the author to Mrs. Onassis, November 1986. — Jane Shadel Spillman. *White House Glassware: Two Centuries of Presidential Entertaining.* Washington, D.C., (1989). — William Kloss, et al. *Art in the White House: A Nation's Pride.* (Washington, D.C., 1992). — and others.

$800–1,200

788 **The White House**

Group of 17 volumes, various sizes. Mostly illustrated. Publisher's cloth and wrappers, many with dust-jackets. Various places, various dates.

Gilson Willets. *Inside History of the White House.* New York, (1908). — Bess Furman. *White House Profile.* Indianapolis, 1951. — Ona Griffin Jeffries. *In and Out of the White House.* New York, (1960), PRESENTATION COPY, inscribed by the author to Mrs. Kennedy, December 1960. — Janet Halliday Ervin. *The White House Cookbook.* Chicago, 1964, PRESENTATION COPY, inscribed by the editor to Mrs. Kennedy, June 1965. — *The White House Library: A Short-Title List.* Washington, D.C., 1967. — J. B. West. *Upstairs at the White House: My Life with the First Ladies.* New York, 1973. — William Seale. *The President's House: A History.* Washington, D.C., 1986, 2 volumes. — An unbound proof copy of the foregoing. — and others.

$600–800

789 **The White House**

Group of 6 volumes, various sizes. First title bound in half green morocco gilt, others in wrappers.

Olmsted Brothers, Landscape Architects. *Report to the President of the United States on Improvements and Policy of Maintenance for the Executive Mansion Grounds.* Brookline, Massachusetts, 1935. Folding plans and illustrations; with the bookplate of Jacqueline Bouvier Kennedy. — Stanley McClure. *The White House.* (Washington, D.C.:) United States Department of the Interior, 1953. Illustrated; 2 copies. — John Carl Warnecke and Associates. *Program for the Historical Preservation and Development of Lafayette Square, including Design of Federal Office Building #7 (FOB #7 Executive Office Building) and Court of Claims and Court of Customs & Patent Appeals Building.* (Washington, D.C., 1962). — *The White House Collection: Preliminary Catalogue, Furniture, Furnishings, Fine Arts, Documents Acquired 1961–Nov. 1964.* (Washington, D.C., 1965). — *The White House Library: A Short-Title List.* Washington, D.C., 1967.

$200–300

790 **Kennedy, John F.**

Discours [trans. J. Bloch-Michel]. *Paris: Club du Livre, 1967*

Together 2 items, book and portfolio of plates (12½ x 9¾ in.) Title in blue and black. Portrait color lithograph frontispiece and color lithograph plates throughout by Mac'Avoy. Dark blue morocco by Michel Kieffer with accompanying chemise and slipcase.

A fine French illustrated *livre d'artiste* of President Kennedy's famous speeches. This is one of 25 *hors commerce* copies, press-numbered 0, "destinés à Madame J. F. Kennedy, à l'illustrateur et aux collaborateurs de l'édition." Printed on japon nacré, with an extra suite of plates in color. Signed by the illustrator.

$600–800

791 **Kennedy, John F.**

January, 1961. [n.p.], [n.d.] A spiral-bound book of fine photoreproductions of the Kennedy Inauguration, including pictures of the swearing in and the party following, of Frank Sinatra and attendees. — Anne H. Lincoln. *The Kennedy White House Parties.* New York: Viking Press, 1967. Specially bound in half blue calf, spine gilt.

Together 2 items.

$400–600

792 **Kennedy, John F.**

A group of 22 volumes by or about John F. Kennedy, various sizes. Publisher's cloth (3 paperbacks). Various places and dates. One title contains a presentation to Jacqueline Kennedy.

James MacGregor Burns. *John Kennedy: Perfil de un politco de valor.* 1960. In Spanish. Green morocco, gilt, in slipcase. John F. Kennedy. *Profiles in Courage.* 1965. Memorial edition. — John F. Kennedy. *The Burden and the Glory.* 1964. — O.M. Artus. *John F. Kennedy in Deutschland.* 1964. 2 copies, one with calligraphic presentation to Jacqueline Kennedy from the Mayor of Brunswick. — T. C. Sorensen. *Kennedy.* 1966. In Italian. Blue morocco in slipcase. — Roger Hilsman. *To Move a Nation: The Politics of Foreign Policy in the Administration of John F. Kennedy.* 1967. — and others.

$800–1,200

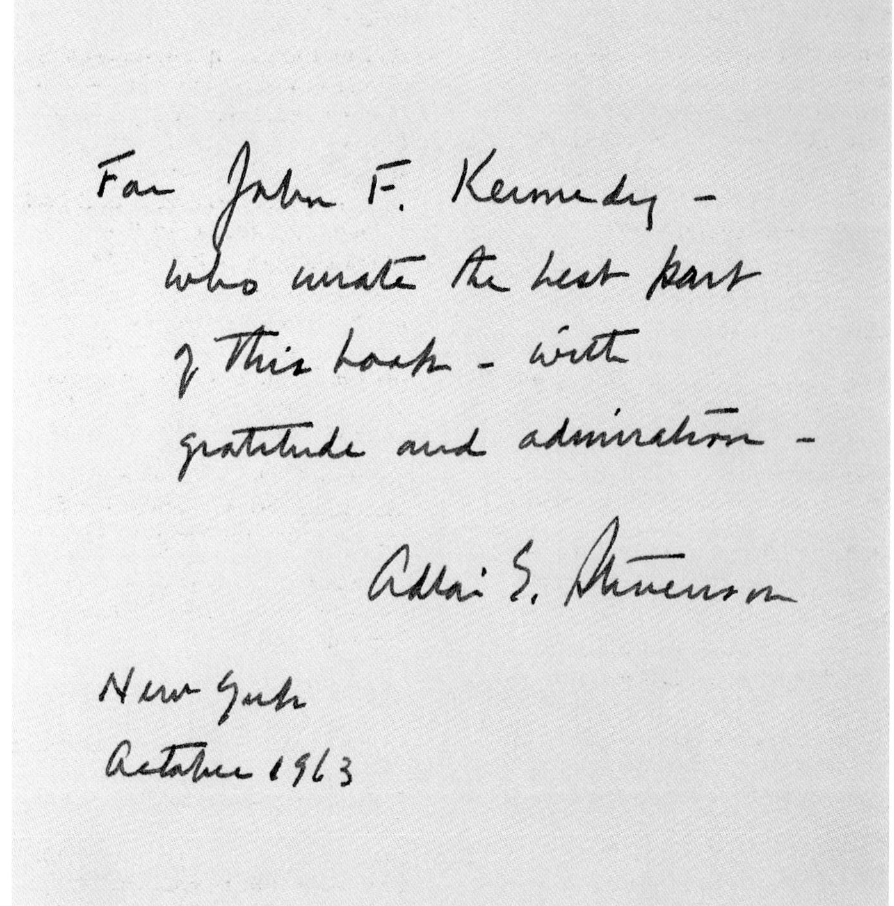
For John F. Kennedy – who wrote the best part of this book – with gratitude and admiration –

Adlai S. Stevenson

New York
October 1963

794

793 **Kennedy, John F.**

A group of 23 volumes, various sizes. Several illustrated. Publisher's cloth or paper. Various places and dates.

John F. Kennedy. *America the Beautiful.* 1964. 2 copies. Dedicated to Jacqueline Kennedy. One copy with her name stamped on the upper cover. — John F. Kennedy. *Profiles in Courage.* 1964. Memorial edition. — John F. Kennedy. *The Burden and the Glory.* 1964. Specially bound edition with President's seal. — Harold Faber, ed. *The Kennedy Years.* 1964. — John F. Kennedy. *Why England Slept.* 1992. — And others.

$500–700

794 **Stevenson, Adlai E.**

Looking Outward. Years of Crisis at the United Nations. Preface by President John F. Kennedy. *New York: Harper & Row, 1963*

(8¼ x 5⅝ in.). First edition. Publisher's blue cloth, spine lettered in silver, dustjacket; price clipped from inside corner of dustjacket.

A FINE PRESENTATION COPY FROM ADLAI E. STEVENSON TO PRESIDENT KENNEDY. Stevenson writes gratefully to the President for his prefatory contribution to *Looking Outward*: "For John F. Kennedy, who wrote the best part of this book—with gratitude and admiration. Adlai S. Stevenson. New York, October 1963." Stevenson, the unsuccessful Democrat candidate for president in 1952 and 1956, served in the Kennedy administration as the United States Ambassador to the United Nations.

$1,500–2,000

795 **American History**

Thomas J. Fleming. *Now We Are Enemies: The Story of Bunker Hill.* New York, (1960). — Harold McCracken. *Portrait of the Old West.* New York, (1952). — F. Van Wyck Mason. *The Young Titan.* Garden City, 1959

Together 3 volumes, various sizes. Various publisher's cloth.

ASSOCIATION COPIES, each bearing the presidential bookplate of John F. Kennedy.

$600–800

796 **American Literature**

Ernest Hemingway. *The Hemingway Reader.* New York, 1953. — John P. Marquand. *The Late George Apley.* (New York, 1940). — Robert Service. *Ballads of a Bohemian.* New York, 1933. — Tennessee Williams. *Summer and Smoke.* (New York, 1948).

Together 4 volumes, various sizes. Various publisher's cloth, last title with dust-jacket.

ASSOCIATION COPIES, each bearing the presidential bookplate of John F. Kennedy.

$800–1,200

797 **Literature: Anthologies and Criticism**

John Mason Brown. *As They Appear.* New York, (1952). — Whit Burnett, ed. *This is My Best.* New York, 1942. — Gilbert Highet. *The Powers of Poetry.* New York, 1960. — *Short Stories from The New Yorker.* New York, 1940.

Together 4 volumes, various sizes. Various publisher's cloth; slightly worn.

ASSOCIATION COPIES, each bearing the presidential bookplate of John F. Kennedy.

$600–800

798 **Literature**

Hilaire Belloc. *Sonnets and Verse.* New York, 1944. — Hilaire Belloc. *Cautionary Verses.* New York, 1949. — Rudyard Kipling. *Barrack-Room Ballads & Departmental Ditties.* Mount Vernon, New York, (ca. 1950). — Abbé Prévost. *Histoire du Chevalier des Grieux et de Manon Lescaut.* Stamford, Connecticut: Overbrook Press, 1958. — George Sand. *La Petite Fadette.* Paris, [n.d.]. — M. H. B. Stendhal. *Lamiel, or The Ways of the Heart.* New York, 1929. — Alfred de Vigny. *Cinq-Mars.* Paris, [n.d.]; volume 1 only from a collected edition.

Together 7 volumes, various sizes. Various publisher's cloth and morocco; several badly rubbed.

ASSOCIATION COPIES, each bearing the presidential bookplate of John F. Kennedy.

$800–1,200

799 **Biography**

William Lyon Phelps. *Autobiography with Letters.* New York, 1939. — Peter Quennell, ed. *Byron: A Self-Portrait, Letters and Diaries 1798 to 1824.* New York, (1950); volume 2 only. — Sir Osbert Sitwell. *Noble Essences: A Book of Characters.* Boston, 1950. — Christopher Sykes. *Four Studies in Loyalty.* New York, (1948). — Captain Malet. *Annals of the Road or Notes on Mail and Stage Coaching in Great Britain.* London, 1876. — Jan-Olof Traung. *Fishing Boast of the World.* London, 1955.

Together 6 volumes, various sizes. Various publisher's cloth and half morocco; slight rubbing.

ASSOCIATION COPIES, each bearing the presidential bookplate of John F. Kennedy.

$800–1,200

800 **Biography**

Arthur Bryant. *The Age of Elegance, 1812–1822.* London, 1950. — John Buchan. *Montrose: A History.* Boston, 1928. — Arthur Hassall. *The Life of Napoleon.* Boston, 1911. — Alfred Noyes. *Voltaire.* New York, 1936. — E. T. Raymond. *Portraits of the Nineties.* New York, 1921. — Louisa Anne Twamley. *The Romance of Nature; or, the Flower-Seasons Illustrated.* London, 1836. — René Guerdan. *Byzantium: Its Triumphs and Tragedy.* New York, (1957).

Together 7 volumes, various sizes. Various publisher's cloth and morocco; most slightly rubbed, Twamley very worn with both covers detached; a few pages of Buchan roughly opened.

ASSOCIATION COPIES, each bearing the presidential bookplate of John F. Kennedy.

$1,000–1,500

801 **Politics and Policy: American**

Leverett S. Lyon, Victor Abramson, et al. *Government and Economic Life: Development and Current Issues of American Public Policy.* Washington, D.C., 1940; volume II only. — Raymond Moley. *After Seven Years.* New York, 1939. — Alfred E. Smith. *Campaign Addresses.* Washington, D.C., (1929). — Irving R. Levine, Sander Vanocur, et al. *Memo to JFK from NBC News.* New York, 1961.

Together 4 volumes, various sizes. Various publisher's cloth, last title with dust-jacket; some slight rubbing and fading.

ASSOCIATION COPIES, each bearing the presidential bookplate of John F. Kennedy. The *Memo to JFK* is also inscribed by the president of the National Broadcasting Company: "To President John F. Kennedy with admiration and best wishes from N.B.C. … 10/5/61." The volume of Governor Smith's presidential *Campaign Speeches* also bears Kennedy's ink-stamp on the front and rear paste-downs.

$1,000–1,500

802 **Kennedy Presidency**

Group of 7 volumes, various sizes, 2 INSCRIBED or presented to Mrs. Onassis, one to PRESIDENT KENNEDY, 3 with bookplate of Jacqueline Bouvier Kennedy. Publisher's cloth or wrappers, one half-leather. Various places, various dates.

William Manchester. *Portrait of a President.* 1962. — Gerald Gardner, ed., *The Quotable Mr. Kennedy.* 1963. "To President John F. Kennedy – with admiration and commitment." — Molly Kazan. *Kennedy.* 1964. "To Jackie with affection, Polly Fitzgerald." — William Manchester. *One Brief Shining Moment.* 1983. Specially bound in black half-morocco, gilt, and INSCRIBED: "For Jackie—With warmest regards And my best wishes, as always, Bill." — and 2 others.

$500–700

805

803 **Kennedy, John F. — Memorials**

Group of 21 volumes, various sizes, most illustrated, being various memoirs and memorials of President Kennedy. Publisher's cloth or wrappers. Various places, various dates.

Summary of the Three-Year Kennedy Record, Government Printing Office, 1964. Specially published, in the words of Sen. Mansfield, "because of the incomprehensible tragedy which occurred on November 22." — *The Shining Moments ... with the Memorial Tribute of Adlai E. Stevenson*. 1964. — Encyclopaedia Britannica. *A Tribute to John F. Kennedy*. 1964. — Harvard Class of 1940. *Twenty-fifth Class Report.* Dedicated to the memory of Pres. Kennedy, and with frontispiece portrait. — Wendell Berry & Ben Shahn. *November Twenty Six Nineteen Hundred Sixty Three*. 1964. — and 16 others.

$400–600

804 **American Politics**

Group of 6 volumes, 2 of which INSCRIBED to Mrs. Onassis. Various sizes. Publisher's cloth or wrappers. Various places, various dates.

W. W. Rostow. *View From the Seventh Floor.* 1964. "To Jacqueline Kennedy with affection and the commitment to do what a man can to make this little book's theme come alive. Walt ..." — Theodore H. White. *The Making of the President 1964*. 1965. "For Jacqueline Kennedy, with everlasting devotion, Teddy." — and 4 others.

$400–600

805 **Kennedy, John F.**

A group of 9 works in 16 stereo albums (33 r.p.m.). Various places and dates.

John F. Kennedy. *Senator Kennedy Speaks*. 1959. Sleeve inscribed with, "Save for JBK." — *The Kennedy Years, 1956-63*. [n.d.] 3 stereo albums, boxed set. — *The Kennedy Wit*. 1964. — ABC Radio Network. *November 22, 1963*. 2 stereo albums. — *J.F.K. ... A Legacy of Laughter*. 1975. — *JFK May 29, 1917 Nov. 22, 1963*. (ca. 1964.). — and 4 other works.

$600–800

806 **Kennedy, John F.**

A group of 8 works including 1 book and 10 phono albums. Various places and dates.

A Tribute to President John F. Kennedy from the Arts. November 24, 1963. 2 phono albums. — Leonard Bernstein. *Symphony no. 3, Kaddish*. n.d. First recording by the New York Philharmonic. — The ABC Radio Network. *November 22, 1963*. 2 phono albums. — *John Fitzgerald as We Remember Him*. 1965. Book and double phono album. In slipcase. — and 4 others.

$300–500

807 **The White House Library**

White House Library List, August 9, 1963. *(Washington, D.C., 1963)*. — The White House Library: A Short-Title List. *Washington, D.C.: The White House Historical Association, 1967* (one cloth-bound, and two paper-bound copies)

Together, 4 volumes, various sizes. Publisher's calf, cloth, and wrappers; first title rubbed at extremities.

An early, unpublished checklist of the White House Library, together with three copies of the published short-title catalogue. Mrs. Kennedy engaged James T. Babb, Librarian Emeritus of Yale University, to collect a library of approximately 2,500 volumes illustrating the American national experience for installation on the first floor of the White House. The project was seen to completion by First Lady Lady Bird Johnson.

$500–700

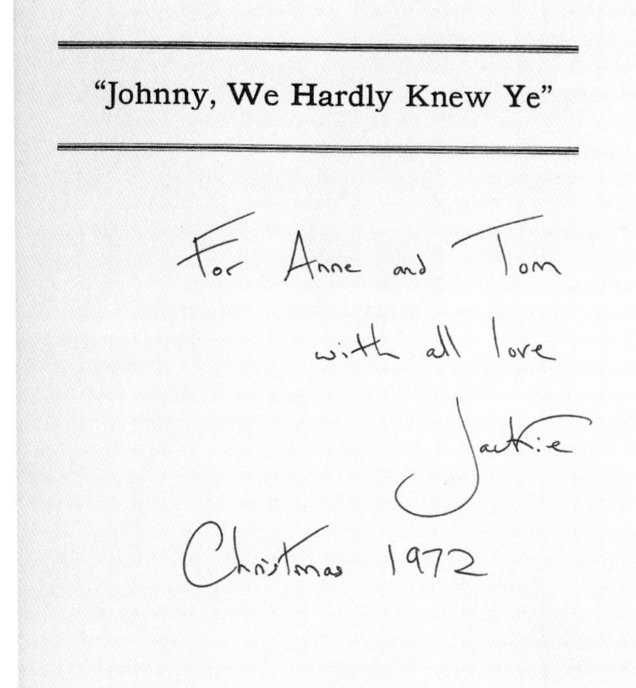

808

808 **O'Donnell, Kenneth P., and David F. Powers**

"Johnny, We Hardly Knew Ye": Memories of John Fitzgerald Kennedy. *Boston: Little, Brown, (1972)*

(9¼ x 6⅛ in.). Publisher's half yellow cloth, dust-jacket; jacket torn with loss.

ASSOCIATION COPY, INSCRIBED AND SIGNED BY JACQUELINE ONASSIS on the half-title: "For Anne and Tom with all love, Jackie, Christmas 1972."

$600–800

809

809 **Kennedy, John F.**

As We Remember Joe. *Cambridge, Mass.: Privately printed at the University Press, 1945*

(9 x 6 in.). Photographic illustrations and facsimile plates. Original maroon cloth gilt; extremities slightly rubbed.

FIRST EDITION, ONE OF APPROXIMATELY 400 COPIES, printed for private distribution to the relatives and friends of Joseph P. Kennedy, Jr. Lt. Joseph Kennedy was killed flying a secret mission to Germany on 12 August 1944; these memorial remarks by his family and comrades were collected and edited by his younger brother, John F. Kennedy.

$1,000–1,500

25TH ANNIVERSARY REPORT

✠ JOHN FITZGERALD KENNEDY

BORN: May 29, 1917, Brookline, Mass. PARENTS: Joseph Patrick Kennedy, '12, Rose Fitzgerald.
PREPARED AT: Choate School, Wallingford, Conn.
YEARS IN COLLEGE: 1936–1940. DEGREES: S.B., *cum laude*, 1940; LL.D. (Notre Dame Univ.), 1950; D.A.O. (Staley Coll.), 1951; LL.D. (Tufts Coll.), 1954; LL.D. (Assumption Coll.), 1955; LL.D. (Boston Univ.), 1955; LL.D. (Harvard Univ.), 1956; S.D., Hon. (Lowell Technological Inst.), 1956; LL.D. (Boston Coll.), 1956; LL.D. (Northeastern Univ.), 1956; LL.D. (Loras Coll.), 1956; LL.D. (Rockhurst Coll.), 1956; LL.D. (Springfield Coll.), 1956; LL.D. (Syracuse Univ.), 1957; D.P.A. Hon. (Suffolk Univ.), 1957; LITT.D. (Quincy Coll., Ill.), 1958; S.D., Hon. (New England Coll. of Pharmacy), 1958; LL.D. (George Washington Univ.), 1961; LL.D. (West Virginia Univ.), 1961; LL.D. (Yale Univ.), 1962.
MARRIED: Jacqueline Bouvier, Sept. 12, 1953, Newport, R.I. CHILDREN: Caroline Bouvier, Nov. 28, 1957; John Fitzgerald, Jr., Nov. 25, 1960; Patrick Bouvier, Aug. 7, 1963 (died Aug. 9, 1963).
HARVARD BROTHERS: Joseph Patrick Kennedy, Jr., '38 (deceased); Robert Francis Kennedy, '48; Edward Moore Kennedy, '54.
DIED: Nov. 22, 1963, Dallas, Texas.
WIDOW: Mrs. John F. Kennedy, New York, N.Y.

JOHN FITZGERALD KENNEDY spent four years with our Class, was a member of our Permanent Class Committee and while an undergraduate was an editor of the *Crimson*, and member of Winthrop House hockey, swimming and football teams. From 1957 to 1963, he served as a member of the Board of Overseers of Harvard College. During World War II, he served four years in the Navy, attained the rank of lieutenant, and was commander of a PT boat in the South Pacific. Retired from the Navy in 1945 because of injuries, he was awarded the Navy and Marine Corps Medals and the Purple Heart. After the war he entered the field of journalism,

[717]

K

811

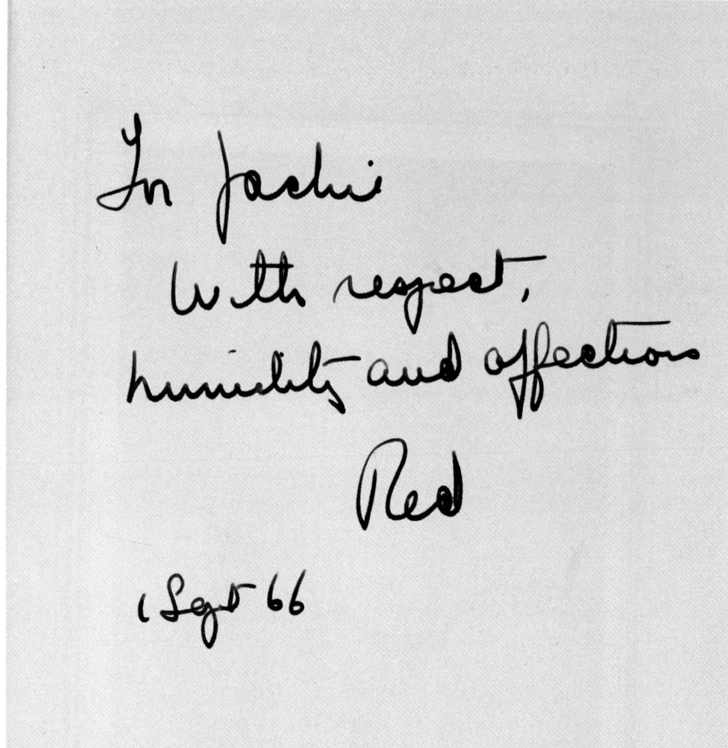

812

810 British Biography

Together 3 volumes, various sizes. All with photographic portrait plates. Various publisher's cloth; slightly rubbed.

John Buchan. *The King's Grace 1910–1935.* London, (1935). — Shane Leslie. *George the Fourth.* London, 1926.— W. N. L. Townsend. *A Biography of H. R. H. the Prince of Wales.* New York, 1929

ASSOCIATION COPIES, each with the presidential bookplate of John F. Kennedy.

$600–800

811 Harvard University

Harvard Class of 1940: Twenty-fifth Anniversary Report. *Cambridge: Printed for the Class, 1965*

(9 x 6 in.). Photographic frontispiece portrait of President Kennedy. Blue morocco gilt, marbled endpapers, gilt edges, thumb-tabbed with a gilt K to the entry on John F. Kennedy. Blue cloth slipcase.

A specially bound copy of the 1940 Harvard Class Report, evidently made for presentation to Mrs. Kennedy. The dedication of the volume reads: "With pride and a deep sense of loss ... We, the Harvard College Class of 1940 Dedicate our Twenty-fifth Anniversary Report To our Classmate John Fitzgerald Kennedy, President of the United States (1961–1963), Member of the Class of 1940, Member of the 1940 Permanent Class Committee, Member of the Board of Overseers."

$800–1,200

812 Fay, Paul B., Jr.

The Pleasure of his Company. *New York: Harper & Row, (1966)*

(8¼ x 5⅝ in.). Photographic frontispiece portrait of John F. Kennedy, plates. Publisher's maroon cloth, dust-jacket.

PRESENTATION COPY, inscribed and signed by the author on the verso of the frontispiece: "For Jackie, With respect, humility and affection, Red, 1 Sept 66." Kennedy met Paul "Red" Fay at a PT-Boat training base in Rhode Island. The two became close friends, and in 1961, the President appointed Fay as Under Secretary of the Navy.

$500–700

813 **American Politics**

A group of 9 volumes, inscribed to Mrs. Kennedy or with her floral bookplate; various sizes. Some illustrated. Publisher's cloth or wrappers.

George W. Malone. *Mainline.* 1958. Bookplate. — Henry Brandon. *As We Are.* 1961. Inscribed. — Michael Harrington. *The Other America.* 1962. Bookplate. — Edward P. Morgan. *Clearing the Air.* 1963. Inscribed. — and others.

$800–1,200

814 **Vrzalik, Larry F., and Michael Minor**

From the President's Pen: An Illustrated Guide to Presidential Autographs. *(Austin, Texas:) State House Press, 1991*

(10 ⅞ x 8¾ in.). Numerous reproductions and facsimiles. Publisher's half blue morocco gilt, endpapers with facsimile presidential signatures.

PRESENTATION COPY, inscribed and signed on the verso of the front free endpaper by Texas Senator Ralph W. Yarborough, who wrote the introduction to the volume: "To Mrs. Jacqueline Kennedy Onassis With fond memories of the Camelot White House, presided over by you with all of your grace and charm, and President Kennedy, one of the most intelligent of all of our Presidents, and the most intelligent person I have ever known personally, and I worked with for three years (precious years) on the Labor and Public Welfare Committee of the U. S. Senate..."

Limited edition, one of 100 numbered copies on the limitation leaf by Yarborough and the authors; this copy out-of-series and numbered "AAA."

$600–800

815 **The Paul Mellon Collection**

Judy Egerton. *British Sporting and Animal Painting 1655–1867.* 1978. — Judy Egerton & Dudley Snelgrove. *British Sporting and Animal Drawings.* 1978. — Dudley Snelgrove. *British Sporting and Animal Prints 1658–1874.* 1981. — John B. Podeschi. *Books on the Horse and Horsemanship: Riding, Hunting, Breeding & Racing.* 1981

Together 4 volumes (11½ x 8¾ in.). Numerous illustrations (many color). Uniform publisher's orange cloth, pictorial dust-jackets.

A set of the catalogues of Paul Mellon's collection of British Sport and Art, published for the Yale Center for British Art.

$300–500

816 **Fox-Hunting**

A group of 6 volumes, various sizes. Publishers cloth (one in sheep, gilt.) Various places and dates.

Earl of Lonsdale. *Fox-Hunting.* The Lonsdale Library VII. 1930. One of 350 copies. — Almet Jenks. *The Huntsmen at the Gate.* 1952. Inscribed, "For Jackie from Michael, Dec. 1st. 1952." — James L. Young. *A Field of Horses: The World of Marshall P. Hawkins.* 1988. Foreword by Jacqueline Kennedy Onassis. Signed by James Young. — Michael Sinclair-Smith. *Don't Trample the Dogs.* 1987. Inscribed, "To Jackie, A great rider across country who can stay with the 'best' ... Michael Sinclair-Smith 27th Feb. 1990." With an autograph letter signed. — Kitty Slater. *The Hunt Country of America Revisited.* 1987. Signed by the author. — Jim Meads.*They Will always Meet at Eleven.* 1991. Inscribed by the author to: "Mrs. Onassis; A great ambassador for America and fox-hunting ... Jim Meads 12/91."

$500–800

817 **Horses and Horsemanship**

A group of 4 volumes, various sizes. All illustrated. Publisher's cloth. Various places and dates.

Mathilde Windisch-Graetz. *The Spanish Riding School.* [n.d.] With the Jacqueline Bouvier Kennedy bookplate. — Harriet Wadsworth Harper. *Around the World in Eighty Years on a Sidesaddle.* 1966. With two inscriptions, one "To Jackie with best wishes Jim Livingston, August 1966," and signed by the author. — Jane McIlvaine. *The Will to Win: The True Story of Tommy Smith and Jay Trump.* 1967. Inscribed by the author, "To Jackie with love." — James L. Young. *A Field of Horses: The World of Marshall P. Hawkins.* Foreword by Jacqueline Kennedy Onassis. 1988. Signed by the author.

$300–500

TREASURES of JAPAN
RENAISSANCE
Kennedy
PARADISO
Universal Limited Art Editions
ITALIAN VILLAS AND PALACES
THE THRONES OF EARTH AND HEAVEN
Henry F. Miller
Boston

THE ESTATE OF JACQUELINE KENNEDY ONASSIS

SESSION VIII
FRIDAY, APRIL 26,
10:00 A.M.

The Dining Room and Living Room of Jacqueline Kennedy Onassis' New York City apartment, showing lots 13, 40, 41, 76, 102, 122, 159, 160, 238, 241, 242, 245, 248, 306, 307, 308, 310, 338, 341, 352, 568, 569, 908, and 989.

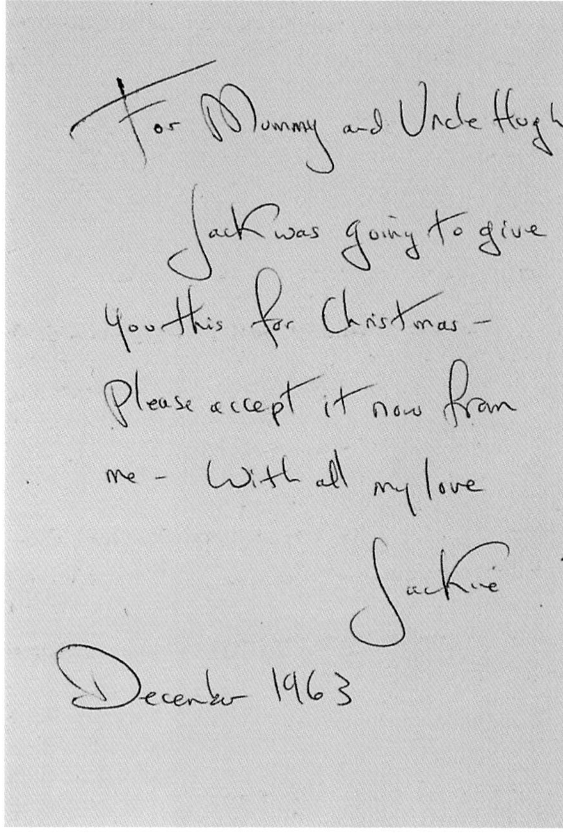

818

(9¼ x 6 in.). Dark blue morocco, gilt with crest of the United States and the name "JACQUELINE KENNEDY."

$800–1,200

818 **Presidents of the United States**

Inaugural Addresses of the Presidents of the United States from George Washington 1789 to John F. Kennedy 1961. *Washington: GPO, 1961*

(9 x 5¾ in.). The address (or addresses for two-term presidents) of each chief executive is headed by an engraved vignette portrait (portraits of Tyler, Fillmore, Johnson, and Arthur, who did not make inaugural addresses, appear on a page facing the table of contents). Polished maroon calf, front cover gilt with double-fillet border and the presidential seal, spine gilt in five compartments with title and star-tool, marbled endpapers, gilt edges; joints rubbed, spine flaking. Marbled slipcase.

ASSOCIATION COPY, SIGNED AND INSCRIBED BY JACQUELINE KENNEDY to her mother and stepfather: "For Mummy and Uncle Hugh, Jack was going to give you this for Christmas — Please accept it now from me — with all my love, Jackie, December 1963."

This copy of the *Inaugural Addresses* is one of eighty-five specially bound copies of a whole edition of 10, 880 copies printed for the use of the Senate and House of Representatives.

$3,000–5,000

819 **[Washington, D.C.] The Times, London.** Capture of the City of Washington. *London, September 27, 1814*

(23 x 15¼ in.), sight. Framed and glazed.

Contemporary newspaper account of the sacking of Washington, D.C. by the English.

$200–300

820 **White House Guides**

A group of various editions, with successive revisions, of *The White House: An Historic Guide* (first published in the summer of 1962 at the request of the First Lady, Jacqueline Kennedy). Approximately 40 copies from the Kennedy years, 7 from Johnson's administration and 1 from Nixon's.

Together approximately 48 volumes, variously publisher's cloth and paper.

$300–500

821 **Kennedy, John F.**

A Compilation of Statements and Speeches during his Service in the United States Senate and House of Representatives. *Washington, DC: Government Printing Office, 1964*

822 **Kennedy, John F.**

Profiles in Courage. Memorial Edition … Special Foreword by Robert F. Kennedy. *New York: Harper & Row, 1964*

Blue cloth, gilt; dust-jacket.

A group of 17 copies.

$400–600

823 **Kennedy, John F.**

45 r.p.m. phonographic album of the Inaugural Address, January 20, 1961, in a pictorial sleeve.

$100–200

824 **Fine and Decorative Arts**

Group of approximately 105 volumes, various sizes, most illustrated. Publisher's cloth. Various places, various dates.

A miscellaneous group of books and journals, including issues of *Horizon* and *Connoisseur* — *Conqueste della Ser. Repp. di Venezia*. 1687.

$400–500

825 **Kennedy, John F.**

The Burden and the Glory … edited by Allan Nevins, Special Foreword by President Johnson. *New York: Harper & Row, 1964*

Black cloth, gilt; dust-jacket.

A group of 20 copies.

$400–600

826 **White House and Presidency**

Group of 50 volumes, various sizes. Illustrated. Publisher's cloth or wrappers, a few in special leather bindings. Various places, various dates.

The White House … Introduction by Jacqueline Kennedy. 1962 (and later editions). — *The Living White House.* 1966 (and later editions) — *The Presidents.* 1964 (and later editions) — *The First Ladies.* 1975 (and later editions). — Anne H. Lincoln. *The Kennedy White House Parties.* 1967.

Most in multiple copies.

$300–500

827 **White House and Presidency**

Group of 50 volumes, various sizes. Illustrated. Publisher's cloth or wrappers, a few in special leather bindings. Various places, various dates.

The White House ... Introduction by Jacqueline Kennedy. 1962 (and later editions). — *The Living White House.* 1966 (and later editions). — *The Presidents.* 1964 (and later editions). — *The First Ladies.* 1975 (and later editions). — Anne H. Lincoln. *The Kennedy White House Parties.* 1967.

Most in multiple copies.

$300–500

828 **White House Guides**

A group of various editions, with successive revisions, of *The White House: An Historic Guide* (first published in the summer of 1962 at the request of the First Lady, Jacqueline Kennedy). Approximately 40 copies from the Kennedy years, 7 from Johnson's administration and 1 from Nixon's.

Together approximately 48 volumes, variously publisher's cloth and paper.

$300–500

829 **Biography**

A group of 8 volumes, mostly 8vo. Most with illustrations. Publisher's cloth. Mostly New York, various dates. All inscribed to Jacqueline Onassis.

Robert Giroux. *A Deed of Death.* 1990. Inscribed by the author, "To Jackie ..." — Janet Flanner. *Men and Monuments.* 1990. Inscribed by the editor. — Jonathan Cott. *Wandering Ghost: The Odyssey of Lafcadio Hearn.* 1991. Inscribed by the author, "Dear Jackie, with great thanks for getting me started on Lafcadio Hearn ..." — Marshall de Bruhl. *Sword of San Jacinto: A Life of Sam Houston.* 1993. Inscribed by the author, "For Jackie..." — and others.

$400–600

830 **Biography**

A group of 34 volumes, mostly 8vo. Many illustrated. Mostly publisher's cloth, some paper. Various places, mostly New York and various dates.

Florence Adele Sloan. *Maverick in Mauve: The Diary of A Romantic.* 1983. — Yves Saint Laurent. *Yves Saint Laurent.* 1986. In French. — Victoria Glendenning. *Rebecca West.* 1987. — Tennessee Williams. *Five O'Clock Angel: Letters* ... 1990. — Slim Keith. *Slim.* 1990. — and others.

$300–500

831 **Russia**

Robert Johnson. *Travels through part of the Russian Empire.* London: Printed for J.J. Stockdale, 1815. Maps, color plates. Contemporary black straight-grain morocco, gilt. — *Costume of the Russian Empire.* London: Printed for W. Miller, 1803. Colored plates. Text in French and English. Contemporary diced red morocco, gilt Greek-key border: upper joint starting. A fine tall copy.

Together 2 volumes on early nineteenth century Russia.

$800–1,200

832 **Modern literature**

A group of 37 volumes, mostly 8vo. Some illustrated. Publisher's cloth and paper. Various places and dates. A few with bookplate, signature or inscribed.

Louis Auchincloss. *The House of Five Talents.* 1960. Jacqueline Bouvier Kennedy bookplate. — Peter Davis. *Hometown.* 1982. Inscribed by the author, "To Jackie..." — Edna O'Brien. *The High Road.* 1988. — Sybille Bedford. *Jigsaw.* 1989. JKO initials. — and others.

$500–700

833 **Cape Cod and summer pastimes**

A group of 13 volumes, various sizes. Several illustrated. Various publisher's cloth or paper. Various places and dates.

Robert Finch. *Common Ground: A Naturalist's Cape Cod.* 1981. — Henry Beetle Hough. *Remembrance and Light: Images of Martha's Vineyard.* 1984. Initialed JKO. — Samuel Chamberlain. *Martha's Vineyard.* n.d. — Vita Sackville-West. *The Illustrated Garden Book.* 1986. — Celia Thaxter. *An Island Garden.* 1988. Modern facsimile, slipcase. — and others.

$200–300

834 **Onassis, Jacqueline Kennedy**

A group of 30 volumes by, or edited by Jacqueline Kennedy Onassis, or published at Doubleday, various sizes. Many illustrated. Publisher's cloth and paper. Mostly New York, and various dates.

Boris Zvorykin. *The Firebird and other Russian Fairy Tales.* 1978. Introduction by Jacqueline Kennedy Onassis. — Diana Vreeland. *Allure.* 1980. Edited by J.K.O. — Olivier Bernier. *The Eighteenth-century Woman.* 1981. Dedicated to J.K.O. — Mary-Sargent Ladd. *The Frenchwoman's Bedroom.* 1991. Edited by J.K.O. — and others including books by Bill Moyers, and a few children's books.

$500–700

835 **Adolphus, J.L.**

Memoirs of Queen Caroline. *London: Jones & Co., 1821*

2 volumes (8 x 5⅛ in.). Engraved titles and hand colored plates. Contemporary tree calf, gilt, yellow edges; rebacked.

$400–600

836 **Egan, Pierce**

Life in London, or, the Day and Night Scenes of Jerry Hawthorn. *London: Sherwood, Neely and Jones, 1821*

(9¾ x 6 in.). Hand-colored plates, folding music; occasional foxing. Red morocco gilt by F. Bedford; joints dry, some minor spotting.

Bound from parts, with the advertisements bound in at the end.

$300–500

837 **Toussaint, Manuel**

La Catedral de Mexico y el Sagrario Metropolitano: su Historia, su Tesoro, su Arte. *Mexico City: Comision Diocesana de Orden y Decoro, 1948*

(18 x 13⅜ in.). Numerous tipped-in plates and text illustrations, decorative initials and tailpieces. Publisher's brown morocco, diced in black, central metal boss and two clasps, pictorial endpapers.

Limited edition, number 929 of 1,100 copies, inscribed to Mrs. Kennedy by Andres Morales Huicochea "En testmonio de especial estamacion y entranable agradecimiento ... 1° de junio de 1962."

$300–500

841

THE
JOHN F. KENNEDY
MEMORIAL
AT
RUNNYMEDE

DEDICATORY REMARKS BY
The Rt. Hon. Harold Macmillan
The Rt. Hon. Harold Wilson
Her Majesty the Queen
The Hon. Dean Rusk

MAY FOURTEENTH, NINETEEN HUNDRED SIXTY-FIVE

841

ALOIS PODHAJSKY / DIE SPANISCHE HOFREITSCHULE

To Mrs Jacqueline Kennedy
in remembrance to her visit at
the Spanish Riding School of Vienna
with best wishes
Vienna June 4th 1961
Podhajsky

842

838 **Manchester, William**

One Brief Shining Moment. *Boston, (1983).* Signed by the author on the front free endpaper. — **Benjamin Bradlee.** That Special Grace. *Philadelphia, (1964).* 15 copies.

Together, 16 volumes, various sizes. Publisher's cloth, dust-jackets.

$200–400

839 **Brittain, Alfred, et al**

Women in All Ages and in All Countries. *Philadelphia: The Rittenhouse Press, (1907-1908)*

(7¾ x 5¼ in.). 8 (of 10?) volumes. Frontispieces. Publisher's red cloth gilt.

ASSOCIATION COPIES, each volume bearing the bookplate of Jacqueline Bouvier Kennedy.

$300–500

840 **The Times History of the War**

London: The Times, (ca. 1920)

(11 ⅞ x 7 ⅞ in.). 22 volumes. Numerous illustrations, maps (some folding), and facsimiles. Publisher's half red sheep; spines very worn with occasional loss.

ASSOCIATION SET of this important history of World War I, each volume bearing the presidential bookplate of John F. Kennedy.

$800–1,200

841 **Kennedy, John F.**

The John F. Kennedy Memorial at Runnymede: Dedicatory Remarks...May Fourteenth, Nineteen Hundred Sixty-Five. *(Privately printed and bound for Mrs. John F. Kennedy, December 1965*

(10½ x 7¾ in., *uncut*). Polished red calf, covers with double gilt-fillet border, front cover gilt with presidential seal, marbled endpapers; spine slightly faded.

LIMITED EDITION, ONE OF ONE HUNDRED COPIES PRINTED FOR MRS. KENNEDY.

In memory of John F. Kennedy, Great Britain gave to the United States an acre of English ground at Runnymede, where the Magna Carta had been signed in 1215. The present volume contains the addresses of the principal speakers at the dedication of the memorial: Queen Elizabeth II, Harold Macmillan, Harold Wilson, and Dean Rusk.

$400–600

842 **Podhajsky, Alois**

Die Spanische Hofreitschule. *Vienna: Adolf Holzhausen, (1959)*

(9¾ x 8 in.). Numerous photographic illustrations. Publisher's two-toned cloth, front cover gilt-stamped with the image of a rearing horse, spine gilt-decorated. Dust jacket; chipped, some wear.

INSCRIBED BY PODHAJSKY, Manager of the Imperial Riding School, "To Mrs. Jacqueline Kennedy in remembrance to her visit at the Spanish Riding School of Vienna, with best wishes, Vienna June 4th 1961. Podhajsky." Mrs. Kennedy visited the riding school during President Kennedy's crucial summit meeting with Nikita Khrushchev in Vienna. With a program from the performance laid in.

$300–500

843 **Giafferi, Paul-Louis de**

L'Histoire du Costume Féminin Français. *Paris: Éditions Nilsson, (ca. 1920)*

(15 x 10¾ in.). Collection of 119 (of 120) pochoir-colored costume plates; many browned and chipped at edges. 10 parts, loose in original blue board portfolio, as issued.

ASSOCIATION COPY, INSCRIBED AND SIGNED BY MRS. KENNEDY on the verso of plate 1 of part 5: "Jacqueline Bouvier Kennedy, given to me by Uncle Hugh [Auchincloss], March 17, 1963, Book I always loved at Merrywood."

$600–800

844

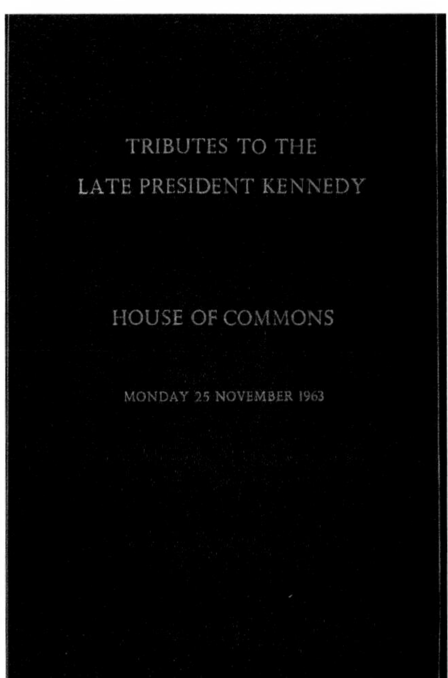

845

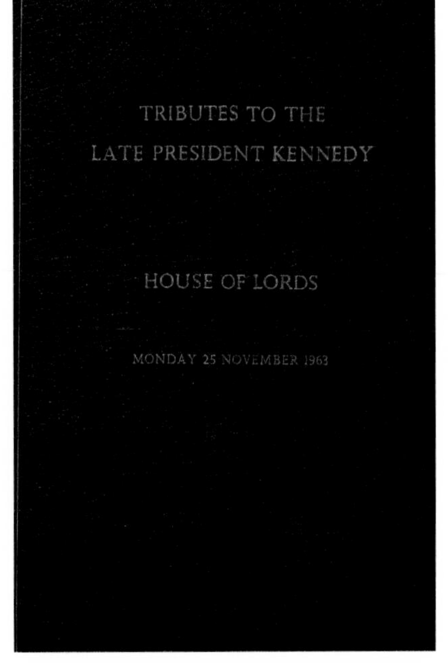

845

844 Ballets Russes

Collection des plus beaux numéros de Comoedia Illustré et des Programmes consacrés aux Ballets & Galas Russes depuis le début á Paris 1909–1921. *Paris: M. de Brunoff, (1922)*

(13 x 10¼ in.). With many illustrated programs from productions of the Ballets Russes bound in. Publisher's cloth, front cover with window mat cut to reveal an inset pictorial panel after Gontcharova, patterned endleaves; backstrip missing, some staining.

A splendid collection of illustrations including designs by Bakst, Picasso, and others, and numerous photographic illustrations of celebrated dancers and productions.

$1,500–2,500

845 Kennedy, John F.

Parliamentary Debates. House of Lords Official Report (Vol. 253, no. 7). Tributes to the Late President Kennedy. *London: Her Majesty's Stationary Office, 25 November 1963.* — Parliamentary Debates. House of Commons Official Report (Vol. 685, no. 10). President Kennedy (Tributes). *London: Her Majesty's Stationary Office, 25 November 1963*

Together, two 4–leaf pamphlets (11 x 7⅞ in.). Uniform crushed blue morocco gilt. Crushed blue morocco slipcase gilt.

The official memorial tributes to President Kennedy made in both houses of Parliament.

$600–800

846 **Propert, W. A.**

The Russian Ballet in Western Europe, 1909–1920. *London: John Lane, 1921*

(12¾ x 10 in.). Additional illustrated and decorations in text by Gontcharova, 63 tipped-in plates, many in color, after Bakst, Picasso, Matisse, Gontcharova, Larionov. Publisher's half white cloth gilt, marbled boards, top edges gilt; spine darkened, extremities rubbed.

LIMITED EDITION, one of 500 numbered copies, this copy number 411.

$400–600

847 **Kennedy, John F.**

To Turn the Tide. *New York: Harper & Brothers, (1962)*

(8⅜ x 5½ in.). Publisher's black cloth gilt, front cover blindstamped with the seal of the United States, dust-jacket; jacket a bit frayed and soiled.

ASSOCIATION COPY, SIGNED by President Kennedy on the front free endpaper. First edition of this compilation of Kennedy's statements and speeches from his election through the end of his first year in office, edited by John W. Gardner.

$1,500–2,500

848 **Decorative Arts**

Group of 25 volumes, various sizes. All illustrated. Publisher's cloth and wrappers. Various places, various dates.

Georges Lechevallier-Chevignard. *Choix de compositions et de projects de décoration.* N.d. — Yvonne Hackenbroch. *The Irwin Untermyer Collection.* (Vol. 1.): *Meissen and Other Continental Porcelain*; (Vol. 2): *Chelsea and Other English Porcelain*; (Vol. 3): *English Furniture*; (Vol. 4): *English and Other Needlework*; (Vol. 6): *English and Other Silver.* 1956–1963. — Edwards and Ramsey, eds. *The Early Victorian Period. 1958.* — Edwin O. Christensen. *The Index of American Design.* 1959. — Esther Stevens Brazer. *Early American Decoration.* 1961. — E. H. Gombrich. *The Sense of Order.* 1979. — and others.

$800–1,200

849 **Interior Design**

Group of 15 volumes, various sizes. Mostly illustrated. Publisher's cloth and wrappers. Various places, various dates.

Collection Connaissance des Arts. Le Style anglais 1750–1850. 1959. — *Connaissance des Arts. Décoration.* 1963. — Claude Arthaud. *Les Maisons du génie.* 1967. — Billy Baldwin. *Billy Baldwin Decorates.* 1972. — Norma Skurka. *New York Times Book of Interior Design and Decoration.* 1979. — Pauline Agius. *Ackermann's Regency Furniture & Interiors.* 1984. — Pauline Metcalf. *Ogden Codman and the Decoration of Houses.* 1988. — and others.

$300–500

850 **Gardens and Garden History**

A group of 21 volumes, various sizes. Publisher's cloth or paper. Various places, various dates.

Ralph Dutton. *The English Garden.* 1950. — Henry Hope Reed. *Central Park.* 1967. — Julia S. Berral. *Histoire illustrée des jardins.* 1968. — Anthony Huxley. *An Illustrated History of Gardening.* 1978. — Maggie Keswick. *Chinese Garden History, Art & Architecture.* 1980. — William T. Stearn and P. Davis. *Peonies of Greece.* 1984 — and others.

$300–500

851 **Gardens, Garden History, and Botanical Illustration**

A group of 16 illustrated volumes, various sizes. Publisher's cloth. Various places, various dates.

Barr Ferree. *American Estates and Gardens.* 1904. — Osvald Sirén. *China and Gardens of Europe.* 1950. — Joseph Ewan. *William Bartram; Botanical and Zoological Drawings.* 1968. — Madison Cox. *Private Gardens of Paris.* 1989. — Mac Griswold and Eleanor Weller. *The Golden Age of American Gardens.* 1991. — Derek Fell. *Impressionist Garden.* 1994. — and others.

$400–600

852 **Versailles**

A group of 21 volumes (some duplicates), various sizes. All or mostly illustrated. Publisher's cloth and wrappers. Various places, various dates.

Henry Racinais, ed. *Un Versailles inconnu; les petits appartements des roys Louis XV et Louis XVI.* 2 vols. 1950. — Ian Dunlop. *Versailles.* 1956. — Lucy Norton, ed. *Saint-Simon at Versailles.* 1980. — *Unseen Versailles.* Intro. by Louis Auchincloss. 1981 (4 copies). — Guy Walton. *Louis XIV's Versailles.* 1986. — and others.

$500–700

853 **France. Châteaux and Monuments**

A group of 15 volumes (some duplicates), various sizes. Mostly French texts, illustrated. Publisher's cloth and wrappers. Various places, various dates.

Ernest de Ganay. *Châteaux de France.* 1950. — René Pichard du Page. *Fontainebleau.* 1955. — *Merveilles des châteaux du Val de Loire.* 1964. — Pierre Lavedan. *Pour connaître les monuments de France.* 1970. — *Unseen Versailles.* Introduction by Louis Auchincloss. 1981(4 copies). — and others.

$200–300

854 **Paris and its environs**

A group of 9 volumes, various sizes, including the Veyrier edition of *The History of Paris.* Illustrated, mostly in French. Publisher's cloth and wrappers. Various places, various dates.

Jacques Silvestre de Sacy. *Le Faubourg de Saint-Germain.* 1966 and 1980. 2 copies of which the first is a LIMITED EDITION of 50 in full crimson morocco richly gilt, out of a total edition of 3,000. — Idem. *Le Marais.* 1980. — Jean-François Barrielle and others. *Champs-Elysées; Faubourg Saint-Honoré; Plaine Monceau.* 1980. — Robert Cameron and Pierre Salinger. *Above Paris.* 1984. — and others.

$700–1,000

855 **Horses and Sporting Art**

A group of 7 volumes, various sizes. All illustrated. Publisher's cloth or paper. Various places, various dates.

Coaching Days of England. 1966. — Basil Taylor. *Stubbs.* 1971. — Terence Doherty. *The Anatomical Works of George Stubbs.* 1976. — Tate Gallery. *George Stubbs, 1724-1806.* 1984. — and others.

$200–300

856 **Horses and Horsemanship**

A group of 9 volumes, various sizes. Mostly illustrated. Publisher's cloth (one in wrappers). Various places, various dates.

J. D. B. Stillman. *The Horse in Motion.* 1882. — Lady Wentworth. *Thoroughbred Racing Stock.* 1960. — Luigi Gianoli. *Horses and Horsemanship.* 1967. — Peter Willet. *The Thoroughbred.* 1970. — and others.

$400–600

857 **Reference**

A group of 23 volumes, various sizes, one bearing the floral bookplate of Jacqueline Bouvier Kennedy. Publisher's cloth and wrappers. Various places, various dates.

E. A. Andrews. *A New Latin Dictionary.* 1898. — *Tabularum geographicarum Lusitanorum.* Facsimile edition. 1960. Bookplate. — Henry George Liddell and Robert Scott. *A Greek-English Lexicon.* 1968. — Sandra Raphael. *An Oak Spring Sylva.* 1989. — Idem. *An Oak Spring Pomona.* 1990. — and others.

$400–600

858 **Periodicals**

Approximately 250 periodicals, mostly American, containing articles and/or photographs of Mrs. Kennedy and members of her family, ca. 1960s–1980s. Included are issues of *Life, Time, People, Cosmopolitan, McCall's, Modern Screen, Ladies' Home Journal, Newsweek,* etc.

$100–200

859 **American History**

Albert Perry Brigham. *Cape Cod and the Old Colony.* New York, 1921. — Henry S. Burrage. *Maine at Louisburg in 1745.* Augusta, 1910. — Harry T. Peters. *Currier & Ives: Printmakers to the American People.* Garden City, (1942). — Eleanor Lee Templeman. *Arlington Heritage: Vignettes of a Virginia County.* Privately Published, (1961).

Together 4 volumes, various sizes. Various publisher's cloth, the last title in pictorial dust-jacket.

ASSOCIATION COPIES, each bearing the presidential bookplate of John F. Kennedy. Templeman has also inscribed her copy on the front free endpaper: "To the President and Mrs. Kennedy … Feb. 1st. 1962."

$800–1,200

860 **English Country Houses**

A group of 12 volumes, various sizes. All illustrated. Publisher's cloth. Various places and dates.

Olive Cook. *The English House through Seven Centuries.* 1968. — Anthony Emery. *Dartington Hall.* 1970. — John Harris. *The Artist and the Country House.* 1979. — Gervase Jackson-Stopo and James Pipkin. *The English Country House: A Grand Tour.* 1985. — and others.

$300–500

861 **School of Paris**

A group of 11 volumes, various sizes. All illustrated. Publisher's cloth and wrappers.

Stéphane Mallarmé. *Madrigaux.* Illustrated by Raoul Dufy. Paris, 1920. LIMITED EDITION. One of 90 copies on Rives, of a whole edition of 1110. — Pablo Picasso. *Toros y Toreros.* 1961. — Idem. *Picasso 347.* 1970 — Henri Matisse. *Jazz.* 1983. — Brenda Richardson. *Dr. Claribel & Miss Etta: The Cone Collection at the Baltimore Museum of Art.* 1985. — and others.

$400–600

862 **Country Houses and Villas**

A group of 12 volumes. Illustrated; mostly in publisher's cloth and wrappers. Varying sizes and conditions.

Rudolf Wittkower. *Gothic vs. Classic; Architectural Projects in Seventeenth-Century Italy.* 1974. — Harold Acton. *The Villas of Tuscany.* 1985. — Michael Muraro . *Venetian Villas.* 1986. — Michael Pratt. *The Great Country Houses of Central Europe.* 1991. — and others.

$300–500

863 **Architecture**

A group of 12 volumes, chiefly monographs and treatises. Illustrated; most in publisher's cloth and wrappers. Varying sizes and conditions.

Ralph Dutton. *The Age of Wren.* 1951. — Christopher Alexander and others. *A Pattern Language.* 1977. 2 copies. — Christopher Alexander. *The Timeless Way of Building.* 1979. 2 copies. — Inigo Jones. *Complete Architectural Drawings.* 1989. — Vincent Scully. *Architecture: The Natural and the Manmade.* 1991. — and others.

$200–300

864 **Isabella I, *Queen of Spain***

Document signed ("yo la reyna"), in Spanish, 1 page (10 x 10 in.), Granada, 5 August 1500, to the secretaries of her chamber; docketed on verso; paper loss at center right affecting numerous character of a few words of text.

Isabella instructs: "I order you to acquit Sancho de Paredes, my chamberlain for an emerald square cut which has been debited to him … acquit him of it without any other formality except by this decree …"

$1,000–1,500

865 **Russia**

A group of 19 volumes, various sizes. Some illustrated. Publisher's bindings.

B. H. Sumner. *Peter the Great and the Emergence of Russia*. 1950. — Lazar Pistrak. *The Grand Tactician*. 1961. — E. M. Almedingen. *The Emperor Alexander I*. 1964. — Svetlana Alliluyeva. *Only One Year*. 1969. — John Bergamini. *The Tragic Dynasty*. 1970. — Edward Crankshaw. *The Shadow of the Winter Palace*. 1976. — and others.

$300–500

866 **English History and Biography**

A group of 26 volumes, various sizes. Some illustrated. Publisher's cloth.

Lord Rosebery. *Pitt*. 1908. — L. G. Pine. *Talen of the British Aristocracy*. 1956. — Sheila Birkenhead. *Peace in Piccadilly*. 1958. — C. V. Wedgwood. *The King's War, 1641-1647*. 1959. — Edward, Duke of Windsor. *Windsor Revisited*. 1960. — Winston S. Churchill. *The Island Race*. 1964. — Harold Macmillan. *At the End of the Day*. 1973. — and others.

$300–500

867 **Middle East**

A group of 21 volumes, various sizes. Some illustrated. Publisher's cloth and wrappers.

Leonard Cottrell. *The Lost Pharaohs*. 1951. — Freya Stark. *The Lycian Shore*. 1956. — Peter Willey. *The Castles of the Assassins*. 1963. — Julien Huxley. *From an Antique Land*. 1966. — Lord Kinross. *Portrait of Egypt*. 1966. — Terence Prittie. *Israel: Miracle in the Desert*. 1967. — and others.

$200–300

868 **French History and Biography**

A group of 36 volumes, various sizes. Some illustrated. Publisher's cloth and wrappers.

Lord Rosebery. *Napoleon: The Last Phase*. 1900. — W. H. Lewis. *The Splendid Century*. 1953. — Harold Nicolson. *Sainte-Beuve*. 1956. — Gilbert Guilleminault. *La Belle Epoque*. 1957. — Henry Lachouque. *The Anatomy of Glory*. 1961. — Guy Mollat. *The Popes at Avignon*. 1963. — André Malraux. *Anti-mémoirs*. 1968. — Jean-Jacques Fiechter. *Un diplomate américain sous la Terreur*. 1983. — Olivier Bernier. *Words of Fire, Deeds of Blood*. 1989. — and others.

$500–700

869 **Biographies of Women**

A group of 43 volumes of biography and autobiography, various sizes. Some illustrated. Publisher's cloth and wrappers.

H. Noel Williams. *Madame de Montespan*. 1903. — Comtesse de Boigne. *Memoirs, 1781-1814*. 1907. — Lewis Gibbs. *The Admirable Lady Mary*. 1949. — André Maurois. *Adrienne: The Life of the Marquise de la Fayette*. 1961. — Santha Rama Rau. *Gifts of Passage*. 1961. — Constance Wright. *Daughter to Napoleon*. 1961. — Ellen Maury Slayden. *Washington Wife*. 1963. — Jean Challon. *Portrait of a Seductress*. 1979. — Madeline Bingham. *Princess Lievan*. 1982. — Olivier Bernier. *Secrets of Marie-Antoinette*. 1985. — Rose Avrillon. *Memoirs*. 1986.

$700–1,000

870 **Classic Literature**

A group of 15 volumes of Greek and Roman literature and several scholarly analyses, including one presentation copy to Jacqueline Kennedy Onassis. Mostly in translation; publisher's cloth and wrappers. Varyings sizes and conditions.

Sophocles. *The Three Theban Plays* (trans. Robert Fagles). 1982. Presentation copy from the translator to Jacqueline Kennedy Onassis. — *The Stoic and Epicurean Philosophers*. 1940. — Nikos Kazantzakis. *The Odyssey. A Modern Sequel*. 1959. 2 volumes, in Greek and English; illustrated; full calf, slipcase. — Aeschylus. *The Oresteia* (trans. Robert Fagles). 1976. — and others.

$300–500

871 **French Literature**

A group of 47 volumes in French and in English translation. Some illustrated. Publisher's cloth and wrappers. Varying sizes and conditions.

Jules Verne. *De la terre à la lune* [and] *Autour de la lune*. [ca. 1870]. 2 vols. Half morocco. — Alfred de Musset. *Oeuvres*. [n.d.]. 2 vols. Full tan morocco, spines richly gilt, by David. — Pierre Loti. *Vers Ispahan*. 1925. — Marguerite Yourcenar. *Memoirs of Hadrian*. 1963. — Madame de Staël. *Corinne, or Italy*. 1987. — and others.

$500–700

872 **Biography**

A group of approximately 50 volumes, comprising biographies, journals, diaries, and collected letters of literary and historical figures with a concentration on English women authors and French literary figures of the 19th and 20th centuries. Most illustrated, some French texts; mostly publisher's cloth and wrappers. Varying sizes and conditions.

André Maurois. *Olympio ou la vie de Victor Hugo*. 1955. Limited edition. — George D. Painter. *Proust: The Early Years; The Later Years*. 1959; 1965; 2 vols. — Millicent Bell. *Edith Wharton & Henry James*. 1965. — Clara Malraux. *Memoirs*. 1967. — André Malraux. *Antimémoires*. 1967. — Francis Steegmuller, trans. *Flaubert in Egypt; A Sensibility on Tour*. 1972. — R. W. B. Lewis. *Edith Wharton*. 1975. — A. L. Rowse. *Milton the Puritan*. 1977. — and others.

$300–500

873 **Literature and Poetry**

A group of 21 volumes of poetry and literature of the East, in English translation. Mostly publisher's cloth and wrappers. Varying sizes and conditions.

Jon and Rumer Godden. *Under the Indian Sun*. 1966. — *Three Mughal Poets: Mir, Sauda, Mir Hasan*. 1968. — Rama Mehta. *Inside the Haveli*. 1977. — *Sanskrit Poetry from Vidyakara's 'Treasury'*. 1979. — *Old Friend from Far Away. 150 Chinese Poems from the Great Dynasties*. 1980. — *The Peacock's Egg: Love Poems from Ancient India*. 1981. — Kabir. *The Bijak*. 1983. — Anita Desai. *Baumgartner's Bombay*. 1988. — and others.

$150–250

874 **Literature and Poetry**

A group of 20 volumes chiefly by modern American and English authors. Publisher's cloth and dust jackets. Varying sizes and conditions.

Norman Mailer. *Advertisement for Myself.* 1959. — Herman Wouk. *This is My God.* 1959. — Leon Uris. *Mila 18.* 1961. — Ernest Hemingway. *A Moveable Feast.* 1964. 2 copies. — Norman Mailer. *Existential Errands.* 1972. — and others.

$150–250

875 **American History**

A group of 31 volumes, including several pamphlets, various sizes.

Lamont Buchanan. *A Pictorial History of the Confederacy.* 1951. — William Smyth. *The Lessons of History.* 1955. — Michael Kraus. *The United States to 1865.* 1959. — Fairfax Downey. *Texas and the War with Mexico.* 1961. — Hermann Warner Williams, Jr. *The Civil War: The Artists' Record.* 1961. — Arthur Herzog. *The War-Peace Establishment.* 1965. — Robert Sherrill. *The Accidental President.* 1967. — James Pope-Hennessy. *Sins of the Fathers: A Study of the Atlantic Slave Traders, 1441-1807.* 1968. — John Barlow Martin. *Adlai Stevenson and the World.* 1977. — and others.

$500–700

876 **India**

Group of 11 volumes, various sizes. Some illustrated. Most in publisher's cloth.

[William Kingston.] *The Private Life of an Eastern King.* 1855. — Janet Dunbar. *Golden Interlude.* 1955. — James Pope-Hennessy. *Verandah.* 1964. — Henri Mouhot. *Diary.* 1966. — Emily Eden. *Up the Country.* 1978. — James Tod. *Annals and Antiquities of Rajast'han.* 2 vols. 1978. — Richard Hough. *Edwina, Countess Mountbatten of Burma.* 1983. — Elizabeth Longford. *A Viceroy's India: Leaves from Lord Curzon's Notebook.* 1984. — and others.

$600–900

877 **Poetry**

A group of 9 volumes of 19th-century English and American poetry. Some illustrated; mostly publisher's cloth and wrappers, with one fine morocco binding by Sangorski and Sutcliffe on the Vale Press edition of Tennyson's *In Memoriam.* Varying sizes and conditions.

Rudyard Kipling. *The Seven Seas.* 1896. — Alfred, Lord Tennyson. *In Memoriam.* 1900. Full brown morocco richly gilt, mosaic panels and spine, by Sangorsky & Sutcliffe. — Elizabeth Barrett Browning. *Sonnets from the Portuguese.* 1954. — Gerard Manley Hopkins. *Poems.* 1967. — and others.

$300–500

878 **Poetry**

A group of 30 volumes chiefly of modern English and American poets. Some illustrated; mostly publisher's cloth and wrappers. Varying sizes and conditions.

Edith Sitwell. *Collected Poems.* 1954. — John Betjeman. *Summoned by Bells.* 1960. — Robert Lowell. *For the Union Dead.* 1964. — Robert Penn Warren. *Selected Poems: New & Old 1923–1966.* 1966. — James Joyce. *Giacomo Joyce.* 1968. Slipcase. — and others.

$200–300

879 **Virginia and Miscellaneous**

A group of 35 books and pamphlets mostly on Virginia and the South, and including a framed map, "Orange County, Middlebury Hunts," removed from the Virginia home of Jacqueline Kennedy Onassis. Publishers cloth or paper. Various dates and sizes. One with Jacqueline Kennedy's signature, another with her initials.

Henry Chandlee Forman. *Early Manor and Plantation Houses of Maryland.* 1934. — W.P.A. *A Guide to the Old Dominion.* 1940. Signed "Jacqueline Kennedy." — Philip Kopper. *Colonial Williamsburg.* 1986. — Edith Clay, ed. *Ramage in South Italy.* 1987. Initialed, "J.K.O." — Mary Emmerling. *American Country South.* 1989. — David King Gleason. *Virginia Plantation Homes.* 1989. — and others.

$600–800

880 **Literature**

A group of 26 volumes of short stories, anthologies, and miscellanies chiefly by American and English authors. Some illustrated; mostly in publisher's cloth and wrappers. Varying sizes and conditions.

Anthony Trollope. *Hunting Sketches.* 1933. Illustrated. — Sacheverell Sitwell. *Poltergeists.* 1940. — Edith Sitwell. *English Eccentrics.* 1957. — Edith Somerville and Martin Ross. *Experiences of an Irish R. M.* 1957. — Charles and Mary Lamb. *Tales from Shakespeare.* 1961. Full crimson calf panelled gilt. — Robert Lowell. *Collected Prose.* 1987. — and others.

$200–300

881 **Literature**

A group of 37 volumes, chiefly by contemporary American and English women authors. Mostly publisher's cloth and wrappers. Varying sizes and conditions.

Mildred Cram. *Forever.* 1948. — Nina Auchincloss Straight. *Ariabella: The First.* 1981. — Molly Keane. *Time after Time.* 1984. — Jamaica Kincaid. *Annie John.* 1985. — Toni Morrison. *Beloved.* 1987. — and others.

$250–350

882 **Auchincloss family**

A group of 3 titles in 4 volumes by Louis Auchincloss and N. A. Straight. Publisher's cloth and dust jackets. Varying sizes, excellent condition.

Louis Auchincloss. *The Cat & the King. A Novel.* 1981. Printed dedication to Jacqueline Kennedy Onassis. — Idem. *False Dawn: Women in the Age of the Sun King.* 1984. — Nina Auchincloss Straight. *Ariabella: The First.* 1981. 2 copies.

$100–200

883 **British and Irish Art**

A group of 12 works in 16 volumes, various sizes. Mostly illustrated. Publisher's cloth. Various places, various dates.

Ludwig Bieler. *Ireland.* 2 vols. 1963. — William Blake. *America, a Prophecy.* 1963. Limited edition, slipcase. — Françoise Henry. *L'art irlandais.* 3 vols. 1963. — H. C. Mariller. *The Early Work of Aubrey Beardsley.* 1967. — Mildred Archer. *British Drawings in the India Office Library.* 2 vols. 1969. — and others.

$300–500

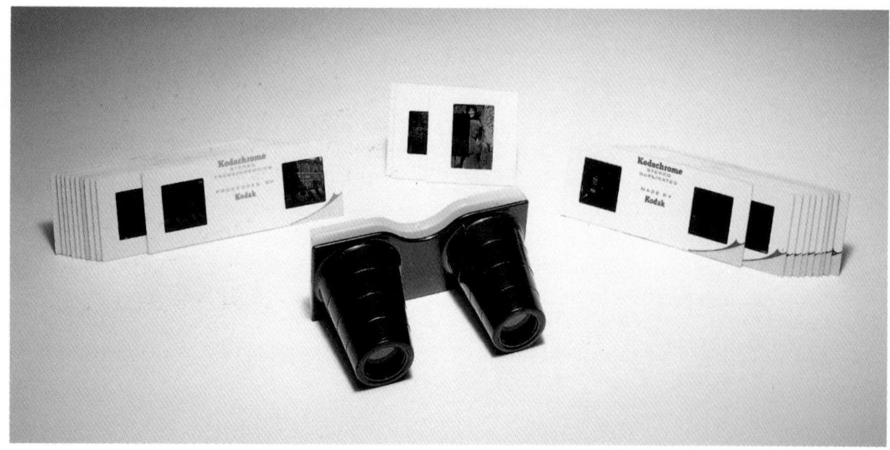

885

884 **White House Guides**

A group of various editions, with successive revisions, of *The White House: An Historic Guide* (first published in the summer of 1962 at the request of the First Lady, Jacqueline Kennedy). Approximately 40 copies from the Kennedy years, 7 from Johnson's administration and 1 from Nixon's.

Together approximately 48 volumes, variously publisher's cloth and paper.

$300–500

885 **Kennedy, John Fitzgerald**

A stereoscopic viewer and 21 slides of JFK as President. In a cardboard box, labeled in ink, "Color slides of JFK."

$400–600

886 **Gardens and Gardening**

A group of 6 books, mostly folio. All illustrated. Publisher's cloth. Various places and dates. Most SIGNED OR INSCRIBED.

Mabel M. Gabriel. *Livia's Garden Room at Prima Porta.* 1955. Signed, "Jacqueline Kennedy." — Russell Page. *The Education of a Gardener.* 1983. Signed "Jacqueline Kennedy Onassis." — Pierre Joseph Redouté. *The Most Beautiful Flowers.* ca. 1980. Inscribed, "Dear Jackie, Merry Christmas, 1988 ... John Kenny."

$600–800

887 **Descourtilz, Jean Théodore**

Pageantry of Brazilian Birds.[Facsimile edition]. *Amsterdam & Rio de Janeiro: Colibris Editora, 1960*

(17 x 11¼ in.). 60 plates (some printed in color); printed note on parchment by the bookbinder bound in. Full blue morocco with inlaid feather of the Brazilian "Ara-Ararauna" ("blue light") bird on the front cover, burnt orange suede doublures and flyleaves of handmade Japanese paper, gilt turn-ins, by Artemis Marques Ferreira; light rubbing and spotting.

$200–300

888 **Literature**

A group of 7 volumes of fiction, poetry, and non-fiction bearing presentation inscriptions, the floral bookplate of Jacqueline Bouvier Kennedy or ownership inscription.

W. S. Lewis, ed. *The Letters to and from Madame du Deffand and Mademoiselle de Lespinasse.* 1938. Bookplate. — *The Letters of Rainer Maria Rilke and Princess Marie von Thurn und Taxis* . 1958. Bookplate. — Frank Waters. *The Man Who Killed the Deer.* 1970. Poetically inscribed: "Jackie, I'm sure the mountains will call you back. Until then, with affection, [Azalea?] and Lloyd." — Yannis Ritsos. *Subterranean Horses.* 1980. Inscribed by Alexis Ladas, Hellenic Heritage Foundation. — Antonio Garrigues y Diaz-Cañabate. *Reflexion sobre las cosas que pasan.* 1984. Cryptically inscribed: "To J. That's all." — Errol Trzebinski. *Silence will Speak.* Ownership inscription and acquisition note by Jacqueline Onassis: "J.K.O. From Anna Cataldi December 1985." _ Osip Mandelstam. *The Moscow Notebooks* (trans. Richard and Elizabeth McKane). 1991. Inscribed by Richard McKane "For Jacqueline Onassis from Richard and Elizabeth McKane. London, June '91 in Mandelstam's 100th year."

$300–500

889 **Montesquieu, Charles Louis de Secondat**

Arsace et Isménie, histoire orientale. *London [i.e., Paris]: Guillaume de Bure, 1783*

(5 x 3 in.). Red straight-grain morocco by Bozérian, covers gilt with foliate-roll border and acorn-tool cornerpieces, flat spine ruled in seven compartments, green marbled endpapers, gilt edges, signed by the binder at the foot of the spine; extremities slightly rubbed.

$200–300

890 **Biography**

A group of 9 volumes of biography and autobiography, bearing presentation inscriptions to, or the ownership inscription of, or floral bookplate of Jacqueline Bouvier Kennedy. Mostly illustrated; chiefly publisher's cloth and wrappers. Varying sizes and conditions.

Augustus John. *Chiaroscuro.* 1952. Bookplate. — Françoise Gilot and Carlton Lake. *Life with Picasso.* 1964. Ownership inscription on flyleaf ("Jacqueline Kennedy | November 1964"). — Sylvia Townsend Warner. *T. H. White.* 1967. Ownership inscription on front free endpaper ("Jacqueline Kennedy"). White is best known for his *Once and Future King,* the basis of the Lerner-Loewe musical *Camelot.* — Janet Dunbar. *Mrs. G.B.S.* 1963. Inscribed by Father Joseph Leonard: "To dearest Jacqueline on her birthday, with love and admiration from her old friend. J.L. 28 July 1963." — Lillian Hellman. *An Unfinished Woman.* 1969. Inscribed by the author. "For Jackie with affection, Lillian." — A. L. Rowse. *Milton the Puritan.* 1976. Inscribed by the author: "For Jacqueline Kennedy Onassis—hommage and admiration, and Welcome to Literature!" — Norman Cousins. *Dr. Schweitzer of Lambaréné.* 1958. Inscribed by the author and dated March 1965. — Arthur Gold and Robert Fizdale. *Misia.* 1980. Inscribed by the authors. — Paul Horgan. *Lamy of Santa Fe.* 1975. Limited edition, inscribed by the author and dated 3 May 1984.

$800–1,200

891

891 **Colum, Padraic**

A Treasury of Irish Folklore: The Stories, Traditions, Legends, Humor, Wisdom, Ballads and Songs of the Irish People. *New York: Crown, (1954)*

(8¼ x 5⅝ in.). Publisher's green cloth; lightly faded and soiled.

An extraordinary association copy from the Kennedy Presidency, inscribed by Mrs. Kennedy at the foot of the front free endpaper: "In JFK's room in the White House, JBK, 1964."

$1,500–2,500

892 **French Biography**

A group of 6 biographies, of which all but 2 bear presentation inscriptions, the ownership inscription or floral bookplate of Jacqueline Bouvier Kennedy. Some illustrated, one in French. Mostly publisher's cloth and wrappers. Varying sizes and conditions.

R. F. Delderfield. *Napoleon in Love.* 1959. Bookplate. — Marcus Cheke. *The Cardinal de Bernis.* 1958. Gift inscription. — Michael of Greece. *Louis XIV: L'envers du soleil.* 1979. Inscribed in French by the author and dated New York, November 1980. — Olivier Bernier. *Louis the Beloved.* 1984. Ownership inscription ("J.K.O."). — John Paul Francis de Gondi, Cardinal de Retz. *Memoirs.* Translated into English. 1896. Bookplate of Walter and Katherine Bliss. — Marguerite de Valois. *Memoirs.* Translated into English. 1896. Bookplate of Walter and Katherine Bliss.

$300–500

893 **Presidents of the United States**

The White House Gallery of Official Portraits of the Presidents. *New York: Gravure Company of America, (1901)*

(19⅝ x 16 in.). Gravure portrait plates on india paper mounted of all presidents from Washington to McKinley, with lettered tissue-guards, each portrait with an accompanying page of text with marginal gravure vignettes; edges browned. Publisher's black morocco, front cover with large inset medallion of the seal of the United States, blue silk moiré doublures, marbled free endpapers, top edge gilt; worn, restored, rebacked.

Number 244 of the Statesmen's Edition.

$400–600

894 **Biography**

Group of 7 volumes, various sizes. Publisher's cloth or wrappers, some with dust-jackets. Various places, various dates.

Edvard Radzinsky. *The Last Tsar.* 1992. Inscribed "To dear Jackie who gave this book life." — King Hussein. *Uneasy Lies the Head.* 1962. Inscribed "With my respect and highest esteem to Mrs Jackline Kennedy." — Rom Landau. *Hassan II: King of Morocco.* 1962. Inscribed by author "For Mrs. John F. Kennedy with the author's profound respect and great admiration." — QueenVictoria. *Leaves from a Journal.* 1961. Inscribed. — Evelyn Abbott. *Lorenzo de' Medici.* 1896. Bookplate of Jacqueline Bouvier Kennedy. — Juan Bosch. *David Biografia de un rey.* 1963. Gilt stamped "Jacqueline Kennedy" on upper cover; with bookplate of Jacqueline Bouvier Kennedy. — Werner Bertram. *A Royal Recluse.* [nd]. Bookplate of Jacqueline Bouvier Kennedy.

$400–600

895 **Onassis, Jacqueline Kennedy and Gloria Steinem**

Ms. Magazine cover [featuring Mrs. Onassis.] "Why Does This Woman Work?" *March, 1979*

Framed (23½ x 15½ in., sight). cover tear-sheet mounted with signatures surrounding.

"From the working women at Ms. to a friend and colleague." Signed by approximately 50 staffers at Ms. magazine and with a presentation from Gloria Steinem (lower right), "Here is to many more good words—in and out of books—Gloria Steinem." The presentation poster commemorates a "conversation" between Mrs. Onassis and Gloria Steinem.

$400–600

896 **A Chinese Export Porcelain Milk Jug and a Cover, circa 1780**

The pear-shaped body painted on the front in rose, purple, iron-red, blue, green and gold with a bowknotted floral bouquet, on each side with a floral sprig and around the neck and spout with a floral garland, the cover (married and with a chip) painted with three rose floral sprigs around the gilt knop.
Height 5 ⅝ in. (14.3 cm.)

$100–150

897 **A French Opaline Glass Small Mug and a Beaker, late 19th Century**

Each cylindrical, the mug painted on the front in pink, iron-red, blue, purple, yellow and green with a cluster of flowers surrounding a black-edged oval panel, the reverse with a loop handle; and the beaker inscribed on the front in gilding *Amitié* within a wreath of yellow-centered blue and red blossoms and gilt leaves between a gilt band around the foot and the gilt rim edge (wear to the gilding). Together with a modern 'floral barometer' formed as an arrangement of colored glass flowers and leaves in a clear glass pot, (some losses). (3)
Heights 3 15/16, 3 3/16 and 4 ⅜ in. (8.4, 8.1 and 11.1 cm.)

$125-175

898 **A Staffordshire Earthenware Cylindrical Mug, circa 1840**

Painted in rose, green, yellow and brown around the circumference with two floral borders between brown bands around the rim (three small hair cracks) and flaring foot, the loop handle also with a brown band, (some discoloration).
Height 3 ¾ in. (9.5 cm.)

$100–150

899 **A Staffordshire Earthenware Cylindrical Child's Mug, circa 1850**

Transfer-printed in black and colored in yellow and salmon with scenes of two ladies conversing and a lady and gentleman mourning at a deathbed alternating with the initials G and H, the reverse with a loop handle.
Height 2 7/16 in. (6.2 cm.)

$100–150

896

898, 899, 1130, 897, 900, 897

900 **Four English Porcelain Tea and Coffee Wares, 1820-50**

Comprising a Derby coffee can painted in blue, rose, yellow and green with sprigs of cornflowers alternating with gilt foliate sprigs beneath a cornflower-vine border, *crowned crossed batons and D mark and numeral 31 in iron-red*; a Derby oval teapot stand (discolored) painted with a central pink rose sprig within a border of pink roses, blue cornflowers, iron-red blossoms and green leaves between gilt bands (slight wear), *similarly marked, but with numeral 31 in iron-red*; a saucer printed in brown and painted in rose, iron-red and green with Chinese Export-style floral sprays within a whorl-pattern border, *pattern number 2/235 in brown*; and a saucer printed and colorfully painted in Sèvres style with a central floral spray within a floral garland border entwined with a shaded turquoise ribbon beneath the gilt dentil edge, *impressed potter's mark and painter's two-dot mark in green enamel.*
Height 2 ¾ in. (7 cm.), length 7 ½ in. (19 cm.), diameters 5 ⅞ and 5 ⅝ in. (14.9 and 14.3 cm.)

$125-175

901, 902, 897

903, 904

901 **A Pair of Italian Earthenware Ashtrays and a Pillivuyt Porcelain Oyster Plate, Modern**

The ashtrays molded with four leafy plants enameled in brown, turquoise and shades of green extending from the center onto the green-edged scalloped and barbed rim, *ITALY marks printed in black*; and the white plate molded with a central circular depression surrounded by four oyster shells against a fluted ground, (two chips), *PILLIVUYT France 654 mark printed in green.*
Diameters 5 7/16 and 9 3/16 in. (13.8 and 23.3 cm.)

$50–75

902 **A Staffordshire Smear-Glazed Stoneware Candlestick, circa 1820**

The columnar stem decorated in relief with pendent leafage above a central ring, and with acanthus leaves and bellflowers below the ring and above a further foliate border around the domed foot, all against a 'Wedgwood-blue' ground, and the flat drip-pan molded with a beadwork border, (small chips), *impressed potter's numeral 4.*
Height 6 3/8 in. (16.2 cm.)

$150–250

903 **A Set of Six Doccia Porcelain Plates, circa 1770**

Each painted in shades of puce, blue, yellow, iron-red and green with three sprays and three sprigs of flowers within a molded rim edge (five cracked and most with slight stacking wear), *painter's numeral 10 or 12 in green enamel.*
Diameter 9 ¼ in. (23.5 cm.)

$200–300

904 **A Set of Eight Royal Worcester Porcelain 'Astley' Pattern Dessert Plates, Modern**

Each painted in black, shades of pink, iron-red, rose, yellow, white, turquoise and green with an oriental design of trailing branches of blossoms and leaves within an iron-red scallop-and-dot border at the gilt edge, *factory and pattern name printed in black above a portrait inscribed FIRST PRODUCED IN DR. WALL'S PERIOD 1751-1783, some also with various impressed marks.*
Diameter 9 ¼ in. (23.5 cm.)

$300–500

906, 905, 906, 905, 906, 908, 907, 909

905 **A Pair of Continental Cream-Colored Earthenware Pierced Miniature 'Orange Tubs', late 19th/early 20th Century**

Each square, the sides formed by vertical staves bisected by a molded floral garland suspended from a bowknot at each corner, *impressed rose in a shield factory marks and mold number 1883 00.*
Height 2 ⅜ in. (6 cm.)

These 'orange tubs' were among the furnishings in Mrs. Kennedy's bedroom at the White House.

$60–90

906 **Two Chinese Export Porcelain-Style Dishes and a Pair of Chinese Porcelain Saucers, Modern**

The first dish of scalloped oval shape and painted in the center with a green, gold, iron-red and blue coat of arms within a rose, purple and green floral garland beneath a border of gilt scallops and dots, *interlaced S's mark for the Samson factory of Paris, and inscribed 'Hand Painted in France'*; the second dish a leaf-shaped sauceboat stand painted in rose, iron-red, purple, green and gold with a bowknotted bouquet of flowers and three sprigs beneath a gilt edge, *ITALY mark printed in green*; and the saucers painted in rose, green and black with lotus around a floral-sprig roundel beneath a gilt-edged rim (worn, and one cracked), *DECORATED IN HONG KONG marks printed in red.* (4)
Lengths 6 ⅞ and 7 ⅞ in. (17.5 and 20 cm.), diameter 5 7/16 in. (13.8 cm.)

$100–150

907 **Three Chinese Porcelain Blue and White Small Bowls and a Dish, late 19th and 20th Century**

Comprising a pair of small bowls painted around the exterior with four ducks swimming amidst lotus, (hair cracks and slight fritting), *four-character marks in underglaze-blue*; a large teabowl painted with a Chinese fisherman standing beneath a willow tree, (small chip); and a dish painted with two recumbent deer beneath a poem and a pine tree near a rock, (large chip), *four-character mark in underglaze-blue.* Together with a Chinese Export porcelain saucer, circa 1765, painted with underglaze-blue and *famille-rose* floral sprigs within peony petal-shaped panels, (restored). (5)
Diameters 4 ⅞ , 3 ¾, 5 ⅞ and 5 ¾ in. (12.4, 9.5, 14.9 and 14.6 cm.)

$400–600

908 **Three Silver Lustre and Gilt Julep Cups and a Nippon Porcelain Coffee Cup and Saucer, 20th Century**

The cups with a silver lustred and heart-'quilted' exterior beneath a gilt rim (one with a tiny chip), the interior fully gilt (some wear); and the hexafoil cup and saucer each painted in shades of brown, green, iron-red, white, blue, grey and black with a Japanese house and a flowering prunus tree in a river landscape beneath a white-dotted brown zigzag border around the rim (chip and a star crack on the saucer), *NIPPON mark printed in russet on the saucer.* (2)
Diameters 4 ¼ and 5 in. (10.8 and 12.7 cm.), heights 2 15/16 and 3 ¾ in. (7.5 and 9.5 cm.)

$150–250

911, 910, 911, 900, 910, 900, 910, 912

909 **Nine Chinese Porcelain Blue and White Small Dishes, 20th Century**

Comprising a set of six sauce dishes (two with tiny chips) and a saucer (rim repaired) painted with three or five stylized lotus blossoms on a trailing vine, *spurious six-character marks in underglaze-blue*; a sauce dish painted with two Chinese travellers amidst rocks and shrubbery, (chipped), *stylized character mark in underglaze-blue*; and a sauce dish painted with censers and scrolls, (damaged), *knot mark in underglaze-blue.* Together with a Japanese porcelain blue and white small saucer painted with three carp, (restored chip issuing a hair crack), *four-character mark in underglaze-blue.* (10)
Diameter 2¾ to 4 in. (7 to 10.2 cm.)

$75–100

910 **A Pair of Shelley Bone China Hexafoil Sugar Bowls and a Berry Dish from a Breakfast Service, Modern**

Each printed in pink and green with rose sprigs in the 'Bridal Rose' pattern within a pink-edged rim (one sugar bowl hair cracked), *printed marks in green and pink.* Together with a Royal Crown Derby porcelain saucer (star crack) printed in colors with two floral bouquets and two sprigs within a gilt-edged rim, *factory mark printed in green*; a Hammersley & Co. bone china saucer printed in green and pink with three bunches of clover within a gilt-edged rim, *factory mark printed in green*; and a set of six Sheffield stainless steel cheese knives mounted with Continental porcelain pistol-shaped handles (two mostly missing, two others damaged), painted with pastel and gilt flowers between spring-green and gilt trelliswork borders. (11)
Diameters 3⅜ to 5 11/16 in. (8.6 to 14.4 cm.), overall length of knives 7 3/16 in. (18.3 cm.)

$75–100

911 **A Pair of English Creamware Enameled Teabowls, probably Leeds, circa 1775**

Each painted in black on the exterior with a floral spray and two sprigs beneath a lightly beaded rim (one repaired, chipped and hair cracked, the other slightly abraded), and on the interior with a small sprig beneath a scalloped band around the rim. Together with a later Staffordshire creamware coffee cup printed in brown and enameled with floral sprigs beneath a daisy border between orange lustre bands, *pattern 2/1387 and a painter's mark in iron-red, and an impressed potter's mark.* (3)
Diameters 2 11/16 and 2¾ in. (6.8 and 7 cm.), height of coffee cup 2 in. (5.1 cm.)

$75–100

912 **An English Porcelain Coffee Cup, Three Saucers and Three Saucer Dishes, 1805-15**

The New Hall cup painted in brown monochrome and gold with a fruiting strawberry vine border between gilt bands (slight wear); the saucers and one dish painted also in brown and gold with a stylized flowering vine border between gilt bands (some wear, and each repaired); and the two largest dishes Derby and painted in iron-red, rose, blue and green with a flowering vine entwined with a gold foliate vine beneath the gilt-edged rim (some wear and both repaired), *crowned crossed batons and D marks and painter's numeral 15 in iron red.* (7)
Height 2⅝ in. (6.7 cm.), diameters 5½ to 8½ in. (14 to 21.6 cm.)

$75–100

913

914, 915, 916, 915

913 An Austrian Painted Tole Vase in the Form of a Costumed Figure, 19th Century

Wearing red shoes, the skirt painted in colors.
Height 10 in. (25.4 cm.)

$600–800

914 A Staffordshire Earthenware Figure of a Whippet, late 19th Century

With a pale tan coat and black eyes, carrying in her mouth a grey dead hare, and standing on a mottled green, yellow and brown (enamel chips) grassy mound above an oval base edged with a black line, (dog's neck repaired, ears restored, and the glaze crackled).
Height 10½ in. (26.7 cm.)

$150–250

915 A Pair of Staffordshire Earthenware Recumbent Whippet Inkwells, late 19th Century

Each with a pale salmon-washed coat, black nose, eyes and paws, and one wearing a black collar, modelled affronté, recumbent on an oval mound pierced with a black-edged quill hole and edged with a black line, (glaze crackled, and each with one ear lost in the firing).
Length 6 in. (15.2 cm.)

$300–400

916 A Staffordshire Earthenware Equestrian Group of the 'Empress of France', late 19th/early 20th Century

Modelled as Empress Eugénie wearing a pink-plumed green headdress, a gilt-dotted cobalt-blue dress and yellow gloves, seated side-saddle above a gilt-edged yellow saddle-blanket on a salmon horse with an iron-red mane and tail above a brown-dashed green (enamel chips) mound and gilt-edged oval base molded and inscribed in gilding EMPRESS OF FRANCE, (her neck repaired, and the glaze crackled).
Height 12 in. (30.5 cm.)
Groups of this model are illustrated by P. D. Gordon Pugh, *Staffordshire Portrait Figures*, p. C 269, pl. 35, fig. 87, and p. C 270, pl. 37, fig. 87, who also illustrates the companion models of Emperor Napoleon III, to whom Eugénie was married in 1853. At the fall of the French Empire in 1870, Eugénie emigrated to England, where she died in 1920 at the age of 94.

$150–250

917, 918, 919, 920

917 **A Wannopee Pottery Co. Glazed Pottery 'Lettuce Leaf' Pattern Part Service, 20th Century**

Each piece naturalistically molded as a slightly curled lettuce leaf shaded in pale green, *some pieces impressed W within a sunburst and/or numeral 194, 197, 198, or 212, and some with "LETTUCE LEAF" TRADE MARK printed in green*; comprising:
Shallow bowl (chip), *width 11 3/8 in. (28.9 cm.)*
Shallow bowl (chip and hair crack), *width 10 3/16 in. (25.9 cm.)*
Twelve plates (some wear and minor discoloration, one repaired and two with a small chip), *diameters 8 5/8 to 8 3/4 in. (21.9 to 22.2 cm.)*
Two salad plates (some wear and discoloration, one with small chips), *diameter 7 5/8 in. (19.4 cm.)*
Three small dishes (two discolored and one of those chipped), *diameters 6 and 6 1/4 in. (15.2 and 15.9 cm.)*
Square teacup and saucer, *height 3 3/8 in. (8.6 cm.), width 6 1/8 in. (15.6 cm.)*
Vase of slightly flaring trefoil section (hair cracks and beveled chips), *height 7 5/8 in. (19.4 cm.)*
(22)

$600–900

918 **A Dodie Thayer Pottery Lettuce Leaf Salad Bowl, circa 1965**

The exterior applied with seven naturalistically modeled overlapping lettuce leaves veined in yellow and colored in bright green, and the circular interior glazed in yellow, (small chips), *impressed pineapple mark and "au bon gout, Palm Beach, Dodie Thayer."*
Width 13 3/16 in. (33.5 cm.)

$150–200

919 **A Pair of Dodie Thayer Pottery Cabbage Leaf Bowls, circa 1965**

Each square and formed as four overlapping leaves veined in yellow and colored on the exterior and interior in bright green, (chips), *impressed pineapple mark and incised "au bon gout, Palm Beach, Dodie Thayer."*
Widths 9 and 9 1/8 in. (22.9 and 23.2 cm.)

$100–150

920 **A Set of Seven Dodie Thayer Pottery Lettuce Leaf Small Dishes, circa 1965**

Each formed as a bright green almost circular leaf with a slightly ruffled edge (chips) and pale yellow veining, (one repaired), *impressed pineapple and "au bon gout, Dodie Thayer" marks.*
Diameter 4 in. (10.2 cm.)

$75–100

921, 921, 921, 922

924, 923, 923

921 **An American Glazed Redware Jar, probably New England, mid-19th Century**

The barrel-shaped body incised around the mid-section and beneath the flaring rim (small chips and abrasions) with concentric lines flanking dark brown splotches, the sides with shallow loop handles, (chips on the footrim). Together with a 20th-century redware tapering cylindrical milk jug with a brown-splotched interior and grooved loop handle set perpendicularly to the spout (chips); and a glazed redware oval baking dish (some abrasion on the edges), *incised Kitty Bright '77.* (3)
Heights 9 7/8 and 3 in. (25.1 and 7.6 cm.), length of dish 18 3/4 in. (47.6 cm.)

$250–350

922 **An English Creamware Jelly Mold, 1820-30**

Of octagonal shape and molded on the interior with a fruit-filled bowl placed on trailing foliage within a 'tongue-and-dart' border around the sides (hair crack on the rim), the underside with two small peg feet (one with a small chip, the other with two glaze cracks).
Length 6 3/8 in. (16.2 cm.)

$75–100

923 **A Set of Nine French Terracotta Cocottes and Covers, Agitna (Placide Saltalamacchia), Vallauris, Modern**

Each circular with reeded strap handles at the sides and mushroom-shaped knops on the covers, the interior of the pots and the exterior of the covers glazed, (minor chips), *impressed AEGITNA, VALLAURIS MADE IN FRANCE, and various other marks.* Together with an American brown-glazed stoneware cocotte and cover, *molded maple leaf USA mark.* (10)
Widths 5 1/2 to 5 5/8 and 5 3/8 in. (14 to 14.3 and 13.7 cm.)

$100–150

924 **A Set of Six French Stoneware Butter Pots, Modern**

Each circular, the interior grey and the exterior covered in a brown ferruginous glaze, *impressed GRES du BERRY, FAIT-MAIN, MADE IN FRANCE marks and numeral 50.*
Diameter 3 to 3 1/8 in. (7.6 to 7.9 cm.)

$75–100

927

928

926, 925, 926, 926

925 **A Set of Five French Porcelain 'Man in Space' Plates, Designed by Piero Fornasetti, December 1966**

Each printed in black and five heightened in orange with a different scene commemorating space exploration, (number 1 repaired), *'Serie de six assiettes specialement dessinées par Fornasetti Pour PARIS MATCH Decembre mille neuf cent soixante six L'HOMME DANS L'ESPACE', the number and title and Copyright marks printed in black, and four with number 2 in black or 5, 6, or 7 in orange. Diameter 9½ in. (24.1 cm.)*

The titles printed on this series are:
1 Le départ
2 L'orbite
3 Le vol
5 Le retour
6 L'histoire.

$250–350

926 **A Set of Five French Porcelain 'Man in Space' Plates, Designed by Piero Fornasetti, December 1966**

Each printed in black with a different scene commemorating space exploration, (number 7 damaged), *'Serie de six assiettes specialement dessinées par Fornasetti Pour PARIS MATCH Decembre mille neuf cent soixante six L'HOMME DANS L'ESPACE', the number and title and copyright marks printed in black.*
Diameter 9½ in. (24.1 cm.)

The titles printed on this series are:
7 Le départ
8 L'orbite
9 Le vol
11 Le retour
12 L'histoire.

$200–300

927 **Five Ceramic Vessels, Modern**

Comprising a compressed spherical pottery vase with a short ring-turned neck, covered in a pale tan glaze, *signed in brown Stewart 1994*; a tan-glazed pottery cylindrical jar, *impressed anchor within an oval and GRESPOTS·DICOIN·FRANCE mark*; a small white-glazed pottery jar; a blue-spattered cream-colored pottery small bowl; and a white porcelain milk jug in the form of an open milk carton, *incised The American Apple Pie Co 1976©.*
Height of vase 4 11/16 in. (11.9 cm.)

$100-150

928 **A Miscellaneous Group of Colorless Glass Table Glassware**

Including 20 large balloon red wine glasses and a quantity of other drinking glasses, decanters and bud vases.

$350–500

932

929 **A Set of Five Lourioux 'Fireproof Porcelain' Pots de Crème and a Circular Stand, Modern**

Each piece printed in burgundy, green and blue with sprays and/or sprigs of cornflowers and other wild flowers within a gilt-edged rim, the loop handles on the fluted pots and the mushroom knops on the covers heightened in gilding, *factory marks and MADE IN FRANCE printed in gilding.*
Height 3⅜ in. (8.6 cm.), diameter of stand 8⅝ in. (21.9 cm.)

$100–150

929

930 **A Set of Eight Derby Porcelain Dessert Plates, circa 1825**

Each decorated in the center with a gilt roundel (two worn), and on the gilt-edged rim with a green and gold berried ivy vine border interrupted with pink rose blossoms and green leaves, (one with a chip and hair crack, all with discoloration and crackled glaze, and with varying degrees of wear to the enamels and gilding), *crowned crossed batons and D marks and various numerals in iron-red or puce and black.*
Diameter 8⅛ in. (20.6 cm.)

$100–150

931 **An American Porcelain Commemorative Cabinet Plate, dated 1962**

Printed in black with a portrait signed *LS Hudson* © '61 and inscribed *Jacqueline Kennedy First Lady of the Land* within a grey-ground rim, (some central scratching), *pseudo coat of arms, above © 1962 and on a banderole DELANO STUDIOS SETAUKET L.I. N.Y. marks printed in black.*
Diameter 10 ¹¹⁄₁₆ in. (27.1 cm.)

$100–150

932 **A Belleek Porcelain 'Shamrock Ware' Part Tea and Coffee Service, 1955-65**

Each piece molded with basketwork superimposed with sprays of green shamrocks issuing from the green and brown stem handles or on the plates and saucers scattered around the rim, the interiors of the jugs, sugar bowl and cups covered in a nacreous chartreuse glaze, *green-printed marks and registry number 0857*; comprising:
Tea or coffee pot (rim chipped and cover missing), *height 5 ⅞ in. (14.9 cm.)*
Two milk jugs, *heights 6 and 4½ in. (15.2 and 11.4 cm.)*
Cream jug, *height 3 ¹¹⁄₁₆ in. (9.4 cm.)*
Sugar bowl (cover missing), *height 2⅛ in. (5.4 cm.)*
Six teacups (two damaged)
Seven saucers
Plate, *diameter 8¼ in. (21 cm.)*
Six cake plates, *diameter 6 ¹¹⁄₁₆ in. (17 cm.)*
Two-handled serving plate, *width 10½ in. (26.7 cm.)*
Ashtray molded with a border of gordian knots interrupted by three cigarette rests, *diameter 4¼ in. (10.8 cm.)*
(27)

Various Belleek 'Shamrock Ware' teawares are illustrated by Richard K. Degenhardt, *Belleek, The Complete Collector's Guide and Illustrated Reference*, pp. 56, 57 and 177.

Given to President Kennedy at Dunganstown, Ireland, June, 1961.

$600–900

Clockwise from top left: 935, 933, 938, 936, 937, 937, 935, 934

933 **A Chinese Export Porcelain Shell-Shaped Dish, 20th Century**

Painted in the center with the Great Seal of the United States: a brown spread-winged eagle emblazoned with a red, gold and blue shield beneath a gilt aura and surrounded by four puce, purple, iron-red, brown and gold floral sprigs repeated on the reeded handle, the cavetto with a gilt spearhead border beneath a purple dotted wavy line entwining an iron-red and blue 'bead-and-reel' band, and the gilt-edged rim (worn) with a salmon and brown foliate border.
Length 10 3⁄8 in. (26.4 cm.)

$150–250

934 **A Pair of Chinese Export Porcelain Plates, 20th Century**

Similarly decorated to the preceding lot.
Diameters 8 15⁄16 and 9 in. (22.7 and 22.9 cm.)

$150–250

935 **A Pair of Chinese Export Porcelain Plates, 20th Century**

Identical to the preceding lot, (one with a chip).
Diameter 9 in. (22.9 cm.)

$125–175

936 **A Chinese Export Porcelain Oval Dish, 20th Century**

Painted in the center with a brown spread-winged American eagle emblazoned with a red, gold and blue shield, and bearing in his beak a rose-edged banderole inscribed with the motto E PLURIBUS UNUM, the cavetto with a gilt spearhead border beneath a gilt-edged and -dotted iron-red band and a salmon-ground brown and gilt foliate border, the gilt-edged rim (some wear) with a gilt husk and blue dot band, and the exterior with four puce, purple, brown and gold floral sprigs.
Length 10 1⁄16 in. (25.6 cm.)

$150–250

937 **A Pair of Chinese Export Porcelain Quatrefoil Dishes, 20th Century**

The center of each similarly decorated to the three preceding lots with a shield-emblazoned brown eagle between puce, purple, brown and gilt floral sprigs within a gilt spearhead border around the cavetto, the rim with a brown and gold guilloche border beneath a brown and salmon scallop band at the gilt edge (worn; one dish repaired).
Lengths 7 13⁄16 and 7 7⁄8 in. (19.8 and 20 cm.)

$100–150

938 **A Chinese Export Porcelain Soap Dish, Cover and Liner, late 19th Century**

The dish and pierced liner decorated under or on the rim with a salmon border patterned with gilt stripes and interlocking circlets, and the dish and cover with a salmon and gilt husk border interrupted on the cover by the gilt monogram *WDW* beneath an iron-red lion rampant crest, (worn).
Length 5 1⁄4 in. (13.3 cm.)

$200–300

940, 939, 939, 940, 941, 941

939 **A Pair of American Pottery Commemorative Mugs, Modern**

Each with a slightly flaring cylindrical body printed on one side with a black trident held by a brown hand emerging from blue waves within a yellow rope-edged oval panel interrupted at the top with a banderole inscribed in brown U.S.S. JOSEPH P. KENNEDY, JR., and at the bottom with a smaller banderole inscribed DD-850, the rim and flaring foot edged with gilt bands, *LGB monogram within a shield beneath a Grecian portico and above ATTLEBORO MASS. MADE IN U.S.A. mark printed in gold, possibly the retailer's mark of L. G. Balfour (now located in North Attleboro).*
Height 3 13/16 in. (9.7 cm.)

The *USS Joseph P. Kennedy, Jr.* was launched in July, 1945 and commissioned in December, 1945. The ship is now in a museum in Fall River, Massachusetts.

$100–150

940 **A Pair of American Pottery Commemorative Mugs, Modern**

Identical to the preceding pair, *identically marked to the preceding lot.*
Height 3 13/16 in. (9.7 cm.)

See the note to the preceding lot.

$100–150

941 **A Pair of American Pottery Commemorative Mugs, Modern**

Identical to the two preceding pairs, (one with a slight flaw in the gilt band around the foot), *identically marked to the two preceding lots.*
Height 3 13/16 in. (9.7 cm.)

See the note to lot 939.

$100–150

942 **A Painted Metal Blackamoor Figure**

(Losses). Together with a green-painted basketwork planter. (2)
Length of figure 5 in. (12.7 cm.)

$50–100

943 **Three Items of Electroplate, American and English, all circa 1950**

Comprising a plain baluster Water Pitcher with loop handle, *Friedman Silver Co., Inc., Brooklyn, New York*; a shaped circular Serving Platter with molded border, *Roberts & Belk Ltd., Sheffield, England, retailed by Wylers, New York*; and a gadroon bordered circular Tray, the center die-stamped with scrolling foliage and shells, *unmarked, probably English.*
Height of pitcher 8¼ in. (21 cm.), diameter of platter 13¾ in. (34.9 cm.), diameter of tray 15¼ in. (38.7 cm.)

$100–150

944 **A Pair of Georgian Style Barley-Twist Oak Candlesticks, Modern**

With brass drip pan, barley-twist stem and dished circular base.
Height 8 in. (20.3 cm.)

$200–300

942

943

944

945

946

945 **A Victorian Green-Painted Wood Gothic Revival Wall Bracket**

Height 8 in. (20.3 cm.), width 8¾ in. (22.2 cm.)

$150–200

946 **A Brass Studded Leather-Covered Storage Trunk, 19th/20th Century**

Rectangular, with coffer top and allover brass nailhead decoration.
Height 18½ in. (47 cm.), length 26½ in. (67.3 cm.)

$600–800

947 **A Late Federal Painted Maple Work Table, second quarter 19th Century**

The rectangular top with rounded corners above a frieze containing a long drawer fitted for sewing and decorated on four sides with summer flowers; the whole raised on painted lyre-form trestles.
Height 28½ in. (72.4 cm.), width 23 in. (58.4 cm.)

This work table was among the furnishings in the West Sitting Room of the White House during President and Mrs. Kennedy's residence.

$1,500–2,000

948 **A Set of Four English Gilt-Decorated Eglomisé Pictures, mid-18th Century**

Depicting various pastoral scenes, including fishing and picnicking, *one cracked.*
Sight 8½ by 12 in. (21.6 by 30.5 cm.)

These pictures were among the furnishings in the Second Floor Oval Room of the White House during President and Mrs. Kennedy's residence.

$1,800–2,400

949 **A Set of Caned Bedside Steps, 19th Century**

(Caning distressed).
Height 27¾ in. (70.5 cm.), width 20¾ in. (52.7 cm.), depth 25½ in. (64.8 cm.)

$400–600

950 **Four Rattan Circular Garden Seats**

(Distressed).

$75–100

947

949

948

950

948

951

951 **A Pair of George III Style Mahogany Side Chairs, Modern**

Each with an arched backrest, interlaced strapwork splat, upholstered seat and square chamfered legs, (both damaged). Together with a George III style carved mahogany stool.

$400–600

952 **A Regency Paint-Decorated and Bamboo-Turned Armchair, Early 19th Century**

The square back with bamboo-turned uprights and shaped arms above a rush seat, on turned, tapering legs joined by stretchers; painted predominantly in tones of yellow and brown.

$250–450

952

953

953 **A Bed Step Pot Cupboard, circa 1840,**

In the form of a box with hinged top and pull-out step, both inset within grain carpet, the whole raised on turned legs.
Height 17 in. (43.2 cm.), length 19¼ in. (48.9 cm.)

$400–600

954 **Two Irish Woolwork Pictures**

One depicting a cottage, the other a lake scene; each constructed from samples of Irish fabric. Together with a needlepoint picture of a lady in a riding costume.
8 by 9½ in. (20.3 by 24.1 cm.)

$300–400

954

954

955 **A Small Maple and Ash Child's Writing Armchair, American, 20th Century**

Height 20 in. (50.8 cm.), width 18½ in. (47 cm.)

$200–300

956 **A Marble Replica of the Head of Hermes from the *Hermes and the Infant Dionysos* by Praxiteles**

The youthful god turned to his left and gazing down, with full parted lips, slightly aquiline nose, and prominent brow, his hair a mass of thick unruly locks.
Height 13½ in. (34.3 cm.)

$4,000–6,000

957 **A Continental Enamel Miniature of the Holy Virgin, third quarter 19th Century**

Mounted in an elaborate brass frame, the hinged door mounted with a further enamel miniature of the Virgin and Child.
Height 7⅝ in. (19.4 cm.)

$300–500

958 **A Greek Icon of the Deesis, early 19th Century**

Depicting the Savior Enthroned flanked by the Holy Virgin and St. John the Baptist.
11 by 7½ in. (27.9 by 19 cm.)

$1,200–1,800

959 **A Greek Icon of the Deesis, 18th Century**

Depicting the Savior Enthroned flanked by the Holy Virgin and St. John the Baptist.
11 by 13 in. (27.9 by 33 cm.)

$900–1,200

955

956

957, 959, 958, 960

961

960 **A Russian Brass Icon Triptych, 18th/Early 19th Century**

Depicting the Savior in the center panel, flanked by the Virgin and St. John the Baptist.
Height 5⅛ in. (13 cm.)

Provenance:
A La Vieille Russie, New York

Together with:

A Greek Icon of St. George Slaying the Dragon, 20th Century

4½ by 3½ in. (11.4 by 8.9 cm.)

$350–600

961 **A Viennese Gold, Enamel and Glass Small Cup, circa 1880**

The fluted glass cup applied with a gold band enameled black with white scrolls and set with diamonds, the handles in the form of winged monsters.
Height 2¼ in. (5.7 cm.)

$1,500–2,000

962, 963, 964

965

962 **A French 19th Century Ormolu Candlestick, Fitted for Electricity**

Overall height 20 in. (50.8 cm.)

$200–300

963 **A Milk-Glass Vase Mounted as an Oil Lamp, Fitted for Electricity**

Overall height 20 in. (50.8 cm.)

$75–100

964 **A Molded Colorless Glass Oil Lamp, Fitted for Electricity**

Height 10 in. (25.4 cm.)

$80–120

965 **A Group of Miscellaneous Wood and Metal Decorative and Household Articles, 19th Century and Later**

Including a 19th century wooden oak box with scales and retailer's label *Joseph Brown, Providence, Rhode Island*, a small mahogany box with brass plaque, a pair of opera glasses, and a small bell; together with a tinware candlestick and a tinware chamberstick with saucer base.

$500–700

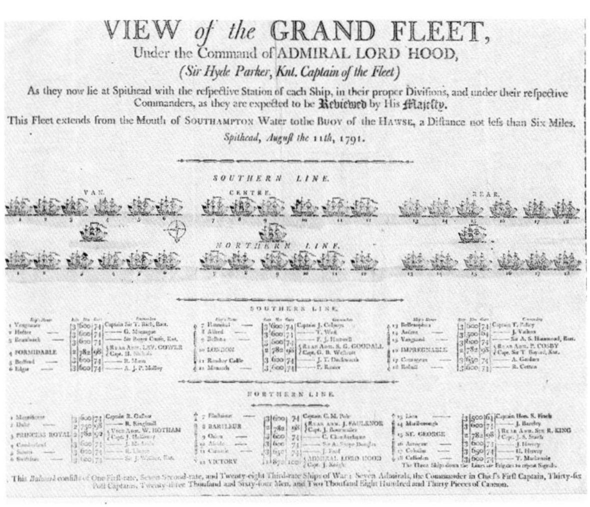

966

966

966

967

966 Three Colored Engravings

THE ESCAPE OF THE BARK *FLORENCE* FROM ARCTIC PERILS, SKETCHES IN BUENOS AYRES, and VIEW OF THE GRAND FLEET (1791)

Three hand colored engravings, with margins and in apparently good condition, framed* (not examined out of the frame) (3)
The largest: 11 ½ by 14 ¼ in. (29.2 by 36.2 cm.)

$200–300

967 A Cut Silhouette Picture of a Gentleman in a Frock Coat, English, 19th Century

The standing figure in a giltwood frame
10 ¼ by 5 in. (26 by 12.7 cm.)

$200–400

968

968 A Christmas Picture

Watercolor, with a beribboned flowering branch, inscribed with name and *Noel 1961* above a landscape with a white house in the distance, (stained). *12 by 8 ½ in. (30.5 by 21.6 cm.)*

$200–300

969 A Group of Four Prints

Comprising:
W. H. Bartlett, *The President's House, from the River* and *The President's House from Washington*, two hand colored engravings published by W. Radclyffe, London, 1839;
E. Sachse & Co. (lithographers), *President's House*, hand colored lithograph, circa 1850; and
P. Sandby (after), *Chatsworth in Derbyshire*, engraving, by M. A. Rooker, published London, 1775, framed* (not examined out of frames) (4)
Each: 6 ¼ by 7 ⅝ in. (15.9 by 19.4 cm.)

$150–200

969

969

969

969

970

970

970 **Cereghetti (Publishers)**

LE CORPS DU PRINCE PONIATOWSKY...; ET LA PRINCESSE PONIATOWSKY...

Two hand colored etchings, circa 1825, published in Paris, framed* (not examined out of frames) (2)
Each 8 ¾ by 11 in. (22.2 by 27.9 cm.)

These etchings were among the furnishings in the Kennedys' Georgetown Residence.

$100–150

971

971

971 **E. B. & E. C. Kellogg (Lithographers)**

HENRY CLAY and JOHN MARSHALL

Two lithographs, printed with beige tint stones, c. 1830, from life by Wm. H. Brown, in generally good condition, framed* (not examined out of frames) (2)
Each approximately 13 ½ by 9 ¾ in. (34.3 by 24.8 cm.)

$100–150

972 **E. B. & E. C. Kellogg (Lithographers)**

ANDREW JACKSON and JOHN RANDOLPH

Two lithographs printed with beige tint stones, c. 1830, from life by Wm. H. Brown, with margins, foxed, water stains, framed* (not examined out of frames) (2)
Each approximately 13 ⅜ by 9 ⅞ in. (34 by 25.1 cm.)

$100–150

972

972

973

973

973 **Cantonese School, Early 19th Century**

GASTERIA and DELAMCANDATUNCTATA: A PAIR OF WATERCOLORS

watercolor and body color on paper
Each 16 by 10¼ in. (40.6 by 26 cm.)

Executed circa 1805

Exhibited:
Eyre & Hobhouse, Lted., London, No. 8 & 9, n.d.

$1,000–1,500

974 **Y. C. Wang**

LION and POLAR BEAR: A PAIR OF PAINTINGS

Lion signed *Y. C. Wang* with artist's insignia, l.l.
Bear signed *YCWang* with artist's insignia, l.c.
each watercolor on board
Each: 13 by 9½ in. (33 by 24.1 cm.)

$300–400

974

974

975

975

976

975 **G. Engelmann (Lithographer)**

PAS NOBLE and PAS COMIQUE

Two hand colored lithographs, circa 1850, framed* (not examined out of frames) (2)
Each: 8½ by 5¼ in. (21.6 by 13.3 cm.)

$100–200

976 **Three Japanese Porcelain Blue and White Saucers, 19th Century**

Each painted in inky underglaze-blue with a central stylized phoenix in flight within a roundel surrounded by sketchily drawn pavilions, figures, scrolls and cloud motifs around the shaped rim. Together with a blue silk box fitted for two of the three saucers. (4)
Diameters 5¼ and 5½ in. (13.3 and 14 cm.)

$300–500

977, 978, 979, 980

977 **A New Hall Porcelain 'Window' Pattern Saucer Dish, circa 1800**

Printed in grey and enamelled in shades of rose, salmon, iron-red, green, blue, turquoise, grey and black with a chinoiserie scene of a figure at a window in a pavilion observing a lady and two boys near a table in a fenced garden within a border of landscape and floral panels interrupting rose diaper and scalework bands, the edge with an iron-red dotted band between black lines (some wear), *pattern number 425 in rose enamel.*
Diameter 8 1/16 in. (20.5 cm.)

$100–150

978 **A Japanese Imari Porcelain Bowl, 20th Century**

Decorated in underglaze-blue, shades of iron-red, green, pale aubergine and gold with a floral medallion surrounded by sketchy landscapes around the sides of the interior beneath an underglaze-blue trelliswork border around the rim repeated on the exterior above floral sprigs.
Diameter 8 ½ in. (21.6 cm.)

$200–300

979 **A Chinese Porcelain Cylindrical Jar and Cover, 20th Century**

Each piece with a pink ground painted in rose, black and green on the slightly ribbed jar with a crane perched in a pine tree and an exotic bird perched in a flowering tree, and on the domed cover with a bird on a rock amidst flowering branches, and each with 'bamboo'-form handles (three with small chips) heightened in gilding on the cover, (hair crack on the jar rim), *seal mark in iron-red.*
Height 8 ¾ in. (22.2 cm.)

$200–300

980 **A Chinese Export Porcelain Bowl, circa 1750**

The exterior painted in underglaze-blue, iron-red, shades of rose, green, blue, white and gold with a pair of pheasants perched on rockwork amongst lushly flowering peonies in a fenced garden, the interior with a central peony sprig beneath an underglaze-blue trellis diaper border interrupted with floral panels around the rim (hair crack, and a small chip on the exterior).
Diameter 10 ⅛ in. (25.7 cm.)

$500-700

981, 981, 982, 983, 907, 907, 981, 981

984

985

981 A Group of Eight Chinese and Japanese Porcelain Dishes, 20th Century

Comprising a pair of Canton *famille-rose* dishes painted in shades of rose, green, iron-red and yellow with a central fruit cluster within four lotus, chrysanthemum, prunus and other floral sprays, *marks in iron-red*; a pair of Chinese dishes painted in underglaze-blue with censers and other precious objects, (both repaired), *peach marks in underglaze-blue*; and four Japanese dishes painted in underglaze-blue with a dragon riding ocean waves within a brown-edged scalloped and barbed rim (one chipped and issuing a small hair crack), *seal marks in underglaze-blue.*
Diameters 8, 6 ⅞ and 6 ¼ in. (20.3, 17.5 and 15.9 cm.)

$400–600

982 A Caughley Porcelain Blue and White Waste Bowl, circa 1785

Transfer-printed in underglaze-blue on the exterior with a floral spray, two sprigs and two insects, and on the interior with a floral sprig beneath a double-line border around the rim, *letter C mark in underglaze-blue.*
Diameter 4 13/16 in. (12.2 cm.)

$150–250

983 A Canton Porcelain Blue and White Bowl, late 19th Century

Painted around the exterior in underglaze-blue with Chinese figures and small boats near island pavilions in a hilly river landscape, the interior with an islet beneath a trellis diaper border edged in spearheads and dots around the rim, (restored area).
Diameter 9 in. (22.9 cm.)

$125–175

984 Two Chinese Porcelain Blue and White Brush Pots and a Rectangular Tray, 19th Century

Each cylindrical pot painted with figures in a landscape with trees and rockwork; the tray with canted corners and painted with an extensive mountainous landscape with pavilions and figures. (3)
Height 4 ¾ in. (12.1 cm.), length 8 ¼ in. (21 cm.)

$400–600

985 Four Japanese Imari Porcelain Scalloped Circular Dishes, 20th Century

Each painted in underglaze-blue, iron-red, green, yellow, lavender, white and gold, three with flowers growing from behind a rock in a central roundel surrounded by three large and three small panels of flowering shrubbery or prunus trees; and the fourth with a gilt-heightened underglaze-blue floral medallion in the center surrounded by three more finely painted panels of birds, prunus and bamboo alternating with quatrefoils of leafy trees beneath a zigzag-patterned border on the rim.
Diameters 8 15/16 to 8 9/16 in. (21.1 to 21.7 cm.)

$300–400

986 **A Set of Four Japanese Imari Porcelain Dishes, 20th Century**

Each painted in the center with a gilt-heightened underglaze-blue stylized floral medallion surrounded by three panels of blue, white, aubergine and green flowering prunus trees alternating with three underglaze-blue, iron-red, aubergine and gold brocaded panels beneath a diaper and floral border around the gilt-edged rim (one chipped).
Diameter 7 ¼ in. (18.4 cm.)

$200–300

987 **A Chinese Ying Qing Bowl, Yuan Dynasty**

Of conical shape, the interior molded with a foliate pattern beneath a pale bluish-green glaze. Together with a blue silk-covered fitted box. (2 pieces)
Diameter 7 ¼ in. (18.4 cm.)

$400–600

988 **A Paris Porcelain Saucer and Three English Porcelain Saucers, circa 1785 and 1820**

The first painted in the center with a blue, tan and black butterfly and a black and red ladybird encircled by five smaller insects beneath a series of tan-shaded black 'cable' and gilt foliate and band borders around the rim (hair crack, and the center with a star crack in the glaze underneath), *crowned M mark of the Clignancourt factory, and monogram for Monsieur, Comte de Provence, stencilled in iron-red*; and the other three decorated in gilding with a central floral sprig (some wear) encircled by a border of floral sprigs issuing from the lower of the gilt bands enclosing a gilt foliate-vine border around the rim. (4)
Diameters 5 7/16 and 5 5/8 in. (13.8 and 14.3 cm.)

$150–250

989 **A Chinese Export Porcelain Blue and White Potpourri Jar and Cover, late 19th Century**

The barrel-shaped body painted with dragons amidst scrolling clouds beneath a dotted scalloped border, and the inset dished cover pierced with five small holes within a 'cloud'-bordered medallion beneath a row of dots within a cable border around the rim (chip and some fritting), *incised characters on the cover interior.*
Height 4 ½ in. (11.4 cm.)

This potpourri jar was among the furnishings in Mrs. Kennedy's bedroom at the White House.

$250–350

990 **Two Staffordshire Porcelain Blue and White Teabowls and Three Saucers, circa 1820 and 1805**

Each piece transfer-printed in underglaze-blue with a version of the 'Willow' pattern beneath a gilt rim edge, the interior rim of the teabowls (one with a small chip and a hair crack, the other slightly discolored) with a 'Fitzhugh'-type border, and the saucers (one damaged and repaired) with a fluted rim decorated also with a 'Fitzhugh'-type border above a gilt foliate-guilloche border. Together with a slightly later Copeland porcelain saucer transfer-printed in underglaze-blue with the 'Two Birds' pattern beneath a trellis diaper border edged in spearheads and dumbbells around the gilt-edged rim, *interlaced C's and COPELAND mark printed in green.* (6)
Diameters 3 3/8, 5 3/8, 5 ½ and 5 5/8 in. (8.6, 13.7, 14 and 14.3 cm.)

$150–250

986

990, 988, 907, 989, 909, 909, 990, 988, 990

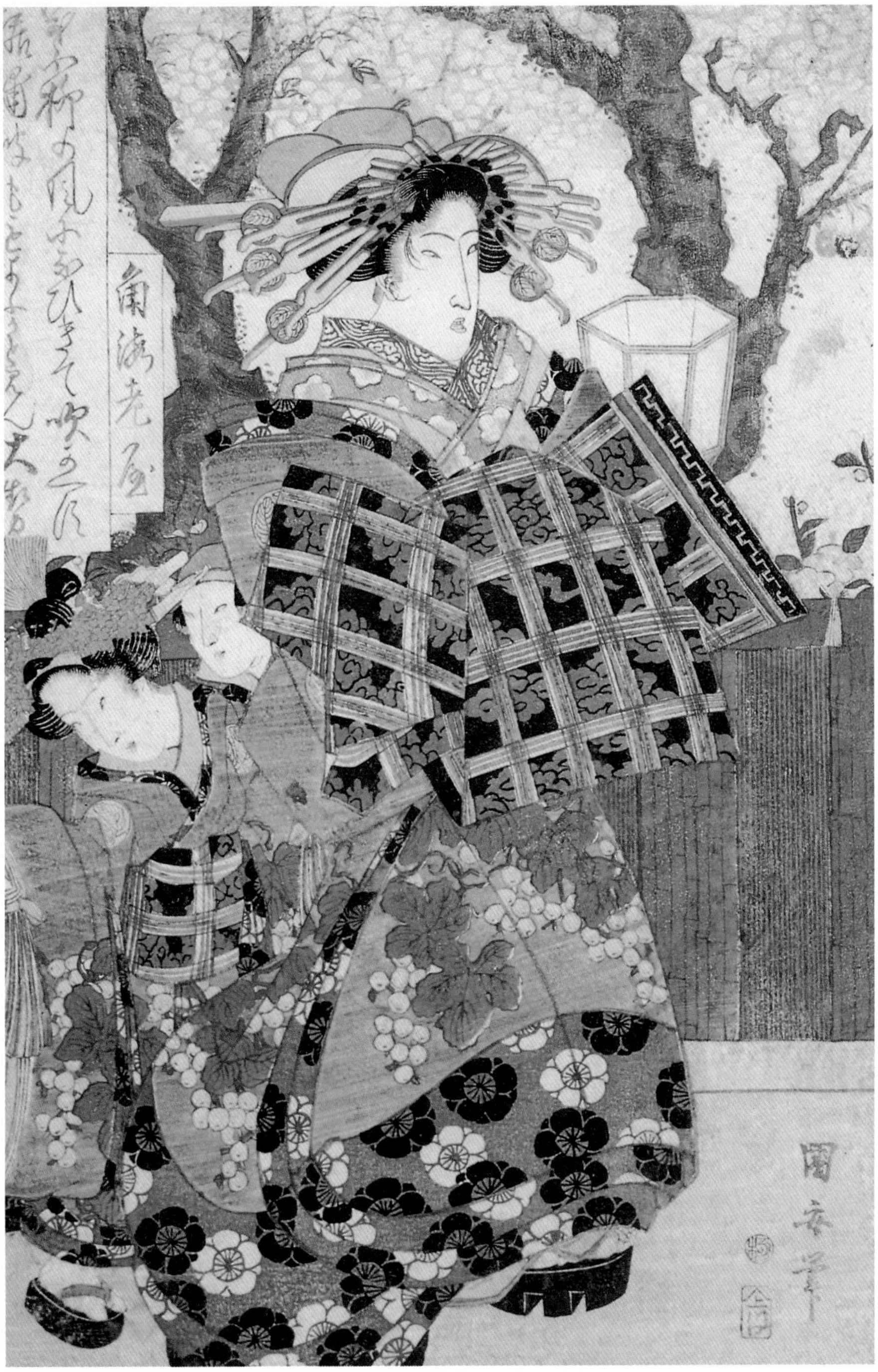

991

992

991 **Kuniyasu**

PORTRAIT OF A COURTESAN AND ATTENDANT

Part of a triptych or pentiptych.
14½ by 9½ in. (36.8 by 24.1 cm.)

(Faded and creased)

$150–250

992 **Charles Sarka** (1879-1960)

BOY IN A LANDSCAPE

signed and dated *July 20*
watercolor on paper
8⅝ by 2¾ in. (21.9 by 7 cm.)

Provenance:
Davis Galleries, New York

$300–500

993

993

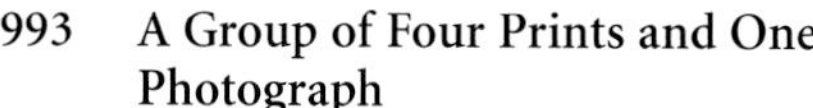

993 **A Group of Four Prints and One Photograph**

Comprising:
James Abbott McNeill Whistler, *Nursemaids: Les Bonnes du Luxembourg* (Way 48; Levy 79), lithograph, 1894, published in *Art Journal*;
Edouard Manet, *Baudelaire de profil en chapeau II* (Harris 59), etching, 1876-68, from a reprint edition;
Auguste Rodin, *Ames du Purgatoire* (Delteil 11), etching, 1893, second state, published in *Vie Artistique*;
Pencil drawing of a street scene, signed in pencil *St. Manetti*(?) and dated '*51*; and
[*Venice at Night*], photograph, framed* (not examined out of frames). (5)
The largest 8 ¾ by 11 ⅞ in. (22.2 by 30.2 cm.)

$300–400

993

993

993

994

995

994 Raymond Crosby (American, 19th Century)

THE BALL

pencil on paper
6 ½ by 8 in. (16.5 by 20.3 cm.)

Executed circa 1900.

Provenance:
Davis Galleries, New York

$500–700

995 Raymond Crosby (American, 19th Century)

THREE WOMEN

pencil on paper
11 ½ by 9 in. (29.2 by 22.9 cm.)

Executed circa 1900.

Provenance:
Davis Galleries, New York

$500–700

996

997

998

996 **Albert York (American, b. 1928)**

GERANIUM IN BLUE POT WITH FALLEN LEAF AND BIRD

oil on wood panel
18 by 17 in. (45.7 by 43.2 cm.)

Provenance:
Davis & Langdale Co., New York

Exhibited:
New York, Davis & Langdale Co., *Albert York Paintings*, 1982, no. 23

$3,000–5,000

997 **Albert York (American, b. 1928)**

A PURPLE ANEMONE WITH ZINNIAS IN A GLASS JAR

oil on canvasboard
14 by 11 in. (35.6 by 27.9 cm.)

Painted in 1987.

Provenance:
Davis & Langdale Co., New York

Exhibited:
New York, Davis & Langdale Co., *Albert York*, March 1988, no. 28

$2,000–4,000

998 **Albert York (American, b. 1928)**

PINK DAISIES IN A GLASS JAR

inscribed *Albert York* on the reverse
oil on panel
12½ by 10⅜ in. (31.7 by 26.4 cm.)

Provenance:
Davis & Langdale Co., New York

Exhibited:
New York, Davis & Langdale Co., *Albert York Paintings: 1963-1991*, March-April 1992

$1,500–2,500

999

1000

999 Reeve Schley (American, 20th Century)

DUNES

signed *Schley* and dated *1981*, l.r.
watercolor on paper
14 by 20 ¼ in. (35.6 by 51.4 cm.)

$800–1,200

1000 Mary Faulconer (American, b. 1912)

BIIRDS, EGGS AND GRASSES

gouache on gessoed panel
10 by 14 in. (25.4 by 35.6 cm.)

Provenance:
Bodley Gallery, New York

$200–400

1001 **Mary Faulconer (American, b. 1912)**

OLIVE OIL

signed *Faulconer* and dated *1978*, l.r.
gouache on gessoed panel
19½ by 15½ in. (49.5 by 39.4 cm.)

Provenance:
Bodley Gallery, New York

$400–600

1002 **Marcel Vertes**

WOMAN IN BIKINI WITH BICYCLE

signed twice
watercolor and pencil on paper
19½ by 25½ in. (49.5 by 64.8 cm.)

$800–1,200

1001

1002

1003

1003 ***Namingha

MASK

signed
oil on canvas
60 by 48 in. (152.4 by 121.9 cm.)

$1,000–1,500

1004 **John Austin (American, b. 1918)**

CLOSE UP OF BRANDT POINT LIGHT, NANTUCKET, MASSACHUSETTS

signed *Austin*, l.r.
oil on board
10 ¼ by 14 ¼ in. (26 by 36.2 cm.)

$150–250

1005 **J. Wood**

THE WHITE WINDOW

signed and dated *'87*
oil on wood
31 ¼ by 22 ¾ in. (79.4 by 57.8 cm.)

$600–800

1005

1004

1006

1006 John Austin (American, b. 1918)

TUCKERNUCK LANDSCAPE, NANTUCKET, MASSACHUSETTS

tempera on board
13 by 19 in. (33 by 48.3 cm.)

Provenance:
The Main Street Gallery, Nantucket, Massachusetts

$100–200

1007 Keith McDaniel

BATH HOUSES

signed
acrylic on canvas
36 ¼ by 45 ¾ in. (92.1 by 116.2 cm.)

$1,500–2,500

1007

1008

1009

1008 Robert Stackhouse

"SAILINGS" AT THE HUDSON RIVER MUSEUM, OAK AND CEDAR, 48' X 14' X 8', 1978

signed and dated *3-1-79*
watercolor and charcoal on paper
42 by 60 in. (106.7 by 152.4 cm.)

$3,000–4,000

1009 R. B. Sprague

A CHURCH WITH THREE CROSSES

signed and dated *'84*
oil on canvas
44 by 50 in. (111.8 by 127 cm.)

$800–1,200

1010

1010 **French School, 20th Century**

OPEN CAR WELCOMING PARADE, FRANCE

indistinctly signed *Pierre S...* and
dated *1961* (?)
oil on canvas
30 by 37 in. (73.7 by 91.4 cm.)

$800–1,200

1011 **Sterling Mulbry**

THE CORNER OF LOUISIANA (FOR WALKER PERCY)

signed and dated *1990* on the reverse
oil on paper, wood and found objects
Closed: 42 by 27 in. (106.7 by 68.6 cm.),
open: 42 by 32 in. (106.7 by 81.3 cm.)

Provenance:
Main Street Gallery, Nantucket

$700–900

1011

1012

1012 **Robert Berk (American, 20th Century)**

JOHN F. KENNEDY: A PORTRAIT BUST

inscribed © *Berk* and dated *'68*
bronze patinated plaster on a black composition base
Height approximately 10 in. (25.4 cm.)

The finisihed bronze portrait of John F. Kennedy, of which this bust is a contemporary patinated plaster version, was installed in time for the opening of the Kennedy Center, Washington, D.C., in September 1971. Berks's full-sized bronze is eight feet high and weighs 3,000 pounds.

$500–1,000

1013 **A Scrimshaw Sperm Whale's Tooth**

The obverse engraved with a portrait of John F. Kennedy above a facsimile of his signature, indistinctly signed on the bottom rim *Patrick ... Nantucket.*
Height 6 ⅜ in. (16.2 cm.)

$300–500

1014, 1015

1014 **Pericle Fazzini (Italian, 1913-87)**

BUTTERO (HORSE AND RIDER)

inscribed *Pericle Fazzini*
bronze, mounted on a half-inch green variegated marble base
Height 10 ½ in. (26.7 cm.)

This bronze was among the furnishings in the White House during President and Mrs. Kennedy's residence.

$1,500–2,500

1015 **Pericle Fazzini (Italian, 1913-87)**

HORSE AND RIDER

inscribed *Pericle Fazzini*
bronze, mounted on a half-inch wooden base
4 by 7 by 1 ¾ in. (10.2 by 17.8 by 4.4 cm.)

$1,000–1,500

1016

1016 ***Radloff**

FRAGMENT OF EDEN (END OF SUMMER)

signed, titled and dated '59 on the reverse
tempera on board
10 ½ by 7 in. (26.7 by 17.8 cm.)

This painting was among the furnishings in Mrs. Kennedy's bedroom at the White House.

$400–600

1017 **Bernard Buffet**

TÊTE DE HIBON (Reinz 248)

drypoint, 1960, signed in pencil and numbered *82/125*, apparently with margins and in good condition, framed* (not examined out of the frame)
8 ¼ by 11 ¾ in. (21 by 29.8 cm.)

$500–700

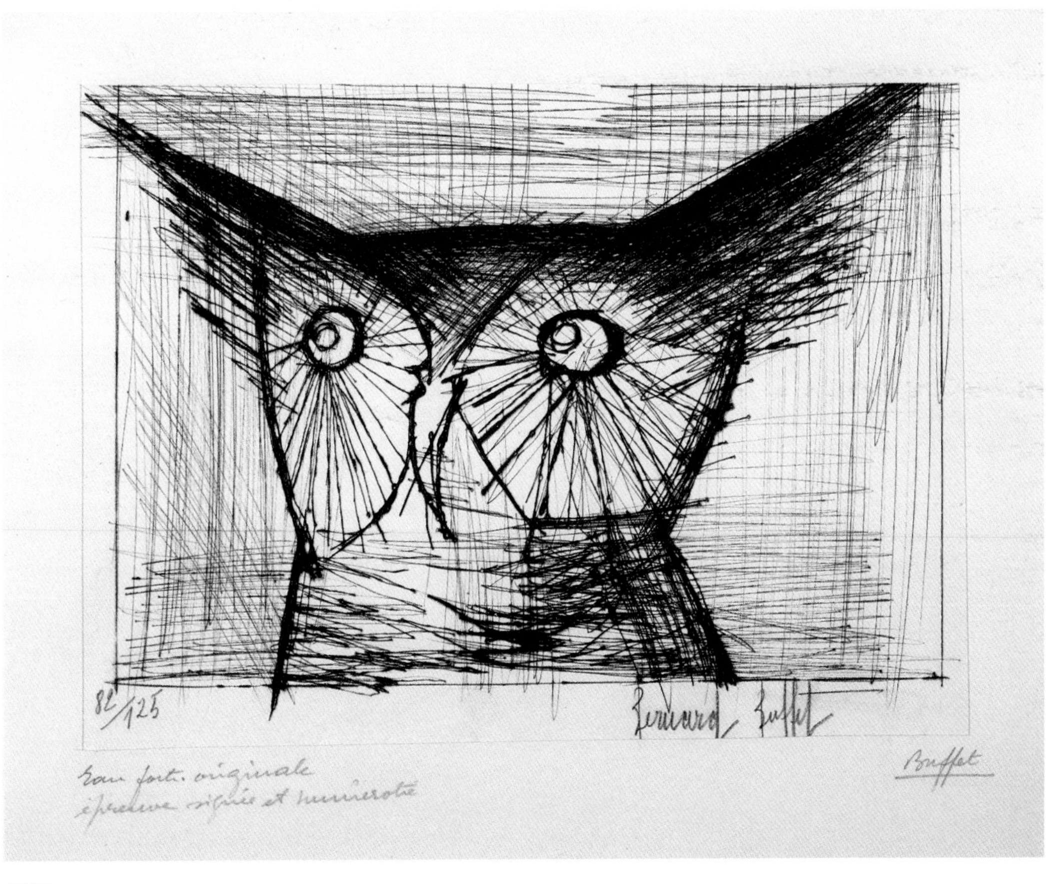

1017

1018

1019

1020

1018 Leonor Fini

PORTRAIT OF A WOMAN

signed
India ink on paper
7 by 5 in. (17.8 by 12.7 cm.)

$300–500

1019 French School, 19th/20th Century

A CAMBODIAN DANCER

bears signature
watercolor and pencil on paper
19 ½ by 14 ½ in. (49.5 by 36.8 cm.)

$200–300

1020 Jacques Villon

AU CONCERT and STUDY OF A WOMAN: a double-sided drawing

signed *recto*
pencil and grey wash *recto*, pencil, ink and blue crayon *verso*
6 ¾ by 4 ½ in. (17.1 by 11.4 cm.)

Provenance:
Mathias Komor, New York

$800–1,200

1021

1021 **Marie Laurencin**

FEMME AU CHEVAL

signed
oil on canvas
21 ¾ by 18 ¼ in. (55.2 by 46.4 cm.)

$60,000–80,000

SOTHEBY'S

1334 York Avenue
New York, NY 10021
Tel: (212) 606-7000

THE ESTATE OF JACQUELINE KENNEDY ONASSIS

AUCTION RESULTS
(continued)

April 23–26, 1996

Sale Number 6834

LOT	U.S.$	LOT	U.S.$	LOT	U.S.$	LOT	U.S.$	LOT	U.S.$	LOT	U.S.$
559P	4,312	**587**	4,600	**623**	6,900	**661**	2,875	**698**	6,900	**710Z**	2,530
559Q	28,750	**588**	19,550	**624**	12,650	**662**	3,450	**699**	10,350	**711**	21,850
559S	4,312	**589**	28,750	**625**	32,200	**663**	3,737	**700**	8,625	**712**	23,000
559T	17,250	**590**	11,500	**626**	43,125	**664**	12,650	**701**	6,325	**713**	35,650
559U	5,750	**591**	9,775	**627**	63,000	**665**	6,900	**702**	6,325	**714**	12,650
559V	4,887	**592**	12,075	**628**	17,250	**666**	16,100	**703**	6,900	**715**	40,250
559W	4,600	**593**	21,850	**629**	34,500	**667**	13,225	**704**	8,050	**716**	24,150
559X	4,255	**594**	27,600	**630**	57,500	**668**	2,587	**705**	26,450	**716A**	12,650
559Y	6,900	**595**	42,550	**631**	18,400	**669**	5,750	**706**	5,750	**717**	13,225
559Z	24,150	**596**	9,775	**632**	7,475	**670**	2,587	**707**	7,475	**718**	16,100
560	8,050	**597**	29,900	**633**	17,250	**671**	5,462	**708**	8,050	**719**	6,900
561	8,050	**598**	6,900	**634**	18,400	**672**	4,312	**709**	2,875	**720**	6,325
562	14,950	**599**	14,950	**635**	9,775	**673**	2,875	**710**	6,325	**721**	7,475
563	5,462	**600**	24,725	**636**	16,100	**674**	2,300	**710A**	2,875	**722**	11,500
564	11,500	**601**	19,550	**637**	16,100	**675**	3,162	**710B**	2,875	**723**	16,100
565	14,950	**602**	5,750	**638**	10,925	**676**	4,312	**710C**	4,887	**724**	8,625
566	13,800	**603**	7,475	**639**	9,775	**677**	1,437	**710D**	3,162	**725**	20,700
567	5,175	**604**	19,550	**640**	12,650	**678**	4,312	**710E**	4,887	**726**	13,800
568	48,875	**605**	19,550	**641**	40,250	**679**	12,650	**710F**	6,900	**727**	25,300
569	57,500	**606**	6,038	**642**	24,150	**680**	4,025	**710G**	5,175	**728**	29,900
570	11,500	**607**	6,900	**643**	35,650	**681**	2,185	**710H**	6,325	**729**	40,250
571	6,900	**608**	7,475	**645**	6,325	**682**	6,900	**710 I**	3,737	**730**	19,550
572	8,050	**609**	11,500	**646**	3,220	**683**	4,025	**710J**	3,450	**731**	12,650
573	6,325	**610**	10,350	**647**	12,650	**684**	6,900	**710K**	2,990	**732**	48,875
574	34,500	**611**	4,600	**648**	43,125	**685**	6,612	**710L**	12,650	**733**	43,125
575	18,400	**612**	20,700	**649**	12,650	**686**	8,625	**710M**	3,162	**734**	90,500
576	19,550	**613**	23,000	**650**	8,625	**687**	3,162	**710N**	1,955	**735**	46,000
577	12,650	**614**	9,200	**651**	14,950	**688**	6,037	**710P**	4,025	**736**	34,500
578	13,800	**615**	5,750	**652**	4,600	**689**	4,887	**710Q**	3,163	**737**	74,000
579	11,500	**615A**	6,900	**653**	43,700	**690**	2,300	**710R**	2,760	**738**	24,150
580	14,950	**616**	34,500	**654**	29,900	**691**	2,587	**710S**	13,800	**739**	14,950
581	5,750	**617**	9,200	**655**	10,350	**692**	24,150	**710T**	2,070	**740**	11,500
582	5,175	**618**	14,950	**656**	6,900	**693**	1,725	**710U**	3,737	**741**	9,775
583	4,600	**619**	11,500	**657**	23,000	**694**	2,587	**710V**	3,162	**742**	20,700
584	4,830	**620**	4,600	**658**	6,900	**695**	2,300	**710W**	4,312	**743**	9,775
585	5,175	**621**	5,175	**659**	3,450	**696**	9,775	**710X**	4,025	**744**	29,900
586	5,175	**622**	6,325	**660**	3,450	**697**	3,450	**710Y**	9,775		

FOR INFORMATION ABOUT SALE RESULTS OR CATALOGUE SUBSCRIPTIONS, PLEASE CALL 1-800-444-3709 (FROM THE U.S. ONLY) OR 203-847-4646 (FROM OUTSIDE THE U.S.)

SOTHEBY'S

1334 York Avenue
New York, NY 10021
Tel: (212) 606-7000

THE ESTATE OF JACQUELINE KENNEDY ONASSIS

AUCTION RESULTS
(continued)

April 23–26, 1996

Sale Number 6834

LOT	U.S.$	LOT	U.S.$	LOT	U.S.$	LOT	U.S.$	LOT	U.S.$	LOT	U.S.$
359	68,500	**395**	11,500	**431**	415,000	**467**	25,875	**503**	9,775	**539**	7,475
360	20,700	**396**	16,100	**432**	34,500	**468**	19,550	**504**	7,475	**540**	40,250
361	37,375	**397**	101,500	**433**	123,500	**469**	12,650	**505**	11,500	**541**	14,950
362	17,250	**398**	13,800	**434**	112,500	**470**	11,500	**506**	6,325	**542**	19,550
363	68,500	**399**	21,850	**435**	43,125	**471**	13,800	**507**	21,850	**543**	19,550
364	85,000	**400**	20,700	**436**	65,750	**472**	9,200	**508**	18,400	**544**	18,400
365	12,650	**401**	40,250	**437**	96,000	**473**	20,700	**509**	5,175	**545**	20,700
366	26,450	**402**	25,875	**438**	129,000	**474**	6,325	**510**	12,650	**546**	23,000
367	20,700	**403**	51,750	**439**	156,500	**475**	12,650	**511**	13,800	**547**	9,775
368	31,625	**404**	12,650	**440**	288,500	**476**	5,175	**512**	14,950	**548**	12,650
369	34,500	**405**	11,500	**441**	17,250	**477**	24,150	**513**	76,750	**549**	27,600
370	29,900	**406**	28,750	**442**	277,500	**478**	19,550	**514**	10,350	**550**	8,050
371	23,000	**407**	31,625	**443**	85,000	**479**	8,625	**515**	10,350	**551**	16,100
372	28,750	**408**	25,875	**444**	360,000	**480**	6,325	**516**	10,350	**552**	101,500
373	31,625	**409**	28,750	**445**	101,500	**481**	6,900	**517**	10,925	**553**	17,250
374	85,000	**410**	33,350	**446**	123,500	**482**	5,750	**518**	10,350	**554**	42,550
375	28,750	**411**	57,500	**447**	156,500	**483**	8,050	**519**	27,600	**555**	28,750
376	31,625	**412**	23,000	**448**	85,000	**484**	13,800	**520**	10,350	**556**	29,900
377	31,625	**413**	18,400	**449**	68,500	**485**	6,900	**521**	85,000	**557**	19,550
378	37,375	**414**	17,250	**450**	250,000	**486**	13,800	**522**	48,875	**558**	16,100
379	34,500	**415**	25,875	**451**	167,500	**487**	14,950	**523**	7,475	**559**	90,500
380	23,000	**416**	43,125	**452**	288,500	**488**	6,900	**524**	7,475	**559A**	6,325
381	37,375	**417**	31,050	**453**	2,587,500	**489**	14,375	**525**	57,500	**559B**	8,050
382	37,375	**418**	17,250	**454**	211,500	**490**	12,650	**526**	18,400	**559C**	8,050
383	46,000	**419**	26,450	**455**	24,150	**491**	19,550	**527**	27,600	**559D**	7,475
384	101,500	**420**	29,900	**456**	20,700	**492**	7,475	**528**	25,300	**559E**	6,325
385	96,000	**421**	25,875	**457**	14,950	**493**	7,475	**529**	17,250	**559F**	6,325
386	57,500	**422**	68,500	**458**	7,475	**494**	17,250	**530**	12,650	**559G**	16,100
387	40,250	**423**	43,125	**459**	8,625	**495**	39,100	**531**	8,625	**559H**	5,175
388	43,125	**424**	34,500	**460**	12,650	**496**	8,625	**532**	18,400	**559 I**	6,900
389	63,000	**425**	63,000	**461**	112,500	**497**	6,325	**533**	7,475	**559J**	4,600
390	74,000	**426**	145,500	**462**	24,150	**498**	5,750	**534**	9,775	**559K**	3,450
391	26,450	**427**	37,375	**463**	9,200	**499**	10,925	**535**	6,900	**559L**	3,910
392	48,875	**428**	96,000	**464**	25,300	**500**	8,050	**536**	14,950	**559M**	17,250
393	31,625	**429**	17,250	**465**	10,925	**501**	5,750	**537**	34,500	**559N**	7,762
394	23,000	**430**	51,750	**466**	13,800	**502**	6,900	**538**	18,400	**559O**	4,600

FOR INFORMATION ABOUT SALE RESULTS OR CATALOGUE SUBSCRIPTIONS, PLEASE CALL 1-800-444-3709 (FROM THE U.S. ONLY) OR 203-847-4646 (FROM OUTSIDE THE U.S.)

THE ESTATE OF JACQUELINE KENNEDY ONASSIS

SESSION NINE

FRIDAY, APRIL 23,

2:00 P.M.

The Living Room of Jacqueline Kennedy Onassis' New York City apartment, showing lots 6, 45, 46, 72, 94, 235, 247, 272, 311, 352, 627, 629, 718, 723, 1019, and 1137.

1022 **Werlich, Robert**

"Beast" Butler. *Washington, D. C.: The Quaker Press, 1962*

(8½ x 5¼ in.). Publisher's grey-blue cloth, gilt lettered on upper cover and spine, dustjacket; clipped quote from *Profiles in Courage* stapled to free front endpaper below inscription, accession ticket dated 22 May 1962 paper-clipped at end.

Together with: John F. Kennedy. *Profiles in Courage*. New York: Harper & Row, 1964. Memorial edition. (9 x 6 in.). Publisher's grey cloth, facsimile signature of John Kennedy stamped in gilt on upper cover, red printed spine label, dustjacket.

A fine inscribed copy to Jacqueline Kennedy alluding to *Profiles in Courage*: "To Jackie Kennedy with best wishes from an old friend. Bob Werlich. 5/20/62. P.S. Judging by 'Profiles in Courage' your husband doesn't particularly like Butler either. R.W." Below the inscription, Werlich attached a quote from *Profiles in Courage* in which Kennedy observed: "The chief prosecutor for the house was General Benjamin F. Butler, 'the Butcher of New Orleans.' A talented but coarse and demagogic Congressman from Massachusetts, when he lost his seat in 1874, he was so hated by his party, as well as his opponents, that one Republican wired concerning the Democratic sweep, 'Butler defeated, everything else lost.'"

$300–500

1023 **American Biography**

A group of 5 volumes bearing presentation inscriptions and/or the floral bookplate of Jacqueline Bouvier Kennedy. Most illustrated; publisher's cloth and wrappers. Varying sizes and conditions.

Frank D. Ashburn. *Peabody of Groton*. 1944. Ownership inscription in pencil ("J. L. Bouvier"); bookplate of Jacqueline Bouvier Kennedy. — Hermann Hagedorn. *The Roosevelt Family of Sagamore Hill*. 1964. Bookplate. — Joseph P. Lash. (Introduction by Franklin D. Roosevelt, Jr.) *Eleanor and Franklin*. 1971. Inscribed by Franklin D. Roosevelt, Jr. and his wife: "For Jackie and Ari, A very Merry Christmas and Happy New Year with love and affection. Felicia and Franklin." — Maxwell D. Taylor (General, U. S. Army, Ret.) *Swords and Plowshares*. 1972. Inscribed by the author: "To Jackie, with the affectionate regards of a former soldier of her guard. Max Taylor." President Kennedy had recalled General Taylor from retirement to analyze the Bay of Pigs fiasco. — Art Buchwald. *"I am not a Crook."* 1974. Inscribed by the author: "To Jackie, I hope my book does as well as yours! Keep laughing!"

$300–500

1024 **Lewis, Wilmarth Sheldon**

One Man's Education. *New York: Alfred A. Knopf, 1967*

(9⅜ x 6 in.). 32 pages of illustrations. Publisher's blue cloth, Lewis's mongram stamped in gilt on upper cover, dustjacket; dustjacket a bit faded.

A fine presentation copy of Lewis's autobiography inscribed "To Jackie, with love, from Uncle Lefty. 22 September 1967." Lewis was an uncle by marriage.

$200–300

1025 **Horne, Alistair**

Harold Macmillan. Volume I: 1894–1956. *New York: Viking, 1988*

(9 x 6 in.). Illustrated. Publisher's plum boards, cloth spine lettered in violet, dustjacket.

A fine presentation copy from the author to Jacqueline Onassis with thanks for her editorial assistance: "With every best wish and *many* grateful thanks for your help on vol.II. Alistair Horne. Newport R. I. 27/3/89."

$200–300

1026 **Ireland and the Irish**

A group of 10 volumes, various sizes. Some illustrated. Publisher's cloth, a few with dust jackets. Various places and dates.

A Memory of John Fitzgerald Kennedy. 1963. About his trip to Ireland in June. — Anne and David Kennedy. *An Outline of Irish History*. [n.d.]. — Alfred Perceval Graves. *The Irish Fairy Book*. [n.d.] Inscribed, "To President Kennedy from Rita Marlow." — Maurice Hennessey. *I'll Come Back in Springtime: John F. Kennedy and the Irish*. 1966. 2 copies. — Eugene Sheehy. *May It Please the Court*. 1951. Presentation by the author to Joseph Leonard, subsequently presented "To Jacqueline, Christmas, 1951." — Henry Glassie. *Irish Folktales*. 1985. Presentation to Jacqueline Kennedy Onassis. — and others.

$300–500

1027 **(Dupuy, Pierre)**

Histoire des plus illustres favoris anciens et modernes. *Leyden: J. Elsevier, 1659*

(5¾ x 3½ in.). Typographical ornaments, head- and tailpieces. Nineteenth-century polished calf gilt, supralibros of the Prince Royal, son of Louis-Philippe, spine in 6 compartments richly panel-gilt, red morocco lettering piece, gilt dentelles, Dutch-combed marbled endpapers, edges gilt, by Simier R. du roi. Joints dry and starting.

With the bookplates of J. Vieillard (Rahir 3369; Willems 852).

$400–600

1028 Smith, Earl

The Fourth Floor: An Account of the Castro Communist Revolution. *New York: Random House, 1962*. — Averell Harriman. Peace with Russia. *New York: Simon and Schuster, 1959.*

Together 2 volumes, both inscribed by their authors to John F. Kennedy. Both men were members of the Kennedy Administration. Averell Harriman became the wandering ambassador. Earl T. Smith was Ambassador to Cuba during the Eisenhower years and was appointed as Ambassador to Switzerland by JFK.

$600–800

1029 **Washington and the White House**

A group of 17 volumes, including 5 association copies bearing the floral bookplate of Jacqueline Bouvier Kennedy or the gift bookplate of the White House Library, presentation inscriptions (2), and a presentation binding modestly printed with Mrs. Kennedy's name on the cover. Some illustrated; mostly in publisher's cloth and wrappers. Varying sizes and conditions.

John B. Ellis. *The Sights and Secrets of the National Capital.* 1869. — Mary Clemmer Ames. *Life and Scenes in the National Capital, as a Woman Sees Them.* 1876. — Amanda M. Douglas. *A Little Girl in Washington.* 1901. Bookplate of Jacqueline Bouvier Kennedy. — United States Congress. House of Representatives. *Development of the United States Capital ... April 25–26, 1929.* 1930. Inscribed by Stephen M. Walter "For my hopeful Jackie" and dated December 3, 1952. — Myrtle Cheney Murdock. *Constantino Brumidi; Michaelangelo of the United States Capitol.* 1950. Inscribed by Myrtle Cheney Murdock to Mrs. Kennedy "with affection and best wishes from her Ladies of the Senate Red Cross Unit. May 1, 1962." — Amy La Follette Jensen. *The White House.* 1958–1962, 2 copies, 2 editions. — Eighty-Ninth Congress. *Pocket Congressional Directory.* January 1965. Gilt stamped "Mrs. John F. Kennedy" on cover. — *The White House Library; A Short Title List.* 1967. Gift bookplate of the White House Library (unaccomplished). — Arden Davis Melick. *Wives of the Presidents.* 1972. — *The Congressional Cookbook.* 1993. — and others.

$400–600

1030 **White House Guides**

A large group of various editions, with successive revisions, of *The White House: An Historic Guide* (first published in the summer of 1962 at the request of the First Lady, Jacqueline Kennedy). Approximately 40 copies from the Kennedy years, 7 from Johnson's administration and 1 from Nixon's.

Together approximately 48 volumes, variously publisher's cloth and paper.

$300–500

1031 **Latin and South America**

A group of 8 works in 9 volumes, various sizes (one a large folio). Mostly illustrated. Publisher's cloth. Various places and dates. Several with inscriptions to President John F. Kennedy and Jacqueline Kennedy.

J.B. Trend. *Bolívar and the Independence of Spanish America.* 1951. Presented to John F. Kennedy by Andres Fuenmayor on a presidential visit to Caracas in 1961. — Guillermo A. Sherwell. *Simón Bolívar: A Sketch of his Life and Work.* 1951. Presented to the President, as above. — Simón Bolívar. *Selected Writings.* 1951. 2 volumes. Presented to the President as above. — Bonifacio del Carril. *Monumenta iconographica ... de la Argentina.* (1964). Presented to Jacqueline Kennedy in Buenos Aires, 1966. — And 4 others.

$500–700

1032 **Travel**

A group of 27 volumes, chiefly on travel in Africa, Asia, and the Middle East, of which 4 bear presentation inscriptions or the ownership signature of Jacqueline Kennedy. Chiefly publisher's cloth and wrappers. Varying conditions and sizes.

Freya Stark. *Letters from Syria.* 1943. Inscribed by the author to Mr. Gannett and dated December 1943. — Freya Stark. *East is West.* 1947. — Lawrence Palmer Briggs. *The Ancient Khmer Empire.* 1951. — Michael Edwards. *The Orchid House.* 1960. Inscribed "Jacqueline Kennedy" on flyleaf. — Kashmir. *Garden of the Himalayas.* Introduction by Raghubir Singh. Inscribed by Singh and dated October 19, 1983. — Marc Riboud. *Capital of Heaven.* 1990. Inscribed by the author "For Jackie, who has always been on the top of CAPITAL OF HEAVEN. I am expecting more summit meetings. With affection." — and others.

$300–500

1033 **Children's Books**

Group of 9 volumes, various sizes. Publisher's cloth. Various places, various dates.

Earl Schenck Miers. *The Story of John F. Kennedy.* 1964. — Flora Strousse. *John Fitzgerald Kennedy: Man of Courage.* 1964. — Lucy Post Frisbee. *John F. Kennedy, Young Statesman.* 1964. — Iris Vinton. *The Story of President Kennedy.* 1966. — Bruce Lee. *Boys' Life of John F. Kennedy.* 1967. — Emery Kelen. *Stamps Tell the Story of John F. Kennedy.* 1968. — and others.

$200–300

1034 **Children's Books**

Group of 13 volumes, various sizes. Publisher's cloth. Various places, various dates.

Earl Schenck Miers. *The Story of John F. Kennedy.* 1964. — Flora Strousse. *John Fitzgerald Kennedy: Man of Courage.* 1964. — Lucy Post Frisbee. *John F. Kennedy, Young Statesman.* 1964. — Robert N. Webb. *The Living JFK.* 1964. — Gene Schoor. *Young John Kennedy.* 1963. — James Playsted Wood. *The Life and Words of John F. Kennedy.* 1964. — and others.

$250–350

1035 **Children's Books on John F. Kennedy**

Group of 10 volumes, various sizes. Publisher's cloth. Various places, various dates.

Martha & Charles Schapp. *Let's Find Out About John Fitzgerald Kennedy.* 1966. — Iris Vinton. *The Story of President Kennedy.* 1966. — Gene Schoor. *Young John Kennedy.* 1963. — James Playsted Wood. *The Life and Words of John F. Kennedy.* 1964. — J. E. Levine. *Young Man in the White House.* 1964. — John F. Kennedy. *Profiles in Courage: Young Readers Memorial Edition,* intro. Robert F. Kennedy. 1964. — and others.

$200–300

1036 **Children's Books on John F. Kennedy**

Group of 8 volumes, various sizes. Publisher's cloth. Various places, various dates.

Iris Vinton. *The Story of President Kennedy*. 1966. — J. E. Levine. *Young Man in the White House*. 1964. — Patricia Miles Martin. *John Fitzgerald Kennedy*. 1964. — Jacqueline Duhème. *John F. Kennedy: A Book of Paintings*. — John F. Kennedy. *Profiles in Courage: Young Readers Memorial Edition*, intro. Robert F. Kennedy. 1964. — and others.

$200–300

1037 **Children's Books on John F. Kennedy**

Group of 13 volumes, various sizes. Publisher's cloth. Various places, various dates.

Earl Schenck Miers. *The Story of John F. Kennedy*. 1964. — Emery Kelen. *Stamps Tell the Story of John F. Kennedy*. 1968. — Robert N. Webb. *The Living JFK*. 1964. — James Playsted Wood. *The Life and Words of John F. Kennedy*. 1964. — and others.

$250–350

1038 **Children's Books on John F. Kennedy**

Group of 18 volumes, various sizes. Publisher's cloth. Various places, various dates.

Iris Vinton. *The Story of President Kennedy*. 1966. — Flora Strousse. *John Fitzgerald Kennedy: Man of Courage*. 1964. — Lucy Post Frisbee. *John F. Kennedy, Young Statesman*. 1964. — Bruce Lee. *Boys' Life of John F. Kennedy*. 1967. — John F. Kennedy. *Profiles in Courage: Young Readers Memorial Edition*, intro. Robert F. Kennedy. 1964. — *The First Book Edition of John F. Kennedy's Inaugural Address*. 1964. — Charles P. Graves. *John F. Kennedy*. 1965. — and others.

$300–500

1039 **Kennedy, John F.**

A group of 19 volumes, various sizes. Several illustrated. Various publisher's cloth or paper. Various places and dates.

Robert J. Donovan. *PT 109: John F. Kennedy in World War II*. 1960. — Arthur M. Schlesinger Jr. *A Thousand Days: John F. Kennedy in the White House*. 1965. — Theodore C. Sorensen. *Kennedy*. 1965. —Paul B. Fay Jr. *The Pleasure of his Company*. 1966. — Evelyn Lincoln. *My Twelve Year with John F. Kennedy*. 1966. — and other personal memoirs.

$300–500

1040 **Read, Thomas Buchanan.** Sheridan's Ride. *N. p., n. d.*

Autograph manuscript fair copy, 2 1/2 pages in a neat script, inlaid into a larger sheet (11 ⅜ x 9 in.) Bound with an mounted oval portrait photograph of Read, signed on the mount, "My Dear Laura Thompson, from T. Buchanan Read," and a steel engraved portrait of Sheridan. Brown morocco by C. Walters, gilt with pink silk liners. With a note on its provenance laid in.

$300–500

1041 **Recueil d'Estampes representant les differents evénemens de la guerre qui a procuré l'indépendance aux Etats Unis de l'Amérique.** *Paris: Nicolas Ponce, [1784]*

(7½ x 8 in.). Engraved throughout, 15 (of 16) plates by Ponce after William, Godefroy and others, including 1 (of 2) maps. Green and beige morocco, by "Dorothy Barrett Moulton, 1941."

$300–500

1042 **Kennedy, John F.**

A group of 25 volumes, various sizes. Many illustrated. Publisher's cloth or paper. Various places and dates.

Harry Golden. *Mr. Kennedy and the Negroes*. 1964. Presentation copy to Mrs. Kennedy from the author. — Seymour Harris. *Economics of the Kennedy Years*. 1964. — William Manchester. *Portrait of a President*. 1967. — Brother Flavius. *In Virtue's Cause: A Story of John F. Kennedy*. 1967. Signed by the author. — Jacques Lowe. *JFK Remembered*. 1993. — and others.

$500–700

1043 **Kennedy, John F.**

A group of 20 volumes (including several duplicates) by or about John F. Kennedy. Chiefly publisher's cloth and wrappers. Varying sizes and conditions.

John F. Kennedy. *To Turn the Tide*. 1964. — Idem. *The Burden and the Glory*. 1964. — Idem. *The Place of the Artist in Society*. 1964. — Idem. *Profiles in Courage*. Memorial Edition. 1964. — Paul B. Fay, Jr. *The Pleasure of His Company*. 1966. — Anne H. Lincoln. *The Kennedy White House Parties*. 1967. — and others.

$300–500

1044 **Kennedy, John F.**

A group of 15 volumes (including several duplicates) by or about John F. Kennedy. Chiefly publisher's cloth and wrappers. Varying sizes and conditions.

Robert J. Donovan. *PT–109: John F. Kennedy in World War II*. 1960. — James MacGregor Burns. *John Kennedy: A Political Profile*. 1961. — John F. Kennedy. *The Place of the Artist in Society*. 1964. — Ram Singh and M. K. Holdar. *Kennedy through Indian Eyes*. 1964. — Paul B. Fay, Jr. *The Pleasure of His Company*. 1966. — Anne Lincoln. *The Kennedy White House Parties*. 1967. — and others.

$250–350

1045 **Kennedy, John F.**

A group of 12 volumes (including one duplicate) by and about John F. Kennedy. Chiefly publisher's cloth and wrappers. Varying sizes and conditions.

James MacGregor Burns. *John Kennedy: A Political Profile*. 1961. — John F. Kennedy. *To Turn the Tide*. 1964. — Idem. *Profiles in Courage*. Memorial Edition. 1964. — Anne H. Lincoln. *The Kennedy White House Parties*. 1967. — Clare Barnes, Jr. *John F. Kennedy: Scrimshaw Collector*. 1969. — and others.

$250–350

1046 **Kennedy, John F.**

A group of 12 volumes (including several duplicates) by or about John F. Kennedy. Chiefly publisher's cloth and wrappers. Varying sizes and conditions.

John F. Kennedy. *Profiles in Courage*. Memorial Edition. 1964. — Jim Bishop. *A Day in the Life of President Kennedy*. 1964. — Arthur M. Schlesinger, Jr. *A Thousand Days*. 1965. — Clare Barnes, Jr. *John F. Kennedy: Scrimshaw Collector*. 1969. — and others.

$250–350

1047 **Kennedy, John F.**

A group of 14 volumes (including one duplicate) by or about John F. Kennedy. Chiefly publisher's cloth and wrappers. Varying sizes and conditions.

Jacques Lowe. *Portrait: The Emergence of John F. Kennedy*. 1961. — John F. Kennedy. *The Burden and the Glory*. 1964. — Jim Bishop. *A Day in the Life of President Kennedy*. 1964. — Evelyn Lincoln. *My Twelve Years with John F. Kennedy*. 1966. — *J. F. K. Words to Remember*. Foreword by Robert F. Kennedy. 1967. — and others.

$250–350

1048 **Kennedy, John F.**

A group of 12 volumes (including one duplicate) by or about John F. Kennedy. Chiefly publisher's cloth. Varying sizes and conditions.

John F. Kennedy. *The Strategy of Peace*. 1960. — Idem. *The Burden and the Glory*. 1964. — Idem. *The Place of the Artist in Society*. 1964. — Arthur M. Schlesinger, Jr. *A Thousand Days*. 1965. — J. Julius Fanta. *Sailing with President Kennedy*. 1968. — and others.

$250–350

1049 **Kennedy, John F.**

A group of 12 volumes (including several duplicates) by or about John F. Kennedy. Chiefly publisher's cloth and wrappers. Varying sizes and conditions.

John F. Kennedy. *The Strategy of Peace*. 1960. — Idem. *Why England Slept*. 1961. — John F. Kennedy. *Profiles in Courage*. Memorial Edition. 1964. — Paul B. Fay, Jr. *The Pleasure of His Company*. 1966. — J. Julius Fanta. *Sailing with President Kennedy*. 1968. — and others.

$250–350

1050 **Kennedy, John F.**

A group of 11 volumes (including one duplicate) by or about John F. Kennedy. Chiefly publisher's cloth and wrappers. Varying sizes and conditions.

John F. Kennedy. *Why England Slept*. 1961. — Idem. *To Turn the Tide*. 1962. — Idem. America the Beautiful in the Words of John F. Kennedy (ed. Michael Dineen). 1964. — Anne H. Lincoln. *The Kennedy White House Parties*. 1967. — Clare Barnes, Jr. *John F. Kennedy: Scrimshaw Collector*. 1969. — and others.

$250–350

1051 **Kennedy, Robert F.**

A group of 23 volumes (including several duplicates) and one broadside by or about Robert F. Kennedy. Chiefly publisher's cloth and wrappers. Varying sizes and conditions.

Robert F. Kennedy. *The Pursuit of Justice*. 1964. — Gerald Gardner. *Robert Kennedy in New York*. 1965. — Robert F. Kennedy. *To Seek a Newer World*. 1967. — Idem. *The Quotable Robert F. Kennedy* (ed. Sue G. Hall). 1967. — Dick Schaap. *R. F. K.* 1967. — Victor Lasky. *Robert F. Kennedy: The Myth and the Man*. 1968. — Edward M. Kennedy. [Eulogy delivered at St. Patrick's Cathedral, New York, 8 June 1968]. [N.d.] Broadside. — Robert F. Kennedy. *Thirteen Days: A Memoir of the Cuban Missile Crisis*. 1969. — William van den Heuvel and Milton Gwirtzman. *On His Own: R.F.K. 1964–68*. 1970. — and others.

$400–600

1052 **Onassis, Jacqueline Kennedy**

Group of approximately 80 volumes, including duplicates, of books edited or with contributions by Mrs. Onassis; various sizes. Publisher's cloth. Various places, various dates.

Jacqueline Onassis. *In the Russian Style*. 1976. — Jacqueline and Lee Bouvier. *One Special Summer*. 1974. — Deborah Turbeville & Louis Auchincloss. *Unseen Versailles*. 1981. — Deborah Nevins. *Grand Central Terminal*. 1982. — *The Fire Bird and Other Russian Fairy Tales*. 1978. — and others.

$600–900

1053 **White House Guides**

A large group of various editions, with successive revisions, of *The White House: An Historic Guide* (first published in the summer of 1962 at the request of the First Lady, Jacqueline Kennedy). Approximately 40 copies from the Kennedy years, 7 from Johnson's administration and 1 from Nixon's.

Together approximately 48 volumes, variously publisher's cloth and paper.

$300–500

1054 **Hunt, Richard M.**

Designs for the Gateways of the Southern Entrances to the Central Park. *New York: D. Van Nostrand, 1866*

(11 ⅞ x 9¼ in.). Title-page printed in red and black, 5 tinted lithographed views, 4 lithographed plans; some browning and offsetting. Publisher's brown cloth gilt, slate-brown endpapers; soiled, worn.

Presentation copy, inscribed and signed by the author on the front flyleaf: "Baron Stockel, with the compliments of R. M. Hunt." The preservation and restoration of Central Park was one of the many New York City projects to which Mrs. Onassis devoted her time. Loosely inserted is a handcolored engraved map of "New-York City, County, and Vicinity" removed from an 1864 Valentine's *Manual of New York City*.

$500–700

1055 **New York City**

Group of 4 volumes, various sizes. Publisher's cloth, boards, or wrappers. Various places, various dates.

Frederick Van Wyck. *Recollections of an Old New Yorker*. 1932. INSCRIBED: "For Jackie, Some words from the older folks – Love, Ruth, Christmas 1977." — Henry Hope Reed. *The New York Public Library*. 1986. INSCRIBED: "To Mrs. Onassis with admiration, Gregorian." — and 2 others.

$200–300

1056 **French Literature**

Group of 6 volumes, various sizes. Publisher's wrappers. Various places, various dates.

André Malraux. *Préface à Sumer*. 1960. No. 6 of 50 copies, INSCRIBED by Malraux: "Vous trouverez des petites déesses ... La vôtre est la XIV-B; qu'elle vous apporte les amitiés da la reine Subad ...". — Prince de Ligne. *Lettres à la Marquise de Coigny*. 1986. Signed "Jacqueline Kennedy Onassis." — Guillaume Apollinaire. *Chroniques d'art*. 1961. INSCRIBED to Jacqueline Kennedy "at the suggestion of Mr. Kenneth Galbraith ..." by the editor, L. C. Breunig. — Guillaume Apollinaire. *Les peintres cubistes*. 1965. INSCRIBED to Jacqueline Kennedy by the editor, L. C. Breunig. — Marx-Antoine Crespi. *Derrière l'avenir*. 1992. INSCRIBED: "Pour Jacqueline à qui je dois des souvenirs aussi précieux que la vie ..." — Philip Roth. *Tromperie*. 1994. INSCRIBED: "March 1994. For Jackie—stay well. Philip."

$500–700

1057 **French Literature**

Group of 11 volumes, various sizes. Most in publisher's wrappers. Various places, various dates.

Pierre Loti. *Au Maroc*. 1925. Signed "Jacqueline Kennedy." — Saint-John Perse. [*Poèmes*]. 1956. Signed "Jacqueline Kennedy from Alexis Leger [=Saint-John Perse] 1967." Postcard inserted to Mrs. Kennedy from Cecile de Rothschild. — André Malraux. *Antimémoires*. 1967. Signed "Jacqueline Kennedy". — and 8 volumes with the bookplate of Jacqueline Bouvier Kennedy.

$1,000–1,500

1058 **French Literature**

Group of 13 volumes, various sizes. Most in publisher's cloth or wrappers. Various places, various dates.

Charles Baudelaire. *Théophile Gautier*. 1859. Presentation inscription from Baudelaire to M. Auguste Vacquerie, label of Docteur André Chauveau; crushed brown morocco janséniste, violet kid doublures, by Huser, wrappers bound in; slipcase. — Mina Moore. *Bernard Shaw et la France*. 1933. Inscribed by the author to unknown recipient, 1934; then "For Jacqueline 27/2/52" and, in Mrs. Onassis's hand, "from Father Leonard, J." — Princesse Bibesco. *La vie d'une amitié*. 1951. Signed "J. Leonard May 1951" and inscribed by him: "For Jacqueline 27/2/52." — and 10 other volumes, most with the bookplate of Jacqueline Bouvier Kennedy.

$800–1,200

1059 **French Literature**

Group of 10 volumes, various sizes, in publisher's cloth or wrappers. Various places, various dates.

Walter G. Langlois. *André Malraux: The Indochina Adventure*. 1966. Signed "Jacqueline Kennedy." — and 9 volumes with the bookplate of Jacqueline Bouvier Kennedy.

$400–600

1060 **French Literature**

Group of 12 volumes, various sizes. Most in publisher's cloth, several with dust-jackets. Various places, various dates.

Edna Nixon. *Voltaire and the Calas Case*. 1961. INSCRIBED by Randolph Churchill: "Jacqueline from Randolph, Christmas, 1961—I think the President will enjoy this. R." — Jacques Casanova de Seingalt. *Histoire de ma vie*. 2 vols. (of 3), 1960. INSCRIBED: "For Jackie, who is also interested in the 18th century, & knows more about it than the giver ... Christmas, 1960." — and 9 other volumes, most with bookplate of Jacqueline Bouvier Kennedy.

$500–700

1061 **Greek Literature**

Group of 6 volumes, various sizes. Publisher's cloth or wrappers. Various places, various dates.

George Seferis. *Poems*. 1961. INSCRIBED: "To Mrs. Jacqueline B. Kennedy with my devoted admiration. George Seferis. Athens. 4.1.'64." — Jan Kott. *The Eating of the Gods*. 1973. INSCRIBED: "For Jackie With my love from Lee, Dec. 25th 1973." — Kimon Friar. *The Spiritual Odyssey of Nikos Kazantzakis*. 1979. INSCRIBED: "For Jacqueline Onassis, That in this book she may embark on a spiritual odyssey of her own. A memento in friendship ..." — and 3 other works, presented to or with the bookplate of Jacqueline Bouvier Kennedy.

$500–800

1062 **French History**

Group of 6 volumes, various sizes, most in publisher's cloth. Various places, various dates.

D. Bingham. *The Marriages of the Bourbons*. 2 vols., 1890. INSCRIBED: "For Jackie, to add to your shelf of little histories, love, Ruth, Christmas '77." — and 4 other volumes, one with the bookplate of Jacqueline Bouvier Kennedy.

$300–500

1063 **English Culture**

Group of 7 volumes, various sizes, most illustrated. Publisher's cloth , 5 with dust-jackets. Various places, various dates.

Wilmarth Lewis. *Collector's Progress*. 1951. INSCRIBED: "To Jackie, With every good wish, from U[ncle] L[efty]. September 1956." — Wilmarth Lewis. *Horace Walpole*. 1960. INSCRIBED: "To Jackie, with love, from Uncle Lefty." — and 5 other volumes, most with the bookplate of Jacqueline Bouvier Kennedy.

$300–500

1064 **Touré, Sékou**

L'Action politique du P. D. G. en faveur de l'émancipation de la jeunesse guinénne. *[1962].*

Red cloth.

A PRESENTATION FROM PRESIDENT TO PRESIDENT. Touré, then president of Guinea, inscribed the book "A Monsieur le président KENNEDY avec l'assurance de mes sentiments respectueux et de notre volonté de sincère et étroite coopération, ce 9–10–62."

$300–500

1065 **Travel**

Group of 4 volumes, various sizes, all INSCRIBED to Mrs. Onassis. Publisher's cloth, with dust-jackets. Various places, various dates.

John F. Donovan. *The Pagoda and the Cross: the Life of Bishop Ford of Maryknoll.* 1967. "To Mrs. John F. Kennedy with ... prayerful good wishes ..." — Peter Mathiessen. *Under the Mountain Wall.* 1962. "For Jackie Kennedy, with all best wishes, Peter M., Nov. 16, 1962." — and 2 others.

$300–500

1066 **Mexico**

Group of 6 volumes, inscribed by Mrs. Onassis or with her bookplate, one presented to her. Most illustrated. Mostly publisher's cloth. Various places, various dates.

Life in Mexico. 2 vols., Boston, 1843. Signed in both volumes "Jacqueline Kennedy, Mexico City, June 30, 1962." — Verna Cook Shipway & Warren Shipway. *Mexican Interiors.* 1965. Signed "Jacqueline Kennedy, Yucatan 1968." — and 4 others.

$300–500

1067 **Coward, Noel**

Present Indicative. *New York, 1937.*

Green cloth, frontispiece portrait. Boldly signed in pencil on flyleaf "Jacqueline Bouvier," with paraph.

$200–300

1068 **Onassis, Jacqueline Kennedy**

Group of approximately 20 volumes, various sizes, about the Bouvier family or Mrs. Onassis, or with contributions by her. Many illustrated. Publisher's cloth, boards, or wrappers. Various places, various dates.

[Bouvier family]. *Our Forbears.* 1940. — *Vassarion 1951* (with picture of Jacqueline Bouvier as former member of the class of 1951, p. 163). — Elisabeth della Santa. *Florilège de la famille Bouvier.* 1987. — Robert T. Harding & A. L. Holmes. *Jacqueline Kennedy: A Woman for the World.* 1966. — Kay Hale, ed. *The Grand Original: Portraits of Randolph Churchill by his friends.* 1971 (including a reminiscence by Mrs. Onassis). — and others.

$400–600

1069 **Kennedy Family**

Group of 9 volumes, various sizes, relating to the history of the Kennedy family. Most publisher's cloth. Various places, various dates.

Richard J.Whalen. *The Founding Father: The Story of Joseph P. Kennedy.* 1964. — Maud Shaw. *White House Nanny.* 1966. — Gail Cameron. *Rose: A Biography of Rose Fitzgerald Kennedy.* 1971. — and 6 others.

$200–300

1070 **White House Guides**

A large group of various editions, with successive revisions, of *The White House: An Historic Guide* (first published in the summer of 1962 at the request of the First Lady, Jacqueline Kennedy). Approximately 40 copies from the Kennedy years, 7 from Johnson's administration and 1 from Nixon's.

Together approximately 48 volumes, variously publisher's cloth and paper.

$300–500

1071 **Russia**

A group of 8 volumes, mostly folio. Illustrated. Various places and dates. A few books printed in Cyrillic. Most with inscriptions.

Suzanne Massie. *The Land of the Firebird.* 1980. INSCRIBED: "For Jacqueline Onassis—who started me on the road which led to this book ... Suzanne Massie." — Mikhail Iroshnikow and others. *The Sunset of the Romanov Dynasty.* 1992. INSCRIBED: "To Jacqueline Kennedy with admiration and a deep cordial devotion from Arseny. June 2, 1993, St. Petersburg." — and others.

$200–300

1072 **Women and Women Authors**

A fine group of 9 volumes, mostly 8vo. Some illustrated. Various publisher's cloth or paper. Various sizes and dates. Each with bookplate or signature or as below.

Mrs. Meer Hassam Ali. *Observations on the Mussulmauns of India.* 1917. Bookseller's label laid-in with "Mrs. J. Onassis" label. — E.L. Tottenham. *Highnesses of Hindostan.* (ca. 1934). Initialed in pencil, "J.K.O. '84" with bookseller's slip laid-in. — Philip Ziegler. *The Duchess of Dino.* 1962. Bookplate. — Ihara Saikaku. *The Life of an Amorous Woman and other Writings.* 1963. Bookplate. — Isak Dinesen. *The Life and Destiny of Isak Dinesen.* 1970. 2 copies (one without bookplate). — and others.

$500–700

1073 **Women Authors**

A group of 8 works in 13 volumes, all 8vo. Publisher's cloth, 2 in paperback. Various places and dates. Mostly with presentations or bookplate.

Edith de Born. *The House in Vienna.* 1957. — *Fielding Castle.* 1960. Bookplates. — Penelope Gilliatt. *A State of Change.* 1968. Signed by the author, "For Jackie– I am so glad you came today, April 7th 1968." — Han Suyin. [Autobiography] *Till Morning Comes.* 1982. Signed, "To Jacqueline Onassis a very wonderful and courageous woman ... Feb. 23/'87." — Han Suyin. [Autobiography] 5 volumes (4 of 5, two copies of *Birdless Summer).* — Anna Akhmatova. *The Complete Poems.* 1989–1990. 2 volumes. With presentation to Jacqueline Onassis from the publishers.— Edna O'Brien. *House of Splendid Isolation.* 1994. Inscribed, "For Jackie with my love and thoughts, always, Edna."

$600–800

1074 **Poetry**

A group of 12 volumes, mostly 8vo. A few are illustrated. Publisher's cloth or paper. Various places and dates. Most with some form of previous Jacqueline Kennedy Onassis ownership.

Dante Gabriel Rossetti. *The Poems.* 1921. Maroon morocco, ex-libris of Cortlandt Field Bishop. — John Hadfield. *A Book of Beauty.* 1952. — John Hadfield. *A Book of Delights.* 1955. Both inscribed by Joseph Leonard, also with JBK bookplates. — William Blake. *Selected Poetry and Prose of William Blake.* 1952. — Edna O'Brien. *On the Bone.* 1989. Inscribed, "For Jackie with much love E.O.B. Sept. '89." — and 7 others.

$600–800

1075 **American Women**

A group of 8 volumes, mostly 8vo. A few illustrated. Publisher's cloth. Various places and dates. Most with Jacqueline Bouvier Kennedy or Onassis bookplates, or as noted below.

Jeanne L. Noble. *The Negro Woman's College Education.* 1956. "Inscribed and presented to Mr. and Mrs. John Kennedy … Jeanne Noble, October 1960." — Betty Friedan. *The Feminine Mystique.* 1963. JBK bookplate. — Dorothy Rodgers. *My Favorite Things.* 1964. Inscribed, "For Jacqueline Kennedy with all good wishes from Dorothy Rodgers." — and 5 others.

$700–1,000

1076 **English Literature**

A group of 14 volumes, various sizes mostly 8vo. A few illustrated. Publisher's cloth or paper. Various places and dates. Most with bookplate or signed.

Joseph Conrad. *A Conrad Argosy.* 1942. Presentation to, Dear Jackie, Christmas '77 … Peter B." — D.H. Lawrence. *The Rainbow.* 1943. Signed, "Jacqueline Kennedy from Lionel Trilling after Nobel dinner April-May 1962." — Ronald Firbank. *The New Rythum and Other Pieces.* 1962. Signed, "Jacqueline Kennedy from Eve Symington June 1963," on the front free endpaper. — Joseph Roth. *The Radetzky March.* 1983. Signed, "Jacqueline Kennedy Onassis." — and 10 others.

$400–600

1077 **English Literature, General**

A group of 15 volumes, various sizes, mostly 8vo. Some with illustrations. Publisher's cloth or paper. Various places or dates. Most with Jacqueline Bouvier Kennedy bookplates or inscription.

Peter Quennell. *Four Portraits: Studies of the Eighteenth Century.* 1946. Signed, "Jacqueline Kennedy." — G.B. Shaw. *To a Young Actress.* 1960. Bookplate. — Max Beerbohm. *The Incomparable Max.* 1962. Presentation, "To Dearest Jacqueline … from her old friend J [oseph] L [eonard]. 28 July 1962." — and 12 others.

$500–700

1078 **English Literature**

A group of 12 volumes, various sizes. A few illustrated. Publisher's cloth or paper. Various places and dates.

William Makepeace Thackeray. *The Rose and the Ring* (facsimile, ed. Gordon N. Ray) 1947. With slipcase. Inscribed, "For Jackie—from Charles [Ryskamp], who also 'particularly loves' this manuscript 16.1.78." — Laura Lovat. *Maurice Baring a post-script.* 1948. Bookplate and inscription from Joseph Leonard. — James Elroy Flecker. *Hassan: The Story of Hassan.* 1923. Limited edition. Bookplate. — William Hickey. *The Prodigal Rake.* 1962. Bookplate. — and 7 others.

$300–500

1079 **American Literature**

A group of 14 volumes, mostly 8vo. Publisher's cloth. Various places and dates. Most with Jacqueline Bouvier Kennedy bookplate or inscription.

Guy Endore. *The King of Paris.* 1956. Bookplate. — John Updike. *Pidgeon Feathers and other Stories.* 1962. Bookplate. — Lillian Hellman. *Six Plays.* 1965. Inscribed on the half title, "Who sends them to Jackie with affection, Lillian, August 1965." — Ellen Gilchrist. *Victory over Japan.* 1984. Signed by the author. — Joanna Scott. *Various Antidotes.* 1994. Inscribed, "To Jacqueline Kennedy Onassis with admiration and gratitude, Joanna Scott." — and 9 others.

$600–800

1080 **Cage, John and Susan Barron.**

Another Song. *New York: Callaway Editions, 1981*

(8 x 7 in.) Mounted photographs by Susan Barron. Letterpress in sepia. Publisher's white paper covers by Carol Joyce, with reproduction of John Cage score on upper cover, dark endpapers with silkscreen printed Cage score. Brown silk folding box with window.

A COLLABORATION BETWEEN JOHN CAGE AND LANDSCAPE PHOTOGRAPHER SUSAN BARRON, SIGNED BY BOTH. A superb production printed by the Stinehour Press and the third book published by Nicholas Callaway. Copy number 39 of 53 with an autograph letter by the photographer explaining the numbering of the edition.

$800–1,200

1081 **Literature and Criticism**

A group of 5 volumes, all 8vo or smaller. Publisher's cloth, all but one in dust jacket. Mostly New York, various dates. All inscribed to Jacqueline Kennedy.

Louis Auchincloss. *Reflections of a Jacobite.* 1961. Inscribed, "Dear Jackie, so pleased that you should want this least selling but favorite of mine … Louis A." — Irwin Shaw. *Selected Short Stories.* 1961. Inscribed, "To Jacqueline Kennedy to be read when the supply of Norman Mailer runs out—with thanks, Irwin Shaw." — Norman Podhoretz. *Doings and Undoings: The Fifties and After in American Writing.* 1964. Inscribed, "To Jackie– These, at least, are lighter than the rocks in Central Park and not nearly so numerous. Fondly, Norman." — F.D. Reeve. *Robert Frost in Russia.* 1964. Inscribed, "For Jacqueline Kennedy close to this trip in every sense from Franklin Reeve, Middletown, 1964." — Lionel Trilling. *Beyond Culture: Essays on Literature and Learning.* 1965. Inscribed, "For Jacqueline Kennedy with friendly greetings, Lionel Trilling."

$500–700

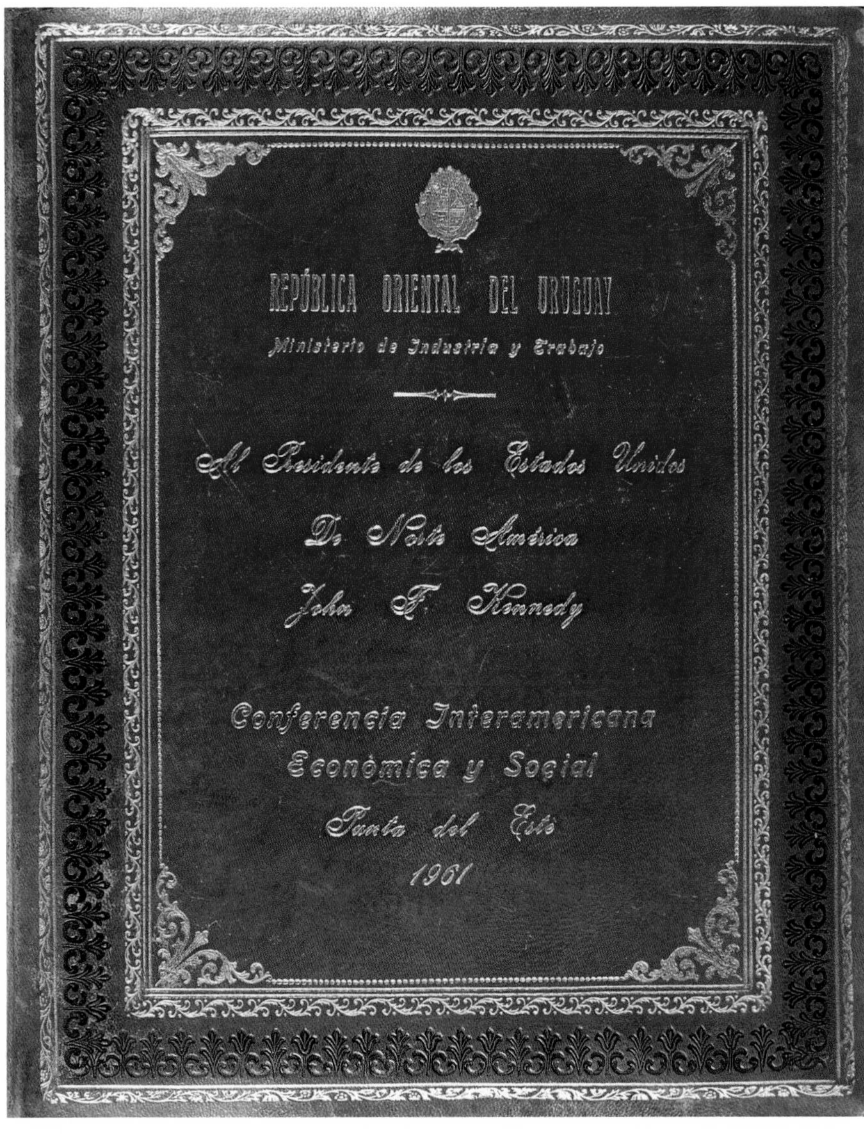

1085

1082 **Literature and Criticism**

A group of 11 volumes, various sizes. Some with illustrations. Publisher's cloth and paper. Various places and dates. Most with bookplate, signature or initials of Jacqueline Kennedy Onassis.

Nell Dorr. *Mother and Child.* 1961. Inscribed, "To Jacqueline Kennedy who speaks to the work in the common language of mother and child … Nell Dorr … 1961." — Roger Shattuck. *The Innocent Eye.* 1984. Signed, "Jacqueline Kennedy Onassis." — *Paris Review* (1963–1964). 2 volumes. Red calf, with initials JK gilt on the spine. — Arnold Samuelson. *With Hemingway: A Year in Key West and Cuba.* 1984. Initialed, "J.K.O." — and 6 others.

$400–600

1083 **History and Politics, Miscellaneous**

A group of 20 volumes, various sizes, mostly 8vo. A few with illustrations. Various publisher's cloth bindings, mostly with dust jackets. Various places and dates.

Newton Minow. *Equal Time.* 1964. Inscribed, dedication copy to President John F. Kennedy, "For Mrs. John F. Kennedy - I was and am dedicated to the President, and so is this book. We send you warmest wishes always, Newt & Jo Minow, December 1964." — Konrad Adenauer. *Memoirs, 1945-53.* 1964. — Don Cook. *Ten Men and History.* 1981. — Jacob Burckhardt. *The Civilization of the Renaissance in Italy.* 1954. — Polly Schoyer Brooks and Nancy Zinsser Walworth. *The World Awakes: The Renaissance in western Europe.* 1962. — Peter Quennell, ed. *Affairs of the Mind: The Salon in Europe and America.* 1980. — and 14 others.

$400–600

1084 **Brookshaw, George**

A New Treatise on Flower Painting, or, Every Lady her Own Drawing Master. *London: Printed for Longman et al., 1816*

(11⅛ x 9 in.) Color printed frontispiece and engraved plates by Brookshaw, (12 in 4 states), finished by hand. Contemporary straight-grain green morocco, gilt roll-tooled frame, spine gilt, gilt edges, marbled endpapers; upper cover detached.

$400–600

1085 **Uruguay, Ministry of Industry and Work**

Conferencia Interamericana Economica y Social. *Punta del Este, 1961*

(11 x 9 in.) Calf post binder, gilt with the seal of Uruguay and the presentation to the President, with calf leaves, felt backed; hinges weak, some drying. With 22 postage stamps tipped in; one is loose.

A FINE PRESENTATION BINDING, GILT-STAMPED: "AL PRESIDENTE DE LOS ESTADOS UNIDOS DE NORTE AMÉRICA JOHN F. KENNEDY." The stamp album contains a set of postage stamps for 1961, of different denominations.

$500–700

1086 **White House Guides**

A large group of various editions, with successive revisions, of *The White House: An Historic Guide* (first published in the summer of 1962 at the request of the First Lady, Jacqueline Kennedy). Approximately 40 copies from the Kennedy years, 7 from Johnson's administration and 1 from Nixon's.

Together approximately 48 volumes, variously publisher's cloth and paper.

$300–500

1087 **American Architecture**

Group of 11 volumes, various sizes. Illustrated. Publisher's cloth, some with dustjackets. Various places, various dates.

Carter Wiseman. *I. M. Pei: A Profile in American Architecture*. 1990. Inscribed by Pei "To Jackie, with affection." — Bruno Suner. *Ieoh Ming Pei*. 1988. Inscribed by Pei "To Jackie: with affectionate regards." — Parke Rouse, Jr. *Living by Design: Leslie Cheek and the Arts*. 1985. Inscribed by Cheek "for Jacqueline K. Onassis with admiration and appreciation." — Philip Johnson and Mark Wigley. *Deconstructivist Architecture*.1988. Inscribed by Johnson "To Jackie, Read *only* my introduction." — Marie Beale. *Decatur House and Its Inhabitants*. 1954. Bookplate of Jacqueline Bouvier Kennedy. — Philip Johnson. *Architecture 1949-1965*. 1966. Inscribed by author "For Jackie Kennedy." — Eleanor Raymond. *Early Domestic Architecture of Pennsylvania*. Signed "Jacqueline Kennedy." — Mary Farland. *In the Shadow of the Blue Ridge*. 1978. Signed "J.K.O." — *Roosevelt Campobello International Park*. [n. d.]. Inscribed by Armand Hammer "To Mrs. John F. Kennedy" and by Jimmy Roosevelt "And with the affectionate best of one of the family *not* born at Campobello!" — and 2 other volumes inscribed to Mrs. Kennedy.

$700–900

1088 **Architecture and Landscape Design**

Group of 12 volumes, various sizes. Illustrated. Publisher's cloth or wrappers, some with dust-jackets. Various places, various dates.

Bates Lowry. *Renaissance Architecture*. 1965. — Inscribed "For Mrs. John Kennedy with sincere thanks for all your help to CRIA." — *The Lacquer Pavilion at Suan Pakkad Palace*. 1960. Inscribed by Princess Chumbhot of Nagara Svarga "For Mrs. Jacqueline Kennedy as a momento of her visit to the Suan Pakkad Colllection of Ancient Thai Art." — Anghelen Phillips. *Gingerbread Houses: Haiti's Endangered Species*. 1975. Signed by the author. — C. P.C. Curran. *Dublin Decorative Plasterwork*. 1967. Inscribed by author "To an overseas lover of Ireland and its culture." — R. Allen Brown. *English Medieval Castles*. 1954. Bookplate of Jacqueline Bouvier Kennedy. — *Chateaux de Bretagne*. 1948. Bookplate of Jacqueline Bouvier Kennedy. — *Chateaux de Bourgogne*.1948. Bookplate of Jacqueline Bouvier Kennedy. — Caroline Constant. *The Palladio Guide*. 1985. Signed "JKO from Harold Adams." — John Martin Robinson. *Temples of Delight*. 1990. Inscribed "for J. from W.H. L." — and 3 others.

$400–600

1089 **Russian Literature**

A group of 10 works in 14 volumes, in translation. Some illustrated. Publisher's cloth and wrappers. Varying sizes and conditions.

Alexander Pushkin. *Boris Godonov*. 1927. Limited edition. Copy 1 of 35 on Japon impérial, with one original watercolor and two suites of the plates in two states; slipcase. — Alexander Pushkin. *Eugene Onegin* (trans. Vladimir Nabokov). 4 vols. 1964. — Leo Tolstoy. *Anna Karenina*. 1992. — and 7 others.

$300–500

1090 **Abelard and Heloise**

Lettres d'Héloise et d'Abaillard. *Paris: L'Imprimerie de Didot le Jeune, l'An quatrième [1796]*

3 vols. (14¼ x 10½ in., *uncut*). 8 engraved plates after Moreau le Jeune by LeMire, Langlois le jeune, and others, half-titles in all three volumes; moderate foxing, chiefly marginal. Contemporary straight-grained red morocco over orange paper boards.

$600–800

1091 **Theatre**

Group of 4 volumes, various sizes. All but one illustrated. Publisher's cloth and one leather album. Various places Various dates.

Theater Palais Lichtenstein. 1888. Album of *carte-de-visite* photographs, with an autograph letter from Anna Farova presenting the volume to Mrs. Onassis. — Tamara Karsavina. *Theatre Street*. 1931. — A. Manera. *Etalages Parisiens*. 1949. Bookplate of Jacqueline Bouvier Kennedy. — Walter Rigdon. *The Biographical Encyclopedia & Who's Who of the American Theatre*. 1966. Binding gilt stamped "Jacqueline Kennedy" and inscribed by author "With admiration and respect."

$300–500

1092 **Children's Literature**

A group of 14 titles in 17 volumes, of which 2 are presentation copies from the illustrators to Jacqueline Kennedy Onassis. Publisher's cloth and wrappers. Illustrated. Varying sizes and conditions.

Hergé. *Les Aventures de Tintin*: (1) *Le lotus bleu*; (2) *L'ile noire*; (3) *Le secret de la licorne*. 1946-1947. — Virginia Lee Burton. *Life Story*. 1962. Alexander Pushkin. *Boris Godonov*. 1982. — Idem. *The Golden Cockerel*. 1990. 4 copies. — Hans Christian Andersen. *The Nightingale*. 1985. Inscribed by the illustrator Beni Montresor "For Jackie from Beni, 1985." — *The Twelve Days of Christmas*. 1990. Inscribed by the illustrator Ilse Plum to Jacqueline Onassis. — and others.

$150–250

1093 **Travel - Europe and the Americas**

A group of 33 volumes of which 4 bear presentation inscriptions and/or the floral bookplate of Jacqueline Bouvier Kennedy. Also included are 31 postcards of Mexico, and one photograph of a [Mexican?] sculpture dated January 1968. Illustrated. Mostly publisher's cloth and wrappers, some pamphlets. Varying sizes and conditions.

Alexander B. Adam, ed. *Thoreau's Guide to Cape Cod*. 1962. Inscribed by the editor: "To Mrs. John Kennedy - Because of your encouragement of arts and letters in America and knowing of your interest in the Cape, I hope that this book brings you pleasure. February 1963"; bookplate. — *Wien* [English edition]. 1963. Bookplate. — J. M. Lara. *El Cordobés*. 1965. Warmly inscribed by the author: "A Jacqueline Kennedy, ilustre dama, de … natural simpatia, y de gran sensibilidad para las bellas artes, con toda admiración y afecto. Sevilla 22.4.66." — Robert Daley. *The Swords of Spain*. 1966. Inscribed by the author and dated 26 April 1966: "For Jacqueline Kennedy. With admiration - and the hope that you not only enjoyed the Feria at Sevilla, but that you will enjoy this too. — Edna O'Brien. *Vanishing Ireland*. 1986. Inscribed and dated December 1986 by the author: "To Jackie with love and a reminder of her Ireland." — Karel Neubert and Jan Royt. *Praga Caput Regni*. 1991. — Matthew Spender. *Within Tuscany*. 1992.

$700–1,000

1094 **Paris and Versailles**

A group of 12 volumes of which 9 bear presentation inscriptions or the floral bookplate of Jacqueline Bouvier Kennedy; one volume interleaved with numerous notecards annotated in the hand of Jacqueline Kennedy Onassis. Illustrated; chiefly publisher's cloth and wrappers. Varying sizes and conditions.

George Pillement. *Les Hôtels du Marais*. 1948. Bookplate. — L. Le Rouzir. *Le trésor de Notre-Dame de Paris*. 1951. Bookplate. — David H. Pinkney. *Napoleon III and the Rebuilding of Paris*. 1953. Humorously inscribed: "JBK. Don't confuse me with Baron Haussmann and I shan't confuse you with Eugenie. XX. W. W. August 1963." — John Russell. *Paris*. 1961. Inscribed by the author "For Jackie from her affectionate friend." — Dominique Lapierre and Larry Collins. *Paris brûle-t-il?* 1964. Inscribed in French by Lapierre: "To Madame J. F. Kennedy, In the hope that these pages will bring to her the faithful echo of the glorious hour of August 1944, when PARIS found … its soul and freedom again. Paris, 1 November 1965." — Christian de Gastyne. *Charme du vieux Quartier Latin*. 1957. Limited edition. Exemplaire nominatif No. VII of 10 (this one for Mrs. Kennedy), of a total edition of 640, warmly inscribed in French by the author/artist: "These pages would like to be a little portion of the heart of France, a dash of Parisian spirit, and also the entire body and soul of the Latin Quarter … June 1961." — Christopher Hibbert. *Versailles*. 1972. Annotated notecards loosely laid in.

$700–1,000

1095 **Italy**

A group of 10 volumes, chiefly about Rome, of which 8 bear presentation inscriptions, the floral bookplate of Jacqueline Bouvier Kennedy, or an accession ticket recording the gift of 4 books (of which 3 are included in the lot) to Mrs. Kennedy during the Presidential trip to Italy in July 1963 by the Mayor of Rome, Hon. Prof. Glauco della Porta. Publisher's cloth and wrappers. Varying sizes and conditions.

Caroline Atwater Mason. *The Spell of Italy*. 1909. Bookplate. — André Castelot. *King of Rome*. 1960. Bookplate. — John H. Davis. *Venice*. 1973. Inscribed: "For Jackie, Elegant as Venice, Affectionately, Cousin Jack." — Pierre Grimal. *The Civilization of Rome*. 1963. Bookplate. — *A History of Rome and the Romans. From Romulus to Pope John XXIII* [1963]. Gift of Mayor della Porta, accession ticket paperclipped to rear endpaper. — G. B. Piranesi. *XXIV Vedute di Roma* [and] *Vedute di Roma, II Serie*. 2 vols. [n.d.] Gifts of Mayor della Porta. — *Roma Nobilis*. Inscribed in Italian by Prof. Avv. Fernando della Rocca, University of Rome: "To Jacqueline Kennedy, in memory of the Eternal City _ 11 March 1962." — and others.

$600–800

1096 **Women's Biography**

A group of 7 volumes chiefly of biographies and autobiographies of women figures in history, all bearing presentation inscriptions to, or the floral bookplate of, Jacqueline Bouvier Kennedy. Some illustrated; chiefly publisher's cloth and wrappers. Varying sizes and conditions.

Miriam MacMillan. *Green Seas and White Ice. Far North with Captain Mac*. 1948. 9th ed. Inscribed by the author to: "Jacqueline Kennedy – *Aksunai! Illitarnamek! (*The Eskimo greeting to a good friend)." — Brian FitzGerald. *Emily, Duchess of Leinster 1731–1814*. 1950. Bookplate. — Idem. *Lady Louisa Conolly*. 1950. Bookplate. — Alden Hatch. *Edith Bolling Wilson: First Lady Extraordinary*. 1961. Inscribed: "To Mrs. John F. Kennedy. This story of one lovely First Lady to another. 17 November 1961." — Helen Hayes. *A Gift of Joy*. 1965. Inscribed by the author: "For Jacqueline B. Kennedy with my admiration and affection. Christmas 1965." — and 2 others.

$500–700

A superb book on Conservation
For President and Mrs Kennedy

To thank them for their
advocacy and support of
the Wilderness Bill.

From The Sierra Club
and
Stewart Udall
Oct 31, 1962

1097 **Porter, Eliot**

"In Wilderness Is the Preservation of the World." *San Francisco: Sierra Club, (1962)*

(13½ x 10¼ in.). Numerous color photographic illustrations. Publisher's gray cloth gilt, pictorial dust-jacket; jacket chipped.

ASSOCIATION COPY, inscribed and signed by the Secretary of the Interior on the front free endpaper: "A superb book on Conservation for President and Mrs. Kennedy, To thank them for their advocacy and support of the Wilderness Bill. From The Sierra Club and Stewart Udall, Oct. 31, 1962."

$700–1,000

1098 **French Style and Design**

A group of 8 volumes, one bearing a joint inscription to the President and Mrs. Kennedy; one to Jacqueline Kennedy Onassis; and two others containing the floral bookplate of Jacqueline Bouvier Kennedy. Illustrated; publisher's cloth and wrappers.Varying sizes and conditions.

André Lévêque. *Histoire de la civilisation française*. 1946. Bookplate. — Cynthia Cox. *Talleyrand's Successor*. 1959. Bookplate. — Katell Le Bourhis ed. *The Age of Napoleon*. [exhibition catalogue of the Costume Institute of the Metropolitan Museum, New York].1989. Inscribed by Le Bourhis: "For Jackie, thanking you for all your interest in this project and for you continuous support and—why not … Vive l'empereur! New York le 18 Dec. 1989." — *Plaisir de la maison*. [n.d.] Loosely laid in is an autograph postcard signed ("Gerald van der Kemp") and clipped return address on brown paper, in French, Versailles, to Mrs. Kennedy thanking her for her unforgettable reception at the White House and enclosing two books (not included). — and others.

$400–600

1099 **White House Guides**

A group of various editions, with successive revisions, of *The White House: An Historic Guide* (first published in the summer of 1962 at the request of the First Lady, Jacqueline Kennedy). Approximately 7 copies from the Kennedy years, 3 from Johnson's administration, 15 from Nixon's, 7 from Carter's and 1 from Reagan's.

Together approximately 33 volumes, variously publisher's cloth and paper.

$75–100

1100 **Hughes, Emmet John**

The Ordeal of Power: A Political Memoir of the Eisenhower Years. *New York: Atheneum, 1963*

(8⅜ x 5¾ in.). Publisher's blue cloth, dust-jacket.

PRESENTATION COPY, inscribed and signed by the author to Mrs. Kennedy on the front free endpaper: "For Mrs. John F. Kennedy—with warm admiration and respect. Emmet John Hughes." Hughes served as an advisor and speechwriter to General Eisenhower during his two presidential campaigns. The volume also bears the bookplate of Jacqueline Bouvier Kennedy.

$300–500

1101 **Women's Biography**

A group of 9 titles in 16 volumes, chiefly biographies and memoirs of women in French history, of which 7 bear the floral bookplate of Jacqueline Bouvier Kennedy, and/or presentation inscriptions including an inscribed copy from André Maurois of his biography of Mme de la Fayette; and another volume with Jacqueline Kennedy Onassis's ownership inscription and acquisition note. Some illustrated; mostly publisher's cloth and wrappers, some volumes in half and full morocco. Varying sizes and conditions.

Countess de Genlis. *Memoirs*. 8 vols. London, 1825. — Pierre de Nouvion and Emile Liez. *Un ministre des modes sous Louis XVI: Mademoiselle Bertin, marchande de modes de la reine*. 1911. Bookplate. — Yvonne de Bremond d'Ars, Chevalier of the French Legion of Honor. *C'est arrivé en plein Paris; passionante aventure d'un antiquaire*. 1957. Inscribed by the author in French: "To Her Excellency, Mrs. Kennedy, *Présidente des Etas-Unis* in remembrance of a prestigious visit, Paris, 2 June 1961"; bookplates of Bremond d'Ars and Jacqueline Bouvier Kennedy. — André Maurois. *Adrienne, ou la vie de Mme de la Fayette*. 1960. Inscribed in French by the author: "For Mrs John Fitzgerald Kennedy, in reverent homage." — Monica Stirling. *A Pride of Lions*. 1961. Bookplate. — *A Woman's Life in the Court of the Sun King. Letters of Elisabeth Charlotte, Duchesse d'Orléans*. Ownership signature and note: "J. K. O. 1985 from Michael of Greece."

$700–1,000

1102

1102 **An Embossed Cordoba Leather Office Set**

Cordovan colored leather embossed with leafage, comprising: a pad holder, an inkwell holder, a blotter holder and a stationery box, impressed *Meryan, Cordoba* and monogrammed *J.F.K.* *Height of blotter 18 in. (45.7 cm.)*

$1,200–1,500

1103 **A Pair of Creamware Cluster-Column Candlesticks, probably Continental, 19th Century**

Each with a scroll-molded flaring nozzle (restored) supported on four clustered columns applied around the top and base with *fleur-de-lis* ornaments and raised on a stepped square plinth (small chips and slight discoloration). *Height 11 $\frac{15}{16}$ in. (30.3 cm.)*

These candlesticks were among the furnishings of Senator and Mrs. Kennedy's Georgetown residence.

$250–350

1103

1113, 1109, 1108, 1110, 1107, 1106, 1105, 1112, 1117, 1117, 1115

1104 **A Wedgwood Creamware Part Dinner Service, circa 1820**

Each piece simply decorated with a bright green band and line around the rim edge, *impressed WEDGWOOD and various potter's marks*; comprising:
Pair of oval soup tureens (seriously damaged) and covers with floral knops, *length 14 ¾ in. (37.5 cm.)*
Pair of oval soup tureen stands, *lengths 14 ⅜ and 14 ½ in. (36.5 and 36.8 cm.)*
Oval platter, *length 19 ⅜ in. (49.2 cm.)*
Oval platter (some scratching), *length 18 7/16 in. (46.8 cm.)*
Pair of oval platters (some scratching), *length 15 ⅝ in. (39.7 cm.)*
Pair of oval platters (one repaired), *length 13 ⅝ in. (34.6 cm.)*
Circular serving plate (repaired), *diameter 12 ½ in. (31.7 cm.)*
Pair of rectangular vegetable dishes (one with some scratching, and both covers missing), *lengths 9 ¾ and 9 15/16 in. (24.8 and 25.2 cm.)*
Pair of oval serving dishes (discolored, and one cracked), *lengths 11 and 11 1/16 in. (27.9 and 28.1 cm.)*
Twenty soup plates (seven chipped and/or cracked, and three with minor enamel flaking), *diameter 9 15/16 in. (25.2 cm.)*
Forty dinner plates (imperfections), *diameter 10 in. (25.4 cm.)*
Eleven butter plates (some discoloration and other imperfections), *diameter 6 ¼ in. (15.9 cm.)*
Twelve dessert plates (ten with imperfections), *diameters 8 ¼ to 8 ⅜ in. (21 to 21.3 cm.)*
(100)

This part dinner service was among the furnishings of the Kennedys' Georgetown residence.

$3,500–5,000

1105 **A Pair of Wedgwood Creamware Covered Oval Butter Tubs on Attached Stands, circa 1820**

En suite with the preceding service, (one cover a plaster replacement), *impressed WEDGWOOD marks and potter's letter S, one stand with a three-dot painter's mark in green enamel, and one cover with pattern 'No 349' in green enamel.*
Lengths 7 15/16 and 8 in. (20.2 and 20.3 cm.)

$300–500

1106 **A Pair of Wedgwood Creamware Large Circular Basins, circa 1820**

En suite with the two preceding lots, (one with a hair crack on the rim), *impressed WEDGWOOD and potter's letter N.*
Diameter 16 9/16 in. (42.1 cm.)

$300–500

1107 **A Pair of Wedgwood Creamware Diamond-Shaped Cress Dishes and Stands, circa 1820 and 1845**

En suite with the three preceding lots, the cress dishes pierced in the center with a foliate design and raised on four conical feet (some small chips), and each piece decorated around the rim with a green enamel line and band border (the later stand with a hair crack and slight discoloration), *impressed WEDGWOOD, one stand also impressed ETRURIA, and various potter's marks, all but the later stand with pattern 'No 349' and a painter's three-dot or one-dot mark in green enamel.* (4)
Lengths 10 7/16 to 10 ⅝ in. (26.5 to 27 cm.)

$300–400

1108 **A Set of Twelve Wedgwood Creamware Dinner Plates, circa 1820**

En suite with the four preceding lots, *impressed WEDGWOOD marks and various potter's marks.*
Diameters 9 ⅞ to 10 in. (25.1 to 25.4 cm.)

$800–1,200

The Mark Shaw Collection / Photo Researchers

Left: *Senator and Mrs. John F. Kennedy dining in their Georgetown residence with Senator and Mrs. John Sherman Cooper.*

1109 **A Set of Twelve Wedgwood Creamware Dinner Plates, circa 1820**

En suite with the five preceding lots, (two with minor chips, some enamel flaking, and one with a star crack), *impressed WEDGWOOD marks and various potter's marks.*
Diameters 9 7⁄8 to 10 in. (25.1 to 25.4 cm.)

$700–1,000

1110 **A Set of Six Wedgwood Creamware Dessert Plates, circa 1820**

En suite with the six preceding lots, *impressed WEDGWOOD marks and various potter's marks.*
Diameter 8 1⁄4 in. (21 cm.)

$250–350

1111 **A Pair of Wedgwood Creamware Diamond-Shaped Dishes, circa 1820**

En suite with the seven preceding lots (small chips, and one with a hair crack), *impressed WEDGWOOD, letters P and S and numeral 2 marks, and pattern 'No 349' and a painter's two-dot or one-dot mark in green enamel.*
Lengths 11 3⁄4 and 11 7⁄8 in. (29.8 and 30.2 cm.)

$150–250

1112 **Two Wedgwood Creamware Diamond-Shaped Dishes, circa 1820**

En suite with the eight preceding lots, (the smaller with faint discoloration spots), *impressed WEDGWOOD marks and a potter's numeral 1 or 2, and the smaller with pattern 'No 349' and a painter's one-dot mark in green enamel.*
Lengths 9 9⁄16 and 11 9⁄16 in. (24.3 and 29.4 cm.)

$150–250

1113 **A Pair of Wedgwood Creamware Oval Dishes, circa 1820**

En suite with the nine preceding lots, (one with a chip and hair crack), *impressed WEDGWOOD marks and potter's numeral 2, and pattern 'No 349' and a painter's three-dot or one-dot mark in green enamel.*
Length 9 1⁄16 in. (23 cm.)

$100–150

1114 **A Wedgwood Creamware Oval Sauce Tureen Stand, circa 1820**

En suite with the ten preceding lots, *impressed WEDGWOOD mark and potter's letter V, and a painter's three-dot mark in green enamel.*
Length 7 7⁄16 in. (18.9 cm.)

$50–75

1115 **A Pair of Wedgwood Pearlware Reticulated Oval Stands, circa 1820**

Each molded around the cavetto with a border of 'gothick' arcading between slightly raised bands colored in green enamel, and further molded around the green-edged rim with a border of pierced ovolos, *impressed WEDGWOOD marks and letter P, and painter's three-dot marks in green enamel.*
Length 10 in. (25.4 cm.)

$400–600

1116 **Another Pair of Wedgwood Pearlware Reticulated Oval Stands, circa 1820**

En suite with the preceding lot, (one slightly discolored, the other with an area of the rim reglued), *impressed WEDGWOOD and letter P, and one with a painter's dot mark in green enamel.*
Length 10 in. (25.4 cm.)

$300–400

1117 **A Wedgwood Creamware Rectangular Vegetable Dish and Six Soup Plates, circa 1820**

Each piece painted with a black line beneath a turquoise-green band around the rim edge (minor imperfections, one plate cracked, and the dish cover missing), *impressed WEDGWOOD marks and a potter's letter or numeral.* (7)
Length of dish 9 3⁄4 in. (24.8 cm.), diameter of plates 9 3⁄4 to 9 7⁄8 in. (24.8 to 25.1 cm.)

$350–500

1119, 1121, 1120, 1122, 1120, 1119, 1118, 1119

1118 **A Set of Five English Creamware Reticulated Small Plates, 1775-85**

Each with a plain center, the rim pierced with dots and foliate motifs beneath a 'feather'-molded edge (one with a chip beneath, and all with some discoloration around the reticulation).
Diameter 7 ¾ in. (19.7 cm.)

$200–300

1119 **Five English Creamware Table Articles, late 18th and mid 19th Century**

Comprising a quatrefoil dish pierced with dots and foliate motifs around the 'feather'-molded scalloped and barbed edge; a shallow circular bowl (damaged) pierced with a border of diamond devices around the beaded edge; a small oval stand molded with basketwork within an openwork edge; and two sauce ladles, one molded on the terminal with three buds, the other (crackled and discolored) molded on the terminal with scrollwork.
Lengths of dishes 8 ¾ and 7 ⅛ in. (22.2 and 18.1 cm.); lengths of ladles 7 ¼ and 6 ⅞ in. (18.4 and 17.5 cm.); diameter of bowl 8 7/16 in. (21.4 cm.)

$250–350

1120 **An English Creamware Reticulated Oval Basket and a Rare Pair of Egg Cups on Stands, late 18th/early 19th Century**

The sides of the basket formed as open arches rising from a border of pierced dots between rope-molded bands around the foot, the rim with similar rope-molded bands enclosing a border of pierced diamonds, hearts and dots and rising to integral pierced foliate-scroll handles (small chips) at the ends; and the goblet-shaped egg cups slightly differently pierced with blossoms around the rim (tiny chips and one with a small hair crack) above a vertically-reeded body, turned stem (one repaired) and circular foot affixed to a saucer-shaped stand (one chipped).
Length of basket 9 13/16 in. (24.9 cm.); height of egg cups 3 ⅛ in. (7.9 cm.)

$200–300

1121 **A Staffordshire Creamware Cruet Stand and a Pair of Cruet Ewers, late 18th Century**

The stand formed as two cylindrical compartments pierced and molded with interlocking C-scrolls bisected by a median border of flowerheads, raised on four paw feet and conjoined below a columnar handle (cracked) surmounted by a fluted urn-form finial (reglued); the ewers each with an ear-form handle and inscribed in Holland in black enamel on one (neck repaired) *Olie*, and on the other (chips) *Azyn*.
Heights 8 13/16 and 5 1/16 in. (22.4 and 12.9 cm.)

A cruet stand of this model with two differently shaped cruet bottles is illustrated by Peter Walton, *Creamware and other English Pottery at Temple Newsam House, Leeds*, p. 118, no. 448, who attributes it to James and Charles Whitehead of Hanley, "1780s-90s," based on the design for an identical cruet stand, p. 14, no. 74 in the Whitehead *Catalogue* of 1798, where it is referred to on p. 5 as an "Oval Single Waiter, for Oil and Vinegar."

$200–300

1122 **A Staffordshire Saltglaze White Charger, circa 1760**

The center plain, and the scalloped and barbed rim molded with panels of dot- and star-diaperwork alternating with panels of basketwork, all divided by foliate scrolls, (small chip under the edge).
Diameter 16 ⅜ in. (41.6 cm.)

$200–300

1123

1124, 1125

1123 **A Royal Worcester Bone China 'Cumberland' Pattern Part Dinner and Coffee Service, dated 1952**

Each piece with a fluted rim or body and decorated with cobalt-blue and gilt sprigs around a central floral medallion and within a cobalt-blue and gilt flowering vine border around the gilt-edged rim, *crowned circular ROYAL WORCESTER MADE IN ENGLAND marks above the date cipher 'W' for 1952 and the pattern name printed in black, and a painter's letter in blue, and most pieces impressed WE C^{o}*; comprising:
Nine dinner plates (one damaged and reglued), *diameter 10 1/2 in. (26.7 cm.)*
Two butter plates, *diameter 6 3/16 in. (15.7 cm.)*
Twelve dessert plates, *diameter 8 1/4 in. (21 cm.)*
Seven demitasse cups, *height 2 3/8 in. (6 cm.)*
Seven saucers (one chipped), *diameter 4 7/16 in. (11.3 cm.)*
(37)

$400–600

1124 **Set of Nine Chinese Export Dinner Plates, circa 1785**

Each painted in a 'Mandarin palette' of rose, purple, iron-red, yellow, green and brown heightened in gilding, the center with a floral bouquet, a spray and sprigs, and the rim with a border of buds and leaves interrupted by stylized pomegranate devices and foliate scrolls beneath eight iron-red fish-roe-patterned panels forming cartouches containing a single floral sprig beneath a *grisaille*-edged gilt line around the edge (some beveling and small chips). Together with four Chinese Export porcelain plates of later date, decorated *en suite.* (13)
Diameters 10 3/16 to 10 7/16 in. (25.9 to 26.5 cm.)

$1,200–1,800

1125 **Set of Twenty-Eight Chinese Export Porcelain Octagonal Plates, circa 1780**

Each painted in the center with a brown cornucopia issuing a spray of rose, iron-red and purple flowers and green leaves surrounded by six ximilarly colored floral sprigs within a rose line around the cavetto interrupted by blossom-and-diamond devices, the rim with a rose blossom-and-diamond swag pendent from iron-red and gilt scrolls and bands at the notched edge (chips, some repaired; and two with a central crack).
Widths 9 to 9 1/8 in. (22.9 to 23.2 cm.)

$2,500–3,500

1126

1127

1126 **A Berlin Porcelain Part Tea and Coffee Service, 20th Century**

Each piece colorfully painted with a bouquet or spray of flowers, small sprigs and butterflies within a gilt-edged basket-molded border,*sceptre marks in underglaze-blue, orb and KPM marks printed in iron-red, various impressed letters, numerals and dots, and painter's marks in colored enamels*; comprising:
'Bullet'-shaped teapot with a gilt-heightened serpent spout, wishbone handle, and cover with a floral-sprig knop, *height 5 ⅞ in. (14.9 cm.)*
Pear-shaped coffee pot with a gilt-heightened scroll-molded spout and domed cover, *height 10 ⅜ in. (26.4 cm.)*
Circular sugar bowl and cover, *height 4 ⅜ in. (11.1 cm.)*
Pear-shaped tripod milk jug, *height 5 3/16 in. (13.2 cm.)*
Four teacups (two with small chips), *diameter 3 ¾ in. (9.5 cm.)*
Twelve saucers (one with a chip), *diameter 6 ¼ in. (15.9 cm.)*
Eleven cake plates, *diameter 7 ½ to 7 ⅝ in. (19 to 19.4 cm.)*
(31)

This part tea and coffee service was among the furnishings in Senator and Mrs. Kennedy's Georgetown residence.

$600–900

1127 **A Meissen Porcelain Part Coffee Service, 20th Century**

Each piece molded in the *Neu-Brandenstein* pattern of spiral fluting on the body beneath a basketwork and florette-molded border on the gilt-edged rim, and colorfully painted with sprays and sprigs of summer flowers, *crossed swords marks, the cups and saucers with dots in underglaze blue, and various impressed, incised and painted numerals*; comprising:
Pear-shaped coffee pot (spout chipped) and cover with a yellow ranunculus-sprig knop (tiny chips), *height 6 ⅝ in. (16.8 cm.)*
Circular sugar bowl (cover missing)
Pear-shaped milk jug (spout damaged, rim worn and footrim chipped), *height 3 ¾ in. (9.5 cm.)*
Six coffee cups
Three saucers (chipped, and one repaired)
(12)

$300–400

1128

1130

1131, 1132, 1133

1128 **A Berlin Porcelain Reticulated Bowl, dated January 1963 (?)**

Of rounded square shape, the sides pierced, heightened on the exterior in gilding interrupted at the intersections with gilt-centered blue florets, and reserved with four gilt-scroll-edged trefoil panels colorfully painted with floral sprays, the decoration of the panels repeated on the interior beneath gilt-edged blue-scalework borders and surrounding a central gilt-edged floral octafoil medallion, *sceptre mark in underglaze-blue, orb and KPM mark printed in iron-red, 13/2 ST and an arrow painted in black, and impressed date cipher for January 1963 (probably) and a bisected circle. Width 11 3/16 in. (28.4 cm.)*

$400-600

1129 **An English Porcelain Scalloped Circular Dish, probably Coalport, mid 19th Century**

Colorfully painted in Sèvres style in the center with a small bird flying toward a cage within a bamboo wreath entwined with a blue ribbon and a flowering vine, the fluted rim with a gilt-berried green laurel garland suspended beneath floral clusters and a gilt circlet-decorated royal-blue border around the gilt dentil edge, (slight wear), *faintly impressed potter's mark. Diameter 9 11/16 in. (24.6 cm.)*

$150–250

1130 **A Chinese Export Porcelain Lotus Bowl, 19th Century**

Painted around the exterior with two rows of rose-shaded and iron-red-veined lotus petals between turquoise-green bands, the interior with an iron-red and green blossom beneath an iron-red band and white and green flowering-vine border; the rim edged in metal. Together with a Chinese Export porcelain cylindrical mug painted with figures, circa 1780, (damaged). (2)
Diameter of bowl 5 3/4 in. (14.6 cm.), height of mug 5 1/8 in. (13 cm.)

$75–125

15, 14, 1134, 1135, 1134, 313, 1136, 1137, 1138

1131 **A Pair of Japanese Porcelain Blue and White Dishes, 20th Century**

Each painted in underglaze-blue in the center with a blossom and five leaves within a pale and dark blue border of stylized waves, clouds, flowers and foliage at the brown-edged rim, *four-character marks in underglaze-blue.*
Diameter 7 in. (17.8 cm.)

$100–150

1132 **A Chinese Porcelain Famille-Rose Snuff Bottle, late 19th Century**

Of ovoid form and painted in shades of green, rose, iron-red, lavender, brown, black and gold with two Mandarin figures conversing on a bridge in a river landscape, with a lady standing on a nearby terrace, (stopper missing).
Height 2⅜ in. (6 cm.)

$100–150

1133 **A Japanese Imari Porcelain Scalloped Bowl, late 19th Century**

Printed in underglaze-blue with a central medallion of foliage within a dashed roundel surrounded by three large panels painted in iron-red and green with flowers and divided by panels of iron-red stylized cash medallions repeated on the exterior beneath the underglaze-blue-edged rim (chips).
Diameter 7½ in. (19 cm.)

$75–125

1134 **Pair of Slip-Glazed Stoneware Baluster Vases Mounted as Lamps**

With a marbleized slip glaze.
Height approximately 17 in. (43.2 cm.)

$600–900

1135 **A Chinese Porcelain Blue and White Small Garden Seat Mounted as a Lamp, early 19th Century**

Of squat barrel form, painted in underglaze-blue within a wide central band, within a lappet border around the base, and across the lappet-edged top with a scrolling foliate vine bearing occasional blossoms, the top pierced with a cash medallion patterned with trellis diaperwork and blossoms; now fitted for electricity and mounted on a wooden circular base.
Height of seat 7 in. (17.8 cm.)

$600–900

1136 **A Louis XV Style Ormolu Candlestick Mounted as a Lamp**

With a circular nozzle and tapered stem above a domed circular base cast with flowerheads and foliate motifs.
Overall height 20½ in. (52.1 cm.)

$400–600

1137 **A Korean Porcelain Blue and White Dragon Jar Mounted as a Lamp, 19th Century**

The ovoid body with a tapered foot, and boldly painted in pale underglaze-blue with a sinuous scaly dragon amongst cloud scrolls; drilled and fitted for electricity.
Height of jar 14½ in. (36.8 cm.)

$3,000–5,000

1139

1138 **A Louis XVI Style Ormolu and Tôle Three-Light Bouillotte Lamp**

With an adjustable green *tôle* shade, three curved candle branches and a circular, dished pierced base. *Fitted for electricity.*

$1,200–1,800

1139 **A Set of Twenty-Two French Green-Cut-to-Clear and Gilt-Decorated Glass Tumblers, St. Louis**

$300–500

1140

1141

1140 A Louis XVI Style Faux Malachite and Gilt-Metal Tazza

Height 4½ in. (11.4 cm.)

$200–300

1141 A Pink Glass Ovoid Boudoir Lamp

Electrified, with brass mounts and turned mahogany base.

Height 8 in. (20.3 cm.)

$200–300

1142 A Mother-of-Pearl-Handled Magnifying Glass and Letter Opener, Modern

With spirally carved handles.
Length of opener 8 in. (20.3 cm.), length of magnifying glass 7 in. (17.8 cm.)

$200–300

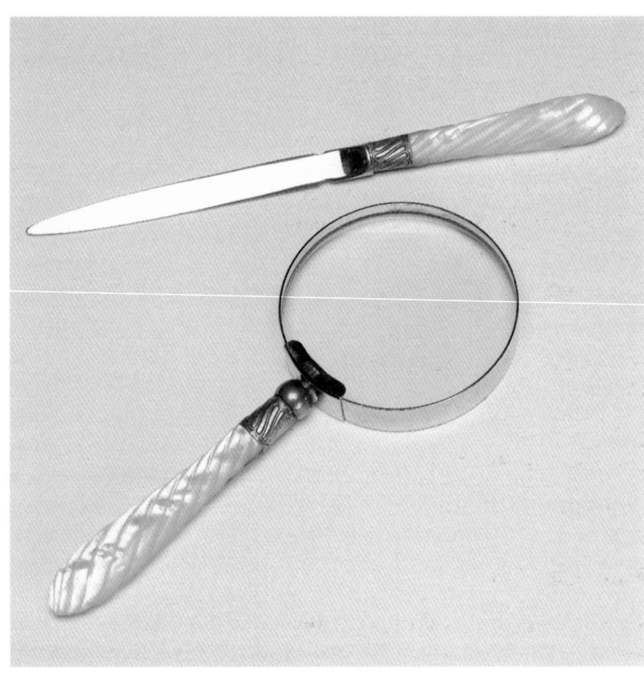

1142

1143

1144

1145

1146

1143 **A Tibetan Turquoise-Inset Silver Amulet Box, 19th Century**

Of square form with triangular projection on each of the four sides, strung with coral, turquoise, and "Z"-bends.
4 by 4 in. (10.2 by 10.2 cm.)

$200–300

1144 **A Painted Plastic Model of Air Force One**

Bearing brass plaque inscribed *Mrs. John F. Kennedy from the Presidential AF Crew and BRIG GEN GODFREY MCHUGH AF Aide to the President.*
13 in. (33 cm.), by 13 in. (33 cm.)

$300–500

1145 **A Black Papier Mâché Tray, 19th Century**

(Chipped).
Length 33 in. (83.8 cm.)

$100–150

1146 **Three Cushions**

Two in striped silk fabric, the other floral.

$50–100

1147, 1148

The Mark Shaw Collection / Photo Researchers

Above: *President Kennedy playing with Caroline and John in the White house nursery while Maud Shaw, the nanny, looks on, 1961.*

1149

1150

1147 **Three-Panel Painted Canvas Screen**

Sparsely decorated with floral ribbons and sprays of flowers.
Height 54 in. (137.2 cm.), width of each panel 14 in. (35.6 cm.)

This screen was among the furnishings in Mrs. Kennedy's bedroom at the White House.

$200–300

1148 **A French Provincial Style Painted Chest of Drawers**

Height 30 in. (76.2 cm.), width 30 in. (76.2 cm.), depth 18 in. (45.7 cm.)

This chest of drawers was among the furnishings in Caroline's bedroom at the White House during President and Mrs. Kennedy's residence.

$500–700

1149 **A Chippendale Style White-Painted Tall Chest of Drawers**

The rectangular top above a case containing three short and four long graduated drawers on ogee bracket feet, *height 47 in. (119.4 cm.), width 36 in. (91.4 cm.).* Together with a white-painted French Provincial style two-drawer commode, *height 30 in. (76.2 cm.), width 29 in. (73.7 cm.).*

This chest of drawers was among the furnishings in Caroline's bedroom at the White House during President and Mrs. Kennedy's residence.

$600–800

1150 **A Black-Painted Three-Legged Stool**

Together with a small green-painted trestle bench.
Height of stool 11 in. (27.9 cm.)

$75–125

1151 **Two Similar Dark Green Painted Turned Ash Side Chairs, early 19th Century**

Each with two rectangular backrests and flaring stiles above a woven seat, on turned tapering legs joined by stretchers; one with rush seat, the other with splint seat.

$200–300

1152

1153

1154

1155

1152 **Two Wooden Wall Mirrors**

One carved.
The larger 31 by 26 in. (78.7 by 66 cm.)

$100–150

1153 **An American Maple Wall Mirror, Second Half 19th Century**

19 by 17 in. (48.3 by 43.2 cm.)

$75–100

1154 **A Dark Green Painted Stool**

With rectangular woven seat, on turned tapering legs joined by stretchers; together with a rush-seat wooden stool. (2)

Height of larger 9 in. (22.9 cm.), length 14 in. (35.6 cm.), width 11 ½ in. (29.2 cm.)

$50–75

1155 **A Paint-Decorated Oval Tray-Top Occasional Table**

The oval top above a plain apron and turned, tapering legs ending in pad feet; painted dark green and cream.
Height 20 in. (50.8 cm.), width 12 ½ in. (31.7 cm.)

$200–300

1156

1157, 1158

1156 **An American Federal Giltwood Rectangular Wall Mirror, circa 1825**

Rectangular, the upper portion with a giltwood panel carved with a basket of flowers and leaves, *losses.*
40 by 20 in. (101.6 by 50.8 cm.)

$200–400

1157 **A Regency Rosewood Three-Tier Etagère, circa 1845**

Height 37½ in. (95.2 cm.), width 15¾ in. (40 cm.), depth 13½ in. (34.3 cm.)

$500–800

1158 **A Victorian Paint-Decorated Etagere, 19th Century**

With four square plateaus, the uprights painted with pendant leafage and bows, on an olive-green ground.
Height 4 feet 2½ in. (128.3 cm.), width 17½ in. (44.4 cm.)

$1,200–1,500

1159 **A Yellow Lacquered Burlap Rectangular Low Table**

On "waved" square-section legs.
Height 17½ in. (44.4 cm.), width 43 in. (109.2 cm.)

$500–700

1159

1160

1161

1160 **Joseph R. Spies**

TOM KITTEN

Gelatin silver print mounted on board, signed, titled and dated in pencil on the mount *"Tom Kitten" alias "Tom Terrific" 3-23-61.* Framed.
13 ¼ by 10 ⅜ in. (33.7 by 26.4 cm.)

"Tom Kitten" was Caroline Kennedy's cat while she lived in the White House.

$50–75

1161 **Artist Unknown**

BIRDCAGE

inscribed *Jackie*
pen, ink and watercolor on paper
4 ¾ by 3 ¾ in. (12.1 by 9.5 cm.)

Painted circa 1966

Together with:

American School, 20th Century

BASKET OF CHERRIES

indistinctly signed
watercolor and pencil on paper
5 ½ by 6 ⅞ in. (14 by 17.5 cm.)

$100–150

1162

1162 **Victorian Child's Puzzle of a Three-Masted Sailing Vessel, late 19th/early 20th Century**

With a lighthouse at lower right, printed in colors, in a giltwood frame.
16 by 21 ¾ in. (40.6 by 55.2 cm.)

$700–900

1163

1164

1166

1163 **Neapolitan School, 19th Century**

MOUNT VESUVIUS

gouache on paper
12 by 17 in. (30.5 by 43.2 cm.)

$1,000–1,500

1164 **Angela Piotrowska Wittman (Austrian, 19th/20th Century)**

ORNAMENT WITH BLUE SHELL-SHAPED FLOWERS

signed
watercolor and black ink over traces of on paper
8½ by 6⅝ in. (21.6 by 16.8 cm.)

Provenance:
Sheperd Gallery, 21 East 84th Street, New York, New York

$200–300

1165 **Contemporary Large Rectangular Brass Cigar Box**

With hinged lid opening to an interior with removable dividers, the lid monogrammed *ASO* in a circle, on brass ball feet
Length 18¾ in. (47.6 cm.), width 12 in. (30.5 cm.)

$200–300

1166 **Two Contemporary Large Rectangular Trays**

En suite with the preceding.
Length 15¾ in. (40 cm.), width 12 in. (30.5 cm.)

$200–300

1168

1167

1169

1167 Artist Unknown

FULL-LENGTH PAINTING OF A GIRL IN A FENCING OUTFIT

oil on canvas
68 by 21 ½ in. (172.7 by 54.6 cm.)

$200–300

1168 William Walton

A POLITICAL RALLY

oil on board, signed
22 by 28 in. (55.9 by 71.1 cm.)

William Walton, an intimate of both John and Jacqueline Kennedy, was born in Jacksonville, Illinois. By 1947 he had settled in Washington upon becoming a reporter for the *New Republic.* In time he left journalism for painting. In 1960 he acted as Kennedy's New York campaign manager. The President later appointed him chairman of the New York Fine Arts Commission.

$800–1,200

1169 Carzou

LE HOFGARTEN À BAYREUTH (GARDEN GATES SURROUNDED BY TREES)

signed *Carzou* and dated *'58*, l.r.
watercolor on paper
24 ¾ by 19 in. (62.9 by 48.3 cm.)

Provenance:
Wildenstein & Co., New York, 1959

This watercolor was among the furnishings in the West Sitting Room of the White House during President and Mrs. Kennedy's residence.

$800–1,200

1170 **Three Decorative Prints of John Fitzgerald Kennedy**

Framed.

The largest 15½ by 20 in. (39.4 by 50.8 cm.)

$200–300

1171 **Malthe M. Hasselriis**

TWO PORTRAIT MINIATURES OF PRESIDENT JOHN F. KENNEDY

the first, signed upper right and dated *1964*; the second signed and dated *1964* lower right
both gouache on card (2)
The first 3 by 4 in. (7.6 by 10.2 cm.); the second oval, 3¾ by 2¾ in. (9.5 by 7 cm.)

$200–400

1172 **Rene Bouché**

PORTRAIT OF JACQUELINE KENNEDY

signed
watercolor and ink on paper

25½ by 19½ in. (64.8 by 49.5 cm.)

$800–1,200

1170

1170

1170

1172

1171

Figure 1

Copyrighted by White House Historical Association

Figure 2

Photo courtesy of Aaron Shikler

1173 **Aaron Shikler (b. 1922)**

STUDY FOR THE WHITE HOUSE PORTRAIT OF JACQUELINE KENNEDY

signed with the artist's initials *AAS* and dated *'69*, l.l.
pastel on board
30 by 19 ¼ in. (76.2 by 48.9 cm.)

This work was a study for the official portrait of Jacqueline Kennedy, which hangs in the White House (1970, oil on canvas, 48 x 32 inches) (figure 1).

Aaron Shikler was born in Brooklyn, New York in March 1922. In the early 1940s, he studied painting at The Barnes Foundation in Marion, Pennsylvania and the Tyler School of Art, Temple University in Philadelphia. In 1949, Shikler returned to his hometown, working in Hans Hoffman's studio for several years. From 1953 to the present, Shikler has had approximately twenty-five one-person exhibitions, most of which were hosted by Davis & Langdale, New York. Shikler is considered by some critics as one of our great contemporary portrait painters.

In 1968, Jacqueline Kennedy's secretary contacted Aaron Shikler to commission a portrait of Caroline and John. Shikler believes that Mrs. Kennedy selected him because she had admired the portrait that he painted of her nieces and nephew, the Lawford children. When Shikler arrived at Mrs. Kennedy's New York apartment for a sketching session, Mrs. Kennedy remarked that "...they [Caroline and John] look just right to me now. I would like to remember them at this age. As they are, just now" (Aaron Shikler, "The Painting of a Legend," *McCall's*, March 1971, p. 79). Caroline was ten and John was seven. The final portrait of Caroline and John includes Mrs. Kennedy reading to them on a sofa in the apartment.

During one of the sketching sessions, Mrs. Kennedy asked Shikler if he would do her official White House portrait as well. Shikler recalls: "I wanted to create a painting that Mrs. Kennedy would feel was right and that would, at the same time, fall within the meaningful tradition of the White House, a tradition which she had done so much to preserve and enhance. I needed to paint a picture of the First Lady of the Land at the same time that I painted a picture of Jacqueline Bouvier Kennedy Onassis" (*ibid*, p. 118).

For the White House portrait, Mrs. Kennedy chose to have herself depicted in a long black skirt and a high-collared white blouse. Shikler executed numerous sketches of Mrs. Kennedy; some in casual poses and others more formal. Shikler recalls that "she was particularly pleased by a charcoal drawing of her reading a book" (*idem.*), but they both agreed that it was not formal enough for the official portrait. Eventually Mrs. Kennedy and Shikler chose a sketch that depicted Mrs. Kennedy standing before her fireplace, confronting the viewer with her direct gaze. Upon its completion, Shikler decided that he was not satisfied with the final version. He felt it was too girlish and coy and it failed to convey her reserve and her strength (figure 2).

Shikler states: "The painting I finally did of her was the result of many studies I had done of her, a composite concept. She might have preferred another study for the White House. She might have wanted something a little more mysterious, a little less finished." However, he emphasized that "she left me completely alone" (Sally Quinn, "Aaron Shikler Talks About Kennedys," *Washington Post*, March 26, 1971). The official White House portrait depicts Mrs. Kennedy standing in a similar pose as the first portrait, wearing a full-length off-white dress with her head slightly turned to one side. Shikler explained that "he wanted a brighter, less troubled image, one that would immediately evoke how he—and the rest of the country—saw her: as an ethereal woman of almost mythological dimensions" (Byron Dobell, "The Forgotten Portrait," *Town & Country*, pp. 77-78).

$10,000–15,000

1173

1174 **Aaron Shikler (b. 1922)**

STUDY OF JACQUELINE KENNEDY, SEATED

signed with the artist's initials *AAS* and dated *'68*, l.l.
watercolor and gouache on green paper
16 by 12 ¾ in. (40.6 by 32.4 cm.)

$8,000–12,000

1174

1175 **Aaron Shikler (b. 1922)**

PORTRAIT OF JACQUELINE KENNEDY SEATED ON A COUCH

signed with the artist's initials *AAS* and dated *'68*, l.l.
charcoal on paper
19 ¼ by 12 ½ in. (48.9 by 31.7 cm.)

Literature:
Aaron Shikler, "The Painting of a Legend," *McCall's*, March 1971, illustrated p. 77

$8,000–12,000

1175

1176 **Aaron Shikler (b. 1922)**

STUDY FOR THE WHITE HOUSE PORTRAIT OF JACQUELINE KENNEDY

signed with the artist's initials *AAS* and dated *'68*, l.l.
watercolor and gouache on paper
20 by 14 in. (50.8 by 35.6 cm.)

$8,000–12,000

1176

1177 **Aaron Shikler (b. 1922)**

STUDY OF JACQUELINE KENNEDY STANDING

signed with the artist's initials *AAS* and dated '69, l.r.
pencil on paper
20 by 14 in. (50.8 by 35.6 cm.)

$5,000–7,000

1177

1178

1179

1180

1178 **Aaron Shikler (b. 1922)**

A STUDY OF CAROLINE AND JOHN KENNEDY

signed with the artist's initials *AAS* and dated '*68*, l.r.
charcoal and chalk on blue paper
10 by 12 ½ in. (25.4 by 31.7 cm.)

$2,000–3,000

1179 **Aaron Shikler (b. 1922)**

JOHN F. KENNEDY, JR. SEATED

signed with the artist's initials *AAS* and dated '*68*, l.r.
colored crayon and pastel on paper
9 ¼ by 6 ½ in. (23.5 by 16.5 cm.)

$2,000–3,000

1180 **Aaron Shikler (b. 1922)**

A STUDY OF CAROLINE KENNEDY STANDING

signed with the artist's initials *AAS* and dated '*68*, l.r.
conté crayon and chalk on paper
9 ¼ by 5 ½ in. (23.5 by 14 cm.)

$1,500–2,500

1181

1182

1181 Aaron Shikler (b. 1922)

JOHN F. KENNEDY, JR., READING

signed with the artist's initials *AAS* and dated '68, l.l.
oil on panel
6 by 10 in. (15.2 by 25.4 cm.)

Literature:
Aaron Shikler, "The Painting of a Legend," *McCall's*, March 1971, illustrated p. 76

$3,500–5,000

1182 Aaron Shikler (b. 1922)

A PORTRAIT STUDY OF JOHN F. KENNEDY, JR.

signed with the artist's initials *AAS* and dated '68, l.l.
oil on board
7 by 9¾ in. (17.8 by 24.8 cm.)

Literature:
Aaron Shikler, "The Painting of a Legend," *McCall's*, March 1971, illustrated p. 76

$1,500–2,500

1183

1184

1185

1185 **Aaron Shikler (b. 1922)**

A PORTRAIT STUDY OF CAROLINE KENNEDY

signed with the artist's initials *AAS* and dated '*68*, l.l.
oil on board
7 by 9½ in. (17.8 by 24.1 cm.)

Literature:
Aaron Shikler, "The Painting of a Legend," *McCall's*, March 1971, illustrated p. 76

$1,500–2,500

1183 **Aaron Shikler (b. 1922)**

A PORTRAIT STUDY OF CAROLINE KENNEDY

signed with the artist's initials *AAS* and dated '*68*, l.l.
oil on paper
8¾ by 6¼ in. (22.2 by 15.9 cm.)

$1,500–2,500

1184 **Aaron Shikler (b. 1922)**

A STUDY OF CAROLINE KENNEDY

signed with the artist's initials *AAS* and dated '*68*, l.r.
pastel on green paper
13 by 10 in. (33 by 25.4 cm.)

$2,000–3,000

1186 **Aaron Shikler (b. 1922)**

VASE OF FLOWERS WITH ONE WHITE ROSE

signed with the artist's initials *AAS* and dated '*85*, l.l.
pastel on board
8 ¼ by 6 in. (21 by 15.2 cm.)

Provenance:
Davis & Langdale Co., New York

Exhibited:
Old Lyme, Connecticut, Lyme Academy of Fine Arts, April-May 1986, no. 3

$750–1,000

1187 **Photograph of an Aaron Shikler Portrait**

JACQUELINE BOUVIER KENNEDY, SEATED, SIDE VIEW

4 by 6 in. (10.2 by 15.2 cm.)

$50–75

1188 **Photograph of an Aaron Shikler Portrait**

JACQUELINE BOUVIER KENNEDY, SEATED, FRONT VIEW

4 by 6 in. (10.2 by 15.2 cm.)

$50–75

1186

1187

1188

1189

1190

1191

1192

1193

1189 **Photograph of an Aaron Shikler Portrait**

JACQUELINE BOUVIER KENNEDY, THREE VIEWS

4 by 6 in. (10.2 by 15.2 cm.)

$50–75

1190 **Photograph of an Aaron Shikler Portrait**

JACQUELINE BOUVIER KENNEDY, SEATED

4 by 6 in. (10.2 by 15.2 cm.)

$50–75

1191 **Photograph of an Aaron Shikler Portrait**

JACQUELINE BOUVIER KENNEDY, SIDE VIEW

4 by 6 in. (10.2 by 15.2 cm.)

$50–75

1192 **Photograph of an Aaron Shikler Portrait**

JOHN F. KENNEDY, JR.: PORTRAIT STUDY

4 by 6 in. (10.2 by 15.2 cm.)

$50–75

1193 **Photographs of Aaron Shikler Portraits**

The official portraits of President and Mrs. John F. Kennedy. Together with a photograph of the portraits at the White House.
Framed: 19¼ by 32½ in. (48.9 by 82.5 cm.)

$75–100

The John F. Kennedy Library

Right: *President Kennedy meeting with a delegation from the NAACP at the White House in the second floor Yellow Oval Room, July 12, 1961.*

1194 **An Oak Rocking Chair**

With caned backrest and seat, loose cushions, padded arms and turned legs ending in rockers, stamped under left arm *Carolina Rocker (P & P Chair Company Asheboro, North Carolina*, (fabric ripped on right arm).
Height 43 ¾ in. (111.1 cm.), width 28 in. (71.1 cm.), depth 33 in. (83.8 cm.)

$3,000–5,000

"A rocker is a rocker and there isn't much you can do to make it look like anything else," Jacqueline Kennedy once said. Rocking chairs were recommended by Dr. Janet Travell to ease President Kennedy's severe back pain. In deference to the President's need for comfortable seating, the comment was one of surrender; Mrs. Kennedy was, after all, attempting to restore the White House state rooms, wherein, she explained, "everything...must have a reason for being there." But in a sense there was a very good historical reason why a rocking chair should have been included among the furnishings of the Oval Room: it is said that no less a personage than Dr. Benjamin Franklin devised the form by applying rockers to the lower extremities of a straight chair.

The pioneer minister Manasseh Cutler wrote after a visit to Franklin's home in July, 1787: "...the Doctor invited me into his library, which is likewise his study.... [He showed us] his great armed chair, with rockers." While Cutler's reference is the earliest dated citation for the usage in the *Oxford English Dictionary*, the antiquarian Dr. Irving I. Lyon found rocking chairs listed in inventories of estates of Hartford County, Connecticut, rather earlier: 1772 in Windsor and 1775 in Enfield. While in the eighteenth century straight slat-back chairs were converted into rockers, there are published advertisements as early as 1810 of fancy chair manufactories that produced rocking chairs, not as a new curiosity, but as an accepted and well-known type.

After 1840 the so-called Boston Rocker, a direct descendant of the Windsor rocker of the 1820s and 1830s, with flat rockers, turned and slightly raked legs, turned stretchers, a wood seat fashioned in a peculiar roll, arms curving over at the ends to fit the hands, and a high back of two stiles and seven slender spindles surmounted by a horizontal dressing with curved outline at the level of the sitter's head, were made in large quantities. About 1825, an Empire touch was added to the entire chair—rolling crest, seat and arms. The *Bridgeport Standard* of July 26, 1845, contains two advertisements in which the 'Boston rocker' is specifically mentioned. The rectangular headpiece was steamed and bent in a shallow curve, and the spindles were also steamed and bent to fit the back. As the Boston rocker began to become more a matter of quantity production in factories, material was conserved and work simplified. A plainer headpiece came into vogue, developing at length, about 1835, into the standard stenciled headpiece of the later Boston rocker, with the top rounded and the straight bottom edge cut with two semicircular notches. Boston rockers were made in great quantities in widely separated places, and become pretty generally standardized in form and construction after 1840. Most were made with pine or whitewood seats, while legs and spindles were made of oak, hickory, ash or maple. The price was low and they were widely distributed by peddlers.

Rocking chairs abounded in Jacksonian America. The Englishwoman Anne Royall abhorred them. She stumbled over their bold crescent projections, departing the country in 1828 with "hardly a sound toe left." Nevertheless, the rocking chair became established in general use during this period. The critical English traveler and writer Harriet Martineau on a visit here in the mid 1830s was reflecting a fairly general attitude among foreigners when she wrote in her *Retrospect of Western Travel* of "The disagreeable practice of rocking in the chair... How this lazy and ungraceful indulgence ever became general, I cannot imagine, but the [American] nation seems so wedded to it, that I see but little chance of its being forsaken."

1195 **A 1992 BMW 325i Four-Door Sedan, VIN# WBACB4319NFF2019**

The six-cylinder in-line engine, bore 75 mm., stroke 84 mm., displacement 2,492 c.c., compression ratio 10:1, producing 189 horsepower at 5900 r.p.m., with dual overhead cams driving 24 valves, Bosch fuel injection, electronic hydraulic transmission, and ABS braking system; wheelbase 2,700 mm., weight 1,405 kg.

This automobile was purchased new by Mrs. Onassis, and comes equipped with all original owner's manuals, leather interior, SRS safety system, ABS brakes, sunroof, climate control system, am/fm stereo cassette player, power windows, power mirrors, power steering, cellular phone, spare tire and assorted tools. The exterior color is *Lagunengrün*-metallic (dark green-metallic), with tan interior. The indicated mileage is 10,032 and is believed to be correct.

The BMW 325i is noted for its sports car-like handling and acceleration, with all the creature comforts of a luxury sedan.

$18,000–22,000

END OF SALE

1195

Glossary of Terms

The following are examples of the terminology used in this catalogue Please note that all statements in this catalogue as to authorship, period, culture, source or origin are qualified statements and are made subject to the provisions of the Conditions of Sale and Terms of Guarantee printed in this catalogue.

Statements in the catalogue regarding the condition of objects in the sale are open to misinterpretation. Therefore condition descriptions rarely appear in the catalogue. Prospective bidders who are unable to view the sale and wish information concdrning condition are welcome to contact the appropriate specialist departments. Please see page 6 for phone numbers.

Notwithstanding any condition reports or catalogue descriptions provided, all lots are offered and sold "AS IS" in accordance with paragraph 1 of the Conditions of Sale.

Glossary for Furniture and Decorations

Louis XV Ormolu-Mounted Marquetry Commode, mid-18th Century
This heading with date included, means that the piece is, in our opinion, of the period indicated with no major alterations or restorations.

Louis XV Ormolu-Mounted Marquetry Commode
This heading without inclusion of the date, indicates that, in our opinion, the piece, while basically of the period has undergone significant restoration or alteration.

Louis XV Style Ormolu-Mounted Marquetry Commode
The inclusion of the word "style" in the heading indicates that, in our opinion, the piece was made as an intentional reproduction of an earlier style.

Glossary for Porcelain

A Meissen Cup and Saucer, circa 1735,
This states that the cup and saucer were made at the Meissen factory around the year 1735.

A Meissen Cup and a Saucer, circa 1735,
Again, this states that the cup and saucer were made at the Meissen factory around 1735, but it also indicates that the cup and saucer may not have been "born" together.

A Meissen Cup and Saucer, 1730-50,
This states that the cup and saucer were made at the Meissen factory some time between 1730 and 1750.

A Meissen Cup and Saucer, dated 1735,
This states that the cup and saucer were made at the Meissen factory, and that the date 1735 appears within the decoration, although it may not be the actual year of manufacture. Only in the case of factories such as Sèvres, Frankenthal and Vienna, which incorporated date letters or numbers into their marks, does the term "Dated" mean the actual year of manufacture.

A 'Meissen' Cup and Saucer, 19th Century,
This states that the cup and saucer are of Meissen type, and although of the date specified, not necessarily made at the Meissen factory.

A Meissen Cup and Saucer
This title without a date simply states that the pieces were made at the Meissen factory, but does not specify when, implying that their age is questionable.

Glossary of Terms

The following are examples of the terminology used in this catalogue Please note that all statements in this catalogue as to authorship, period, culture, source or origin are qualified statements and are made subject to the provisions of the Conditions of Sale and Terms of Guarantee printed in this catalogue.

Glossary for Paintings

**Gustave Courbet*
Followed, under the heading "Authorship," by the words "ascribed to the named artist ." In our opinion, a work by the artist, (when the artist's forename is not known, a series of asterisks followed by the surname of the artist, whether preceded by an initial or not indicates that, in our opinion, the work is by the artist named). While this is our highest category of authenticity, no unqualified statement as to authorship is made or intended.

Attributed to Gustave Courbet
In our opinion, probably a work by the artist but less certainty as to authorship is expressed than in the preceding category.

Studio of Gustave Courbet
In our opinion, a work by an unknown hand in the studio of the artist which may or may not have been executed under the artist's direction.

Circle of Gustave Courbet
In our opinion, a work by an as yet unidentified but distinct hand closely associated with the named artist but not necessarily his pupil.

Style of . . . Follower of Gustave Courbet
In our opinion, a work by a painter working in the artist's style, contemporary or nearly contemporary, but not necessarily his pupil.

Manner of Gustave Courbet
In our opinion, a work in the style of the artist and of a later date.

After Gustave Courbet
In our opinion, a copy of a known work of the artist.

The term *signed* and/or *dated* and/or *inscribed* means that, in our opinion, a *signature* and/or *date* and/or *inscription* are from the hand of the artist.

The term *bears* a signature and/or a date and/or an inscription means that, in our opinion, a signature and/or date and/or inscription have been added by another hand.

Unless otherwise stated in the description, all pictures are framed and all measurements are given with the height preceding the width.

Glossary For Sculpture

Bronze Figure of a Woman, Maurice Giraud-Rivière, circa 1925
This heading indicates that the casting was done by the artist or with his direct authorization or supervision.

Bronze Figure of a Woman, after Maurice Giraud-Rivière, circa 1925
This heading indicates the casting was done by another, i.e., artisans at a foundry.

Glossary of Terms

The following are examples of the terminology used in this catalogue Please note that all statements in this catalogue as to authorship, period, culture, source or origin are qualified statements and are made subject to the provisions of the Conditions of Sale and Terms of Guarantee printed in this catalogue.

Glossary for Rugs

Tekke Rug, Turkestan, first quarter 20th Century.
This attribution and ascribed date indicate that, in our opinion, the rug is an early 20th Century Turcoman rug with no major alteration or restoration. Please note that while every effort is made to maintain accuracy and consistency in terms of date, the dating of rugs and carpets is necessarily inexact, and often a matter of opinion. Therefore, the Terms of Guarantee only apply to the Bold Type Heading and do not apply to our statement of the age of a rug or carpet.

Daghestan Rug, Caucasus, circa 1875. Reduced in length, rewoven areas.
This attribution and ascribed date indicate that, in our opinion, the rug was woven in the Caucasian district of Daghestan around 1875. It also indicates that the rug has been altered in length and has major reweaves. The notation of condition in catalogue descriptions is as consistent as possible. However, bidders should read the Important Notice below and not that Sotheby's liability with regard to these comments is limited by the Conditions of Sale printed in the front of the catalogue.

Technical Analysis
The technical analyses appearing after desciptions of tribal, village and nomadic pile rugs are provided exclusively as a service for those interested in the structure of pile weavings. Please note that all such technical analyses are qualified statements and are made subject to the Conditions of Sale and Terms of Guarantee printed in the catalogue.

The following abbreviations are employed:
H - Horizontal
V - Vertical
S - Clockwise direction of spin
Z - Counter-clockwise direction of spin

Z2S -
The spin of the individual strands is clockwise, 2 of these strands are then plied together counter-clockwise to form the yarn. For a thorough description of this method of structural analysis, please refer to David Black, ed., World Rugs and Carpets, London, Robert Adkinson, 1985, pp. 20-21, and Irene Emery, The Primary Structure of Fabrics, New York, The Spiral Press, 1966.

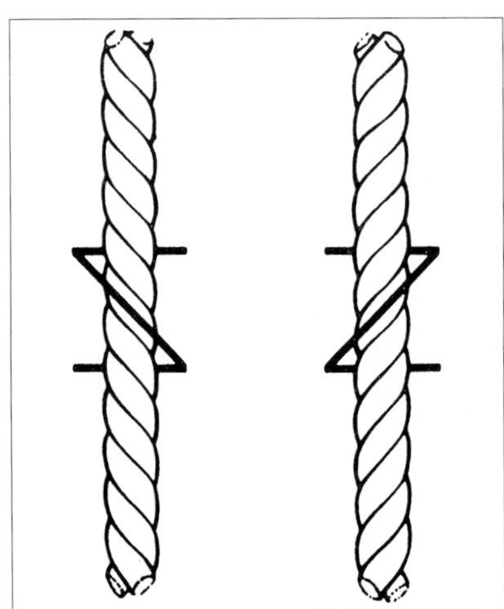

Yarns are spun and plied in either an 'S' or a 'Z' direction

Glossary of Terms

Glossary of Print Terms

Name of Artist
Subject to Conditions of Sale and Terms of Guarantee set forth in this catalogue, each lot is guaranteed to be the work of the artist whose name appears in Bold Type Heading. This heading may precede a single lot or a series of lots by the same artist.

Title
If there is a generally accepted title for the print, that title is given at the beginning of the lot description. If the work does not have a title or the title is not known to us, a descriptive title is given in brackets.

References
Wherever possible, standard catalogues of the artist's works are cited in parentheses following the title. This is done to facilitate identification and to indicate where the reader might seek further information with respect to any of the subjects mentioned below.

Medium
The primary medium is identified following the title or reference. The terms used are intended as a general description and may not cover all the techniques employed by the artist. It is generally understood, for example, that a work described as an "etching" may include a few touches of "drypoint"; conversely, a work described as a "drypoint," or as an "aquatint," according to its predominant character, may in many instances have some underlying etched lines.

Date
Unless otherwise indicated, the date given is the date of execution of the "plate" or "master." For works printed after 1949, if the date or approximate date of printing is other than the date of execution of the "plate" or "master," this will be indicated.

A date preceded by "c." (circa) represents a generally accepted approximate date, or our best judgment of the approximate date. A date set off with brackets is intended only as a rough indication of the period of execution and/or printing.

State
Unless otherwise indicated, the print is an impression of the only state, final state, or only published state.

Signature
A print is described as "signed" only if it has, in our opinion, a manuscript signature of the artist. A manuscript signature which, in our opinion, is probably that of the artist, but which we consider to be open to serious question is described as "signed(?)."

In any case in which the name of the artist or engraver appears on the print, and this name is not described as a manuscript signature or otherwise specifically described, this name constitutes a signature "in the plate."

Edition
Within the limits of available information, every reasonable effort is made to state fully the relevant information as to the extent of the edition or editions of a given print. If the print described is an artist's proof or Hors Commerce, etc., the size of the regular edition is usually given. Unless otherwise indicated, each work described in this catalogue which is printed after 1949 is offered as part of a limited edition. For these, the size of the edition is indicated explicitly or implicity (as in the case of works marked with the individual print number and the aggregate number in the edition, separated by a slash: e.g. "numbered 27/50").

Quality and Condition
When deemed relevant, and within practical limitations, an attempt is made to characterize quality and to indicate significant defects in condition. This is done as an aid to prospective bidders, but clients are advised that all prints should be carefully inspected personally, as quality and the seriousness of defects may prove to be a matter of personal judgment. If the margins are known or believed to be full (as printed or published), this is stated. It should be noted that this service in no way negates paragraph 1 of the Conditions of Sale which states that all lots are sold "AS IS."

*An asterisk at the end of a description indicates that an item has not been examined outside of the frame.

Framing
Whenever possible,"framed" prints are sold in the frames in which they have been received. Sotheby's takes responsibility neither for the appearance of frames nor for their conformity to proper standards of conservation.

Buyers are advised to check the materials used in framing any print against the guidelines provided in Sotheby's pamphlet "Framing and Preservation of Works of Art on Paper," or any other standard reference work on conservation. In no event will we be liable for damage to glass or frames, regardless of the cause.

Measurements
Measurements are given height before width, in inches and in centimeters. Unless otherwise indicated, etchings and engravings are measured by the maximum dimensions of the indentation produced by the plate. Woodcuts, lithographs and serigraphs are measured by the maximum dimensions of the image.

Guide for Prospective Sellers

If you have property you wish to sell at auction, please call the appropriate specialist department to arrange for a consultation. (A list of specialist departments appears in the back of this catalogue.) If you are unsure which department would handle your property, or if you have a variety of objects to sell, please call one of our general representatives:

Fine Arts Representative, Thomas Denzler, (212) 606-7120

Decorative Arts Representative, Timothy Hamilton, (212) 606-7100

Inspection of Property

You may bring your property, or photographs if it is not portable, directly to our galleries where our specialists will give you auction estimates and advice. There is no charge for this service, but we request that you telephone ahead for an appointment. Inspection hours are 9:30 am to 5 pm, Monday through Friday.

Our specialists will provide a free preliminary auction estimate, subject to a final auction estimate after first-hand inspection, if you send a clear photograph of each item, or a representative group of photographs if you have a large collection. Please be sure to include the dimensions, artist's signature or maker's mark, medium, physical condition, and any other relevant information.

Evaluations of property can also be made at your home. The fees for such visits are based on the scope and diversity of the collection. Travel expenses are additional. These fees may be rebated if you consign your property for sale at Sotheby's.

Specialists from our Beverly Hills office are available for inspection visits in the western United States. For more information please call (310) 274-0340.

Standard Commission Rates

All private, trade and institutional sellers are required to pay a commission, which is based on the successful hammer price of property sold, for further details regarding specific commission rates, please refer to the cards that are available at our galleries, or contact the relevant specialist department. Other charges, including shipping, insurance, illustration, restoration, unsold lots and minimum handling fees will be charged as applicable. (For more information about reserves, please refer to "Reserves" in the Guide to Prospective Buyers.)

Shipping Arrangements

Sotheby's Art Transport Department and the staff at any of our regional offices can assist you in making arrangements to have your property delivered to our galleries. This service is free, but actual packing, shipping and insurance charges are payable by our clients. (While we may recommend packers and shippers, we are not responsible for their acts or omissions.) For further information, please call Mary Mancuso Klindt at (212) 606-7511.

Appraisals

Sotheby's Appraisal Company can prepare appraisals for insurance, estate tax, charitable contributions, family division or other purposes.

Appraisal fees vary according to the nature and amount of work to be undertaken, but will always be highly competitive. Flat rates can be quoted based on specialist time required, value and processing costs. Travel expenses are additional.

We shall be pleased to refund the appraisal fee pro rata if the appraised property is consigned to us for sale within one year after the appraisal is completed. For further information please call (212) 606-7440.

Financial Services

Sotheby's offers a wide range of financial services. These financial services include advances on consignments and loans secured by art collections which are not intended for sale. It is Sotheby's general policy, subject to exceptions, to lend no more than 40% of the total of its low estimates for such property. It is also Sotheby's general policy, subject to exceptions, that the minimum loan for consignor advances is $50,000, and the minimum loan for secured loans is $1,000,000. For further information regarding qualifications, conditions, and terms, please call Mitchell Zuckerman at (212) 606-7077.

Catalogues, Price Lists and Newsletter

Illustrated catalogues, prepared by Sotheby's specialists, are published for all regularly scheduled auctions and may be purchased singly or by annual subscription. (Catalogue subscribers automatically receive Sotheby's Newsletter at no additional charge.)

Printed lists of the prices realized at each auction are available at our galleries approximately three weeks following the auction, and are sent directly to catalogue purchasers and subscribers.

Sotheby's Newsletter, published seven times a year, provides an advance calendar of all Sotheby's sales worldwide and full-color photographs of auction highlights. A complimentary copy is available upon request. Annual subscriptions are $25 ($35 overseas).

For more information, or to subscribe to our catalogues or *Newsletter*, ask for our brochure. Write or call Sotheby's Subscription Department, P.O. Box 5111, Norwalk, CT 06856.
Telephone: 1-800-444-3709.

Guide for Prospective Buyers

The following will help explain some of the words and symbols commonly used throughout this catalogue. All bidders should read the Conditions of Sale and Terms of Guarantee in this catalogue, as well as any Glossary or other notices. By bidding at auction, bidders are bound by those Conditions of Sale and Terms of Guarantee, as amended by any oral announcement or posted notices, which together form the contract of sale between the successful bidder (purchaser), Sotheby's and the seller (consignor) of the lot.

Symbol Key

This is a key that explains the symbols you may see inside this catalogue:

□ *Reserves.* Lots with this symbol are subject to reserve. A reserve is the confidential minimum price established between Sotheby's and the seller. This symbol will only be used if some, but not all, lots in the catalogue are offered subject to a reserve.

◪ *Guaranteed property.* Lots with this symbol indicate that Sotheby's has assured the seller a minimum price from one auction, or a series of auctions. This symbol will only be used if some, but not all, lots in the catalogue are offered subject to a guarantee.

⊠ *Property owned by Sotheby's.* Lots with this symbol indicate that Sotheby's owns the lot in whole or in part.

Please remember that all property is sold "As Is" and is only subject to rescission as stated in any applicable Terms of Guarantee. If you have any questions concerning the information below or any other auction practices, please contact Roberta Louckx at 606-7414.

Estimates

Each lot in the catalogue is given a low and high estimate. The estimates are guides for prospective bidders and, where possible, reflect prices that similar objects have sold for in the past. The estimates are determined several months before a sale and are therefore subject to revision to reflect current market conditions or currency fluctuations. Estimates should not be relied upon as a representation or prediction of actual selling prices. If you have any questions concerning a lot, please contact the specialist in charge of the sale whose name is printed in the front of the catalogue.

Specialist Advice; Exhibitions

Prospective bidders may be interested in specific information which is not included in the catalogue description of a lot. Do not hesitate to contact a Sotheby's specialist in charge listed in the front of the catalogue, or Sotheby's Client Services Department, for additional information. A few days prior to every sale, there will be an exhibition of the property to be offered. Specialists will be available at the exhibition to answer questions about the property or to provide any other assistance with the auction process. The dates and times of the exhibition are printed in the front of this catalogue.

Bidding

In order to bid at an auction, you must qualify and register for a paddle when entering the salesroom. If you are the successful bidder on a lot, the auctioneer will acknowledge your paddle number. Unless you have previously qualified to bid at Sotheby's, please be prepared to provide requested information to a Sotheby's representative. Issuance of a bid paddle is in Sotheby's sole discretion.

Bidding will be in accordance with the lot numbers listed in the catalogue or as announced by the auctioneer, and will be in increments determined by the auctioneer. There are three ways in which you may bid at auction. You may bid in person by attending the auction, submit an Absentee Bid Form, or in certain circumstances, by telephone. If you are unable to attend the sale, please see the Absentee Bid Form and Guide for Absentee Bidders which contains additional information on absentee bidding.

Unless otherwise noted in the catalogue or by an announcement at the auction, Sotheby's acts as agent on behalf of the seller and does not permit the seller to bid on his or her own property. It is important for all bidders to know that the auctioneer may open the bidding on any lot by placing a bid on behalf of the seller and may continue bidding for the seller by placing responsive or consecutive bids, but only up to the reserve (see the next paragraph below for information regarding reserves). The auctioneer will not place consecutive bids on behalf of the seller above the reserve.

Currency Conversion Board

For your convenience, in many sales Sotheby's operates a display board which converts United States dollars into various foreign currencies. All foreign currency amounts displayed are approximations based on recent exchange rate information and may not be relied upon as a precise invoice amount. Sotheby's assumes no responsibility for any error or omission in foreign or United States currency amounts shown.

Reserves

Unless otherwise indicated, all lots in this catalogue are offered subject to a reserve. A reserve is the confidential minimum price established between Sotheby's and the seller. The reserve is generally set at a percentage of the low estimate and will not exceed the low estimate of the lot. If any lots in the catalogue are offered without reserve, the lots subject to a reserve will be designated by a box (□).

Property in which Sotheby's has an interest

On occasions, Sotheby's offers property for sale and guarantees a minimum price to the consignor. Such property is also offered subject to a reserve and will be designated by the following symbol (▨). Where every lot in a catalogue is guaranteed, Sotheby's will not designate each lot with the symbol, but will state in the Conditions of Sale page that every lot in the sale is subject to a guaranteed minimum price.

If Sotheby's owns property, in whole or in part, such property will be offered subject to a reserve and will be designated by the following symbol (☒).

Hammer Price (or Successful Bid Price) and the Buyer's Premium

For lots which are sold, the last price for a lot as announced by the auctioneer is the hammer, or successful bid price. A buyer's premium will be added to the successful bid price and is payable by the purchaser as part of the total purchase price. The buyer's premium will be the amount stated in Paragraph 3 of the Conditions of Sale in the front of this catalogue.

Payment for Purchased Property

If you are the successful bidder on a lot, payment is to be made immediately following a sale. You will not be permitted to take delivery of your purchases until payment is made, unless a credit arrangement has been established. Please contact the specialist in charge of the sale, or Arlene Kick at (212) 606-7491, for information on a specific lot.

Payment for a lot may be made in United States dollars by cash, check, or coin transfer. Payment may also be made by Visa or MasterCard, subject to the following conditions.

Payment by Credit Card

If you wish to pay for any purchase with your MasterCard or Visa, you must present the card *in person* to Sotheby's. All charges are subject to acceptance by Sotheby's and by MasterCard or Visa, as the case may be. In the case a charge is not approved, you will nevertheless be liable to Sotheby's for all sums incurred by you. Credit card purchases may not exceed $25,000.

Payment by check

If you wish to pay by check, please see our cashier and fill out a Check Acceptance Account form. Until approved, you will not be permitted to remove purchases paid for by check until the check has cleared. Check Acceptance privileges are reviewed from time to time by Sotheby's, and may be granted or withdrawn in Sotheby's sole discretion. Checks drawn on foreign banks may not be accepted for values under $500, and credit card purchases may not exceed $25,000. There will be a collection charge minimum of $100 on checks drawn on foreign banks located outside of the continental United States.

Sales Tax

New York sales tax is charged on the successful bid price, buyer's premium and any other applicable charges on any property picked up or delivered in New York State, regardless of the state or country in which the purchaser resides or does business, unless Sotheby's has been given, in advance of the release of the property, a valid exemption from taxes by the State of New York. Sotheby's will also collect taxes on purchases shipped to California, Connecticut, Florida, Illinois, Massachusetts, Minnesota, New Jersey, Pennsylvania and Washington, D.C. If you have any questions concerning this, please contact our Customer Billing Department at (212) 606-7464.

Removal of Property; Packing and Shipping

Unless otherwise agreed by Sotheby's, all purchases should be removed by the 10th day following a sale. Purchases which are not removed by the 10th day will be subject to a handling charge as outlined in paragraph 8 of the Conditions of Sale.

As a courtesy to purchasers who come to Sotheby's to pick up property, Sotheby's will assist in the packing of lots, although Sotheby's may, in the case of fragile articles, choose not to pack or otherwise handle a purchase. Sotheby's will not be responsible or liable for damage to glass covering paintings, drawings or other works, or damage to frames, regardless of the cause.

Sotheby's Art Transport Department and the staff at Sotheby's regional offices may be able to assist you in making arrangements for delivery and insuring of purchases. The purchaser will be responsible for shipping and insurance expenses. Sotheby's will also, upon request, provide names of professional packers and shippers known to the Art Transport Department, although Sotheby's shall have no liability or responsibility for providing this information. If you have any questions or wish further information, please contact the Art Transport Department at (212) 606-7511.

Export Permits

Certain property sold at auction may be subject to the provisions of the Endangered Species Act of 1973, the Marine Mammal Protection Act of 1972, the Migratory Bird Act of 1982 and the New York State Environmental Conservation Law. Although licenses can be obtained to export some items which are the subject of these laws, other items may not be exported (such as items containing whale bone), and some property may not be resold in the United States. Upon request, Sotheby's is willing to assist a purchaser in attempting to obtain appropriate licenses. However, there is no assurance that an export license can be obtained. Sotheby's will charge a minimum fee of $150 per item if it is able to obtain an export license. Please check with the specialist department or with the Art Transport Department if you are uncertain as to whether an item is affected by the above laws or other related laws which restrict exportation. The sale of a purchased lot will not be cancelled if Sotheby's,or a purchaser, is not able to obtain an export permit.

Absentee Bids

If you are unable to attend an auction in person, and wish to place bids, you may give Sotheby's Bid Department instructions to bid on your behalf. Our representatives will then try to purchase the lot or lots of your choice for the lowest price possible, and never for more than the top amount you indicate. This service is free and confidential. Please note: Sotheby's offers this service as a convenience to clients who are unable to attend the sale, and although we will make every effort, Sotheby's will not be responsible for error or failure to execute bids.

Placing Absentee Bids

To place bids, please use the absentee bid form provided in this catalogue. Be sure to accurately record the lot numbers and descriptions and the top price you are willing to pay for each lot. "Buy" or unlimited bids will not be accepted. Always indicate a "top limit"— the amount to which you would bid if you were attending the auction yourself.

Alternative bids should be indicated by using the word "OR" between lot numbers. Then if your bid on an early lot is successful, we will not continue to bid on other lots for you. Or, if your early bids are unsuccessful, we will continue to execute bids for alternative lots until a bid is successful. Bids must always be placed in the same order as the lot numbers appear in the catalogue.

Each absentee bid form should contain bids for one sale only; the number and code name should appear in the top right-hand corner of the form. Please place your bids as early as possible. In the event of identical bids, the earliest received will take precedence.

Telephone Bids

Bids may be placed by telephone, but are accepted only in Sotheby's discretion and at the caller's risk. In Sotheby's discretion, telephone bids may be recorded. By bidding on the telephone, prospective purchasers consent thereto.

Buyer's Premium

The "top limit" you indicate on your bid form is for the hammer price exclusively. Please keep in mind that a buyer's premium will be added to the successful bid price of each lot you buy and is payable by you, together with the applicable sales tax which is applied to the total cost of your purchase (the total cost includes the buyer's premium). The buyer's premium will be the amount stated in paragraph 3 of the Conditions of Sale in the front of this catalogue.

Successful Bids

Successful bidders will be notified and invoiced within a few days of the sale. All bidders will receive a list of sale results if they purchased the sale catalogue or enclose a stamped self-addressed envelope with their absentee bid form.

For More Information

To place telephone bids, or for further information, please call Frederica Lauder at (212) 606-7414, or the regional office in your area.

GUIDE FOR SHIPMENT OF PURCHASES

Shipping/Forwarding Instructions

If your bid is successful, we can arrange to have your property shipped to you. As shipping costs can be expensive, we suggest that you request a quotation from our Art Transport Department at (212) 606-7511. If an estimate of shipping costs is not requested prior to shipment, we will act according to the instructions you provide. All shipments will be C.O.D.

The packing and shipping of items by Sotheby's employees is undertaken solely at our discretion. Furniture, larger items and high-valued property may require the services of professional packers.

Upon receipt of payment, Sotheby's will instruct packers and carriers. Your attention is drawn to the Conditions of Sale which require payment and clearance promptly after the sale. In default of those terms, lots may be transferred to a public warehouse at the risk and expense of the purchaser. As stated in the Conditions of Sale, we are not responsible for the acts or omissions of carriers or packers, whether or not recommended by us. Packing and handling of purchased lots by us is at the entire risk of the purchaser.

Please allow 4 – 6 weeks for delivery.

Methods of Transport

Air Freight—Not to be confused with air mail, this method employs air freight carriers to ship property that has already been packed.

Registered Parcel Post—Parcels which do not exceed the size and weight limits set by the United States Postal Service may be sent by this method. In case of international shipments, it is not always possible to insure parcels for their full value. Please consult the Art Transport Department for details.

Truck—This method is recommended for large shipments and the transport of any item of furniture. There are also "shuttle services" which can transport uncrated paintings and works of art to specific areas in the United States. The Art Transport Department can supply complete details.

Book Post—This is a less expensive, but slower, method of shipping books via the United States Postal Service. Parcels shipped in this manner can be insured only for a maximum of $400.

For More Information

To receive an estimate of shipping costs, or for further information, please call Art Transport at (212) 606-7511, or the regional office in your area.

Absentee Bid Form

Special Notice

Catalogue descriptions may indicate sustantial repairs or damages. This is a cataloguing service intended as an aid to prospective bidders, but is not comprehensive in nature. Clients are advised to inspect all lots personally, or call for a condition report prior to the sale date. Please see page 6 for a list of appropriate phone numbers.

Sale Title The Estate of Jacqueline Kennedy Onassis

Date April 23-26, 1996

Sale Code "JKO" 6834

Name *(please print or type)* Date

Sotheby's Card # Sotheby's Account #

Address

City State Zip Code

Telephone/Home Business

Fax

☐ Please check if this is a new address.

Payment Note:

If you wish to pay for any purchase made by absentee bid with a Visa or Mastercard, you must present the card in person to Sotheby's.

Bank reference or deposit *(if bidder is unknown to Sotheby's)*

Bank Name Account

Contact Telephone

I agree that I am bound by the "Conditions of Sale" and any "Terms of Guarantee" which are published in the catalogue for the sale and govern all purchases at auction that I make.

Signed *(We must have your signature to execute this bid.)*

Sotheby's
1334 York Avenue
New York, N.Y. 10021
Bid Department (212) 606-7414

Important
Please see "Guide for Absentee Bidders" opposite this sheet.

I wish to place the following bids for this sale to be held on April 23-26, 1996. These bids are to be executed by Sotheby's up to but not exceeding the amount or amounts specified below. Each bid is PER LOT, as indicated, and all bids will be executed and are accepted subject to the "Conditions of Sale" and "Terms of Guarantee" printed in the catalogue of this sale. Please note that a buyer's premium in the amount stated in paragraph 3 of the "Conditions of Sale" in the front of this catalogue will be added to the hammer price as part of the total purchase price, plus any applicable sales tax.

Arranging Payment
In order to avoid delays in receiving purchases, buyers unknown to us are advised to make payment arrangements or supply credit references in advance of the sale date.
If such arrangements are not made, purchases cannot leave our premises until checks have been cleared.

Please mail or fax to
Sotheby's Bid Department
1334 York Avenue
New York, N.Y. 10021
Fax (212) 606-7016

Lot Number	Catalogue/Description	Top Limit of Bid not including the buyer's premium
		$
		$
		$
		$
		$
		$
		$
		$
		$
		$

(please print or type) *(Bid is per lot number as listed in the catalogue)*

AMERICAN DECORATIVE ARTS & FURNITURE
Leslie B. Keno 606–7130
William W. Stahl, Jr. 606–7110
Wendell Garrett 606–7137

AMERICAN FOLK ART
Nancy Druckman 606–7225
Kara D. Short

AFRICAN & OCEANIC ART
Jean G. Fritts 606–7325

AMERICAN INDIAN ART
Ellen Napiura Taubman 606–7540

AMERICAN PAINTINGS, DRAWINGS & SCULPTURE
Peter B. Rathbone 606–7280
Dara Mitchell

ANIMATION & COMIC ART
Dana Hawkes 606–7424
Francie Ingersoll
Jerry Weist
Consultant

ANTIQUITIES
Richard M. Keresey 606–7328
R. Seth Bright

ARMS & ARMOUR
Nicholas McCullough 606–7260
Consultant

ART NOUVEAU & ART DECO
Barbara E. Deisroth 606–7170
Gregory A. Kuharic
Frank Maraschiello

BOOKS & MANUSCRIPTS
David N. Redden 606–7386
Dr. Paul Needham 606–7385
Selby Kiffer
Marsha Malinowski
Justin E. Caldwell
Kimball E. Higgs
Elizabeth R. Muller

CHINESE PAINTINGS
Gong Jisui 606–7334
Noah Kupferman

CHINESE WORKS OF ART
Carol Conover 606–7332
Lark E. Mason, Jr.
Dr. Hugo K. Weihe
Jiyoung Koo
Dick Ning Wang

COINS
Paul Song 606–7391

COLLECTIBLES
Dana Hawkes 606–7424
Robert Levine
Alison Kurke
Consultant

CONTEMPORARY PAINTINGS, DRAWINGS & SCULPTURE
Robert Monk 606–7254
Leslie Prouty
Tracy Williams
Wendy Cromwell
Midwest
Helyn Goldenberg (312) 664–6800
West Coast
Nora Halpern (310) 274–0340

ENGLISH FURNITURE
Larry J. Sirolli 606–7577
Peter Lang
William W. Stahl, Jr. 606–7110

EUROPEAN FURNITURE
Phillips Hathaway 606–7213
Gillian M. Arthur
Mary Frances Cunningham
Thierry Millerand 606–7349

EUROPEAN WORKS OF ART & TAPESTRIES
Margaret H. Schwartz 606–7250

GARDEN STATUARY
Elaine Whitmire 606–7285

IMPRESSIONIST & MODERN PAINTINGS, DRAWINGS AND SCULPTURE
David J. Nash
Alexander Apsis 606–7360
David Norman 606–7360
Laurel Beckett
Scholarship and Research
John L. Tancock
Midwest
Helyn Goldenberg (312) 664–6800
West Coast
Nora Halpern (310) 274–0340

ISLAMIC WORKS OF ART
Richard M. Keresey 606–7328
R. Seth Bright

INDIAN, HIMALAYAN, SOUTHEAST ASIAN WORKS OF ART & CONTEMPORARY INDIAN PAINTINGS
Carlton C. Rochell, Jr. 606–7304

JAPANESE ART
Suzanne Mitchell 606–7339
Ryoichi Iida 606–7338
Gretchen Good

JEWELRY
John D. Block 606–7392
Paul Russo
Antique
Jacqueline Fay
Business Development
Prince Dimitri of Yugoslavia
Eve J. Reppen
Cataloguing and Research
Valerie Vlasaty
Arcade
Ann Limer Lange
Hilary Humphrey
West Coast
Tracy Sherman (310) 274–0340
Carol Elkins
Midwest
Gary Schuler (312) 664–6800
Canadian Sales
Tracy Sherman (416) 926–1774
Karen Hausman

JUDAICA
Silver
Kevin Tierney 606–7160
Books and Manuscripts
Dr. Paul Needham 606–7385
Tel Aviv Liaison
Jennifer Roth

KOREAN WORKS OF ART
Suzanne Mitchell 606–7339
Ryoichi Iida 606–7338
Jiyoung Koo 606–7286

LATIN AMERICAN PAINTINGS
August Uribe 606–7290
Isabella Hutchinson
Rachael Palacios

MUSICAL INSTRUMENTS
Rachel Gaul 606–7938

19TH CENTURY EUROPEAN PAINTINGS, DRAWINGS & SCULPTURE
Nancy Harrison 606–7140
Benjamin F. Doller
Paula Robinson-Pradines
Evelyn Tompkins
Sculpture
Christopher Gow

19TH CENTURY FURNITURE, DECORATIONS & WORKS OF ART
Elaine Whitmire 606–7285

OLD MASTER PAINTINGS & DRAWINGS
George Wachter 606–7230
Heidi Chin
Christopher Apostle
Drawings
Scott Schaefer

PAPERWEIGHTS & GLASS
Lauren K. Tarshis 606–7180

PHOTOGRAPHS
Denise Bethel 606–7240
Cristina Enriquez Bocobo
Christopher Mahoney

PORCELAIN: EUROPEAN & CHINESE EXPORT
Letitia Roberts 606–7180

POSTAGE STAMPS
Robert A. G. A. Scott 606–7288

PRE-COLUMBIAN ART
Stacy Goodman 606–7330
Fatma Turkkan-Wille
Consultant

PRINTS (OLD MASTER AND MODERN)
Mary Bartow 606–7117
Dr. Nancy Bialler
Blake Koh

PRINTS (CONTEMPORARY)
Nina del Rio 606–7113

RUGS & CARPETS
Mary Jo Otsea 606–7996

RUSSIAN ART, ICONS, OBJECTS OF VERTU
Gerard Hill 606–7150

SILVER
Kevin L. Tierney 606–7160
Ian Irving

SPORTS MEMORABILIA
Robert Levine 606–7424

VINTAGE CARS
David Patridge 606–7920
Daniel I. Sargent 783–5969
Consultant

WATCHES, CLOCKS & SCIENTIFIC INSTRUMENTS
Daryn Schnipper 606–7162
Kevin L. Tierney 606–7160

WINE
Serena Sutcliffe 606–7207
Jamie Ritchie

SOTHEBY'S ARCADE AUCTIONS
Jennifer Roth 606–7516
Decorations
Wiebke Moore 606–7409
Victoria Ayers
Andrew Cheney
Matthew Taylor
Paintings
Jennifer Roth 606–7516
Orla Coleman
Helen Papoulias
Furniture
Amanda Everard 606–7588
Constanza Doerr
Lara Schmidt
Jewelry
Ann Limer Lange 606–7392
Hilary Humphrey
Rugs
Daisy Edelson 606–7996

CLIENT SERVICES

24 HOUR SALE & EXHIBITION INFORMATION
606-7245

24 HOUR SALE RESULTS INFORMATION
606-7901

APPRAISALS
Chapin Carson 606-7440

CATALOGUE SUBSCRIPTIONS
To order catalogues & price lists:
(800) 444-3709
Inquiries:
Diane Pia (203) 849-4928

CLIENT SERVICES DIVISION
Bid Department
For assistance in placing absentee bids for North American Auctions.
606-7414
Frederica R. Lauder
Margot Moes
Courtney Ridenour
Ashley Riviere
Brad Bentoff
Kate Nelson
Lyn Grant

Client Advisory Group
For information and assistance in all aspects of buying at auction in North America. Also assistance for non-English speaking clients.
Roberta Louckx 606-7415
Mallory Hathaway 606-7447
Lisa Heller 606-7468
Geraldine Nager 606-7568
Mish Tworkowski 606-7419
Brooke Douglass de Ocampo 606-7251
Tiffany Dubin 606-7263
Tom Cashin 606-7262
Jean Kim 606-7257
Dulany Cain 606-7279

Client Service Exhibition Representative
Susan V. P. Barrett 606-7087
Client Service Representative
Carole Bellidora 606-7116
International Client Services
For information and assistance in all aspects of buying at auction outside of the U.S. Also assistance for non-English speaking clients.
Rose Balbo 606-7400

CLIENT ACCOUNTING
Arcade
Beverly Banks 606-7147
Buyer Accounts
Arlene Kick 606-7491
Seller Accounts
Alexandra Tyndall 606-7320

CORPORATE COLLECTIONS
Sealy H. Hopkinson 606-7575

FINANCIAL SERVICES
For Consignors & Collectors
Mitchell Zuckerman 606-7077
Shelly Fischer 606-7004

INTERNATIONAL CLIENT ADVISORY
Raul J. Suarez 606-7274

MUSEUM SERVICES
Katherine Ross 606-7303
Wendell Garrett 606-7137

RESTORATION: FURNITURE & DECORATIONS
John Stair 860-5446

SHIPPING & CUSTOMS INQUIRIES
Mary Mancuso Klindt 606-7511

SPECIAL EVENTS
Hilary Cushing 606-7375

SOTHEBY'S EDUCATIONAL STUDIES
Kathleen Martin 606-7958
Elisabeth D. Garrett 606-7988
Jessica Deutsch 606-7838

TRUST & ESTATE SERVICES
Warren P. Weitman, Jr. 606-7198
Richard S. Wolf 606-7099
Christine Wheale 606-7445
Kathryn Wilmerding 606-7259
New England
William S. Cottingham (617) 247-2851
Middle Atlantic
Angela V. B. Hudson (215) 751-9540
South
Robert Ruggiero (704) 627-6001
Midwest
Laura MacLennan (612) 332-8938
Deborah Schmidt (312) 664-6800
Florida
David G. Ober (407) 833-2582
West Coast
Sarah Blanchard (310) 274-0340

ADMINISTRATIVE DEPARTMENTS

EXHIBITIONS
Alfred Bristol 606-7460

FACILITIES & OPERATIONS
Kenneth Schoenfelder 606-7152
Larry Seid 606-7433

FINANCE & ADMINISTRATION
Martha Sayre 606-7393
Jerry Kasdan 606-7820
Karen Schuster 606-7410
Gail Skelly 606-7399

FINANCIAL OPERATIONS
Tricia Carberry 774-5337
Peter Dondero 606-7829
Elsie Spencer 606-7410

INFORMATION SYSTEMS
Joseph Williams 606-7807
Winston Poyser 606-7881

INVESTOR RELATIONS
Jeff Pierne 606-7390

LEGAL
Marjorie E. Stone 606-7175
Rena Moulopolous 606-7163
Allison Miller 606-7173

MARKETING
Suzanne McMillan 606-7354
Richard Buckley 606-7527
Tove Nedergaard 606-7539
Ronald Varney 606-7189
Kae Jonsons 606-7178

PERSONNEL
Susan Alexander 606-7204
Daryl Krimsky 606-7202

PHOTOGRAPHY
Ben Cohen 606-7210

PRESS OFFICE / CORPORATE AFFAIRS
Diana Phillips 606-7176
Matthew Weigman

REGIONAL OPERATIONS
Stuart Seigel 606-7449
Monique Lodi 606-7582
Wendy Armacost 606-7442

TREASURY
John Brittain 606-7220
Jeff Pierne 606-7390

CREDITS

GENERAL PHOTOGRAPHY
Ken Adlard, Leslie Jean-Bart and Matthew Marsten

JEWELRY PHOTOGRAPHY
Michael Oldford

INTERIOR PHOTOGRAPHY
Ben Cohen

DESIGN DIRECTOR
Emil T. Micha

ART DIRECTOR
Jeanne Arnold

PRODUCTION MANAGER
Martha E. Sullivan

CREATIVE CONSULTANTS
Carbone Smolan Associates

PRINTING AND SEPARATIONS
Danbury Printing and Litho

United Kingdom and Ireland

London
34–35 New Bond Street
and Bloomfield Place
(off New Bond Street)
London W1A 2AA
Telephone: (0171) 493 8080
Fax: (0171) 409 3100

SOUTH EAST

Sussex
Michael Thomson-Glover
Alistair Morris
Summers Place, Billingshurst
West Sussex RH149AD
Telephone: (1403) 783 933
Telex: 87210 GAVEL
Fax: (1403) 785 153

The Hon. George Plumptre
Ashford, Kent
Telephone: (1233) 860 566
Fax: (1233) 860 045

THE MIDLANDS, WALES AND SOUTH WEST

John Harvey
18 Imperial Square
Cheltenham
Gloucestershire GL50 1QZ
Telephone: (1242) 510500
Fax: (1242) 250252

The Hon. Mrs. d'Erlanger
Hensleigh Cottage
Hensleigh, Tiverton
Devon, EX 16 5NH
Telephone: (1884) 243663
Fax: (1884) 258692

Wessex
Colin Thompson
Cheviot House
69–73 Castle Street
Salisbury, Wiltshire SP1 3TN
Telephone: (1722) 330793
Fax: (1722) 330982

East Anglia
George Archdale
Lady Victoria Leatham
The George Hotel Mews
Station Road, Stamford
Lincolnshire PE9 2LB
Telephone: (1780) 51666
Fax: (12780) 62086

The Lord Cranworth
Grundisburgh Hall
Grundisburgh
Woodbridge, Suffolk
1P13 6TW
Telephone: (1473) 735581
(1473) 735485
Fax: (1473) 738278
(1473) 738278

Sara Foster
Cokesford Farm
Tittleshall
King's Lynn, Fakenham
Norfolk, PE32 2RQ
Telephone: (1328) 700032
Fax: (1328) 700155

NORTH WEST

Timothy Wonnacott, A.R.I.C.S.
Booth Mansion
28 Watergate Street
Chester CH1 2NA
Telephone: (1244) 315531
Fax: (1244) 346984

Lord Ralph Kerr
Melborne Hall
Melborne
Derbyshire, DE 73 1EN
Telephone: (1332) 862263

Yorkshire
John Phillips
William Sheepshanks
8–12 Montpellier Parade
Harrogate
North Yorkshire HG1 2TJ
Telephone: (1423) 501466
Fax: (1423) 520501

SCOTLAND AND BORDER COUNTIES

John Robertson
Nicholas Linzee Gordon
112 George Street
Edinburgh EH2 4LH
Telephone: (131) 226 7201
Fax: (131) 226 6866

Anthony Weld Forester
130 Douglas Street
Glasgow G2 4HF
Telephone: (141) 221 4817
Fax: (141) 204 2502

Aberdeenshire
Telephone: (1330) 824007

Matthew Festing
11 Osborne Terrace, Jesmond
Newcastle-upon-Tyne
NE2 1NE
Telephone: (191) 281 8867
Fax: (191) 212 0141

NORTHERN IRELAND

William Montgomery
The Estate Office, Greyabbey
Newtonards, Co. Down
Telephone: (124 77) 88 666/8
Fax: (124 77) 88 652

IRELAND

Anne Dillon
William Montgomery
51b Dawson Street, Dublin 2
Telephone: 353 (1) 671 1786
and 353 (1) 671 1431
Fax: 353 (1) 679 7844

CHANNEL ISLANDS

Els Cevat
3 Clos Des Fontaines
La Villette, St. Martin's
Guernsey, C.I.
Telephone: (0481) 38009
Fax: (0481) 36115

Clare d'Abo
Jersey
Telephone: (071) 408 5363

Europe and Middle East

AUSTRIA

Dr. Agnes Husslein
Managing Director–Austria & Hungary
Vienna
Tel: 43 (1) 512 4772/3 and
513 3774
Fax: 43 (1) 513 4867

Vienna
Dr. Agnes Husslein
Palais Breuner
Singerstrasse 16, 1010 Vienna
Tel: 43 (1) 512 4772/3 and
513 3774
Fax: 43(1) 513 4867

Graz
Dr. Soraya Stubenberg
Schloss Gutenberg, A-8160 Weiz
Telephone: 43 (3172) 8133
Fax: 43 (3172) 8133 12

Klagenfurt
Villacher Strasse 813
A-9020
Telephone: 43 (463) 50 44 84
Fax: 43 (463) 50 44 82

BELGIUM

Count Hubert d'Ursel
Managing Director
Count de Limburg Stirum
32 Rue Jacques Jordaens
1050 Brussels
Telephone: 32 (2) 648 0080
Fax: 32 (2) 648 0757

CYPRUS

Rita C. Severis
15 Them Dervis Str.
P.O. Box 1139, Nicosia, Cyprus
Telephone: 357 (2) 461410
Fax: 357 (2) 444897

CZECH REPUBLIC

Dr. Katharina Grafin von Podewils
Celetna 10
110 00 Prague 1
Telephone: 42 (2) 26 94 90
Fax: 42 (2) 232 42 93

DENMARK

Baroness Hanne Wedell-Wedellsborg
Bredgade 6
1260 Copenhagen K, Denmark
Telephone: 45 (33) 135556
Fax: 45 (33) 930119

FINLAND

Carla Enbom
Nylandsgatan 14
Uudenmaankatu 14
SF 00120 Helsinki
Telephone: 358 (0) 64 67 46
Fax: 358 (0) 68 01 208

FRANCE

Paris
Princess de Beauvau Craon
(P.D.G., France)
Alexandre Pradere
Francis Simon
Anne de Lacretelle
Associate
Prince Abdel 'Azis Toussoun
Associate
3 rue de Miromesnil
75008 Paris
Telephone: 33 (1) 4266 4060
Telex: SPBF A 640084 F
Fax: 33 (1) 474 222 32

Bordeaux
France de Sainte Croix
Telephone: 33 56 44 95 23
Fax: 33 56 01 09 26

Montpellier
Beatrice Viennet
Telephone: 33 67 24 95 72
Fax: 33 67 24 93 52

Strasbourg
Marie-France Ludmann
Telephone: 33 88 60 00 61
Fax: 33 88 60 00 61

GERMANY

Dr. Christoph Graf Douglas
Managing Director–Germany
Frankfurt
Telephone: 49 (69) 74 0787

Frankfurt
Johannes Ernst
Nina Buhne
Beethovenstrasse 71
D-60325 Frankfurt-am-Main 1
Telephone: 49 (69) 74 0787
Fax: 49 (69) 746 901

Berlin
Isabella von Bethmann-Hollweg
Lucy Dew
Palais am Festungsgraben
Unter den Linden/Neue Wache
D-10117 Berlin
Telephone: 49 (30) 204 4119
Fax: 49 (30) 394 3080

Cologne
Ursula Niggemann
St. Apern-Strasse 17–21
Kreishaus Galerie
D-50667 Cologne
Telephone: 49 (221) 257 4956/7 or
257 4972
Fax: 49 (221) 257 4359

Hamburg
Tatiana von Hessen
Axel Benz
Innocentiastrasse 19
D-20149 Hamburg
Telephone: 49 (40) 44 40 80
Fax: 49 (40) 410 7082

Munich
Heinrich Graf von Spreti
Andreas Narzt
Odeonsplatz 16
D-80539 München 22
Telephone: 49 (89) 291 31 51
Fax: 49 (89) 299 271

Lower Saxony
Susanne von Luneburg
Rittergut Essenrode
D-38165 Essenrode
Telephone: 49 (5301) 1366
Fax: 49 (5301) 1227

Stuttgart
Heide Rentschler
Bodenseestrasse 23
88138 Sigmarszell
Telephone: 49 (8389) 323
Fax: 49 (8389) 32707

Karlsruhe
Cornelia von Griesheim
Guntherstrasse 14
D-76185 Karlsruhe
Telephone: 49 (721) 858213
Fax: 49 (721) 858273

GREECE

Rita C. Severis
15 Them Dervis Str.
P.O. Box 1139, Nicosia, Cyprus
Telephone: 357 (2) 461 410
Fax: 357 (2) 444 897

HOLLAND

John van Schaik
102 Rokin, 1012 KZ Amsterdam
Telephone: 31 (20) 550 2200
Telex: 13267 MAKSO NL
Fax: 31 (20) 550 2222

HUNGARY
Dr. Soraya Stubenberg
Attila utca 111/4th Floor/1
H-1012 Budapest
Telephone: 36 (1) 175 2961
Fax: 43 (3172) 8133 12

ICELAND
Sigridur Ingvarsdottir
1 Hofsvallagata, 107 Reykjavik
Telephone: 354 (1) 204 37
Fax: 354 (1) 62 04 37

ISRAEL
Rivka Saker Managing Director
Daniella Luxembourg
38 Gordon Street
Tel Aviv 63414
Telephone: 972 (3) 522 3822 or 524 6897
Fax: 972 (3) 522 5454

ITALY
Giuseppe Ceccatelli
Managing Director

Milan
Giuseppe Ceccatelli
Palazzo Broggi
Via Broggi 19
20129 Milan
Telephone: 39 (2) 295001
Fax: 39 (2) 29518595

Rome
Julien Stock
Piazza di Spagna 90
00186 Rome
Telephone: 39 (6) 699 41791 or 678 1798
Fax: 39 (6) 679 6167

Florence
Clementina Bartolini Salimbeni
Telephone: 39 (55) 234 8768
Fax: 39 (55) 247 4828

Turin
Laura Russo
Corso Galileo, Ferraris 18B
10121 Turin
Telephone: 39 (11) 544898
Fax: 39 (11) 547675

LIECHTENSTEIN
Henriette Huber-von Goldschmidt Rothschild
Josef Rheinbergerstr, 11A
FL9490 Vaduz
Telephone: 41 (75) 232 4914
Fax: 41 (75) 233 1738

LUXEMBOURG
Nadia Meyer-Quiring
156A Route de Luxembourg
L-7374 Bofferdange
Telephone: 352 33 97 47
Fax: 353 33 51 60

MONACO
Alain Renner
Mark Armstrong
B.P. 45, Le Sporting d'Hiver
Place du Casino
MC 98001 Monaco Cedex
Telephone: 33 (93) 30 88 80
Fax: 33 (93) 25 24 98

NORWAY
Ingeborg Astrup
Bjornveien 42
0387 Oslo 3, Norway
Telephone: 47 (22) 14 72 82
Fax: 47 (22) 49 38 36

PORTUGAL
Frederico Horta e Costa
Calcada do Combro, 38A - 1
1200 Lisbon
Telephone: 351 (1) 343 1041
Fax: 351 (1) 342 1118

SPAIN

Madrid
Edmund Peel
Plaza de la Independencia 8
28001 Madrid
Telephone: 34 (1) 522 2902
Fax: 34 (1) 521 4482

Barcelona
Rocio Tassara
Luis Monreal Tejada
Associate
Pasaje de Domingo 2
08007 Barcelona
Telephone: 34 (3) 487 6845/5272
Fax: 34 (3) 216 0792

SWEDEN
Hans Dyhlen
Arsenalsgatan 6
111 47 Stockholm
Telephone: 46 (8) 679 5478/9
Fax: 46 (8) 611 4826

Gothenburg
Vivianne Kempe
Telephone: 46 (31) 937 150
Fax: 46 (31) 937 550

South Sweden
Baroness Catharina von Blixen-Finecke
Telephone: 46 (411) 85130
Fax: 46 (411) 85128

SWITZERLAND
Simon de Pury
Chairman–Europe
Geneva
Telephone: 41 (22) 732 8585

Geneva
Simon de Pury
David Bennett
Daniella Luxembourg
13 Quai du Mont Blanc
CH-1201 Geneva
Telephone: 41 (22) 732 8585
Fax: 41 (22) 731 6594

Zurich
Ully Wille
20 Bleicherweg, CH-8002 Zurich
Telephone: 41 (1) 202 0011
Fax: 41 (1) 201 2042

Lugano
Diego Cassina
Via Peri 21, 6900 Lugano
Telephone: 41 (91) 9238562
Fax: 41 (91) 9238563

Basel
Ruedi Staechelin
Schifflande 2
CH-4051 Basel
Telephone: 41 (61) 261 10 20
Fax: 41 (61) 261 10 77

SYRIA AND JORDAN
Antoine Touma
P.O. Box 2011
Damascus, Syria
Telephone: 963 (11) 429 502

Asia

CHINA
Gillian Tso
The Shanghai Hilton, Suite 723
250 Hua Shan Road
Shanghai 20040
Telephone: 86 (21) 248 0000 Ext. 723
Fax: 86 (21)248 3848

HONG KONG
Mee Seen Loong
309–310 Exchange Square Two
8 Connaught Place
Central, Hong Kong
Telephone: (852) 2 524 8121
Fax: (852) 2 810 6238

INDIA
Javed Abdulla
113 Sunder Nagar
New Delhi 110003
Tel and fax: 91 11 463 8385

Dr. Usha Ramamrutham
12 Juhu Ajanta
Gulmohar Road
J.V.P.D. Scheme
Bombay 400 049
Tel and fax: 91 (22) 620 2321

Patrick Bowring (London)
Telephone: 071 408 5407

JAPAN
Dr. Peter Huggler
Chairman–Japan
Tetsuji Shibayama
Managing Director
John Tancock
Fuerte Kojimachi Bldg. 3F
1–7 Kojimachi
Chiyoda-ku, Tokyo 102
Telephone: 81 (3) 3230 2755
Fax: 81 (3) 3230 2754

KOREA
Stephen Joh
2F, 192–11 Kwanhoon-Dong
Jongro-Gu, Seoul
Korea 110–300
Telephone: 82 (2) 733 5733
Fax: 82 (2) 733 4733

MALAYSIA
Walter Cheah
25 Jalan Pudu Lama
50200 Kuala Lumpur
Telephone: 6 (03) 230 0319
Fax: 6 (03) 230 6833

SINGAPORE
Quek Chin Yeow
1 Cuscaden Road
01–01 The Regent Singapore
Singapore 1024
Telephone: (65) 732 8239
Fax: (65) 737 0295

TAIWAN R.O.C.
Rita Wong
1st Floor, No. 79
Sec. 1, An Ho Road
Taipei, Taiwan R.O.C.
Telephone: 886 (2) 755 2906 or 704 6002/3
Fax: 886 (2) 709 3949

AUSTRALIA

Sydney
Robert Bleakley
Chairman
Justin Miller
13 Gurner Street, Paddington
Sydney, New South Wales 2021
Telephone: 61 (2) 9 332 3500
Fax: 61 (2) 9 332 2409

Melbourne
Paul Sumner
926 High Street, Armadale
Melbourne, Victoria 3143
Telephone: 61 (3) 9 509 2900
Fax: 61 (3) 9 563 5067

Latin America

ARGENTINA
Adela MacKinlay de Casal
Consultant
Avenida Callao 1777 (P.B.)
1024 Buenos Aires
Telephone: (541) 811 2965
(541) 42 21 59
Fax: (541) 814 5033

BRAZIL

Rio de Janeiro
Katia Mindlin Leite Barbosa
Consultant
Caixa Postal 62619
Rio de Janeiro, RJ CEP 22250-970
Telephone: 55 (21) 551 6775
Fax: 55 (21) 551 5899

Heloise Guinle
Consultant
Estrada da Gavea 611
Bloco 1, Apt 2503, São Conrado
22610-000 Gavea
Rio de Janeiro
Telephone: 55 (21) 322 4500
Fax: 55 (21) 322 6397

São Paulo
Pedro Corrêa do Lago
Consultant
Rua João Cachoeira 267
São Paulo SP CEP 04535-010
Telephone: 55 (11) 282 0066
Fax: 55 (11) 282 6559

MEXICO

Mexico City
Françoise Reynaud de Velez
Consultant
Suzy de Gilly
Consultant
Kepler 189
Mexico 11590 D.F.
Telephone: (525) 531 0595
Fax: (525) 545 6971

Gonzalo Gonzalez
Consultant
Schiller 325-7, Polanco
Mexico 11570 D.F.
Telephone: (525) 531 1686/1806
Fax: (525) 250 8734

Monterrey
Barbara Perrusquia de Lobeira
Consultant
Via Triumphalis 127 PTE.
Fuentes Del Valle
Monterrey 66220, N.L.
Telephone: (528) 356 9209
Fax: (528) 378 2432

VENEZUELA
Axel Stein
Consultant
C. C. C. T. Primera Etapa
Piso 3 Of. 312
Chuao, Caracas 1060
Telephone: (582) 959 2249
Fax: (582) 959 1832

Headquarters
1334 York Avenue
New York, New York 10021
Telephone: (212) 606–7000
Fax: (212) 606–7107
(212) 606–7016 (Bids only)

Representatives and Associates

U.S.A.

Atlanta
Associate
Virginia Groves Beach
2585 Habersham Road, NW
Atlanta, Georgia 30305
Telephone: (404) 233–4928
Fax: (404) 237–3457

Baltimore
Associate
Aurelia Bolton
P.O. Box 250
Riderwood, Maryland 21139
Telephone: (410) 252–4600
Fax: (410) 561–9738

Beverly Hills
Managing Director, West Coast
Andrea L. Van de Kamp
Trusts & Estates
Sarah Blanchard
Jewelry
Tracy Sherman
Carol Elkins
Fine Arts
Nora Halpern
Decorative Arts
Katherine Watkins
Associate
Eleanore Phillips Colt
Associate
Christine Eisenberg
Associate
Nancy O. Livingston
9665 Wilshire Blvd.
Beverly Hills, California 90212
Telephone: (310) 274–0340
Fax: (310) 274–0899

Chicago
Midwest Fine Arts and Managing Director
Helyn Goldenberg
Jewelry
Gary Schuler
Trusts & Estates
Deborah A. Schmidt
Administrator
Robert Tilendis
International Representative
Marjorie S. Susman
325 West Huron Street
Suite 200
Chicago, Illinois 60610
Telephone: (312) 664–6800
Fax: (312) 664–3152

Dallas
Associate
Frasher Hudson Pergande
International Representative
Nancy Strauss Halbreich
8409 Pickwick Lane, #284
Dallas, Texas 75225–5323
Telephone: (214) 265–9958
Fax: (214) 369–0332

Honolulu
Associate
Andrea Song Gelber
P.O. Box 177
Honolulu, Hawaii 96810
Telephone: (808) 732–0122
Fax: (808) 531–6963

Houston
Associate
Laura H. Morris
International Representative
Windi Phillips
2476 Bolsover, Suite 143
Houston, Texas 77005
Telephone: (713) 524–0044
Fax: (713) 520–1602

Long Island
Associate
Kim Coleman
3–1 Park Plaza, Suite 170
Old Brookville, New York 11545
Telephone: (516) 621–7240
Fax: (516) 625–2919

Miami
Stefanie Block Reed
Consultant
Dolores C. Smithies
Douglas Entrance
800 Douglas Road, Suite 125
Coral Gables, Florida 33134
Telephone: (305) 448–7882
Fax: (305) 448–7168

Minneapolis/St. Paul
Laura MacLennan
2030 Foshay Tower
821 Marquette Avenue
Minneapolis, Minnesota 55402
Telephone: (612) 332–8938
Fax: (612) 332–7456

Naples
Barbara Deisroth
Telephone: (813) 261–6787
Fax: (813) 263–5860

New England
Managing Director
William S. Cottingham
Representative
Patricia Ward
99 Newbury Street
Boston, Massachusetts 02116
Telephone: (617) 247–2851
Fax: (617) 247–1779

New Orleans
Associate
Debe Cuevas Lykes
Telephone: (504) 523–7059

North Carolina
Robert V. Ruggiero
Box 231, Route 3
Clyde, North Carolina 28721
Telephone: (704) 627–6001
Fax: (704) 627–2059

New York City/Southampton
Associate
Barbara D. Cates
1334 York Avenue
New York, New York 10021
Telephone: (212) 644–5310
Fax: (704) 644–0468

Palm Beach
Managing Director, Florida
David G. Ober
Administrator
Susan Sencer
Senior Associate
Hope P. Kent
Associate
Louis J. Gartner
Associate
Kim Coleman
225 Peruvian Avenue
Palm Beach, Florida 33480
Telephone: (407) 833–2582
Fax: (407) 655–4583

Philadelphia
Wendy T. Foulke
Trusts & Estates
Angela Hudson
1831 Chestnut Street, Suite 601
Philadelphia, Pennsylvania 19103
Telephone: (215) 751–9540 or
(215) 751–9349
Fax: (215) 751–0936

Puerto Rico
Marta Gutierrez
P.O. Box 13171
Santurce, Puerto Rico 00908
Telephone: (809) 791–1971

St. Louis
International Representative
Marjorie S. Susman
Telephone: (314) 991–4939

San Francisco
Jennifer Seymour Foley
Associate
Mrs. Prentis Cobb Hale
International Representative
Mrs. John N. Rosekrans
214 Grant Avenue, Suite 350
San Francisco, California 94108
Telephone: (415) 772–9028
Fax: (415) 772–9031

Sante Fe
International Representative
Windi Phillips
Telephone: (713) 524–0044
Fax: (713) 524–1962

Seattle
Jeannie Johnston
P.O. Box 4356
Seattle, Washington 98104
Telephone: (206) 667-9575
Fax: (206) 667-9576

Tampa
Associate
Debe Cuevas Lykes
P.O. Box 13782
Tampa, FL 33681–3782
Telephone: (813) 832–4741
Fax: (813) 832–4542

Washington, D.C.
Associate
Sally E. Chapoton
2201 Wisconsin Avenue, N.W.,
Suite 390
Washington, D.C. 20007
Telephone: (202) 457–1910
Fax: (202) 457–8100

CANADA
President
Christina Orobetz
Vice President
Brian Watson
9 Hazelton Avenue
Toronto, Ontario M5R 2E1
Telephone: (416) 926–1774
Fax: (416) 926–9179

Associate
Kenzie Selman
301–2245 West Broadway
Vancouver, B.C. V6K 2E4
Telephone: (604) 732–6501
Fax: (604) 684–0567

Associate
Gillian Stewart
3230 Beach Drive
Victoria, B.C. V8R 6L8
Telephone: (604) 370–1021
Fax: (604) 592–2884

Sotheby's International Realty
President
Stuart N. Siegel
980 Madison Avenue
New York, New York 10021
Telephone: (212) 606–4100
Fax: (212) 606–4199

Sotheby's Appraisal Company
(Insurance and Estate Appraisals)
Director
Chapin Carson
1334 York Avenue
New York, New York 10021
Telephone: (212) 606–7446
Fax: (212) 606–7022

Sotheby's Restoration
(Furniture)
Director
John Stair
1425 York Avenue
New York, New York 10021
Telephone: (212) 860–5446
Fax: (212) 876–1064

Sotheby's Financial Services, Inc.
President
Mitchell Zuckerman
1334 York Avenue
New York, New York 10021
Telephone: (212) 606–7077
Fax: (212) 606–7023

International Representatives
Marion Oates Charles
Newport, Washington D.C.
Nancy Strauss Halbreich
Dallas
Windi Phillips
Houston, Santa Fe
Mrs. John N. Rosekrans
San Francisco
Marjorie S. Susman
Chicago, St. Louis
Lee Copley Thaw
New York City
Joan F. Tobin
Washington, D.C.
Virginia Guest Valentine
New York City, Richmond
Telephone: (212) 606–7442
Fax: (212) 606–7022

Last Name *(please print or type)*	First Name

Lot Number	Catalogue/Description	Top Limit of Bid not including the buyer's premium
		$
		$
		$
		$
		$
		$
		$
		$
		$
		$
		$
		$
		$
		$
		$
		$
		$
		$
		$
		$

(please print or type)

(Bid is per lot number as listed in the catalogue)

GUIDE FOR ABSENTEE BIDDERS

All bids are subject to the **"Conditions of Sale"** and **"Terms of Guarantee"** in the catalogue

Absentee Bids
If you are unable to attend an auction in person, and wish to place bids, you may give Sotheby's Bid Department instructions to bid on your behalf. Our representatives will then try to purchase the lot or lots of your choice for the lowest price possible, and never for more than the top amount you indicate. This service is free and confidential. Please note: Sotheby's offers this service as a convenience to clients who are unable to attend the sale, and although we will make every effort, Sotheby's will not be responsible for error or failure to execute bids.

Placing Absentee Bids
To place bids, please use the absentee bid form provided in this catalogue. Be sure to accurately record the lot numbers and descriptions and the top price you are willing to pay for each lot. "Buy" or unlimited bids will not be accepted. Always indicate a "top limit"— the amount to which you would bid if you were attending the auction yourself.

Alternative bids should be indicated by using the word "OR" between lot numbers. Then if your bid on an early lot is successful, we will not continue to bid on other lots for you. Or, if your early bids are unsuccessful, we will continue to execute bids for alternative lots until a bid is successful. Bids must always be placed in the same order as the lot numbers appear in the catalogue.

Each absentee bid form should contain bids for one sale only; the number and code name should appear in the top right-hand corner of the form. Please place your bids as early as possible. In the event of identical bids, the earliest received will take precedence.

Buyer's Premium
The "top limit" you indicate on your bid form is for the hammer price exclusively. Please keep in mind that a buyer's premium will be added to the successful bid price of each lot you buy and is payable by you, together with the applicable sales tax which is applied to the total cost of your purchase (the total cost includes the buyer's premium). The buyer's premium will be the amount stated in paragraph 3 of the Conditions of Sale in the front of this catalogue.

Successful Bids
Successful bidders will be notified and invoiced within a few days of the sale. All bidders will receive a list of sale results if they purchased the sale catalogue or enclose a stamped self-addressed envelope with their absentee bid form.

For More Information
For further information, please call Frederica Lauder at (212) 606-7414, or the regional office in your area, and consult your catalogue for the sale.

Absentee Bid Form

Special Notice

Catalogue descriptions may indicate substantial repairs or damages. This is a cataloguing service intended as an aid to prospective bidders. Clients are advised to inspect all lots personally or call for a condition report prior to the sale date. Please see page 6 for a list of appropriate phone numbers.

Sotheby's
1334 York Avenue
New York, N.Y. 10021
Bid Department (212) 606-7414

Important
Please see "Guide for Absentee Bidders" on the reverse of this sheet.

I wish to place the following bids for this sale to be held on April 23-26, 1996. These bids are to be executed by Sotheby's up to but not exceeding the amount or amounts specified below. Each bid is PER LOT, as indicated, and all bids will be executed and are only accepted subject to the **"Conditions of Sale"** and **"Terms of Guarantee"** printed in the catalogue of this sale. Please note that a buyer's premium in the amount stated in paragraph 3 of the "Conditions of Sale" in the front of this catalogue will be added to the hammer price as part of the total purchase price, plus any applicable sales tax.

Arranging Payment
In order to avoid delays in receiving purchases, buyers unknown to us are advised to make payment arrangements or supply credit references in advance of the sale date.
If such arrangements are not made, purchases cannot leave our premises until checks have been cleared.

Sale Title The Estate of Jacqueline Kennedy Onassis
Date April 23-26, 1996
Sale Code "JKO" 6834

Name *(please print or type)* Date

Sotheby's Card # Sotheby's Account #

Address

City State Zip Code

Telephone/Home Business

Fax

☐ Please check if this is a new address.

Payment Note:
If you wish to pay for any purchase made by absentee bid with a Visa or Mastercard, you must present the card in person to Sotheby's.

Bank reference or deposit *(if bidder is unknown to Sotheby's)*

Bank Name Account

Contact Telephone

I agree that I am bound by the "Conditions of Sale" and any "Terms of Guarantee" which are published in the catalogue for the sale and govern all purchases at auction that I make, and that I have read the information on the back of this form.

Signed *(We must have your signature to execute this bid.)*

Please mail or fax to
Sotheby's Bid Department
1334 York Avenue
New York, N.Y. 10021
Fax (212) 606-7016

☐ **Please check here**
if you have placed additional bids on the reverse of this sheet.

Lot Number	Catalogue/Description	Top Limit of Bid not including the buyer's premium
		$
		$
		$
		$
		$
		$
		$
		$
		$
		$

(please print or type) *(Bid is per lot number as listed in the catalogue)*